Tutorial:
COMPUTER COMMUNICATIONS:
Architectures, Protocols, and Standards

William Stallings

IEEE CATALOG NUMBER EH0226-1
LIBRARY OF CONGRESS 85-60383
IEEE COMPUTER SOCIETY ORDER NUMBER 604
ISBN 0-8186-0604-5

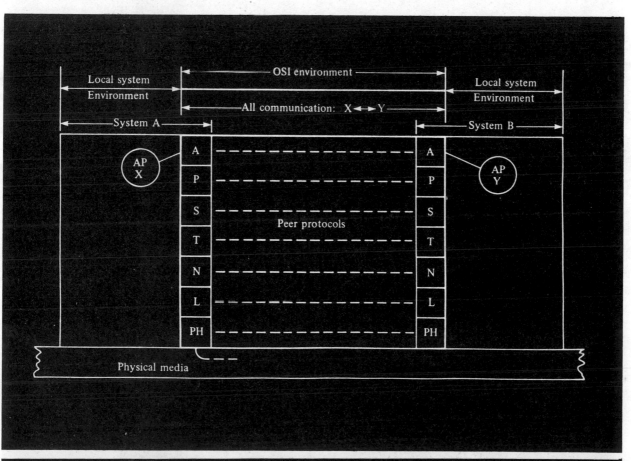

IEEE COMPUTER SOCIETY   COMPUTER SOCIETY PRESS   THE INSTITUTE OF ELECTRICAL AND ELECTRONICS ENGINEERS, INC

Published by IEEE Computer Society Press
1109 Spring Street
Suite 300
Silver Spring, MD 20910

IEEE Catalog Number EHO226-1
Library of Congress Number 85-60383
IEEE Computer Society Order Number 604
ISBN 0-8186-0604-5 (Paper)
ISBN 0-8186-4604-7 (Microfiche)

Order from: IEEE Computer Society.   IEEE Service Center
Post Office Box 80452   445 Hoes Lane
Worldway Postal Center   Piscataway, NJ 08854
Los Angeles, CA 90080

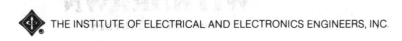

THE INSTITUTE OF ELECTRICAL AND ELECTRONICS ENGINEERS, INC.

PREFACE

In the early 1970's, networks that interconnected computers and terminals began to appear. The primary motivations were to share expensive computing resources and to minimize data transmission costs. Since that time, the rapid proliferation of minicomputers and personal computers has increased the demand for data communications between computers, between terminal and computer, and between terminals. Such communication is accomplished by means of protocols. Typically, the task is too complex for a single protocol. Rather, a structured set of protocols forming a communications architecture is used.

P.1 TUTORIAL FOCUS

The focus of this tutorial is twofold. First, the tutorial presents the motivations for, and design principles of, a communications architecture. Considerable attention is devoted to the open systems interconnection (OSI) model. This model has achieved near-universal acceptance, providing both a framework within which protocols are developed and the terms of reference for discussing communication system design. In addition, a somewhat dissimilar view of communications architecture, evolving out of the ARPANET experience, is examined. The contrast between these two viewpoints serves to highlight the important design issues for a communications architecture.

Second, this tutorial presents a broad overview of communication protocols. It explores the key issues in the field in the following general categories:

- *Principles:* The tutorial provides an understanding of protocols in general, and explores the design principles common to all protocols.

- *Services and mechanisms:* A protocol provides services to its user, which is generally a higher-level protocol. To provide these services, a set of mechanisms are implemented. The services and mechanisms of various protocols are examined.

- *Standards:* It is essential that standard protocols be used to allow the greatest possible degree of interoperability among systems. This view has now been accepted by suppliers as well as users. The nature and current status of protocol standards are presented.

This tutorial, of necessity, strives for breadth rather than depth. Both the bibliography (Section 8) and the references contained in each article suggest additional sources for the interested reader.

P.2 INTENDED AUDIENCE

This tutorial is intended for a broad range of readers interested in computer-communications architecture and protocols:

- *Students and professionals in data processing and data communications:* The tutorial is a convenient means of reviewing some of the important papers in the field. Its organization and the original material aid the reader in understanding this exciting area of data processing and data communications.

- *Protocol designers and implementers:* The tutorial discusses the critical design issues and explores approaches to meeting communications requirements.

- *Computer system customers and managers:* The tutorial provides the reader with an understanding of what features and structures are needed in a communications capability, as well as a knowledge of current and evolving standards. This information provides a means for assessing a specific vendor's offering.

Most of the material can be comfortably read with no background in data communications. The glossary and original material provide supporting information for the reprinted articles.

P.3 ORGANIZATION OF MATERIAL

This tutorial is a combination of original material and reprinted articles. Because the OSI model has become the almost universally accepted context both for designing protocols and for professional discourse on computer communications, the structure of this tutorial is based on that model. The organization of the sections is as follows:

1. *Communications Architecture:* A communications architecture is a structured set of protocols that perform the communications task. The OSI model has become the basis for protocol development and standardization. Although the OSI model is almost universally accepted as the framework for discourse in this area, there is another point of view which grows out of the extensive research and practical experience of ARPANET. Both points of view are presented in this section.

2. *Physical and Data Link Protocols:* The physical and data link protocols are concerned with providing a direct communications path between two devices. This section includes a survey of physical level protocols plus a look at one of the most important standards at that level, RS 449. There are several papers on data link protocols. Finally, there is a paper on the IEEE 802 physical and data link standards.

3. *Network Access Protocols:* Network protocols provide an interface by which devices may access a communications network. The two most important existing protocols at this level are X.25 for packet-switched networks and X.21 for circuit-switched networks. The most important forthcoming protocols are those that will provide access to the Integrated Services Digital Network (ISDN). Papers are included for all these standards.

4. *Internetworking:* Increasingly, there will be a requirement for communication across multiple interconnected networks. The OSI model does not easily accommodate this requirement which seems to call for a protocol between layers 3 and 4. Two major approaches have been taken for internetworking: X.75 and the Internet Protocol. Both are covered in this section.

5. *Transport and Session Protocols:* The transport and session layers provide end-to-end communication service. Of the two the transport layer is far more complex and important. This section examines some of the design considerations for these protocols and surveys existing standards.

6. *Presentation and Application Protocols:* For layers 5 (session) and below, there will be relatively few distinct protocols at each level. At the presentation and application levels, however, there will be a variety of protocols to provide a broad range of user-oriented services. This section includes an overview of these protocols plus some representative examples.

7. *Glossary:* Includes definitions for most of the key terms appearing in this text.

8. *Bibliography:* Provides a guide to further reading.

P.4 RELATED MATERIALS

Data and Computer Communications (Macmillan, 1985) by William Stallings is a companion to this tutorial text, and follows the same topical organization. It is intended as a textbook as well as a reference book for the professionals (available from Macmillan Publishing; 866 Third Avenue; New York, NY 10022; 800-223-3215). A videotape course specifically designed for use with this tutorial text is available from the Association for Media-Based Continuing Education for Engineers, Inc. 500 Tech Parkway, NW; Suite 200A; Atlanta, GA 30313 (404) 894-3362).

Two other texts from the IEEE Computer Society cover related topics. *Computer Networks, A Tutorial* (Fourth Edition, 1984) by Marshall Abrams and Ira Cotton and *Principles of Communication and Networking Protocols* (1984) by Simon Lam. The book by Abrams and Cotton is directed toward the network user and includes a coverage of technical considerations, including lower level protocols and communications network technology. The remainder of the text concerns network applications and management issues, such as network control, security, and planning.

The text by Lam focuses on the technical details of protocols: algorithms, design and analysis techniques, formal models, and verification methods. Whereas *Computer Communications* explores the communications architectures and protocols used by *end systems* (computers and terminals) to communicate and cooperate, Lam emphasizes the techniques and protocols used to manage the intervening *communications* network. For example, technical approaches to access control, routing, and traffic control for packet radio, packet-switched, and local networks are examined in considerable detail. Thus, the present tutorial and Lam's are complementary texts.

Table of Contents

SECTION 1   COMMUNICATIONS ARCHITECTURES

1.1 OVERVIEW

The concepts of distributed processing and computer networking imply that entities in different systems need to communicate. We use the terms "entity" and "system" in a very general sense. Examples of entities are user application programs, file transfer packages, data base management systems, electronic mail facilities, and terminals. Examples of systems are computers, terminals, and remote sensors. Note that in some cases the entity and the system in which it resides are coextensive (e.g., terminals). In general, an *entity* is anything capable of sending or receiving information, and a *system* is a physically distinct object that contains one or more entities.

When computers, terminals, and/or other data processing devices exchange data, the scope of concern is broad. Consider, for example, the transfer of a file between two computers. There must be a data path between the two computers, either directly or via a communications network. But more is needed. Typical tasks to be performed:

- The source system must either activate the direct data communication path, or inform the communications network of the identity of the desired destination system.
- The source system must ascertain that the destination system is prepared to receive data.
- The file transfer application on the source system must ascertain that the file management program on the destination system is prepared to accept and store the file.
- If the file formats used on the two systems are incompatible, one or the other system must perform a format translation function.

It is clear that there must be a high degree of cooperation between the two computer systems. The exchange of information between computers for the purpose of cooperative action is generally referred to as *computer communications*. Similarly, when two or more computers are interconnected via a communications network, the set of computer stations is referred to as a *computer network*. Since a similar level of cooperation is required between a user at a terminal and a computer, these terms are often used when some of the communicating entities are terminals.

In discussing computer communications and computer networks, two concepts are paramount:

- Protocols.
- Computer-communications architecture.

1.2 PROTOCOLS

For two entities to successfully communicate, they must "speak the same language." What is communicated, how it is communicated, and when it is communicated must conform to some mutually acceptable set of conventions between the entities involved. The set of conventions is referred to as a *protocol*, which may be defined as a set of rules governing the exchange of data between two entities. The key elements of a protocol are:

- *Syntax:* includes such things as data format, coding, and signal levels.
- *Semantics:* includes control information for coordination and error handling.
- *Timing:* includes speed matching and sequencing.

Some important characteristics of a protocol are:

- Direct/indirect.
- Symmetric/asymmetric.
- Standard/nonstandard.
- Monolithic/structured.

Communication between two entities may be *direct or indirect*. If two systems share a point-to-point link, the entities in these systems may communicate directly; that is, data and control information pass directly between entities with no intervening active agent. If systems connect through a switched communications network, a direct protocol is no longer possible. The two entities must depend on the functioning of other systems to exchange data. A more extreme case is a situation in which two entities do not even share the same switched network, but are indirectly connected through two or more networks. A set of such interconnected networks is termed a *catenet*.

An important protocol design consideration is raised by the latter two possibilities, namely, the extent to which the entities and hence their protocol must be aware of the characteristics of intervening systems. Ideally, the intervening systems would be transparent and the protocol between the two entities would be the same as for a point-to-point link. We shall see that this ideal cannot be met.

A protocol may be either *symmetric or asymmetric*. Most of the protocols that we shall study are symmetric; that is, they involve communication between peer entities. Asymmetry may be dictated by the logic of an exchange (e.g., a "user" and a "server" process), or by the desire to keep one of the entities or systems as simple as possible.

A protocol may be either *standard or nonstandard*. A nonstandard protocol is one built for a specific communications situation or, at most, a particular model of a computer. Thus, if K different kinds of information sources have to communicate with L types of information receivers, K x L different protocols are needed without standards and a total of 2 x K x L implementations are required. If all systems shared a common protocol, only $K + L$ implementations would be needed. The increasing use of distributed processing and the decreasing inclination of customers to remain locked in to a single vendor dictate that all vendors implement protocols that conform to an agreed-upon standard. Section 1.4 lists the key organizations involved in standards development.

1.3 ARCHITECTURE

Another characteristic of a protocol is whether it is *monolithic or structured*. It should become clear as this tutorial proceeds that the task of communication between entities on different systems is too complex to be handled as a unit. For example, consider an electronic mail package running on two computers connected by a direct link. To be truly monolithic, the package would need to include all of the link control logic. If the connection was over a packet-switched network, the package would still need the link control logic to attach to the network. It would also need logic for breaking up mail into packet-sized chunks, logic for requesting a virtual circuit, and so forth. Mail should only be sent when the destination system and entity are active and ready to receive. Logic is needed for that kind of coordination, and, as we shall see, the list goes on. A change in any aspect means that this huge package must be modified, with the risk of introducing difficult-to-find bugs.

An alternative is to use structured design and implementation techniques. Instead of a single protocol, there is a set of protocols that exhibit a hierarchical or layered structure. Lower level, more primitive functions are implemented in lower-level entities that provide services to higher-level entities. That structure is referred to as a *computer-communications architecture*.

Figure 1.1 suggests, in general terms, a structured set of protocols, and shows the most extreme case of two stations connected via multiple switched networks. Stations 1 and 2 each have one or more applications that wish to communicate. Between each like pair (e.g., electronic mail modules), an application-oriented protocol is needed which coordinates the activities of the two application modules, and assures common syntax and semantics. This protocol need know little about the intervening communications facility, but makes use of a network services entity that does. The network services entity will have a process-to-process protocol with a corresponding entity in the other station. This protocol might handle such matters as flow control and error control. There must also be a protocol between station 1 and

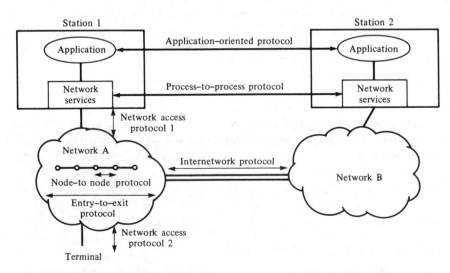

Figure 1-1: Relationship among Communication Protocols

2

network A, and between station 2 and network B. Note that a different, simpler network access protocol might be provided for less intelligent devices such as terminals. Finally, an internetwork protocol is required between networks.

It was mentioned that it is desirable to standardize protocols. It should be clear that to standardize the full range of protocols needed for communications, a common or standardized architecture must be defined. This line of reasoning led the International Organization for Standardization (ISO) in 1977 to establish a subcommittee to develop such an architecture. The result was the *Open Systems Interconnection* (OSI) reference model, which is a framework for defining standards for linking heterogeneous computers. The OSI model provides the basis for connecting "open" systems for distributed applications processing. The term "open" denotes the ability of any two systems conforming to the reference model and the associated standards to connect.

A widely accepted structuring technique, and the one chosen by ISO, is *layering*. The communications functions are partitioned into a vertical set of layers. Each layer performs a related subset of the functions required to communicate with another system. It relies on the next lower layer to perform more primitive functions and to conceal the details of those functions. It provides services to the next higher layer. Ideally, the layers should be defined so that changes in one layer do not require changes in the other layers. Thus we have decomposed one problem into a number of more manageable subproblems.

The task of the ISO subcommittee was to define a set of layers and the services performed by each layer. The partitioning should group functions logically, and should have enough layers to make each layer manageably small, but should not have so many layers that the processing overhead imposed by the collection of layers is burdensome. The resulting OSI reference model has seven layers, which are listed with a brief definition in Table 1.1. This table defines, in general terms, the functions that must be performed in a system for it to communicate. Of course, it takes two to communicate, so the same set of layered functions must exist in two systems. Communication is achieved by having corresponding "peer" entities in the same layer in two different systems communicate via a protocol.

The attractiveness of the OSI approach is that it promises to solve the heterogeneous computer communications problem. Two systems, no matter how different, can communicate effectively if they have the following in common:

- They implement the same set of communications functions.
- These functions are organized into the same set of layers. Peer layers must provide the same functions,

TABLE 1.1 THE OSI LAYERS

1 PHYSICAL	Concerned with transmission of unstructured bit stream over physical medium. Deals with the mechanical, electrical, functional, and procedural characteristics of accessing the medium.
2 DATA LINK	Provides for the reliable transfer of information across the physical link. Sends blocks of data (frames) with the necessary synchronization, error control, and flow control.
3 NETWORK	Provides upper layers with independence from the data transmission and switching technologies used to connect systems. Responsible for establishing, maintaining, and terminating connections.
4 TRANSPORT	Provides reliable, transparent transfer of data between endpoints. Provides end-to-end error recovery and flow control.
5 SESSION	Provides the control structure for communication between applications. Establishes, manages, and terminates connections (sessions) between cooperating applications.
6 PRESENTATION	Provides independence to the application processes from differences in data representation (syntax).
7 APPLICATION	Provides access to the OSI environment for users and also provides distributed data processing services.

but note that it is not necessary that they provide them in the same way.

- Peer layers must share a common protocol.

To assure the above, standards are needed. Standards must define the functions and services to be provided by a layer (but not how it is to be done—that may differ from system to system). Standards must also define the protocols between peer layers (each protocol must be identical for the two peer layers). The OSI model, by defining a seven-layer architecture, provides a framework for defining these standards.

1.4 STANDARDS

It has long been accepted in the communications industry that standards are required to govern the physical, electrical, and procedural characteristics of communications equipment. In the past, this view has not been embraced by the computer industry. Whereas communications equipment vendors recognize that their equipment will generally interface to and communicate with other vendors' equipment, computer vendors have traditionally attempted to monopolize their customers. The proliferation of computers and distributed processing has made that an untenable position. Computers from different vendors must communicate with each other and, with the ongoing evolution of protocol standards, customers will no longer accept special-purpose protocol conversion software development.

In this tutorial, the most important standards that are in use or being developed for various aspects of data and computer communications are described. Some of the standards-making bodies that are most important to our discussion:

- *International Organization for Standardization (ISO):* a voluntary, nontreaty organization whose members are designated standards bodies of participating nations, and nonvoting observer organizations. One of ISO's technical committees (TC97) is concerned with information systems. This committee developed the OSI model and is developing protocol standards at various layers of the model.

- *International Telegraph and Telephone Consultative Committee (CCITT):* a U.N. treaty organization made up primarily of the Postal, Telegraph, and Telephone (PTT) authorities of the member countries. The U.S. representative is the Department of State. As its name indicates, CCITT is involved in a broad range of communication areas. The organization works closely with ISO on communication protocol standards.

- *American National Standards Institute (ANSI):* a non-profit, non-governmental organization composed of manufacturers, users, communications carriers, and other interested organizations. It is the national clearinghouse for voluntary standards in the United States. It is also the U.S. designated voting member of the ISO. ANSI's interests roughly parallel those of ISO.

- *National Bureau of Standards (NBS):* a part of the Department of Commerce. It issues Federal Information Processing Standards (FIPS) for equipment sold to the federal government. The Department of Defense (DOD) need not, and frequently does not, comply. The concerns of NBS are broad, encompassing the areas of interest of both CCITT and ISO. NBS is attempting to satisfy federal government requirements with standards that, as far as possible, are compatible with international standards.

- *Federal Telecommunications Standards Committee (FTSC):* an interagency advisory board responsible for establishing standards (FED-STD) for federal procurements to assure interoperability of government-owned communications equipment. FTSC tends to concentrate on standards corresponding to the lower layers of the OSI model, whereas NBS is more focused on higher layers. However, there is an unre- solved area of overlap between the two sets of standards.

- *Defense Communications Agency (DCA):* promulgates communications-related military standards (MIL-STD). DOD feels that its requirements in some areas are unique, and this is reflected in DCA standards that are unlike those used elsewhere.

- *Electronics Industries Association (EIA):* a trade association of electronics firms and a member of ANSI. It is concerned primarily with standards that fit into OSI layer 1 (physical).

- *The Institute of Electrical and Electronics Engineers, Inc. (IEEE):* a professional society and also a member of ANSI. Their concerns have been primarily with the lowest two layers of the OSI model (physical and data link).

- *European Computer Manufacturers Association (ECMA):* composed of computer suppliers selling in Europe, including the European divisions of some American companies. It is devoted exclusively to the cooperative development of standards applicable to computer technology. ECMA serves as a non-voting member of CCITT and ISO and also issues its own standards. Because of the rapidity of their efforts, they have had considerable influence on OSI work.

There are a number of advantages and disadvantages to the standards-making process. We list here the most striking ones. The principal advantages of standards are:

- A standard assures that there will be a large market for a particular piece of equipment or software. This encourages mass production, and in some cases, the use of large-scale-integration (LSI) or very-large-scale-integration (VLSI) techniques, resulting in lower costs.

- A standard allows products from multiple vendors to communicate, giving the purchaser more flexibility in equipment selection and use.

The principal disadvantages are:

- A standard tends to freeze the technology. By the time a standard is developed, subjected to review and compromise, and promulgated, more efficient techniques are possible.

- There are multiple standards for the same thing. This is not a disadvantage of standards per se, but of the current way things are done. Fortunately, in recent years the various standards-making organizations have begun to cooperate more closely. Nevertheless, there are still areas where multiple conflicting standards exist.

1.5 ARTICLE SUMMARY

The first article provides an overview of the OSI model. It discusses the motivation for the model and provides a formal description. Tanenbaum looks closely at the individual layers of the model and the services they provide. The article by Bowers and Connell contains a handy checklist of protocol functions by OSI layer. The article shows clearly both the similarities and differences among the layers. Specific examples of layered communications architectures are presented in the article by Konangi and Dhas.

The final two articles present the somewhat different perspective on communications architecture growing out of the ARPANET research. Cerf and Cain define an architecture and set of protocols that have been standardized by the Department of Defense. Padlipsky contrasts the result with the OSI model.

Reprinted with permission from *Open Systems Data Transfer*, Number 1, June 1982, pages 2-21. Copyright © 1982 by OMNICOM, Inc.—All rights reserved.

A TUTORIAL ON THE OPEN SYSTEMS INTERCONNECTION REFERENCE MODEL

Harold C. Folts
Omnicom, Inc.

BACKGROUND

Although standards development activities for data communications applications started during the early 1960's, the real momentum did not build until the 1970's. By 1976, a number of standards were approved for public data networks, including CCITT Recommendation X.25 for packet-switched operation. Also near completion were the bit-oriented data-link control procedures (ADCCP in the USA and HDLC internationally). It was then realized that there was no master plan or structure for determining what standards were needed and whether all aspects of future distributed information systems were properly covered. Data communications standards work has been responding to immediate requirements, with little consideration given to the relationships among the various standards, proprietary protocols, and systems architecture.

The realization of this dilemma came about in 1977 when the International Organization for Standardization (ISO) Technical Committee 97 established a new Subcommittee (SC 16) to deal directly with this problem. SC 16, entitled Open Systems Interconnection, was chartered to develop an architecture to provide a framework for the definition, development, and validation of standards in the new generation of distributed information systems. The work was first directed toward a basic structure to define the functionality needed for communications among application processes remotely separated in different heterogeneous user end-systems.

The International Telegraph and Telephone Consultative Committee (CCITT) also recognized the importance of establishing a sound architecture and appointed a Special Rapporteur to study the problem and to work in close liaison with ISO. While the ISO work is more general, CCITT is directing its efforts to the application of the OSI to telecommunications services.

The Reference Model that has resulted from this intense effort has now evolved through 4 drafts and is in the final stages of approval in ISO. Currently identified as Draft International Standard (DIS) 7498 (February 1982), it is expected to be approved by the end of 1982 as an International

Standard. While the ISO Reference Model has been going through the approval process since mid-1981, the CCITT work has continued to advance editorially and has maintained full consistency with the principles established by ISO. A copy of the March 1982 CCITT Draft, Reference Model of Open System Interconnection for CCITT Applications, is included in Omnicom's OSI Reference.

The basic architecture specified by the OSI Reference Model is only the first in a family of standards that will result from this work. From the established principles of OSI, layer service definitions are now being developed that will then enable further development of the necessary protocols for communications among distributed application processes within the Open Systems Interconnection structure. The work will be ongoing and evolutionary. Now is the time to start to apply the new standardized OSI principles to all implementations that will be part of the worldwide distributed information era.

INTRODUCTION

The term 'open' is used to convey the ability of an end-system of one manufacturer (or design) to interconnect with any other end-system according to the OSI Reference Model and the associated standard peer protocols. This will enable application processes to communicate with each other through the resulting Open Systems Interconnection Environment (OSIE). Figure 1 illustrates an abstract of an Open Systems Interconnection - the OSIE is enclosed by the heavy line.

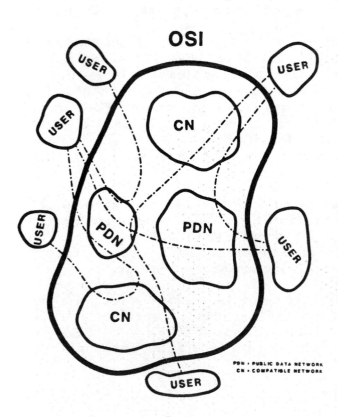

FIGURE 1

The 'user' is actually an Application Process (AP), which can be any sort of task from a simple program to a very complex operation. Examples of AP's include: a person operating a manual keyboard entry terminal, a credit checking program, an industrial production-line control program or sensor, plus an endless range of distributed computer processing applications. AP's may be one or a group of activities executing a set of procedures according to instructions established within the system to perform designated functions. In performing the overall task, AP's must be able to communicate, in order to share processing resources, access data bases, and deliver an output to an appropriate destination.

The user is outside of the OSIE, and when operating within its own end-system is considered to be closed. When a communication with another remotely located AP is needed, the OSIE is accessed, so that the user end-system becomes open. A number of intermediate systems may be transited from user to user through the OSIE. Shown in Figure 1 as Public Data Networks (PDN) or private Compatible Networks (CN), the telecommunications facilities are also an essential part of the overall OSI structure.

THE LAYERED ARCHITECTURE

A continuum of functions is involved in a communication, and they must be arranged in a logical order so that they can be understood. The technique of layering has been employed for this purpose in the OSI Reference Model. The first decision that had to be made was "how to slice the cake." There is almost an unlimited number of ways, and the final decision will always be somewhat arbitrary. Too many layers would make the structure too complex, while too few would lead to very complex protocols. It is also important to group functions that are most logically related to each other in supporting the communication. In the end, however, the decision made must be acceptable to the widest range of interests, both politically as well as technically. The division of seven layers of functionality has now been agreed upon worldwide to serve as a basis for the OSI architecture.

The layers of the OSI Reference Model are shown in Figure 2, and are briefly described as follows:

APPLICATION LAYER -
Directly serves AP by providing access to the Open Systems Interconnection Environment and provides the distributed information services to support the AP and manage the communication

PRESENTATION LAYER -
Provides the services that allow the AP to interpret the meaning of the information being transferred - syntax selection and conversion

SESSION LAYER -
Supports the dialog between co-operating AP's, binding and un-binding them into a communicating relationship

TRANSPORT LAYER -
Provides end-to-end control and information interchange with the reliability and quality of service that is needed for the AP

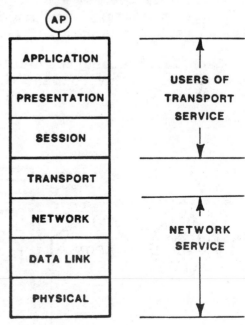

LAYERS OF MODEL

FIGURE 2

NETWORK LAYER -
Provides the switching and routing functions needed to establish, maintain, and terminate switched connections and transfer data between the communicating end-systems (NOTE - The term "network" as used here is a specific OSI technical term and should not be taken as denoting a

communications network in the conventional sense.)

DATA LINK LAYER -
Provides for the transfer of information over the physical link with the necessary synchronization, error control, and flow control functions

PHYSICAL LAYER -
Provides the functional and procedural characteristics to activate, maintain, and deactivate the physical links that transparently pass the bit stream of the communication.

The upper three layers provide the functions in direct support of the application process, while the lower three layers are concerned with the transmission of the information between the end-systems of the communication. The Transport Layer is the essential link between these two groups of functions; it provides end-to-end integrity of the communication, ensuring that the appropriate quality of service from the lower three layers meets the requirements of the upper three layers.

The specification of the characteristics of each layer individually provides the modularity that enables the functions and protocols to be defined independently - each performing its own task in supporting the communication. It then become possible to change a protocol at one layer without affecting the other layers and their protocols. Therefore, as technology evolves and new requirements emerge, OSI can advance into the future. This also enables application of the OSI structure now, and where suitable protocols are not available, temporary ones can be used. As the OSI protocols develop, then they can replace the ones in place without disturbing the whole system.

Each layer spans the whole interconnection within the Open Systems Interconnection Environment (OSIE) that supports the communication between cooperating AP's. As shown in Figure 3, within the OSIE, there are peer

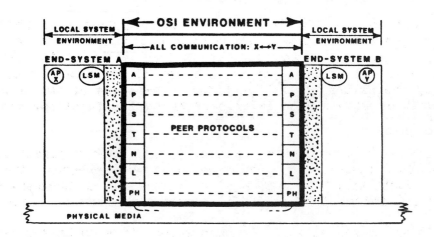

FIGURE 3

protocols that are needed to perform the control functions that support the communication. Each communicating application process is shown in the end-system within the local system environment. When a communication is desired, the AP, through the action of the Local System Manager (LSM), accesses the OSIE through the Application Layer. The OSIE is the area that is enclosed within the heavily outlined box. The physical media and the local system environment are external.

<u>**LAYER PRINCIPLES**</u>

As shown in Figure 4, each layer can be viewed individually as an (N) layer having an (N+1) layer as an upper boundary and an (N-1) layer as a lower boundary. The (N) layer receives services from the (N-1) layer and provides services to the (N+1) layer. In the case of the Physical Layer, however, the lower boundary is with the physical media rather than a (N-1) layer. The upper boundary of the Application Layer is with the application process.

CONCEPT OF A LAYER

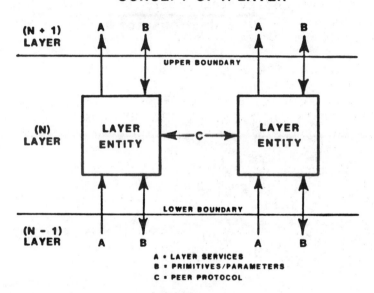

A • LAYER SERVICES
B • PRIMITIVES/PARAMETERS
C • PEER PROTOCOL

<u>**FIGURE 4**</u>

Each layer contains a logical grouping of functions that provide the specific <u>services</u> for facilitating a communication. A function, or a group of functions, within a layer makes a functional unit that is called an <u>entity</u>. An entity accepts one or more inputs (arguments) and produces outputs (values) determined by the nature of the functions. There may be two or more instances of active entities within each layer performing the functions that support the communication.

There are also interactions between entities of adjacent layers, in the form of requests, indications, responses, and confirmations. These are called <u>primitives</u>. Each primitive may also have associated parameters that convey detailed control information needed to support the communication.

There is an active entity, for each layer, in each system involved in the interconnection. Entities in the same layer communicate with each other using <u>peer protocols</u> that convey the necessary control information to support the communications between the cooperating AP's. While standard definitions are being developed for the services to be provided by each layer and for the associated interaction primitives, the OSI peer protocols that result will be the standards that will enable full OSI compatibility among systems.

(N-1) CONNECTION

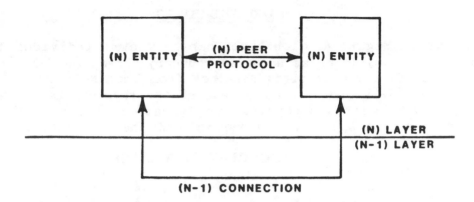

FIGURE 5

Information is exchanged between the layer entities through the use of the services of the (N-1) layer, which provides the logical connection path - the (N-1) connection shown in Figure 5 - between (N) layer entities. In turn, each layer utilizes the services of the lower layers, which are cumulatively reflected as the (N-1) services.

Entities of adjacent layers interconnect via layer service access points, as shown in Figure 6. The (N+1) layer knows the associated service access point by a service access point name, while the (N) layer knows the same point by a (N) service access point address. Mapping of addresses layer by layer for a connection may be accomplished either by hierarchical address mapping (inherent in the address structure) or through address mapping tables.

SERVICE ACCESS POINTS

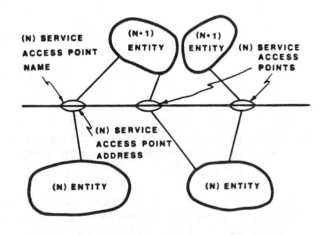

FIGURE 6

Interactions between adjacent layers are also key elements in supporting a communication. The primitives either initiate an action or advise the result of an action. Referring to Figure 7, the primitives are:

REQUEST - is initiated by the (N+1) layer to the (N) layer to activate a particular service

INDICATION - is provided by the (N) layer to advise of the activation of a particular service

INTERACTION PRIMITIVES

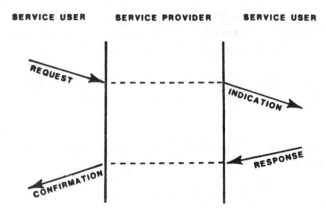

SERVICE USER   SERVICE PROVIDER   SERVICE USER

REQUEST

INDICATION

RESPONSE

CONFIRMATION

FIGURE 7

RESPONSE - is provided by the (N+1) layer in reply to an indication primitive

CONFIRM - is returned to the requesting (N+1) layer by the (N) layer upon completion of a requested service

Each primitive can have a number of associated parameters that convey additional specific information for the respective service. For example, a connection request primitive can contain the destination address, quality of service requirement, and data received from the next upper layer.

Information transfer takes place between peer entities within a layer as well as between entities of adjacent layers within the same system. The transfer is accomplished in the form of various types of data units, which are made up of control information and data. The basic construction of the information flow is shown in Figure 8.

The (N) Protocol Control Information (PCI) is exchanged between peer entities to coordinate their joint operation.

DATA UNITS

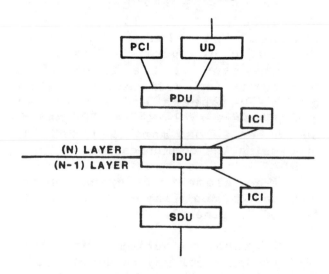

PCI   UD

PDU

ICI

(N) LAYER
(N-1) LAYER   IDU

ICI

SDU

FIGURE 8

The (N) <u>User Data (UD)</u> may also be transferred between peer entities as required. In the (N-1) layer the UD becomes the (N) Service Data Unit (SDU).

The (N) <u>Protocol Data Unit (PDU)</u> is a combination of the (N) PCI and the (N) UD or (N) SDU. The (N) PDU is the total information that is transferred between peer entities as a unit.

The (N) <u>Interface Control Information (ICI)</u> provides the interaction between the adjacent layer entities. These are referred to as "Primitives" in the layer service definitions that are under development.

The (N) <u>Interface Data (ID)</u> is transferred between adjacent layer entities for the transmission to the peer entity via the (N-1) connection.

The (N) <u>Interface Data Unit (IDU)</u> is the total unit of information transferred across the service access point.

The (N-1) <u>Service Data Unit (SDU)</u> is the part of the IDU, whose identity is preserved between the ends of the connection.

This structure is followed layer by layer as the communication is processed through the interconnection. The terms for the different units used above are those as defined by the ISO DIS 7498. The CCITT Reference Model defines an (N) <u>Boundary Data Unit (BDU)</u> instead of IDU and does not define ICI or ID. (NOTE - The term "interface" is used in OSI to mean the boundary between adjacent layers and should not be taken as a connection between equipment.)

As the control information and data are processed by the entity within a layer the units may be segmented into smaller units or blocked into larger units as illustrated in Figure 9. This allows optimization of the information transfer through efficient utilization of the resources en route. For example, a very large (N) PDU may be segmented across many (N-1) PDU's in processing the communication.

Many elements of operation are common to most layers and can be treated in general. These are:

Protocol selection - More than one protocol may be defined for a layer to meet different requirements and applications.

SEGMENTING

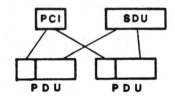

BLOCKING

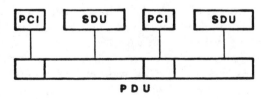

<u>FIGURE 9</u>

Therefore, a mechanism is required to properly identify the protocol for the specific communicating application process.

Connections - An (N) connection is an association for communication between two or more (N+1) entities. Connections are established and released as needed during a communication. They may be point-to-point or multipoint.

Multiplexing - An entity may support the connection of more than one (N+1) entity over a single (N) connection.

Splitting - A layer may use more than one (N) connection to support a single (N+1) layer entity.

Data transfer - Normal data transfer takes place over the primary path, while expedited data can bypass the normal data to support recovery or other infrequent operations.

Flow control - Because of limited capacity to hold data while the control information is being processed, it is necessary to manage the flow of the information both between entities of adjacent layers and between peer entities within a layer.

Sequencing - In some networking configurations, it may be possible for the information to arrive at the destination in a different order from that sent by the source. Before it can be processed further, it may be necessary to put the information back into its original order.

Acknowledgement - Receipt of confirmation that data has been received at the appropriate destination and is acceptable may be necessary at several layers, depending on the quality of service requirements of the corresponding application processes.

Reset - If synchronization is lost or some unrecoverable error occurs, it may be necessary to reinitialize the connection between peer entities.

Routing - This function enables the communications to be relayed by a chain of entities within the layer.

Not all functions are necessarily invoked in each layer for every communication. Only those that are needed to support the specific application are activated. It is also possible that there may not be a need for any functions within a particular layer. What will be considered the minimum functionality of any individual layer is still being debated.

For any system to operate properly, there must be orderly management to ensure all components work in harmony. The management aspects of OSI include the control of initiation, termination, monitoring, and handling of abnormal conditions. There are three management areas that need to be considered:

Application management - involves: initialization of parameters; initiation, maintenance, and termination of the communication; detection and prevention of OSI resource interference and deadlock; integrity and commitment control; security control; and checkpointing and recovery control.

Systems management - involves control of the OSI resources and their status across all the layers.

Layer management – is concerned with the activation process, error control, and coordination of activities within a layer.

Development work in these management areas is in the early stage and is now getting more attention as the work on the basic reference model has reached a good level of maturity and wide agreement.

COOPERATING OPEN SYSTEMS

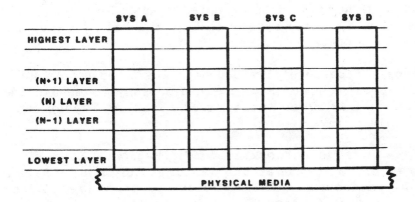

FIGURE 10

As earlier mentioned, each layer logically transverses all the interconnected systems that are in a cooperating relationship in the OSIE. At each interconnected system there are layer entities that interact with peer entities in the other connected systems via the peer protocols to facilitate the communication. As shown in Figure 10, the physical media provides the connecting path between the respective systems. While all seven layers in the

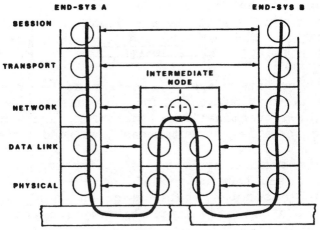

FIGURE 11

connected end-systems are functionally active, intermediate (or relay) systems may only have active entities in the lower three layers, as in the case of a packet-switched network, shown in Figure 11. The circles show the activated entity at each layer in each interconnected system. In this case, there are two physical connections and two data links that are in tandem to make up the full network connection. The active network layer entity in the intermediate system performs the relay function between the two links and provides continuity of communication path. A typical relay system may involve only the physical layer. An intermediate system involving all seven layers is an example used for store and forward message transfer.

There are unlimited configurations that can be created when mapping the OSI structure into an actual system or in designing a new system. By using diagrams like Figure 11, it becomes much easier to identify the actual structure of the total system at hand. This technique is now being used in CCITT for the development of the standards for the new Integrated Services Digital Networks (ISDN).

AN OSI SCENARIO

To illustrate the OSI principles in operation, a simple scenario is presented, using the configuration in Figure 12. The two communicating end-systems are shown, while the relay systems are only implied in this example. In each peer relationship the (N) protocol control information is shown as a header (H), which, combined with the data unit, creates the (N) protocol data unit that is logically transferred between the peer entities. For the Data Link Layer the actual X.25 format is shown rather than a general header. The peer relationships are horizontal, while the actual information flow follows the dotted line.

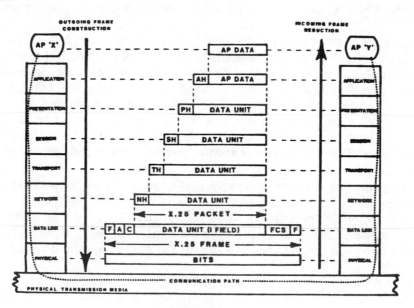

FIGURE 12

Application Process X finds a need to communicate with Application Process Y in a remotely located system. AP X then accesses the OSIE by requesting the Application Layer to establish the required communication. The Application Layer determines the availability of the OSI resources to support the communication. If available, the communications establishment begins with a series of request primitives that repeat from layer to layer down through the next six layers as each layer entity is activated in the originating end-system. At the bottom, the Physical Layer entity activates the physical link and the respective peer entity. Then the Data Link Layer activates the peer protocol, and the Network Layer establishes the network connection to the destination end-system. In turn the end-system to end-system peer relationships for the Transport, Session, Presentation, and Application Layers are established. As this takes place each layer is advised of the incoming communication from the layer below by indication primitives, and acceptance is returned to the next lower layer through a response primitive. In completion of the activation of each layer's peer relationship and the communication path, a confirmation primitive is returned to each layer upward at the originating end-system. When this process is completed, the communication between the AP's proceeds.

AP X passes the data to the Application Layer, where the application protocol header (AH) is added to convey the peer protocol information to the application entity in the destination end-system. This is the application protocol data unit that becomes the service data unit at the Presentation Layer (assuming a one-to-one relationship). The Presentation Layer then adds its protocol control information header (PH) that will be carried to its peer at the other end-system. The presention entity may also perform a syntactic transformation on the application data. The appending of protocol control information onto the data units follows layer by layer as the outgoing frame is constructed through the Data Link Layer. At the Physical Layer the information is seen only as a flow of bits to the transmission media. En route there may be a number of relay systems where switching and routing functions are performed at the network layer or between transmission media at the Physical Layer. A relay function within the Data Link Layer is also possible if, for example, certain types of Local Area Networks are traversed.

At the destination end-system the bit flow enters the Physical Layer from the transmission media and is passed on to the Data Link Layer. The flags (F) of the X.25 frame synchronize the information while the address (A), control (C), and frame check sequence (FCS) information is used for the various data-link control functions. These are then removed from the frame and the data unit of the I field is passed to the Network Layer. (In the X.25 example, this is a packet.) The network entity then looks at the header (NH), performs its required function, and passes the remaining data unit to the Transport Layer. Each layer in turn looks at its header, performs the required functions, and passes the remaining data unit to the next upper layer until the final application process data is delivered to AP Y. This construction and reduction of the information flow associated with the communication takes place in both directions until the communication is completed. Then the resources are released and become available for subsequent communications.

Although this scenario is simplified and represents only one of many possible situations, the basic OSI process is shown. Some applications may activate all the peer relationships in parallel during the establishment procedures, while others may activate each layer sequentially one at a time. While this example may give the impression of an excessive amount of overhead and control information to transfer the data between the application processes, bear in mind that only the functions that are needed are actually invoked. Furthermore, larger data units from upper layers may be segmented or blocked according to the resources and nature of the communication. In overall system operation the total protocol control information should be small compared to the AP data being transferred.

LAYER SERVICE DEFINITIONS

The basic OSI Reference Model provides only the general description of each layer. The next step in the OSI development process is the preparation of a service definition for each layer that will define the functions, services and associated primitives in greater depth. When the service definitions are completed, the layer protocols can then be identified, if existing, or developed where they do not exist. The latter is generally the case except for a few existing protocols that will be fully adapted into the OSI structure, such as X.25, X.21, and HDLC. Further details of the layer service definitions and protocols will be subjects of future OSI Data Transfer tutorials. Below are brief presentations of the functions and services that are defined in the basic OSI Reference Model.

Application Layer

The Application Layer serves as the window for the application process to access the Open Systems Interconnection Environment. This is the only layer that provides services directly to the application process. These services, however, reflect the accumulation of the results of all the services provided by the underlying layers. The definition of the Application Layer is just now starting to take shape and settle.

APPLICATION LAYER ELEMENTS

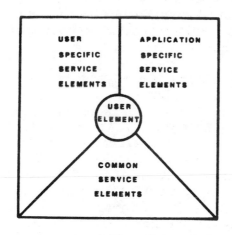

USER SPECIFIC SERVICE ELEMENTS

APPLICATION SPECIFIC SERVICE ELEMENTS

USER ELEMENT

COMMON SERVICE ELEMENTS

FIGURE 13

The advanced definition in the CCITT OSI Reference Model identifies three categories of service elements (see Figure 13) - common, application-specific, and user-specific. The common elements furnish the capabilities for an OSI communication independent of the nature of the specific application. The application-specific elements are required by certain categories of applications to support the functions of the information transfer process, such as file transfer, virtual terminal, and job transfer and manipulation. The user-specific elements apply to the functions that are unique to the specific application area, such as airline reservations and banking.

For particular communications, functions from all three service elements may be invoked. While the common elements provide and control the access of the AP to the OSIE, the file transfer elements may be used from the application-specific elements together with electronic funds transfer elements that are user-specific. As a result, eventually there will be a large number of protocols developed for the application layer to meet the wide variety of specific user needs. Work in the area of file transfer and virtual terminal is now making good progress in developing general-purpose Application Layer protocols.

Presentation Layer

The Presentation Layer ensures that the information is delivered to the communicating application process in a form that can be used and understood. While the meaning - semantics - of the information is fully preserved, the format and language differences - syntax - are resolved.

If the communicating application processes both use the same syntax, the functionality of the Presentation Layer does not have to be invoked. With open systems, however, this is not always the normal situation. Therefore, the Presentation Layer provides for syntax selection to specify the format of the data and choose from alternative encodings.

Within a communication, it is possible to have the information appear in three different syntaxes - local to source, local to destination, and between Presentation Layer entities. The illustration in Figure 14 shows an example where three syntaxes are used, French, English, and German, and where the translation is accomplished in both end-systems.

Work is proceeding well in this area. ECMA has issued a general-purpose data-presentation protocol. In CCITT there is an active issue to resolve the presentation syntax and protocol for Videotex applications. There are presently 15 possible code sets that can be employed out of the North American and European proposals. The issue at hand is to resolve a common procedure for selecting the appropriate code set for a particular Videotex communication.

PRESENTATION LAYER

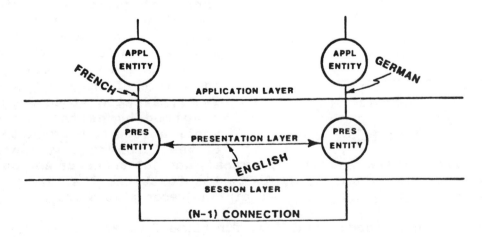

FIGURE 14

Session Layer

The Session Layer provides the means for the cooperating presentation entities to organize and synchronize their dialog and manage their data exchange. As with other layers, the Session Layer provides a connection to bind the upper layer entities and application processes into a logical communicating relationship.

As shown in Figure 15, consecutive session connections may be established and terminated over one continuous transport connection. On the other hand, one continuous session connection can be maintained over a number of transport connections that are established and terminated sequentially. Before connections are released, however, the session entity ensures that all the information en route has been received at the destination, so data are not inadvertently lost.

Both normal and expedited data exchange can take place. The expedited data may bypass normal data flow to facilitate recovery procedures or some other occasional special procedure needed for operation.

A quarantine service is provided by the Session Layer so data can be held and released for delivery to the destination only upon explicit command from the source. It may also be decided by the source, after preparing the quarantined data, that it is not to be delivered and is to be purged. (This feature was challenged and was omittedinthefinalversions.)

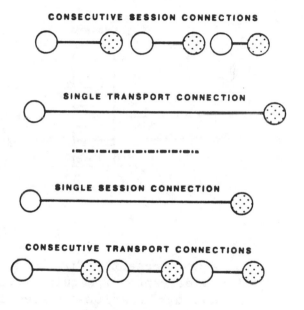

SESSION CONNECTIONS

CONSECUTIVE SESSION CONNECTIONS

SINGLE TRANSPORT CONNECTION

SINGLE SESSION CONNECTION

CONSECUTIVE TRANSPORT CONNECTIONS

FIGURE 15

The Session Layer also provides for interaction management of the communication. In applications where dialog control is needed, management of whose turn is it to send is handled - two-way alternate or two-way simultaneous. When errors occur in the data flow, a resynchronization procedure can be invoked to recover the missing data.

Currently there are two standards published for session protocols. The first is CCITT Recommendation S.62, which was developed initially for the new Teletex services - communication among office word processing systems. CCITT is using this as the basis of further work for facsimile and videotex services as well as a general purpose superset. ECMA published their first session protocol standard, ECMA 75, in January 1982. This will also serve for initial implementations and provide a basis for further work. In June 1982, ISO/TC 97/SC 16 passed a resolution that would enable the draft Session Protocol to be balloted as a Draft Proposal in early 1983.

Transport Layer

The Transport Layer is the lowest layer, whose peer entities are always in the communicating end-systems (see Figure 16). The functions of this layer do not become involved in an intervening telecommunications network or relay nodes. The basic purpose of the Transport Layer is to provide a consistent Transport Service in association with the lower three layers. It will optimize the use of the network services and correct for deficiencies in quality of service to meet the requirements of the upper layers and communicating application processes.

TRANSPORT CONNECTION

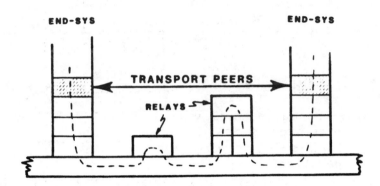

FIGURE 16

There are presently five classes of transport protocols being developed to meet a wide range of requirements. Since the Transport Layer is the bridge between the application-related functions and the transmission-related functions, it is key to the operation of the OSI. If the underlying network services are poor and the application requires a high quality of service, the transport protocol must take care of the differences. On the other hand, if the network services meet the requirements of the application, little transport functionality is needed.

Among the functions that may be performed by the Transport Layer are: establishment of transport connections, error recovery, multiplexing, flow control, and error detection. As with other layers, only the functions that are needed for the particular situation are invoked for a specific communication. These can be negotiated during the establishment of the communication.

In 1980 CCITT published the first transport protocol in Recommendation S.70 for the new teletex services. It was a very minimal protocol to serve the specific application. In January 1981, ECMA published their transport protocol, ECMA 72. This has served as the basis for the further work in both ISO and CCITT. The National Bureau of Standards has also contributed to the development of the highly functional class 4 of the family of transport protocols. In June 1982, ISO/TC 97/SC 16 approved the draft Transport Protocol to beballoted as a Draft Proposal. If all goes well, it could be approved by mid-1983.

Network Layer

The Network Layer is responsible for the routing and relay functions through switched telecommunications media. It provides the network connection between transport entities and can multiplex two or more network connections over a single data link access to a relay node, as shown in Figure 17.

NETWORK ROUTING & SWITCHING

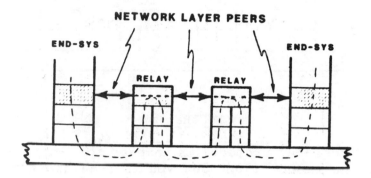

FIGURE 17

Among the other services that the Network Layer provides are both normal and expedited data transfer, error notification, peer flow control, sequenced data, and reset. Another service optionally provided is receipt confirmation. When requested by the transport entity, the network entity will monitor the delivery and receipt of information to the destination transport entity. When the destination transport entity returns an acknowledgement to the network entity, notification is conveyed to the source transport entity via the network peer protocol and indication acknowledge primitive.

As a result of the ISO/TC 97/SC 16 meeting in Tokyo inJune 1982, the receipt confirmation service will be recognized by the OSI Reference Model for optional use by only one class of Transport Layer protocol when the features of CCITT Recommendation X.25 are applied.

Data Link Layer

The Data Link Layer is responsible for the reliable transfer of information over the physical transmission media. A connection between end-systems may comprise a number of data links in tandem (see Figure 18) - each functioning independently, but contributing to the total communication process.

The Data Link Layer provides the synchronization of the information to delimit the flow of bits from the Physical Layer and give it identity. It also provides for peer flow control of the information so that receiving buffers do not become overloaded. Finally, the Data Link Layer provides for detection of transmission errors and mechanisms to recover from lost, errored, or duplicated information.

TANDEM DATA LINKS

ERROR CONTROL
FRAMING
FLOW CONTROL

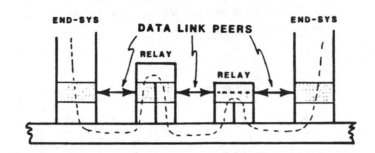

FIGURE 18

If a fully functional protocol is invoked for this layer, upper layers can assume that the information received is free of transmission errors, although there is always a finite probability that there will be undetected errors.

Existing protocols that fall within the Data Link Layer are the well-established character-oriented procedures, ANSI X3.28 or ISO 1745, known as basic mode or Bisync. The new bit-oriented procedures of ANSI X3.66, Advanced Data Communication Control Procedures (ADCCP), ISO's High Level Data Link Control (HDLC), LAP B of CCITT Recommendation X.25, and the single link procedure of CCITT Recommendation X.75 are also within the definition of the OSI Data Link Layer.

Physical Layer

The Physical Layer provides the functional and procedural characteristics to activate, maintain, and deactivate the physical link through the transmission media. In ISO's DIS 7498 the Physical Layer definition also includes the electrical and mechanical characteristics. These have been eliminated from the advanced CCITT draft of the OSI Reference Model. Since layer entities deal only with logical relationships, CCITT proposes that the electrical and mechanical characteristics actually represent the physical interface with the transmis-

PHYSICAL LAYER CONNECTIONS

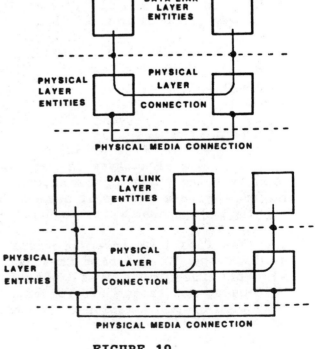

FIGURE 19

sion media. Thus the logical physical connection between peers, when activated, does not directly represent the physical media. The physical media is
outside of the OSIE and only represents the path over which the bits flow.

The Physical Layer deals only with bits received from and passed up to
the Data Link Layer. It may provide a multiplexing function for multiple data
links over a single Physical Layer connection. Physical Layer connections may
be either point-to-point or multipoint, as shown in Figure 19. The relay
function also applies where the connection is made up of tandem transmission
media.

Existing standards within the Physical Layer include the well-known EIA
RS-232-C as well as EIA RS-449, CCITT V.24, and physical elements of CCITT
Recommendation X.21.

CONCLUSION

During the first four years of the OSI development work, substantial
progress has been made through active and intense effort. Now that the basic
structure and principles are well agreed upon, the progress of the work is
gaining a much more rapid pace. If one asks, "When will OSI be finished?" the
answer is "never." The work will be ongoing and evolutionary as technology
advances and new requirements emerge. Those that start applying the OSI
principles now will also be able to evolve their systems with the OSI work.
Where particular parts are not complete, proprietary designs will have to be
employed, but if they are done within the OSI framework, they can be replaced
with OSI standards in the future.

The approval process in ISO is slow; therefore, a delay of 18 to 24
months can be expected from completion of a Draft Proposal to final approval
of the International Standard. The CCITT, however, has speedier mechanisms
for timely approval when needed.

The ISO Reference Model DIS 7498 is expected to be approved by the end of
1982, while the more advanced version for CCITT Applications is expected to be
processed under the accelerated procedures and approved by Spring of 1983.

The Transport protocol started the ISO approval process in June 1982, and
CCITT may invoke the accelerated procedures, which could give overall approval
by mid-1983. The work on Session Layer protocols is advancing, with ISO and
CCITT drafts expected in 1983. It should be noted that ECMA 75 and CCITT
Recommendation S.62 already exist.

The remaining upper layer work is also making progress, with mature
drafts expected in 1984. Again ECMA is pioneering the way and will be issuing
the first standards for the Presentation and Application Layers during 1982
and 1983.

In addition to the protocols, active work is underway to develop a formal
specification language that will be used to define unambiguously the OSI peer
protocols as well as the OSI Reference Model itself. This work is expected to
be completed by 1984. Activity on the OSI management aspects and associated
protocols is just getting underway, but the pace is expected to quicken, so
the results should be only a couple of years away.

The OSI Reference Model presently deals only with a connection-oriented mode of operation. That is where a path for the communication to follow is established prior to the communication. A connectionless mode of operation also has some popularity and is being prepared as an addendum to the OSI Reference Model. Connectionless communications do not pre-establish a path, but route individual units of information as they are sent. The optional datagram service in CCITT Recommendation X.25 is an example of connectionless operation, while virtual circuit service is an example of a connection-oriented communication.

Some think the above statements may be very optimistic, but industry is quickly realizing the importance of the new generation of standards for distributed information systems. These are key to the realization of compatible operation worldwide. The days are now passing where any one manufacturer's design becomes the de facto standard in the market place. OSI is leading the way to sensible, usable standards that will serve the widest range of interests and applications in the very near future.

Network Protocols

ANDREW S. TANENBAUM

Wiskundig Seminarium, Vrije Universiteit, Amsterdam, The Netherlands

During the last ten years, many computer networks have been designed, implemented, and put into service in the United States, Canada, Europe, Japan, and elsewhere. From the experience obtained with these networks, certain key design principles have begun to emerge, principles that can be used to design new computer networks in a more structured way than has traditionally been the case. Chief among these principles is the notion of structuring a network as a hierarchy of layers, each one built upon the previous one. This paper is a tutorial about such network hierarchies, using the Reference Model of Open Systems Interconnection developed by the International Organization for Standardization as a guide. Numerous examples are given to illustrate the principles.

Key Words and Phrases: computer network, data communication, ISO OSI Reference Model, layered architecture, network, protocol

CR Categories: 1.3, 4.9, 6.9

INTRODUCTION

Ten years ago, only a handful of computer networks existed, mostly experimental networks built by research organizations. Today dozens of national and international networks and innumerable local networks operate on a commercial basis around the clock. From the beginning, many networks were designed hierarchically, as a series of layers, each one building on the one below. At first, each network design team started out by choosing its own set of layers. However, in the past few years, a consensus has begun to develop among network designers, a consensus embodied in the International Organization for Standardization's Reference Model of Open Systems Interconnection (ISO OSI). In this paper we present an informal introduction to computer networking using this model as a guide. A more thorough treatment of the ISO OSI model itself can be found in ZIMM80.

Before getting into the subject of network protocols, it is worth saying a few words about what we mean by a computer network. A computer network is a collection of computers, called *hosts*, that communicate with one another. The hosts may be large multiprogrammed mainframes or small personal computers. Networks can be classified as *local networks* or *long-haul networks*. The hosts on a local network are typically contained in a single building or campus and are connected by a high-bandwidth cable or other communication medium specifically designed for this purpose. Long-haul networks, in contrast, typically connect hosts in different cities using the public telephone network, an earth satellite, or both.

Local networks are nearly always completely owned by a single organization, whereas long-haul networks normally involve at least two organizations: the *carrier*, which operates the communication facility (telephone lines, microwave dishes, satellite, etc.), and the users, who own the hosts. This division of labor into (1) the provider of the communication facility and (2) the

Computing Surveys, Vol. 13, No. 4, December 1981

CONTENTS

---

users of the communication facility has important ramifications for network architectures, as we shall see later.

The communication facility in a long-haul network is called the (*communication*) *subnet*, and often consists of a collection of minicomputers variously called *IMPs* (interface message processors), *nodes*, or *switches* connected by high-bandwidth leased telephone lines or a satellite. Figure 1 shows a network using telephone lines. Such a network is called a *point-to-point* or *store-and forward* network, as opposed to a *broadcast* network, such as a satellite network. The terms "host," "IMP," and "communication subnet" come from the U.S. Department of Defense's ARPANET, one of the first large-scale networks [McQu77]. We use this terminology gener-

ically because no consensus on nomenclature exists.

When the IMPs are connected by telephone lines, they are normally located on the carrier's premises, with each IMP servicing multiple hosts. To save on long-distance leased-line line charges, hosts and terminals are often funneled through remote concentrators. When the IMPs are connected by a satellite, the IMPs may be located on the customer's premises (e.g., on the roof). Local networks do not have IMPs; instead, each host has an interface card inserted into its backplane to control access to the network. This card is attached to the communication subnet, which is typically just a cable.

Although the ISO Reference Model can be used for both long-haul and local networks, it was designed primarily with the former in mind. Accordingly, in this paper we also treat both kinds of networks, but we emphasize slightly the long-haul variety, since issues such as routing and congestion control play a more prominent role in long-haul networks than in local networks.

In passing, we note that the subject of connecting distinct networks together is an increasingly important one, although it lies beyond the scope of this article. For an introduction to this subject see BOGG80 and POST80.

Protocols

As mentioned above, networks are almost always organized as a hierarchy of layers. Each layer performs a small set of closely related functions. The ISO Reference Model has seven layers:

(1) the physical layer,
(2) the data link layer,
(3) the network layer,
(4) the transport layer,
(5) the session layer,
(6) the presentation layer,
(7) the application layer,

as shown in Figure 2. All layers are present on the hosts, but only layers 1, 2, and 3 are present on the IMPs.

Each layer should be thought of as a program or process (possibly embedded in a hardware device) that communicates with

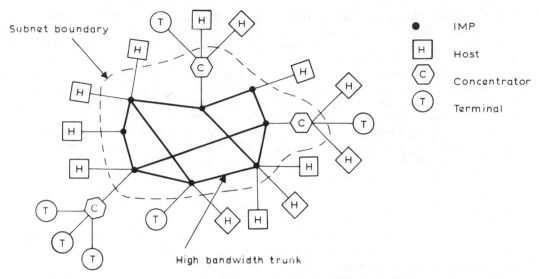

Figure 1. A typical point-to-point long-haul network.

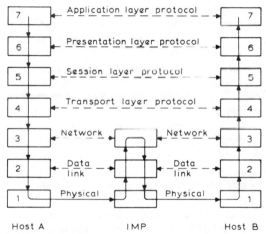

Figure 2. The seven-layer ISO Reference Model.

the corresponding process on another machine. In Figure 2, host layers 1, 2, and 3 think that they are communicating with their corresponding layers on the IMP, called *peers*. (In this example, hosts *A* and *B* are serviced by a common IMP; in general, multiple IMPs may intervene.) Layers 4–7, in contrast, communicate directly with their peer layers on the other host. The rules governing the layer *k* conversation are called the *layer k protocol*. The ISO model thus has seven protocols.

In reality, data are not transmitted horizontally, from machine to machine within a given layer, but are passed vertically down

the layers of the sending machine and up the layers of the receiving machine. Only in layer 1 does actual intermachine communication occur. When an application program, running in layer 7 on host *A*, wants to send a message to the application in layer 7 on host *B*, it passes the message down to the presentation layer on its own machine. The presentation layer transforms the data, adds a layer 6 *header* containing control information used by the layer 6 protocol, and passes the resulting message down to the session layer. The session layer then adds its own header and passes the new message down to the transport layer. The complete path from layer 7 on host *A* to layer 7 on host *B* is shown in Figure 2 by the solid line. The boundary between adjacent layers is called an *interface*. The layers, interfaces, and protocols in a network form the *network architecture*.

No layer is aware of the header formats or protocols used by other layers. Layer *k* on the sending machine regards its job as getting the bits that come in from layer *k* + 1 over to the receiving machine somehow (using the services of the lower layers). It neither knows nor cares what the bits mean.

A three-layer analogy may be helpful in understanding how multilayer communication works. Consider the problem of the

Computing Surveys, Vol. 13, No. 4, December 1981

two talking philosophers. Philosopher 1 lives in an ivory tower in Kenya and speaks only Swahili. Philosopher 2 lives in a cave in India and speaks only Telugu. Nevertheless, Philosopher 1 wishes to convey his affection for *Oryctolagus cuniculus* to his Indian colleague (the philosophers are layer 3 peers). Since the philosophers speak different languages, each engages the services of a translator (layer 2 process) and an engineer (layer 1 process).

To convey his thoughts, Philosopher 1 passes his message, in Swahili, to his translator, across the 3/2 interface. The translator may convert it to English, French, Dutch, or some other language, depending only on the layer 2 protocol. The translator then hands his output to his engineer across the 2/1 interface for transmission. The physical mode of transmission may be telegram, telephone, computer network, or something else, depending only on the layer 1 protocol. When the Indian engineer receives the message, he passes it to his translator for rendition into Telugu. Finally, the Indian translator gives the message, in Telugu, to his philosopher.

This analogy illustrates three points. First, each person thinks of his communication as being primarily horizontal, with his peer (although in reality it is vertical, except in layer 1). For example, Philosopher 1 regards himself as conversing with Philosopher 2, even though his only physical communication is with translator 1. Second, actual communication is vertical, not horizontal, except in layer 1. Third, the three protocols are completely independent. The philosophers can switch the subject from rabbits to guinea pigs at will; the translators can switch from English to Dutch at will; the engineers can switch from telegram to telephone at will. The peers in any layer can change their protocol without affecting the other layers. It is for precisely this reason that networks are designed as a series of layers—to prevent changes in one part of the design (e.g., caused by technological advances) from requiring changes in other parts.

Overview of the ISO OSI Layers

The remainder of this article concerns the various layers in the ISO Reference Model,

one section per layer. Before looking at the layers in detail, we first present a brief overview of each layer, to put the hierarchy in perspective.

The physical layer protocol is concerned with the transmission of a raw bit stream. Its protocol designers must decide how to represent 0's and 1's, how many microseconds a bit will last, whether transmission is full- or half-duplex, how the connection is set up and torn down, how many pins the network connector has, what each pin is used for, and other electrical, mechanical, and procedural details.

The data link layer converts an unreliable transmission channel into a reliable one for use by the network layer. The technique for doing so is to break up the raw bit stream into frames, each containing a checksum for detecting errors. (A *checksum* is a short integer that depends on all the bits in the frame so that a transmission error will probably change it and thus be detectable.) The data link protocol usually ensures that the sender of a data frame will repeatedly transmit the frame until it receives an acknowledgment frame from the receiver.

The network layer in a point-to-point network is primarily concerned with routing and the effects of poor routing, namely, congestion. In a broadcast network, routing is not an issue, since only one channel exists.

The task of the transport layer is to provide reliable host-to-host communication for use by the session layer. It must hide all the details of the communication subnet from the session layer, so that, for example, a point-to-point subnet can be replaced by a satellite link without affecting the session, presentation, or application layers. In effect, the transport layer shields the customer's portion of the network (layers 5–7) from the carrier's portion (layers 1–3).

The session layer is responsible for setting up, managing, and tearing down process-to-process connections, using the host-to-host service provided by the transport layer. It also handles certain aspects of synchronization and recovery.

The presentation layer performs generally useful transformations on the data to be sent, such as text compression. It also performs the conversions required to allow an interactive program to converse with any one of a set of incompatible intelligent terminals.

The content of the application layer is up to the users. Nevertheless, standard protocols for specific industries, such as airlines and banking, are likely to develop, although few exist now. For this reason we say no more about the application layer in this paper.

Although the ISO OSI Reference Model says nothing about how the layers are to be implemented, one possible configuration might have the physical layer in hardware, the data link layer in a special protocol chip, the network layer in a device driver, the transport and session layers in the operating system proper, the presentation layer in a set of library routines in the user's address space, and the application layer be the user's program.

At this point we have covered enough background material to say a little bit about the ISO OSI Reference Model itself. Basically, it is a framework for describing layered networks. It discusses the concept of layering in considerable detail, and introduces a uniform terminology for naming the various entities involved. Finally, it specifies the seven layers mentioned thus far, and for each layer gives its purpose, the services provided to the next higher layer, and a description of the functions that the layer must perform. The value of the model is that it provides a uniform nomenclature and a generally agreed upon way to split the various network activities into layers.

However, the ISO OSI Reference Model is *not* a protocol standard. By breaking a network's functions up into layers, it suggests places where protocol standards could be developed (physical layer protocols, data link layer protocols, and so on), but these standards themselves fall outside the domain of the model. With the model in hand, other organizations such as the Consultative Committee for International Telephony and Telegraphy (CCITT), the International Federation for Information Processing (IFIP), and the American National Standards Institute (ANSI) may develop specific protocol standards for the various layers. Although these standards may even-

tually be officially approved by ISO, such work is still in progress and, in any event, falls far outside the scope of the model.

As a final note, before plunging into the details of the various layers, we would like to point out that this article is about network protocols, with the ISO OSI Reference Model used as a guide; it is *not* an article about the model itself. We emphasize the communication algorithms and protocols themselves, a subject about which the Reference Model says nothing.

1. THE PHYSICAL LAYER

In this section we look at a variety of aspects related to the physical layer. Our emphasis is on the conceptual organization of the physical transmission facilities, not on the hardware details themselves. Point-to-point, satellite, and local networks are discussed. We conclude with a brief discussion of the X.21 physical layer protocol.

The function of the physical layer is to allow a host to send a raw bit stream into the network. The physical layer is in no way concerned with the way the bits are grouped into larger units, or what they mean. Nor does it rectify the problem of some bits being garbled by transmission errors. Recovery from such errors is up to the data link layer.

The communication subnet can be organized in one of two ways. In *circuit switching*, a fixed amount of transmission capacity (bandwidth) is reserved when the source initiates a conversation and released only when the conversation is over. The telephone system uses circuit switching. When someone calls a time-sharing service in a distant city, the connection is established after dialing and remains in force until one end hangs up. If the user goes out to lunch while still logged in, the connection remains intact and the charges continue to accumulate, even though the connection is actually idle.

With *packet switching*, in contrast, the user initially sets up a connection between his terminal or host and the nearest IMP, not the destination host. (We assume that the destination host also is connected to some IMP.) Whenever the user has data to send, he sends them to the IMP as a series of *packets*, typically 10–1000 bytes long.

Packets are routed from IMP to IMP within the subnet, until they get to the IMP which services the destination host. No circuits are reserved in advance within the subnet for the terminal-to-host connection (except the terminal-to-IMP and IMP-to-host circuits). Instead, the high-bandwidth IMP–IMP lines are dynamically shared among all the users on a demand basis; IMP–IMP bandwidth is only tied up when data are actually being transmitted.

Although the above discussion is cast in terms of a point-to-point network, the same considerations apply to broadcast channels. If a portion of the channel (e.g., one frequency band) is dedicated to a given conversation throughout its duration, without regard to actual usage, the network is circuit switched. If, however, the channel is dynamically requested, used, and released for every packet, the network is packet switched.

Circuit-switched networks are best suited to communication whose bandwidth requirements do not change much over time. Transmission of human speech is such an application, so it makes sense for the telephone network to be circuit switched. Terminal-to-computer and computer-to-computer traffic, however, is usually bursty. Most of the time there are no data to send, but once in a while a burst of data must be transmitted. For this reason, most computer networks use packet switching to avoid tying up expensive transmission facilities when they are not needed. However, in the future, all digital transmission systems will allow computers to dial a call, send the data, and hang up, all within a few milliseconds. If such systems become widespread, circuit switching may come back into favor.

1.1 The Telephone System

Since most existing long-haul networks use the telephone system for their transmission facilities, we shall briefly describe how the latter is organized. Most telephones are connected to a nearby telephone company switching office by a pair of copper wires known as a *local loop*. The switching offices themselves are connected by high-bandwidth *trunks* onto which thousands of unrelated calls are multiplexed. Although

some trunks utilize copper wire, many utilize microwave relays, fiber optics, or wave guides as the transmission medium.

Because the bandwidth of the local loop is artificially limited to about 3000 Hz (hertz), it is difficult to transmit information over it by using, for example, +5 volts for a binary one and 0 volts for a binary zero. Such square wave signaling depends on high-frequency harmonics that are well above the 3000-Hz cutoff frequency. Only with very low date rates might enough information be below 3000 Hz to be intelligible. Instead, a device called a *modem* is inserted between the host and the telephone line. The input to the modem is pure digital data, but the output is a modulated sine wave with a base frequency of generally between 1000 and 2000 Hz. Since the modulated sine wave has fewer high-frequency components than the original square wave, it is affected less by the limited bandwidth.

A sine wave has three properties that can be modulated to transmit information: an amplitude, a frequency, and a phase. In amplitude modulation, two different amplitude values are used to represent 0 and 1. In frequency modulation, different frequencies are used for 0 and 1, but the amplitude is never varied. In phase modulation, neither the amplitude nor the frequency is varied, but the phase of the sine wave is abruptly switched to send data. In the most common encoding scheme, phase shifts of 45, 135, 225, and 315 degrees are used to send 00, 01, 10, and 11, respectively. In other words, each phase shift sends two bits. The three methods can be combined to increase the transmission capacity.

Many such transmission systems have been standardized and form an important class of physical layer protocols. Unfortunately, in many cases, the standards in the United States and Canada differ from those used by the rest of the world. For example, those ubiquitous 300-bit-per-second frequency modulation modems found near terminals around the world use different signaling frequencies in North America and Europe.

Probably the best known physical layer standard at present is RS-232-C, which specifies the meaning of each of the 25 pins on a terminal connector and the protocol governing their use. However, a new standard, RS-449, has been developed to replace this aging workhorse. RS-449 is upward compatible with RS-232-C but uses a 37-pin connector to accommodate the new signals. Unfortunately, 37 pins are insufficient, so users wishing to take advantage of all the features of RS-449 (notably the secondary channel) need a second 9-pin connector as well.

The transmission technology and protocols used on the interoffice trunks are different from those used on the local loop. In particular, digital rather than analog techniques are becoming increasingly widespread. The most common digital system is *pulse code modulation* (PCM), in which the analog signal coming in from the local loop is digitized by sampling it 8000 times per second. Eight bits (seven data and one control) are transmitted during each 125-μs (microsecond) sampling period. In North America, 24 such PCM channels are grouped together into 193-bit frames, with the last bit being used for synchronization. With 8000 193-bit frames per second, the gross data rate of this system, known as T1, is 1.544 Mbits/s (megabits per second). In Europe, the 1.544-Mbit/s PCM standard uses all 8 bits for data, with the 193rd bit (which is attached to the front rather than rear of the frame) used for signaling. Two different (and incompatible) 32-channel PCM standards running at 2.048 Mbits/s are also widely used outside North America. For more information about the telephone system see DAVI73 and DOLL78.

1.2 Communication Satellites

Although most existing long-haul networks use leased telephone circuits to connect the IMPs, satellite-based networks are becoming increasingly common. A communication satellite is a big repeater in the sky. Incoming signals are amplified and rebroadcast by a transponder on the satellite. The upward and downward signals use different frequencies to avoid interference. A typical communication satellite has 5–10 independent transponders, each with a capacity of about 50 Mbits/s.

Communication satellites are put into geosynchronous equatorial orbit at an altitude of 36,000 kilometers to make them appear stationary in the sky when viewed from the earth. Consequently, the ground station antenna can be pointed at the satellite when the antenna is installed and never moved. A moving satellite would require a much more expensive steerable antenna and would also have the disadvantage of being on the other side of the earth half the time. On the other hand, the great altitude required to achieve a 24-hour period implies an up-and-down propagation delay of 270 ms (milliseconds), which seriously affects the data link layer protocols and response time.

To avoid mutual interference, communication satellites using the 4/6-GHz (gigahertz) frequency band must be separated by an angle of 4 degrees as viewed from the earth. Since some orbit slots have been allocated by international agreement to television, military, and other use, the number of equatorial orbit slots available to data communication is limited. (As an aside, the allocation of orbit slots has been a political battleground, with every country, especially those in the Third World, asking for its fair share of slots for the purpose of renting them back to those countries able to launch satellites.) The 12/14-GHz band has also been allocated to data communication. At these frequencies, an orbit spacing of 1 degree is sufficient, providing four times as many slots. Unfortunately, because water is an excellent absorber of these short microwaves, multiple ground stations and elaborate switching are needed in order to avoid rain.

Three modes of operation have been proposed for satellite users. The most direct but most expensive mode is to put a complete ground station with antenna on the user's roof. This approach is already feasible for large multinational corporations and will become feasible for medium-sized ones as costs decline. The second approach is to put a small, cheap antenna on the user's roof to communicate with a shared satellite ground station on a nearby hill. The third approach is to access the ground station via a cable (e.g., a leased telephone circuit or even the same cable used for cable television).

Computing Surveys, Vol. 13, No. 4, December 1981

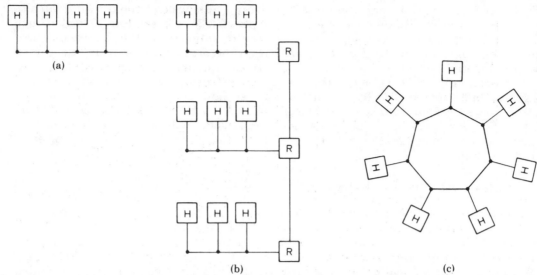

Figure 3. Local network topologies. (a) Linear cable with four hosts. (b) Segmented cable with repeaters and hosts. (c) Ring.

Physical layer satellite protocols typically have many PCM channels multiplexed on each transponder beam. Sometimes they are dedicated (circuit switched); at other times they are dynamically assigned as needed (packet switched). For more information about communication satellites see MART78.

1.3 Local Networks

In most local networks, the hosts are connected by a linear, tree-shaped, or ring-shaped cable, as shown in Figure 3. In Figure 3a, all hosts tap onto a common cable. In Figure 3b, multiple cables are used (e.g., one per floor of an office building), with repeaters connecting the segments. In Figure 3c, all hosts tap onto a unidirectional ring.

A widely imitated linear or tree-shaped local network is the Ethernet™ network [METC76]. The proper term for this kind of network is CSMA/CD (Carrier Sense Multiple Access/Collision Detect), although many people incorrectly use the term "Ethernet" (which is a trademark of the Xerox Corporation) in a generic sense. In these networks, only one packet may be on the cable at any instant. The cable is known as the *ether*, after the luminiferous ether through which electromagnetic radiation was once alleged to propagate. The principle behind CSMA/CD is simple: when a

host wishes to send a packet, it first listens to the ether to see if the ether is being used. If it is, the host waits until the current transmission finishes; if not, the host begins transmitting immediately.

The interface hardware must detect collisions caused by two hosts simultaneously starting a transmission. Collision detection is done using analog circuitry, in essence monitoring the ether to see if it agrees with the signal being transmitted. When a host interface (the analog of an IMP in this system, since the ether itself is totally passive) detects a collision, it informs the data link layer. The collision recovery action consists of aborting the current transmission, broadcasting a noise burst to make sure that everyone else detects the collision as well, waiting a random length of time, and then trying again. Collision detection is only feasible if the round-trip propagation delay is short compared to the packet transmission time, a condition that can be met with cable networks, but not, for example, with satellite networks.

Cable networks similar to the Xerox Ethernet network, but without the collision detect feature, also exist. Network designers can trade off the cost of collision detection circuitry against the time lost by not aborting colliding packets quickly.

Ring nets use a different principle: in effect, the whole ring is a giant circular shift

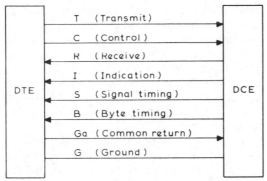

Figure 4. The DTE/DCE interface in X.21.

register. After each shift, the host interface can read or write the bit just shifted into it. Several different kinds of rings have been proposed [CLAR78, FARB72, FRAS75, LIU78, WILK79], differing primarily in their layer 2 organizations, which we describe later. Both CSMA/CD networks and rings typically operate at data rates of 1–10 Mbits/s. A substantial bibliography about local networks can be found in FREE80 and SHOC81.

1.4 An Example Physical Layer Protocol: X.21

At present, most physical layer standards, like RS-232-C and RS-449, utilize analog signaling. In the future, true digital interfaces will be needed. Recognizing this need, CCITT, the international standardization body for telephony, has developed a fully digital interface called *X.21*. X.21 is intended to be used to connect a host computer to a network. This connection remains established as long as the host wants to communicate with the network. Consequently, X.21 is a circuit-switched protocol, but host–host connections set up over the X.21 line may be either circuit switched or packet switched.

In X.21 terminology, the host is a *DTE* (Data Terminal Equipment) and the IMP is a *DCE* (Data Circuit-Terminating Equipment). The DTE–DCE interface consists of eight lines, as shown in Figure 4. The *S* line provides a clock signal to define bit boundaries. The (optional) *B* line provides a pulse every eighth bit, to allow byte alignment. The *C* and *I* lines are used for control signaling, analogous to the on-hook/off-hook signal on a telephone. The *T* and *R* lines are used for data and also for signaling.

To see how X.21 works, let us examine how a DTE calls another DTE, talks to it, and then hangs up. When the interface is idle, *T*, *R*, *C*, and *I* are all 1. The series of events is as follows (with a telephone analogy in parentheses):

(1) DTE drops *T* and *C* (DTE picks up phone).
(2) DCE sends "++++++···+++" on *R* (DCE sends dial tone).
(3) DTE sends callee's address on *T* (DTE dials number).
(4) DCE sends call progress signals on *R* (phone rings).
(5) DCE drops *I* to 0 (callee answers phone).
(6) Full duplex data exchange on *T* and *R* (talk).
(7) DTE raises *C* to 1 (DTE says goodbye).
(8) DCE raises *I* to 1 (DCE says goodbye).
(9) DCE raises *R* to 1 (DCE hangs up).
(10) DTE raises *T* to 1 (DTE hangs up).

The call progress signals in Step 4 tell whether the call has been put through, and if not, why not. The shutdown procedure in Steps 7–10 operates in two phases. After either party has said goodbye, that party may not send more data but it must continue listening for incoming data. When both sides have said goodbye, they then hang up, returning the interface to idle state, with 1's on all four lines. RS-449 and X.21 are described in more detail in BERT80 and FOLT80.

2. THE DATA LINK LAYER

As we have seen, neither X.21, RS-232-C, nor any other physical layer protocol makes any attempt to detect or correct transmission errors. Nor do these protocols recognize the possibility that the receiver cannot accept data as fast as the sender can transmit them. Both of these problems are handled in the data link layer. In the following sections we first discuss the relevant principles and then we give an example of a widely used data link protocol, HDLC (High-Level Data Link Control). Following the HDLC example, we look at some data link protocols for satellite and local networks.

As mentioned earlier, the approach used in the data layer is to partition the raw physical layer bit stream into frames so each transmitted frame can be acknowledged if need be. An obvious question is: "How are frames delimited?" In other words, how can the receiver tell where one frame ends and the next one begins?

Three methods are in common use on long-haul networks: *character count, character stuffing,* and *bit stuffing.* With the first method, each frame begins with a fixed-format frame header that tells how many characters are contained in the frame. Thus, by simply counting characters, the receiver can detect the end of the current frame and the start of the following one. The method has the disadvantage of being overly sensitive to undetected transmission errors which affect the count field; it also has the disadvantage of enforcing a specific character size. Furthermore, lost characters wreak havoc with frame synchronization. Digital Equipment Corporation's DDCMP (Digital Data Communication Message Protocol) uses the character count method, but few other protocols do. Use of character counts to delimit frames is likely to diminish in the future.

The second method for delimiting frames, character stuffing, is to terminate each frame with a special "end-of-frame" character. The problem here is what to do with "end-of-frame" characters that accidently appear in the data (e.g., in the middle of a floating point number). The solution is to insert an "escape" character before every accidental "end-of-frame" character. Now what about accidental "escape" characters? These are rendered as two consecutive escapes. Although these conventions eliminate all ambiguity, they do so at the price of building a specific character code into the protocol. IBM's BISYNC (BInary SYNchronous Communication) protocol uses character stuffing, but, like all other such protocols, it is gradually becoming obsolete.

Modern data link protocols for long-haul networks all use bit stuffing, a technique in which frames are delimited by the bit pattern 01111110. Whenever five consecutive one bits appear in the data stream, a zero bit is "stuffed" into the bit stream (normally by hardware). Doing so prevents user data from interfering with framing, but does not impose any character size on the data.

On local networks, one can use any of the above methods, or a fourth method: detecting frames by the presence or absence of a signal on the cable. This method is much more direct, but it is not applicable to long-haul networks.

Virtually all data link protocols include a checksum in the frame header or trailer to detect, but not correct, errors. This approach has traditionally been used because error detection and retransmission requires fewer bits on the average than forward error correction (e.g., with a Hamming code). However, with the growing use of satellites, the long propagation delay makes forward error correction increasingly attractive.

A simple checksum algorithm is: compute the Exclusive OR of all the bytes or words as they are transmitted. This algorithm will detect all frames containing an odd number of bits in error, or a single error burst of length less than the checksum, and many other combinations. In practice, a more complex algorithm based on modulo 2 polynomial arithmetic is used [PETE61, SLOA75].

2.1 Stop-and-Wait Protocols

As a first example of a data link layer protocol, consider a host *A* wishing to send data to another host *B* over a perfectly reliable channel. At first glance you might think that *A* could just send at will. However, this idea does not work, since *B* may not be able to process the data as fast as they come in. If *B* had an infinite amount of buffer space, it could store the input for subsequent processing. Unfortunately, no host has infinite storage. Consequently, a mechanism is needed to throttle *A* into sending no faster than *B* can process the data. Such mechanisms are called *flow control* algorithms. The simplest one calls for *A* to send a frame and then wait for *B* to send explicit permission to send the next frame. This algorithm, called *stop-and-wait,* is widely used.

More elaborate protocols are needed for actual channels that make errors. An obvious extension to our basic protocol is to

Sender

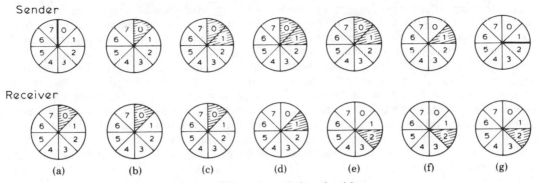

Receiver

      (a)   (b)   (c)   (d)   (e)   (f)   (g)

Figure 5. The sliding-window algorithm.

have A put a sequence number in each data link frame header and to have B put in each acknowledgment frame both a sequence number and a bit telling whether the checksum was correct or not. Whenever A received a negative acknowledgment frame (i.e., one announcing a checksum error), it could just repeat the frame.

Unfortunately, this protocol fails if either data or acknowledgment frames can be lost entirely in noise bursts. If a frame is lost, A will wait forever, creating a deadlock. Consequently, A must time out and repeat a frame if no acknowledgment is forthcoming within a reasonable period. Since each frame bears a sequence number, no harm is done if A has an itchy trigger finger and retransmits too quickly; however, some bandwidth is lost.

2.2 Sliding-Window Protocols

Stop-and-wait works well if the propagation time between the hosts is negligible. Consider, for a moment, how stop-and-wait works when 1000-bit frames are sent over a 1-Mbit/s satellite channel:

Time (ms)	Event
0	A starts sending the frame
1	Last bit sent; A starts to wait
270	First bit arrives at B
271	Last bit arrives at B
271	B sends a short acknowledgment
541	The acknowledgment arrives at A

For each millisecond of transmission, A has to wait 540 ms. The channel utilization is thus 1/541, or well below 1 percent. A better protocol is needed.

One such protocol is the *sliding-window* protocol, in which the sender is allowed to have multiple unacknowledged frames outstanding simultaneously. In this protocol, the sender has two variables, S_L and S_U, that tell which frames have been sent but not yet acknowledged. S_L is the lowest numbered frame sent but not yet acknowledged. The upper limit, S_U, is the first frame not yet sent. The current send window size is defined as $S_U - S_L$.

The receiver also has two variables, R_L and R_U, indicating that a frame with sequence number N may be accepted, provided that $R_L \leq N < R_U$. If $R_U - R_L = 1$, then the receiver has a window of size 1, that is, it only accepts frames in sequence. If the receiver's window is larger than 1, the receiver's data link layer may accept frames out of order, but normally it will just buffer such frames internally, so that it can pass frames to the network layer in order.

To keep sequence numbers from growing without bound, arithmetic is done modulo some power of 2. In the example of Figure 5, sequence numbers are recorded modulo 8. Initially (Figure 5a), $S_L = 0$, $S_U = 0$, $R_L = 0$, and $R_U = 1$ (receiver window size is 1 in this example). The current window is shown shaded in the figure. When the data link layer on the sending machine receives a frame to send (from the network layer), it sends the frame and advances the upper edge of its window by 1, as shown in Figure 5b. When it receives the next frame from the network layer, it sends the frame and advances the window again (Figure 5c). When the first frame arrives at the receiver, the receiver's window is rotated by advanc-

Computing Surveys, Vol. 13, No. 4, December 1981

ing both edges (Figure 5d), and an acknowledgment is sent back. If frame 1 arrives at the receiver before the acknowledgment gets back to the sender, the state will be as shown in Figure 5e. When the first acknowledgment arrives, the lower edge of the sender's window is advanced (Figure 5f). Figure 5g shows the variables after both acknowledgments arrive.

As with stop-and-wait, the sliding-window protocol uses timeouts to recover from lost frames. The sender maintains a timer for each frame currently in its window. Whenever the lower edge of the window is advanced, the corresponding timer is stopped. Suppose, for example, that frames 0–4 are transmitted, but frame 1 is lost. The receiver will acknowledge frame 0, but discard frames 2–4 as they arrive, because they are outside the receive window (still size 1 in our example). Eventually, frames 1–4 will all time out and be retransmitted.

How many frames may our example sender have outstanding at any instant? The answer is seven, not eight, as might at first appear. To see why, consider the following scenario:

(1) The sender transmits frames 0–7.
(2) All eight frames arrive and are acknowledged.
(3) All eight acknowledgments are lost.
(4) The sender times out and retransmits the eight frames.
(5) The receiver unknowingly accepts the duplicates.

The problem occurs after Step 2, when the receiver's window has rotated all the way around and it is prepared to accept frame 0 again. Unfortunately, it cannot distinguish frame 9 from frame 0, so the stream of frames passed to the network layer will contain undetected duplicate frames.

The solution is to restrict the sender's window to seven outstanding frames. Then, after Step 2 above, the receiver will be expecting frame 7, and will reject all the duplicate frames, informing the sender after each rejection that it expects frame 7 next.

In the above example, whenever a frame is lost, the receiver is obligated to discard subsequent frames, even though they are correctly received. To avoid this inefficiency, we can allow the receiver's window

to be greater than 1. Now let us look at the lost frame problem again, with both the sender's and receiver's windows of size 7. When frames 2–4 come in, the receiver keeps them internally. Eventually frame 1 times out and is retransmitted. The receiver replies to the correct receipt of frame 1 by saying that it expects frame 5 next, thereby implicitly acknowledging frames 2–4 and preventing their retransmission. With frames 1–4 now safely in hand, the data link layer can pass them to the network layer in sequence, thus completely shielding the latter from the lost frame and its recovery. This strategy is often called *selective repeat*, as opposed to the *go back n* strategy implied by a receiver window size of 1.

Unfortunately, even with the window settings used above, the protocol can fail. Consider the following scenario:

(1) The sender transmits frames 0–6.
(2) All frames arrive; the receiver's window is now 7, 0, 1, 2, 3, 4, 5.
(3) All seven acknowledgments are lost.
(4) The sender times out and retransmits frames 0–6.
(5) The receiver buffers frames 0–5 and says it wants frame 7 next.
(6) The sender transmits frames 7–13 (sequence numbers 7, 0, 1, 2, 3, 4, 5).
(7) The receiver accepts frame 7 but rejects frames 0–5 as duplicates.

At this point the receiver has frames 7, 0, 1, 2, 3, 4, and 5 buffered. It passes them all to the unsuspecting network layer. Consequently, undetected duplicates sneak through again. To prevent this, the window size must be restricted to not more than half the size of the sequence number space. With such a restriction, the receiver's window after having received a maximum batch of frames will not overlap what it was before having received the frames. Hence no ambiguity arises about whether a frame is a retransmission or an original.

2.3 An Example Data Link Protocol: HDLC

As an example of a data link protocol that is widely used, we now briefly look at HDLC (High-Level Data Link Control). HDLC has many brothers and sisters (e.g., SDLC, ADCCP, LAP, LAPB), each having

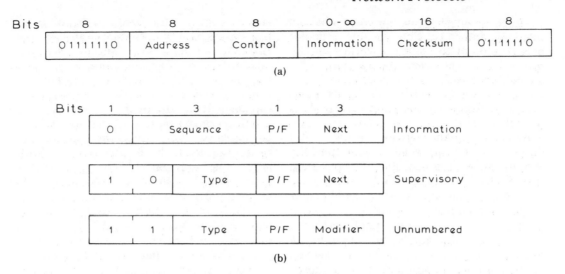

Figure 6. (a) The HDLC frame format. (b) The control byte for the three kinds of frames.

minor, but irritating, differences in the control frames. How this situation came about has to do with how certain large bureaucracies view certain other large bureaucracies, a stone best left unturned here.

HDLC and its friends all use bit stuffing for delimiting frames. Their format is shown in Figure 6a. The *Address* field is used for addressing on multipoint lines (lines connecting more than two computers). The *Control* field is different for each of the three classes of frames (see Figure 6b). In *Information* frames (i.e., ordinary data), the *Sequence* and *Next* fields contain the sequence number of the current frame and of the next frame expected, respectively. When *A* sends a frame to *B*, the *Sequence* field is the number of the frame being sent and the *Next* frame is an acknowledgment to *B* saying that *A* has correctly received all frames sent by *B* up to but not including *Next*. Attaching an acknowledgment field to an outgoing data frame is widely known as *piggybacking*. The practice saves bandwidth by requiring fewer frames. Reducing the number of frames *sent* also reduces the number of frames *received*, and hence reduces the number of I/O interrupts on the receiving machine.

When no reverse traffic is present on which to piggyback acknowledgments, a *Type* = 0 supervisory frame is used. The

other types of supervisory frames are for negative acknowledgment, selective repeat, and receiver temporarily not ready. The *P/F* bit stands for *Poll/Final* and has miscellaneous uses, such as indicating polling frames on multipoint lines and the final frame in a sequence.

Unnumbered frames consist of a hodgepodge of control information and comprise the area of greatest difference between the various HDLC-like protocols. Most of these frames are used to initialize the line and to report certain abnormal conditions.

Although Figure 6 depicts HDLC as having a 3-bit sequence number, an alternate format with 7-bit sequence numbers also exists, for use on satellite or other channels where large windows are needed to keep the channel busy. Gelenbe et al. [GELE78] have constructed a mathematical model of HDLC that can be used to calculate the throughput as a function of window size.

2.4 Channel Allocation in Satellite Networks

At this point we switch from the data link layer of point-to-point networks to that of broadcast networks, in particular, satellite and local networks. Broadcast networks are characterized by having a single channel that is dynamically requested and released by hosts for every packet sent. A protocol is needed for determining who may use the channel when, how to prevent channel overload, and so on. These problems do not occur in point-to-point networks. On the other hand, since every host receives every packet, broadcast networks usually do not have to make any routing decisions. Thus the main function of the network layer is not relevant.

As a consequence of these fundamental differences, it is not really clear where the channel-access protocol should be placed in the ISO OSI Reference Model, which does not mention the issue at all. It could be put in the data link layer, since it deals with getting packets from one machine to the next, but it could equally well be put in the network layer, since it also concerns getting packets from the source host to the destination host. Another argument for putting it in the network layer is that the main task of the access protocol is to avoid congestion on the channel, and congestion control is specifically a network layer function. Last, in most broadcast networks the transport layer is built directly on top of this protocol, or in some cases on top of an internetwork protocol, something lacking in the ISO OSI Reference Model. Nevertheless, we treat the subject as part of the data link layer because the IEEE local network standards committee (802) is probably going to put it there. By analogy, the contention resolution protocol for satellite channels also belongs in the data link layer.

A satellite link can be operated like a terrestrial point-to-point link, providing dedicated bandwidth for each user by time-division or frequency-division multiplexing. In this mode the data link protocols are the same as in point-to-point networks, albeit with longer timeouts to account for the longer propagation delay.

Another mode of operation, however, is to dynamically assign the channel among the numerous competing users. Since their only method of communication is via the channel itself, the protocol used for allocating the channel is nontrivial. Abramson [ABRA70] and Roberts [ROBE73] have devised a method, known as *slotted ALOHA,* that has some interesting properties. In their approach, time is slotted into units of a (fixed-length) packet. During each interval, a host having a packet to send can

either send or refrain from sending. If no hosts use a given slot, the slot is just wasted. If one host uses a slot, a successful transmission occurs. If two or more hosts try to use the same slot, a collision occurs and the slot is also wasted. Note that with satellites the hosts do not discover the collision until 270 ms after they start sending the packets. Owing to this long delay, the collision detection principle from CSMA/CD is not applicable here. Instead, after detecting a collision, each host waits a random number of slots and tries again.

Clearly, if few hosts have packets to send, few collisions will occur and the success rate will be high. If, on the other hand, many hosts have packets to send, many collisions will occur and the success rate will be low. In both cases the throughput will be low: in the first case because of lack of offered traffic, in the second case because of collisions. Hence the throughput versus offered traffic curve starts out low, peaks, and then falls again. Abramson [ABRA73] showed that the peak occurs when the mean offered traffic is one packet per slot, which yields a throughput of $1/e$ or about 0.37 packets per slot. Hence the best one can hope for with slotted ALOHA is a 37 percent channel utilization.

Slotted ALOHA has another problem, in addition to the low throughput: stability. Suppose that an ALOHA system has many hosts. By accident, during one slot k hosts transmit and collide. After detecting the collision, each host decides to retransmit during the next slot with probability p (a parameter of the system). In other words, each host picks a random number between 0 and 1. If the number is less than p, it transmits; otherwise it waits until the next slot to pick another random number.

If $kp \gg 1$, many hosts will retransmit during each succeeding slot and practically nothing will get through. Worse yet, these retransmissions will compete with new packets from other hosts, increasing the number of hosts trying to use the channel, which just makes the problem worse. Pretty soon all hosts will be trying to send and the throughput will approach zero, collapsing the system permanently.

The trick to avoid collapse is to set the parameter p low enough that $kp < 1$ for the

k values expected. However, the lower p is, the longer it takes even to attempt retransmission, let alone succeed. Hence a low value of p leads to a stable system, but only at the price of long delay times.

One way to set p is to use a default value on the first retransmission, say 0.5, on the assumption that two hosts are involved in the collision. On each subsequent collision, halve p. Gerla and Kleinrock [GERL77] have another proposal; they suggest that each host monitor the channel all the time, just to measure the collision rate. When the collision rate is low, the hosts can set p high; when the collision rate is high, the hosts can set p low to minimize collisions and get rid of the backlog, albeit slowly.

A completely different way to avoid collisions is to attempt to schedule the slots in advance rather than have continuous competition for them. Crowther et al. [CROW73] proposed grouping slots into n-slot time slices, with the time slice longer than the propagation delay. In their system, contention is used initially, as described above. Once a host has captured (i.e., successfully used) a slot, it is entitled to use the same slot position in the next slice, forbidding all other hosts from trying to use it. This algorithm makes it possible for a host to transmit a long file without too much pain. If a host no longer needs a slot position, it sets a bit in the packet header that permits other users to contend for the slot the next time around.

Roberts [ROBE73] also proposed a method of reducing contention. His proposal also groups slots into time slices. One slot per slice is divided into minislots and used for reserving regular slots. To send a packet, a host must first compete for a minislot. Since all hosts see the results of the minislot contention, they can all keep track of how long the queue is and hence know who gets to send when. In effect, the use of minislots greatly reduces the amount of time wasted on a collision (like the CSMA/CD rule about aborting collisions as soon as they are detected).

2.5 Channel Allocation in Local Networks

As mentioned earlier, when a CSMA/CD host detects a collision, it jams the channel, aborts the current packet, waits a random time, and tries again. How long should it wait? Metcalfe and Boggs [METC76] decided to use a default maximum time interval on the first collision, with the actual waiting time being picked by multiplying a random number in the range 0.0–1.0 by the maximum time interval. On each successive collision the maximum time interval is doubled and a new random number is generated. They called their algorithm *binary exponential backoff*.

Various other algorithms have been proposed for CSMA/CD, including some that prevent all collisions. For example, Chlamtac [CHLA76], Chlamtac et al. [CHLA79], and Scholl [SCHO76] have suggested slotting time into intervals equal to the channel acquisition time (the round trip propagation delay). After a successful transmission by host n, the next bit slot is then reserved for host $(n + 1)$ (modulo the number of hosts). If the indicated host does not claim its right to use the channel, the next host gets a chance during the succeeding bit slot, and so on. In effect, a virtual baton is passed from host to host, with hosts only allowed to transmit when holding the baton.

Rothauser and Wild [ROTH77] have also proposed a collision-free CSMA/CD protocol. To illustrate their suggestion, we shall assume that there are 1024 hosts, numbered from 0 to 1023 (in binary, although other radices can also be used). After a successful transmission, ten bit slots will be used to determine who goes next. Each host attempts to broadcast its 10-bit number in the ten slots, subject to the rule that as soon as a host realizes that a higher numbered host wants the channel, it must stop trying. If, for example, the first three bits are 011, then some host in the range 368–511 wants the channel, and so hosts below 368 must desist from competing on the current round. No host above 511 wants the channel, as evidenced by the leading 0 bit. In effect, the channel is allocated to the highest numbered contender. Since this system gives high-numbered stations an advantage, it is desirable to make the host numbers virtual, rotating them one position after each successful transmission.

Protocols that allow only a limited number of collisions have also been proposed [CAPE79a, CAPE79b, KLEI78]. Capetanakis'

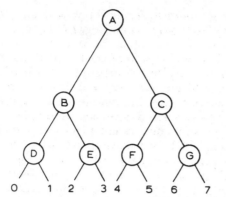

Figure 7. Eight machines organized in Capetanakis' (virtual) tree.

idea is illustrated in Figure 7 for a system with eight hosts. Initially, all hosts may compete. If a collision occurs, only those hosts under node B of the tree, namely, 0, 1, 2, and 3, may compete. If another collision occurs, the only descendants of node D may try, and so forth. As an example, suppose hosts 2, 3, and 4 all want the channel. After initial collisions for A (2, 3, and 4) and B (2 and 3), it will be node D's turn and the channel will lie idle. Next comes node E and another collision. Then 2 and 3 each get a private slot, followed by C. At low load, the algorithm allows pure contention, but under high load it walks the tree looking for hosts that want to send.

Although more could be said about CSMA/CD protocols, we now turn our attention to ring networks. In one of the best-known rings [FARB72], an 8-bit token circulates around the ring when there is no traffic. When a host wants to transmit, it must first capture and destroy the token. Having done so, it may send its packet. When it is finished, it must put the token back, giving the next host downstream a chance to seize it.

If the token is ever lost (e.g., as a result of a ring interface malfunctioning), some mechanism is needed to regenerate it. One possibility is that each host wishing to send must monitor the ring. Having failed to see a token within the worst case interval—namely, all other hosts sending a maximum-length packet—the host generates a new token itself. However, with a little bad luck, two hosts might generate tokens si-

multaneously. Hence, it appears that token recovery in a ring net is similar to contention in CSMA/CD in systems. Clark et al. [CLAR78] have taken this observation to its logical conclusion and proposed a contention ring that is a hybrid of the token ring and CSMA/CD.

Yet another type of ring is exemplified by the Cambridge Ring [NEED79, WILK79]. This 10-Mbit/s ring contains several small slots around it, each slot consisting of 16 bits of data, an 8-bit source address, an 8-bit destination address, a bit telling whether the slot is full or empty, and a few other control bits. To transmit, a host interface just waits for a free slot and fills it up. When the slot arrives at the destination, the receiving interface sets the control bits telling whether it was accepted or not. About 10 μs after transmission, the slot comes back around again so that the sender can find out what happened to it. The sender is not permitted to reuse the slot immediately, as an antihogging measure. By having such small slots and preventing their immediate reuse, the ring guarantees an extremely short delay for small packets, but at the price of higher overhead than the token ring under heavy load.

Still another design is discussed in LIU78. In Liu's design, each ring interface has a shift register equal in length to the maximum packet size. When a host wants to send a packet, it loads up the shift register and inserts the shift register into the ring between two packets. This mechanism leads to low delay, since a host need only wait until the current packet has passed through. When the shift register becomes empty (through a period of low traffic), it can be removed from the ring.

From the above discussion, it should be obvious that many local network protocols have already been devised, with more being threatened all the time. Without standards, the most likely development would be a proliferation of local networks from various vendors, all incompatible; vendor A's terminal would not talk to vendor B's CPU because they would have different protocols embedded in their hardware. In an attempt to nip this incipient chaos in the bud, the Institute of Electrical and Electronics Engineers (IEEE) set up a committee in February 1980 to develop a standard for local network protocols. Although the standard, IEEE 802, was not completed at the time of this writing, the general picture looks as if it will probably be as follows:

The standard treats the physical and data link layers. The physical layer allows for base-band, broad-band, and fiber optics communication, and describes the interfacing of the host (DTE) to the cable. The data link layer handles channel access, as mentioned earlier, as well as addressing, frame format, and control.

The data link layer is split up into two sublayers, media access and data link control, with a third optional sublayer for internetworking (whose presence in the data link layer instead of in the network layer is certainly arguable). The media access sublayer handles channel allocation. It is here that a choice had to be made between CSMA/CD and some kind of ring. The arguments for CSMA/CD were that it was fair, easy to implement on a single chip, had six years of operational experience, and had three major companies (DEC, Intel, and Xerox) already publicly committed to it.

The token ring supporters' counterarguments were as follows: rings, unlike CSMA/CD, provide a guaranteed worst case access time (needed for real-time work, such as speech transmission); rings can be logical as well as physical, accommodating various topologies and allowing important hosts better access by inserting them into the logical ring in several places; and ring performance does not degrade at high load, as does CSMA/CD owing to the many collisions. Unfortunately, neither camp had the necessary two-thirds majority required by IEEE rules, and so a compromise was made in which both CSMA/CD and a token ring were included.

The data link control sublayer was designed to be as compatible with HDLC as possible, on the theory that the last thing the world needed was yet another brand-new data link protocol. Two types of service are provided for: connection oriented and pure datagram. In the former, the data link layer times out and retransmits lost frames, guarantees arrival in sequence, and regulates flow using the standard HDLC sliding-window protocol. In the latter, the data link layer guarantees nothing; once sent, the frame is forgotten (at least by the data link layer).

The major difference between the 802 frame and HDLC's is the presence in 802 of two addresses, source and destination, instead of the one address in HDLC, and the use of variable-length addresses (from 1 to 7 bytes), instead of fixed-length, 1-byte addresses. HDLC was designed for two-party, point-to-point lines, where no address is needed, and for multipoint master/slave lines, in which only the slave's address is needed. In contrast, 802 is aimed at multipoint symmetric lines, where any machine can send to any other machine, and so two addresses are required. The decision to have variable-length addresses up to 7 bytes is intended to allow processes to be designated by a worldwide unique address. Three of the 7 bytes are to be administered by an as-yet-unidentified international organization, and 4 are for local use. Most networks will only need 1- or 2-byte addresses for internal traffic.

3. THE NETWORK LAYER

When a frame arrives at an IMP in a point-to-point network, the data link layer strips off the data link header and trailer and passes what is left, called a *packet*, to the network layer. The network layer must then decide which outgoing line to forward the packet on. It would be nice if such decisions could be made so as to avoid having some lines congested and others idle. Hence congestion control is intimately related to routing. We first look at routing and then at congestion control, both for point-to-point networks. With the channel acquisition protocol for broadcast networks in the data link layer, the network layer for these networks is essentially empty.

Two opposing philosophies exist concerning the network layer. In most local networks and some long-haul networks, the network layer provides a service for delivering independent packets from source to destination with a high probability of success (although less than 1.0). Each packet carried is unrelated to any other packet, past or future, and must therefore carry a full destination address. Such packets are called *datagrams*.

The other approach, taken in many public data networks (especially in Europe), is to require a transmitter to first send a setup packet. The setup packet chooses a route for subsequent traffic and initializes the IMPs along the route accordingly. The user chooses, or is given, a *virtual circuit number* to use for subsequent packets going to the same destination. In this organization, data packets belonging to a single conversation are not independent, since they all follow the same route, determined by the virtual circuit number in them.

The advantage of using virtual circuits is that it guarantees that packets will be delivered in order and helps reduce congestion by making it possible to reserve resources (e.g., buffers) along the route in advance. The disadvantage is that a lot of IMP table space is taken up by idle connections and that there is a lot of overhead in setting up and closing down circuits, the latter a great concern in transaction-oriented database systems [MANN78]. With a datagram system, a query–response requires just two packets. With a virtual circuit system it requires six packets: setup, acknowledgment, query, response, close circuit, and acknowledgment.

3.1 Routing in Point-to-Point Networks

Many routing algorithms have been proposed, for example, BARA64, FRAT73, McQu74, RUDI76, SCHW80, and SEGA81. Below we sketch a few of the more interesting ones. The simplest algorithm is *static* or *directory* routing, in which each IMP has a table indexed by destination, telling which outgoing line to use. When a packet comes in, the destination address is extracted from the network layer header and used as an index into the routing table. The packet is then passed back down to the data link layer (see Figure 2) along with the chosen line number.

A variant algorithm provides two or more outgoing lines for each destination, each with a weight. When a packet arrives, a line is chosen with a probability proportional to its weight. Allowing alternatives eases congestion by spreading the traffic around. Note that when virtual circuits are used

within the subnet, the routing decision is only made for setup packets, not data packets.

Several proposals have been made for determining the routes to be put in the tables. Shortest path routing, which minimizes the number of hops (IMP–IMP lines), is an obvious candidate. In FRAT73 another method, based on flow deviation, is given.

The problem with static routing is just that—it is static—it does not adapt to changing traffic patterns and does not try to route packets around congested areas. One way to have the network adapt is to have one host function as a routing control center. All IMPs send it periodic reports on their queue lengths and line utilizations, from which it computes the best routes and distributes the new routing tables back to the IMPs.

Although seemingly attractive, centralized routing has more than its share of problems [McQu74]. To start with, if the routing control center malfunctions, the network will probably be in big trouble. Second, the complete optimal routing calculation for a large network may require a large dedicated host and even then may not be able to keep up with the traffic fluctuations. Third, since IMPs near the routing control center get their new tables before more distant IMPs do, the network will operate with mixed old–new tables occasionally, a situation that may cause traffic (including the new routing tables) to loop. Fourth, if the network is large, the traffic flow into and out of the routing control center may itself get to be a problem.

One of the earliest routing algorithms [BARA64] adapts to changing traffic, but does so without any central control. In *hot-potato routing*, when a packet arrives, it is assigned to the output line which has the shortest transmission queue. This strategy gets rid of the packet as fast as possible, without regard to where it is going. A much better idea is to combine static information about the suitability of a given output line with the queue lengths. This variant is known as *shortest queue plus bias*. It could be parameterized, for example, to use the shortest queue unless the line is going the wrong way, or to use the statically best line unless its queue exceeds some threshold.

Computing Surveys, Vol. 13, No. 4, December 1981

Algorithms like this are known as *isolated adaptive* algorithms [McQu74].

Rudin's *delta routing* [Rudi76] combines some features from centralized and isolated adaptive algorithms. In this method, IMPs send periodic status reports to the routing control center, which then computes the k best paths from each source to each destination. It considers the top few paths equivalent if they differ (in length, estimated transit time, etc.) by an amount less than some parameter δ. Each IMP is given the list of equivalent paths for each destination, from which it may make a choice based on local factors such as queue lengths. If δ is small, only the best path is given to the IMPs, resulting in centralized routing. If δ is large, all paths are considered equivalent, producing isolated adaptive routing. Intermediate strategies are obviously also possible.

A completely different approach is distributed adaptive routing [McQu74], first used in the ARPANET, but replaced after ten years owing to the problems with looping discussed below. With this algorithm, each IMP maintains a table indexed by destination giving the estimated time to get to each destination and also which line to use. The IMP also maintains an estimate of how long a newly arrived packet would take to reach each neighbor, which depends on the queue length for the line to that neighbor.

Periodically, each IMP sends its routing table to each neighbor. When a routing table comes in, the IMP performs the following calculation for each destination. If the time to get the neighbor plus the neighbor's estimate of the time to get to the destination is less than the IMP's current estimate to that destination, packets to that destination should henceforth be routed to the neighbor.

As a simple example, consider a five-IMP network. At a certain instant, IMP 2 has estimates to all possible destinations, as shown in Figure 8a. Suddenly the routing table from IMP 3 (assumed to be adjacent to IMP 2) arrives, as shown in Figure 8b. Let us assume that IMP 2 estimates the delay to IMP 3 to be 10 ms, on the basis of the size of its transmission queue for IMP 3. IMP 2 now calculates that the transit

Destination

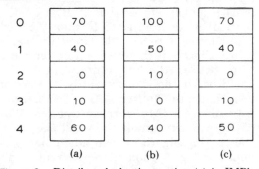

Figure 8. Distributed adaptive routing. (a) An IMP's original routing table. (b) Routing table arriving from a neighboring IMP. (c) The new routing table, assuming a 10-ms delay to the neighbor.

time to IMP 0 via IMP 3 is 10 + 100 ms. Since this time is worse than the 70 ms for its current route, no change is made to entry 0 of the table. Similarly 10 + 50 > 40, and so no change is made for destination 1 either. However, for destination 4, IMP 3 offers a 40-ms delay, which, when combined with the 10-ms delay to get to IMP 3, is still better than the current route (10 + 40 < 60). Therefore, IMP 2 changes its estimate of the time required to get the IMP 4 to 50 ms, and records the line to IMP 3 as the way to get there. The new routing table is given in Figure 8c.

Although this method seems simple and elegant, it has a problem. Suppose that A, B, and C are connected by lines AB and BC. If number of hops is used as a metric, B thinks it is one hop from A, and C thinks it is two hops from A. Now imagine that line AB goes down. B detects the dead line directly and realizes that its delay to A is now infinite via AB. Sooner or later, however, C offers B a route to A of length two hops. B, knowing that line AB is useless, accepts the offer, and modifies its tables to show that A is three hops away via C. At this point B is routing packets destined for A to C, and C is sending them right back again. Having packets loop forever is not considered a good property to have in one's routing algorithm. This particular problem causes great anguish for the transport layer, as we shall see shortly.

To get around the problem of looping packets, several researchers (e.g., Chu78, Sega81) have proposed using the *optimal-*

ity principle to guarantee loop-free routing. This principle states that if B is on the optimal route from A to C, then the best route from B to C falls along the same route. Clearly if there were a better route from B to C, the best route from A to C could use it too. Consequently, the set of best routes to C (or any other destination) from all other IMPs forms a tree rooted at C. By explicitly maintaining all the trees, the routing algorithm can adapt but prevent looping. A good survey of routing algorithms can be found in SCHW80.

3.2 Congestion Control in Point-to-Point Networks

Now we turn to the problem of congestion in point-to-point networks. Actually, little is known about how to deal with it, and all the proposed solutions are rather ad hoc. Davies [DAVI72] suggested starting each network with a collection of special packets called *permits* that would roam about randomly. Whenever a host wanted to send a packet, its IMP would have to capture and destroy a permit before the new packet could be injected into the network.

This mechanism guarantees that the maximum number of packets in the network can never exceed the initial number of permits, which helps somewhat, but still does not guarantee that all the legal packets will not someday end up in one IMP, overloading it. Furthermore, no one has been able to devise a way to regenerate permits lost in IMP crashes (short of deadstarting the whole network, which is unacceptable). If these permits are not generated, carrying capacity will be permanently lost.

Another congestion control scheme is due to Irland [IRLA78]. This scheme calls for IMPs to monitor the utilization of each outgoing line. When a line utilization moves above a trigger value, the IMP sends a *choke packet* back to the source of each new packet needing that line, telling the source to slow down.

Kamoun [KAMO81] has proposed a congestion control scheme based on the observation that when packets must be discarded in an overloaded IMP, some packets are better candidates than others. In particular, if a packet has already made k hops, throwing it away amounts to discarding the investment in resources required to make those k hops. This observation suggests discarding packets with the smallest k values first. A variation of this idea that does not require a hop counter in each packet is to have IMPs discard newly injected packets from local hosts in order to salvage transit traffic with $k \geq 1$.

The limiting case of a congested network is a deadlocked network. If hosts A, B, and C are all full (no free buffers), and A is trying to send to B and B is trying to send to C and C is trying to send to A, a deadlock can occur, as shown in Figure 9.

Merlin and Schweitzer [MERL80a, MERL80b] describe several ways to prevent this kind of *store-and-forward deadlock* from occurring. One way is to provide each IMP with $m + 1$ packet buffers, where m is the longest path in the network. A packet newly arriving in an IMP from a local host goes into buffer 0. At the next IMP along the path it goes in buffer 1. At the following IMP it uses buffer 2. After having made k hops, it goes in buffer k. To see that the algorithm is deadlock free, consider the set of all buffers labeled m. Each buffer is in one of three states:

(1) empty,
(2) holding a packet destined for a local host,
(3) holding a packet destined for a distant host.

In Case 2 the packet can be delivered and the buffer freed. In Case 3 the packet is looping and must be discarded. In all cases the complete set of buffers labeled m can be made empty. Consequently, all packets in buffers labeled $m - 1$ can be either delivered or discarded, one at a time. The process can then be repeated, freeing the buffers labeled $m - 2$, and so on.

Other kinds of deadlocks in computer networks are discussed in GUNT81.

3.3 An Example Network Layer Protocol: X.25

To help standardize public long-haul networks, CCITT has devised a three-layer protocol of its own. The physical layer is X.21 (or X.21 bis, a stopgap analog interface to be used until the digital network arrives).

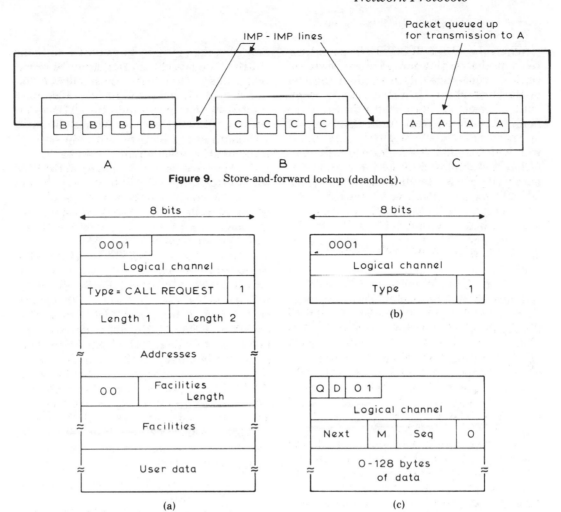

Figure 9. Store-and-forward lockup (deadlock).

Figure 10. X.25 headers. (a) CALL REQUEST packet. (b) Control packet. (c) Data packet.

The data link layer consists of two variants of HDLC (LAP and LAPB). Whether the next layer is network layer protocol or a transport layer protocol is a matter of some debate in the network community. Let us call it a network layer protocol and discuss it now.

X.25 (which is the collective name for all three layers) is virtual circuit oriented [RYBC80]. To set up a virtual circuit, a host (DTE) sends a CALL REQUEST packet into the network. The remote host can either accept or reject the incoming call. If it accepts it, the virtual circuit is set up; otherwise the circuit is cleared.

Figure 10a shows the format of the CALL REQUEST packet. The first 4 bits are 0001.

The next 12 bits are the virtual circuit number chosen by the originating host. The third byte is the type code of CALL REQUEST. The next byte gives the number of decimal digits in the caller's and callee's addresses, followed by up to 30 bytes containing the addresses themselves in binary coded decimal. (The telephone community has been using decimal numbers for 100 years, and old habits die hard.) The *Facilities* field is used to request services such as calling collect. Since the facilities field is variable length, a length field is needed. Finally, the user data field can be used in any way the user chooses, for example, to indicate which process within the called host expects the call.

When the CALL REQUEST packet arrives at the destination, that machine accepts or rejects the call by sending a packet of the form shown in Figure 10b. Acceptance or rejection is indicated in the *Type* field. Once the virtual circuit has been set up, both sides may send data packets at will, which makes the connection, by definition, full duplex. Either side may terminate the call by sending a CLEAR REQUEST packet, which is acknowledged by a CLEAR CONFIRMATION packet.

An ordinary data packet is shown in Figure 10c. The *Sequence* and *Next* fields are analogous to those in HDLC. Like HDLC, X.25 layer 3 also has an optional format with 7-bit sequence numbers. The *M* bit can be used by a host to indicate that more data follow in the next packet, thus partitioning the packet stream into multipacket units.

The meaning of the *Q* bit is not specified, but it is provided to allow the transport layer a means for distinguishing transport layer data packets from control packets. The *D* bit stands for Delivery confirmation. If a host sets it on all the packets sent on a certain virtual circuit, the *Next* field will contain a true acknowledgment from the remote host, producing an end-to-end confirmation. If, however, it is always set to 0, then the *Next* field just means that the local IMP (DCE) received the packet specified, not that the remote host did. Conceivably, when $D = 0$, the local IMP could write all the packets on magnetic tape to be mailed to the remote IMP for delivery in a couple of days (bargain basement service).

In the original version of X.25, only $D = 0$ was provided. That point generated so much controversy that delivery confirmation was added later, as was a pure datagram facility and something called *Fast Select*. With the Fast Select facility, the user data field in the CALL REQUEST packet is extended to 128 bytes and a similar field is added to the CLEAR REQUEST packet (used to reject incoming calls). Thus a host can send a short query in the CALL REQUEST packet and get the reply in the CLEAR REQUEST packet, without having to open a virtual circuit.

Because layers 2 and 3 in X.25 have so much overlap, it is perhaps useful to point out that the layer 2 sequence numbers and acknowledgments refer to the traffic between host and IMP for all virtual circuits combined. If a host sends the IMP seven packets (frames), each one for a different virtual circuit, the host must stop sending until an acknowledgment comes back. The layer 2 protocol is required to keep the host from flooding the IMP. In contrast, in layer 3, the sequence numbers are per virtual circuit and therefore flow control each connection separately.

X.25 layer 3 also has a few control packets. These include RESET and RESET CONFIRMATION, used to reset a virtual circuit; RESTART and RESTART CONFIRMATION, used to reset all virtual circuits after a host or IMP crash; RECEIVER READY, used for acknowledgments; RECEIVER NOT READY, used to indicate temporary problems and stop the other side even though the window is not full; and INTERRUPT and INTERRUPT CONFIRMATION, used to send out-of-band signals, such as breaks. All these control packets use the format of Figure 10b, in some cases augmented with an additional byte or two for additional information.

4. THE TRANSPORT LAYER

The network layer does not necessarily ensure that the bit stream sent by the source arrives intact at the destination. Packets may be lost or reordered, for example, owing to malfunctioning IMP hardware or software. The X.25 standard provides a mechanism (RESET and RESTART packets) for the network to announce to a host that it has crashed and lost track of both the current sequence numbers and any packets that may have been in transit. To provide truly reliable end-to-end (i.e., host-to-host) communication, another layer of protocol is needed: the transport layer. (Note that X.25 with $D = 1$ comes close to being end to end, but is not quite enough since it provides no way to transparently recover from network RESETs and RESTARTs.)

Another way of looking at the transport layer is to say that its task is to provide a network independent *transport service* to the session layer. The session layer should not have to worry about any of the implementation details of the actual network. They must all be hidden by the transport layer, analogous to the way a compiler must hide the actual machine instructions from the user of a problem-oriented programming language.

4.1 The Transport Station

The program within the host that implements the transport service is called the *transport station*. Its chief functions are to manage connection establishment and teardown, flow control, buffering, and multiplexing. Although a transport station might conceivably offer only datagram primitives to its users, most offer (and emphasize) virtual-circuit primitives. As a bare minimum, the following primitives or their equivalents are normally available:

connum = CONNECT(local, remote),
connum = LISTEN(local),
  status = CLOSE(connum),
  status = SEND(connum, buffer, bytes),
  status = RECEIVE(connum, buffer, bytes)

The primitives for establishing a transport connection, CONNECT and LISTEN, take *transport addresses* as parameters. Each transport address uniquely identifies a specific transport station and a specific *port* (connection endpoint) within that transport station. For example, CCITT has decreed that X.25 will use 14-digit numbers for addressing. The first three identify the country, and the fourth identifies the network within the country. (Multiple country codes have been assigned to countries that expect to have more than ten public networks.) The last ten digits of the X.25 address are assigned by each network operator, for example, five digits to indicate hosts and five digits for the hosts to allocate themselves.

In our example, the LISTEN command tells the transport station that the process executing it is prepared to accept connections addressed to the indicated local address. The process executing the LISTEN is blocked until the connection is established, at which time it is released, with the variable *connum* being set to indicate the connection number. The connection number is needed because multiple connections may be open at the same time and a subsequent SEND, RECEIVE, or CLOSE must be able to tell which connection is meant. If something goes wrong, an error number can be returned in *connum* (e.g., positive for connection established, negative for error).

The CONNECT command tells the transport station to send a message (e.g., X.25 CALL REQUEST) to another host to establish a connection. When the connection has been established (or rejected, for example, due to illegal addresses), the connection number or error code is returned in *connum*.

An important design issue is what should the transport station do if a CALL REQUEST packet comes in specifying a transport address for which no LISTEN is pending? Should it reject the request immediately, or should it queue the request in the hope that a LISTEN will be done shortly? If the request is queued, should it time out and be purged if no LISTEN is forthcoming within a reasonable time? If so, what happens if the LISTEN finally occurs after the timeout?

In the above example, both LISTEN and CONNECT are blocking primitives, that is, the caller is halted until the command completes. Some transport stations use nonblocking primitives. In other words, both calls complete immediately, perhaps only checking the syntactic validity of the addresses provided. When the connection is finally established, or definitively rejected, the respective processes are interrupted. Some transport stations that use nonblocking primitives also provide a way for a process to cancel an outstanding LISTEN or CONNECT, as well as a method for a listening process to inspect an incoming connection request before deciding to accept or reject it.

The primitive CLOSE speaks for itself. The status returned would normally be "OK" if the connection actually existed and "error" if it did not.

The SEND and RECEIVE primitives do the real work of message passing. For the sake of clarity, we refer to the entities exchanged here as "messages," to distinguish them from the "packets" of the network layer and "frames" of the data link layer. A message will be encased in a packet, which will be inserted into a frame before transmission, of course. SEND specifies the connection on which to send, the buffer address, and the number of bytes. RECEIVE has the same parameters, although here *bytes* might initially contain the buffer size and later be filled in with the size of the received message. Again, both of these could be provided in nonblocking as well as blocking versions.

A more elaborate transport station could offer commands to send and receive datagrams, to send and receive interrupt signals, to reset the connection in the event of error, and to interrogate the status of the other side, a facility particularly useful for recovering from network layer failures.

4.2 Establishing and Closing Connections

As we pointed out earlier, one consequence of adaptive routing is that packets can loop for an indefinite period of time. If a packet gets trapped, the sending transport station will eventually time out and send a duplicate. If the duplicate gets through properly, but the original packet remains trapped for a while, problems can arise when it finally escapes and is delivered. Imagine, for example, what would happen if a message instructing a bank to transfer a large sum of money were stored and later repeated, long after the transaction had already been completed.

A useful first step is to limit the amount of time that a packet can exist in the network. For example, a counter could be put in the packet header. Each time the packet was forwarded, the counter could be decremented. When the counter reached zero, the packet would be discarded. Alternatively, a timestamp in the packet could be used to render it obsolete after a certain interval.

The next step is to have the transport stations use a sequence space so large (e.g., 32 bits) that no packet can live for a complete cycle. As a result, delayed duplicates can always be detected by their sequence numbers. However, if all new connections always start with sequence number 0, pack-

ets from previous connections may come back to plague later ones. Therefore, it is necessary to have each new connection initialize its sequence numbers to a value known to be higher than that of any existing packet.

Unfortunately, not even these measures are enough. Since each host has a different range of sequence numbers outstanding, each one must specify the initial sequence number for packets it will send. Assume that sequence numbers are chosen during the call establishment phase. With some bad luck, the following scenario could occur at an instant when *A* wanted to set up a connection with sequence number 100 to *B*:

(1) *A* sends a CALL REQUEST packet with sequence number 100.
(2) The packet is lost.
(3) An old CALL REQUEST with sequence number 50 suddenly arrives at *B*.
(4) *B*'s CALL ACCEPT packet, with sequence number 700, is lost.
(5) An old CALL ACCEPT from *B* with sequence number 650 suddenly arrives at *A*.

At this point the connection is fully established, with *A* about to send packet 100, but *B* expecting packet 50. Similarly, *B* intends to send packet 700, but *A* expects 650. The result is a deadlock.

Tomlinson [ToмL75] proposed a connection establishment protocol that works even in the face of delayed control packets. It is called the *three-way handshake*. An example follows (S means sequence, A means acknowledgment):

(1) *A* sends a CALL REQUEST packet with S = 100.
(2) *B* sends a CALL ACCEPTED packet with S = 700, A = 100.
(3) *A* sends a packet with S = 101, A = 700.

Now consider what happens in the face of the same lost and duplicate packets that lead to deadlock above. When *B* receives the CALL REQUEST with S = 50, it replies with S = 700, A = 50. If this packet gets through, *A* sees the bad acknowledgment and rejects the connection. The only way *A* can be spoofed is for an old CALL AC-

CEPTED packet with A = 100 to appear out of the blue. Such a packet could only be generated in response to an *old* CALL REQUEST packet with S = 100, something *A* has not sent for a long time. Sunshine and Dalal (SUNS78] discuss this problem in more detail.

By now you should be convinced that the protocol required to establish a transport layer connection in the face of an unreliable network layer is nontrivial. What about closing a connection? Surely that, at least, is easy: *A* sends *B* a request to close, and *B* sends back a close acknowledgment. Unfortunately, things are not that simple. As an example, let us briefly consider the two-army problem.

Two divisions of the white army are encamped on the opposite walls of a valley occupied by the blue army. If both divisions attack simultaneously, the white army will win; if either division attacks alone, it will be massacred. The white army divisions must synchronize their attack using an unreliable channel (e.g., a messenger subject to capture). Suppose that white's *A* division sends the message: "Let's attack at teatime," and gets the reply "OK." Division *B* has no way of being sure that the reply got back. If it just goes ahead and attacks, it might get slaughtered. Furthermore, *A* is well aware of this line of reasoning and hence may be afraid to attack, even after having received an acknowledgment.

At this point you may be thinking: "Why not use a three-way handshake here?" Unfortunately, it does not work. *A* could confirm receipt of *B*'s acknowledgment, but because this confirmation could get lost, *A* does not know which situation holds:

(1) *B* got the confirmation and the war is on.
(2) The confirmation got lost and the war is off.

How about a four-way handshake? This is no better. An *n*-way handshake? Still no good. In all cases, the sender of the last message cannot tell whether or not it arrived. If its arrival is essential to starting the war, the sender has no way of telling whether the receiver is going to attack or not. If its arrival is not essential to starting the war, one can devise an equivalent pro-

tocol not containing it and apply the above reasoning to the new protocol.

The implication of all this is that a closing protocol in which neither side can hang up until it is convinced that the other side also intends to hand up is, at the very least, more complicated than it at first appears. The issue is discussed further in SUNS78 and YEMI79.

4.3 Flow Control and Buffering

An important design issue in the transport layer is flow control. Since no transport station has an infinite amount of buffer space, some way must be provided to prevent a fast sender from inundating a slow receiver. Flow control is well known in other contexts, such as operating systems design, where it is known as the producer-consumer problem. Although it also occurs in the data link and network layers, some new complications are present in the transport layer.

To start with, the data link layer usually has one connection for each adjacent IMP—a handful at most—whereas the transport layer in a large multiprogrammed computer may have many connections open simultaneously. A stop-and-wait protocol in the transport layer is usually undesirable, since both sender and receiver would have to be scheduled and run for every message sent. If each machine had a response time of 500 ms between the moment a process became ready to run and the time it ran, the transport connection could support two messages per second, at best, and probably fewer. Consequently, large windows are needed to achieve high throughput, but the combination of large windows and many open connections necessitates many buffers, most of which are idle most of the time.

An alternative design is not to dedicate buffers to specific connections, but to maintain a buffer pool and pull buffers out of the pool and assign them to connections dynamically, as needed. This strategy entails some risk, since no buffer may be available when one is needed. To avoid this risk, a buffer reservation protocol is needed, increasing traffic and overhead. Furthermore, if the buffers are of fixed size and messages

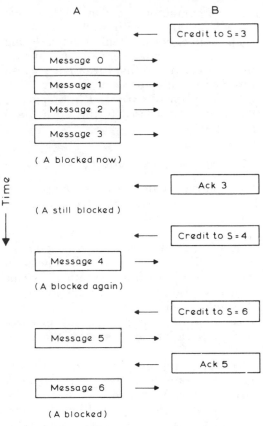

Figure 11. Flow control using credits.

vary from a few characters to thousands of characters, a pool of fixed-sized buffers is not attractive either. No one solution is best. Each transport station must make compromises appropriate to its expected work load.

Another important issue is the relation of flow control to error control. With the sliding-window protocol, an acknowledgment message has two distinct functions: to announce that a message has arrived and to grant the sender permission to send another message. In the transport layer, this coupling is not always desirable.

To see why, consider the dilemma of a transport station that is chronically short of buffer space. What should it do if a message arrives, but the process using the connection has no RECEIVEs outstanding? If it does nothing, the sending transport station will eventually time out and send it again. If it sends an acknowledgment, the other transport station may send

yet another message. The problem comes from the fact that the transport station has no control over the rate at which the user does RECEIVEs. Earlier, we more or less assumed that the network layer was always hungry for new packets—a reasonable assumption, since the network code has little else to do.

One way out of this dilemma is to decouple acknowledgments and flow control. To do so, we introduce two kinds of control messages: acknowledgments and credits. An acknowledgment simply says that a certain message (and by implication, all lower numbered messages) has arrived safely. Upon receiving an acknowledgment, the sender may release the buffers containing all the acknowledged messages, since none of them will ever be retransmitted. However, an acknowledgment does *not* imply permission to send any more messages.

Such permission is granted by a credit message. When a connection is established, the receiver grants some credits to the sender. These credits may be for so many messages or so many bits or both. Every time a message is sent, the credits for message count and/or bit count are decremented. When the credits are all used up, the sender must stop sending until more credits arrive. Such credits may be sent as distinct messages or they may be piggybacked onto data or acknowledgment messages. This scheme provides a simple and flexible mechanism for preventing unnecessary retransmissions in the presence of heavy and variable demands on limited buffer space. An example is given in Figure 11.

4.4 Connection Multiplexing

Multiplexing of connections plays an important role in several layers. In lower layers, for example, packets and frames ultimately destined for different hosts are multiplexed onto the same output lines. In the transport layer, two different forms of multiplexing occur. In *upward multiplexing* (shown in Figure 12a) several transport connections are multiplexed onto the same network connection (e.g., the X.25 virtual circuit). Upward multiplexing is often financially better, since some carriers charge by the packet and also by the second for each virtual circuit that is open.

Now consider the plight of an organization (e.g., an airline) that has 100 telephone operators to handle customer inquiries. If each operator is assigned to a separate virtual circuit, 100 virtual circuits to the central computer will be open all day. The other option would be to use a single virtual circuit to the computer, with the first byte of data being used to distinguish among the operators. The latter has the disadvantage that if the traffic is heavy, the flow control window may always be full, thus slowing down operation. With a dedicated virtual circuit per operator, full windows are much less likely to occur.

The other form of multiplexing, *downward multiplexing* (Figure 12b), becomes interesting when the network layer window is too small. Suppose, for example, a certain network offers X.25, but does not support the 7-bit sequence number option. A user with a large number of data to send might find himself constantly running up against full windows. One way to make an end run around the problem is to open multiple virtual circuits for a single-transport connection. Packets could be distributed among the virtual circuits in a round-robin fashion, first a packet on circuit 0, then a packet on circuit 1, then one on circuit 2, and so on.

Conceivably the two forms could even be combined. For n connections, k virtual circuits could be set up with traffic being dynamically assigned.

5. THE SESSION LAYER

In many networks, the transport layer establishes and maintains connections between hosts. The session layer establishes and maintains connections, called *sessions*, between specific pairs of processes. On the other hand, some networks ignore the session layer altogether and maintain transport connections between specific processes. The ISO OSI Reference Model is exasperatingly vague on this point, stating only that the session layer connects "presentation-entities" and that the transport layer connects "session-entities."

To keep the following discussion from

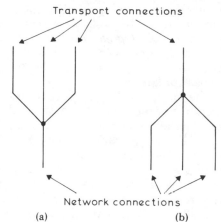

Transport connections

Network connections

(a)   (b)

Figure 12. (a) Upward multiplexing. (b) Downward multiplexing.

vanishing in a linguistic fog, we assume that transport connections are between hosts and session connections are between processes. Thus, when a process wants to talk to another process, it makes its desires known to the session layer, which then engages the services of the transport layer to set up a transport connection to the remote host for use by the session.

A principal task of the session layer is to connect two processes together into a session. Since it is inconvenient for users to be aware of hard transport addresses, the session layer could allow them to refer to destinations by symbolic name, with the session layer doing the mapping onto transport addresses. For example, a user could say, in effect, "Give me a phototypesetter process," with the session layer worrying about where such beasts were to be found.

When a session is set up, an activity often call *session binding*, certain conventions about the coming session can be established. Typical conventions are half-duplex versus full-duplex data transfer, character codes, flow control window sizes, the presence or absence of encryption or text compression, and how to recover from transport layer failures.

Another task that the session layer can perform is particularly useful in networks where the user primitives for sending and receiving messages are nonblocking, and where the user may have multiple requests outstanding on the same session at any instant. Under these circumstances, replies

Computing Surveys, Vol. 13, No. 4, December 1981

may come back in an order different from that in which the requests were sent. The session layer's *dialog control* function can keep track of requests and replies and reorder them if need be to simplify the design of the user programs.

Another aspect of dialog control is bracketing groups of messages into atomic units. In many database applications it is highly undesirable that a transaction be broken off part way, as a result of a network failure, for example. If the transactions consists of a group of messages, the session layer could make sure that the entire group had been successfully received at the destination before even attempting to start the transaction.

Our discussion of the session layer is now complete. The brevity of this section is directly related to the fact that few networks make much of a distinction between the transport and session layers. In fact, many networks have neither a session layer nor any of the dialog control functions belonging to the session layer. While there are no internationally accepted standards for the transport layer yet, there are at least a few serious proposals that have been under discussion for several years [DEPA76, INWG78]. Session layer protocols have not come as far yet. This situation has occurred because the protocol community has been tackling the layers more or less bottom up and is currently in the vicinity of layer 4. Higher layer standards will no doubt be forthcoming in the future.

6. THE PRESENTATION LAYER

The function of the presentation layer is to perform certain generally useful transformations on the data before they are sent to the session layer. Typical transformations are text compression, encryption, and conversion to and from network standards for terminals and files. We examine each of these subjects in turn.

6.1 Text Compression

Bandwidth is money. Sending thousands of trailing blanks across a network to be "printed" is a good use of neither. Although the network designers could leave the matter of text compression to each user pro-

gram, it is more efficient and convenient to put it into the network architecture as one of the standard presentation services.

Obvious candidates for text compression are runs of repeated bits (e.g., leading zeros) and repeated characters (e.g., trailing blanks). Huffman coding is also a possibility. Since text compression is such a well-known subject outside the network context (see, e.g., DAVS76), we do not consider it further here.

6.2 Encryption Protocols

Information often has great economic value. As an example, just think about the data transmitted back by oil companies from exploratory sites. With more and more data being transmitted by satellite, the problem of data security looms ever larger. The financial incentive to erect an antenna to spy on competitors is great and the cost is low. Furthermore, privacy legislation in many countries puts a legal requirement on the owners of personal data to make sure such data are kept secret. All these factors combine to make data encryption an essential part of most networks. The December 1979 issue of *Computing Surveys* [COMP79] is devoted to cryptography and contains several introductory articles on it.

An interesting question is: "In which layer does the encryption belong?" In our view, encryption is analogous to text compression: ordinary data go in and compressed or indecipherable data come out. Since everyone agrees that text compression is a presentation service, logically encryption should be too. For historical reasons and implementation convenience, however, it is often put elsewhere, typically the transport layer or the data link layer.

The purpose of encryption is to transform the input, or *plaintext*, into an output, or *ciphertext*, that is incomprehensible to anyone not privy to the secret *key* used to parameterize the transformation. Thus plaintext is converted to ciphertext in the presentation layer of the source machine and reconverted to plaintext in the presentation layer of the destination machine. In neither machine should the user programs be aware of the encryption, other than having specified encryption as an option when the session was bound.

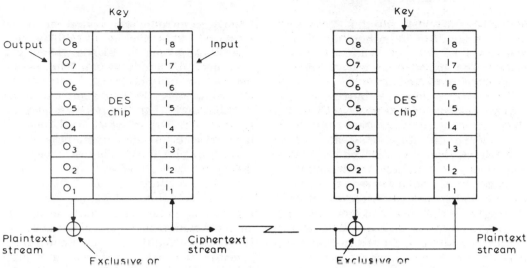

Figure 13. A stream cipher using DES. Data arrives from the left and is encrypted for transmission. The destination machine decrypts it and outputs the plaintext.

One of the best-known encryption methods is the *substitution cipher*, in which a unit of plaintext is converted into a unit of ciphertext. In a *monoalphabetic cipher*, each letter is converted into another letter according to a fixed rule. For example, "a" becomes "M," "b" becomes "R," "c" becomes "G," etc. In this example, the encryption key is MRG . . . , that is, the ciphertext corresponding to the plaintext abc. . . . Although 26! different monoalphabetic substitutions exist, these ciphers can be broken by a clever ten-year-old using the frequency statistics of natural language.

Most computer ciphers use the same principle, but on a larger scale. The U.S. federal government has adopted a substitution cipher that is fast becoming a de facto standard for nongovernmental organizations as well. The *DES* (Data Encryption Standard) cipher takes a 64-bit plaintext input block and produces a 64-bit ciphertext output block. The transformation is driven by a 56-bit key. Conceptually, at least, one could prepare a big table, with 2^{64} columns, one for each possible input, and 2^{56} rows, one for each possible key. Each table entry is the ciphertext for the specified input and key.

DES can also be operated as a *stream cipher*, as shown in Figure 13. The input shift registers on both source and destination machine are initialized to the same 8-byte (random) number, $I_1, \ldots, I_8$. Data are presented for encryption 1 byte at a time, not 8 bytes at a time. When a byte arrives, the DES chip converts the 8 bytes $I_1, \ldots, I_8$ into the output $O_1, \ldots, O_8$. Then O_1 is Exclusive Or'ed with the input to form the ciphertext byte. The ciphertext byte is both transmitted and fed back into I_1, shifting I_2 to I_3, and so on. I_8 is shifted out and lost. Decryption at the other end is similar. Note that feeding back the ciphertext into the DES input register makes subsequent encryption dependent on the entire previous plaintext, and so a given sequence of 8 plaintext bytes will have a different ciphertext on each appearance in the plaintext.

DES has been the subject of great controversy since its inception [DAVA79, DIFF76a, HELL79, HELL80]. Some computer scientists feel that a wealthy and determined intruder who knew, for example, that a certain message was in ASCII, could determine the key by trying all keys until he found one that yielded ASCII plaintext (i.e., only codes 0–127 and not 128–255). If the ciphertext is k bytes long, the probability of an incorrect key yielding ASCII input is 2^{-k}. For even a single line of text, it is unlikely that any key but the correct one could pass the test.

The dispute centers about how much a DES-breaking machine would cost. In 1977, Diffie and Hellman [DIFF77] designed one and computed its cost at 20 million dollars.

The DES supporters say this figure is too low by a factor of 10, although even they concede DES cannot hold out forever against the exponential growth of very large-scale integrated circuits.

To use DES, both the source and destination must use the same key. Obviously the session key cannot be sent through the network in plaintext form. Instead, a master key is hand carried in a locked briefcase to each host. When a session is set up, a key manager process somewhere in the network picks a random key as session key, encrypts it using the master key, and sends it to both parties for decryption. Since the plaintext of this message is a random number, it is hard to break the cipher using statistical techniques. Numerous variations of the idea exist, typically with master keys, regional keys, local keys, and the like.

Shamir [SHAM79] has devised a clever way to share (master) keys in a flexible way among a large group of people, so that n arbitrary people can get together and assemble the master key, but $n - 1$ people can gain no information at all. Basically, each person is given a data point that lies on a degree $n - 1$ polynomial whose y intercept is the key. With n data points, the polynomial, hence the key, is uniquely determined, but with $n - 1$ data points it is not. Modulo arithmetic is used for obfuscatory purposes.

All the master key methods have a significant drawback, though: it is impossible for computers that have not previously had any contact with each other to agree on a session key in a secure way. Considerable academic research has been done on this topic in recent years (not without its own controversy—see SHAP77 and SUGA79), and some interesting results have been achieved. Merkle [MERK78a], for example, has suggested that two strangers, A and B, could establish a key as follows. A sends k ciphertext messages to B with the instruction to pick one of them at random and break it by brute force (i.e., try all possible keys until a plaintext starting with 64 0's appeared). The rest of the message consists of two random numbers, the key number and the key itself. Having broken the cipher, B then sends the key number back to A to indicate which message was broken.

Clearly an intruder will have to break $k/2$ messages on the average to find the right one. By adjusting k and the difficulty of breaking a message, A can achieve any degree of security desired.

A completely different approach to key distribution is that of *public key cryptography* [DIFF76b] in which each network user deposits an encryption key E in a publicly readable file. The user keeps the decryption key D secret. The keys must satisfy the property that $D(E(P)) = P$ for an arbitrary plaintext P. (This is essentially the definition of a decryption key.) The cipher system must be such that D cannot be deduced from the publicly known E.

With this background, the encryption system is obvious and trivial: to send a message to a stranger, you just encrypt it with his publicly known key. Only he knows the decryption key and no one can deduce it from the encryption key, so the cipher cannot be broken. The utility of the whole system depends on the availability of key pairs with the requisite properties. Much effort has gone into searching for ways to produce such key pairs. Some algorithms have already been published [MERK78b, RIVE78, SHAM80]. The scheme of Rivest et al. effectively depends on the fact that given two huge prime numbers, generating their product (the public key) is computationally easy, but given the product, finding the prime factors (the secret key) is very hard. In effect, their system takes advantage of the fact that the computational complexity of factorization is high.

Another area where cryptography plays a major role is in authentication. Suppose that a customer's computer instructs a bank's computer to buy a ton of gold and debit a certain account. The bank complies, but the next day the price of gold drops sharply and the customer denies ever having issued any purchase order. How can the bank protect itself against such unscrupulous customers? Traditionally, court battles over such matters have focused on the presence or absence of an authorized handwritten signature on a piece of paper. With electronic funds transfers and similar applications the need for "digital" (i.e., electronic) signatures is obvious.

With a slight additional restriction, pub-

Computing Surveys, Vol. 13, No. 4, December 1981

lic key cryptography can be used to provide these badly needed digital signatures. The restriction is that the encryption and decryption algorithms be chosen so that $D(E(P)) = E(D(P))$. In other words, the order of applying encryption and decryption must be interchangeable. The M.I.T. algorithm [RIVE78] has this property.

Now let us reconsider the ton-of-gold problem posed earlier. To protect itself, the bank can insist that a customer C use the following protocol for sending signed messages. First, the customer encrypts the plaintext message P with his secret key; that is, the customer computes $D_C(P)$. Then the customer encrypts this result with the bank's public key E_B, yielding $E_B(D_C(P))$. When this message arrives, the bank applies its decryption key D_B to get

$$D_B(E_B(D_C(P))) = D_C(P).$$

Now the bank applies the customer's public key, E_C, to recover P. The bank also saves P and $D_C(P)$ in case trouble arises.

When the angry letter from the customer arrives, the bank takes both P and $D_C(P)$ to court and asks the judge to decrypt the latter using the customer's public key. When the judge sees that the decryption works, he will realize that the bank must be telling the truth. How else could it have come into possession of a message encrypted by D_C, the customer's secret key? Since the bank does not know any of its customer's secret keys, it cannot forge messages (to generate commissions); hence customers are also protected against unscrupulous banks. While in jail, the customer will have ample time to devise interesting new public key algorithms.

Unfortunately, as Saltzer [SALT78] has pointed out, the public key digital signature protocol suffers from some nontechnical problems. For example, immediately after the price of gold drops, the management of the gold-buying company could run to the police claiming it had just become aware of yesterday's key burglary. Depending on local laws, the company might or might not be able to weasel out of obligations undertaken with the "stolen" key. (As an aside, note that the owner of a stolen credit card usually has only a small liability for its subsequent misuse.)

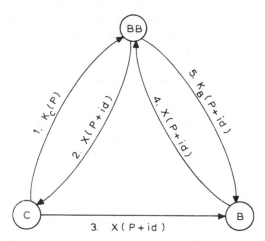

Figure 14. A digital signature protocol with conventional cryptography.

Saltzer also points out that a company is free to change its public key at will. Stronger yet, it may be company policy to do so regularly. If the company changes its key before accusing the bank of fabricating the purchase order, it will be impossible for the bank to convince the judge. This observation suggests that some central key registration authority may be needed. However, if such a central authority, call it Big Brother (BB), exists, conventional cryptography can also be used to achieve digital signatures [NEED78, POPE79].

The signature protocol using DES is illustrated in Figure 14. When a new customer C joins the system, the customer hand carries a secret (DES) key, K_C, to BB. Thus, BB has each user's secret key and can therefore send and receive secure messages from each user. In addition, BB has a secret key of its own, X, that it never discloses to anyone. The protocol for buying gold is as follows (P is the plaintext purchase order):

(1) The customer sends $K_C(P)$ to BB.
(2) BB decrypts the message and returns $X(P + \text{identification})$.
(3) The customer sends $X(P + \text{identification})$ to the bank.
(4) The bank sends $X(P + \text{identification})$ to BB.
(5) BB sends $K_B(P + \text{identification})$ back to the bank.

Computing Surveys, Vol. 13, No. 4, December 1981

The "identification" appended to the message by BB consists of the customer's identity, something that BB can guarantee since the incoming message is encrypted by a key only known to one user, plus the date, time, and perhaps a sequence number. Messages encrypted by X can be freely sent through the network, since only BB can decrypt them, and BB is assumed to be trusted. If a dispute arises, the bank can go to the judge with $X(P + \text{identification})$, which the judge can then order BB to decrypt. The judge will then see the identification and know who sent the original message. While in jail, the customer will have ample time to devise interesting new signature protocols using conventional cryptography.

6.3 Virtual-Terminal Protocols

Dozens of brands of terminals are in widespread use, no two of which are identical. Needless to say, a network user who has just been told that the program or host he wishes to use does not converse with his brand of terminal is not likely to be a happy user. For example, if the program treats carriage returns and line feeds as equivalent and the user's terminal only has a "newline" key, which generates one of each, the program will perceive alternate lines as being empty.

To prevent such difficulties, protocols have been invented to try to hide terminal idiosyncracies from application (i.e., user) programs. Such protocols are known as *virtual-terminal protocols*, since they attempt to map real terminals onto a hypothetical network virtual terminal. Virtual-terminal protocols are part of the presentation layer.

Broadly speaking, terminals can be divided up into three classes: scroll mode, page mode, and form mode. Scroll-mode terminals do not have any intelligence. When a key is struck, the character is sent over the line and perhaps printed as well. When a character comes in over the line, it is just displayed. Most hard-copy terminals, and some of the less expensive CRT terminals, are scroll-mode terminals.

Even though scroll-mode terminals are simple, they still can differ in many ways: character set, line length, half duplex/full duplex, overprinting and the way line feed,

carriage return, tab, vertical tab, backspace, form feed, and break are handled.

Page-mode terminals are typically CRT terminals with 24 or 25 lines of 80 characters. Most of these have cursor addressing, so that the operator or the program can randomly access the screen. Some of them have a little local editing capability. They have the same potential differences as scroll-mode terminals, and, additionally, problems with screen length, cursor addressing, blinking, reverse video, color, multiple intensities, and the details of the local editing.

Form-mode terminals are sophisticated microprocessor-based devices intended for data entry. They are widely used in airline reservations, banking, and many other applications. In a typical situation the computer displays a form for the operator to fill out using cursor control and local editing facilities. The completed form is then sent back to the computer for processing. Sometimes the microprocessor can perform simple syntax checking, to make sure, for example, that a bank account field contains only numbers.

Two kinds of virtual-terminal protocols are commonly used. The first one is intended for scroll-mode terminals and is based on the ARPANET Telnet protocol [DAVD77]. When this type of protocol is used, the designers invent a fictitious virtual terminal onto which all real terminals are mapped. Application programs output virtual-terminal characters, which are mapped onto the real terminal's character set by the presentation layer at the destination. Supporting a new kind of real terminal thus requires modifying the presentation layer software to effect the new mapping, but does not require changing any of the application programs.

Since most of the current research in virtual-terminal protocols focuses on page- or form-mode terminals, let us move on to them. A general model that has been widely accepted is the data structure model of Schicker and Duenki [SCHI78]. Roughly speaking, protocols based on this approach use the model of Figure 15. Each end of a session has a data structure that represents the state of the virtual terminal.

The data structure consists of a collection

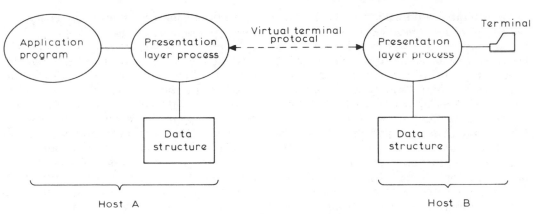

Figure 15. Virtual-terminal protocol model.

of fields, each of which contains certain attributes. Typical attributes are the size of the field, whether it accepts numbers, letters, or both, its rendition (an abstract concept used to model color, reverse video, blinking, and intensity), whether it is protected against operator modification or not, and so forth. The program is written using abstract operations on the data structure. Every time the program changes the data structure on its machine, the presentation layer sends a message to the other machine telling it how to change its data structure. The remote presentation layer is responsible for updating the display on the real terminal to make it correspond to the newly changed data structure. Similarly, changes made to the display by the human operator are reflected in the data structure on the operator's side of the session. Messages are then sent to bring the other side up to date. The protocol used for these messages is the virtual-terminal protocol.

Although a clever presentation layer can come a long way toward hiding the properties of the real terminal from the user program, it cannot work miracles. If the program needs a 24 × 80 screen with cursor addressing and four renditions, the presentation layer will be hard pressed to map everything onto a simple hard-copy terminal. Consequently, virtual-terminal protocols always have an option negotiation facility that is used to establish what each end of the connection is able to provide and what it wants from the other end.

This negotiation can be symmetric or asymmetric. In symmetric negotiation, each end announces its capabilities, inspects its partner's, and sets the parameters to the lowest common denominator. For example, if one end has a 24 × 80 screen, and the other has a 25 × 72 screen, the screen used will be 24 × 72. In asymmetric negotiation, one side makes a proposal and the other side accepts or rejects the proposal. If the proposal is rejected, the proposer may try again. Symmetric negotiation solves the problem of who should go first, but requires more complicated rules to determine what the result of an exchange is. It can also fail, for example, if both sides want to work in alternating (half-duplex) mode, and each wants to go first.

Another important design issue in virtual-terminal protocols is how to handle interrupts (attentions). When a user hits the "break" or "quit" key to terminate an infinite loop with a print statement in it, the presentation layer must purge the pipe of input already queued up; otherwise break will have no apparent effect. It is easy for the presentation layer on the terminal side to begin discarding input upon seeing a break, but it is much harder to determine when to stop discarding. Waiting for the prompt character does not work, since it might occur in the data to be discarded. A special out-of-band signaling protocol is needed. A survey of virtual-terminal protocols is given in DAY80.

6.4 File Transfer Protocols

The most common uses of computer networks at present are for logging onto remote machines and transferring files between machines. These two areas are similar in that just as there is a need for programs to talk to a variety of incompatible terminals, there is a need for programs to read a variety of incompatible files. In principle, the same approach can be used for file transfer as for terminals: define a network standard format and provide a mapping from and to each existing file format.

In practice, this approach seems to work fairly well for terminals, but less well for files, primarily because the differences between terminals are not as great as between file types. Mapping reverse video onto blinking is straightforward compared to mapping 60-bit CDC floating point numbers onto 32-bit IBM floating point numbers, especially when the numbers are strewn randomly throughout the file.

Files are transferred for four primary reasons:

(1) to store a file for subsequent retrieval;
(2) to print a remote file on the local printer;
(3) to submit a file as a remote job;
(4) to use a remote file as data input or output.

Each category of use has its own peculiarities.

When a file is stored for subsequent retrieval, it must be possible to produce an exact, bit-for-bit copy of it upon request. Clearly transmission must be fully transparent, without escape codes that do funny things. The number of bits in the file must be recorded in the stored file, to allow transport between machines with differing word lengths. The last word on the storage machine may be partially full, and so some record of how many bits are in use is required.

When a file is transferred to be printed, problems can arise as a result of different print conventions. Some machines store print files in FORTRAN format, with fixed-length records (with or without some fudge for trailing blanks), and carriage control characters in column 1. Other machines use ASCII style variable-length records, with line feeds and form feeds for indicating vertical motion. When the file is being moved to be used for remote job entry, the same problems are present.

Moving data files containing mixtures of integers, floating point numbers, characters, etc., between machines is nearly impossible. In theory, each data item (e.g., integer, floating point number, character) could occupy one record in a canonical format, with the data type and value both explicitly stored. In practice the idea does not seem to work well, not only because of problems of interfacing existing software to it, but also because of the high overhead and the problems involved in converting floating point numbers from one format to another.

Another aspect of file transfer is file manipulation. Users often need to create, delete, copy, rename, and otherwise manage remote files. Most file transfer protocols tend to concentrate on this aspect of the problem because it is not as hopeless as the conversion aspect. Gien [GIEN78] has described a file transfer protocol in some detail.

7. SUMMARY

Computer networks are designed hierarchically, as a series of independent layers. Processes in a layer correspond with their peers in remote machines using the appropriate protocol, and with their superiors and subordinates in the same machine using the appropriate interface. The ISO OSI Reference Model has been designed to provide a universal framework in which networking can be discussed. Few existing networks follow it closely, but there is a general movement in that direction.

The seven-layer ISO model can be briefly summarized as follows. The physical layer creates a raw bit stream between two machines. The data link layer adds a frame structure to the raw bit stream, and attempts to recover from transmission errors transparently. The network layer handles routing and congestion control. The transport layer provides a network-independent transport service to the session layer. The session layer sets up and manages process-to-process connections. The presentation layer performs a variety of useful conversions. Finally the application layer is up to the user, although some industry-wide protocols may be developed in the future.

The literature on computer networks is huge. Readers unfamiliar with it, but wishing to continue their study of the subject, may be interested in the textbooks by Davies et al. [DAVI79] and Tanenbaum [TANE81], or the book edited by Kuo [KUO81].

ACKNOWLEDGMENTS

I would like to thank Yogen Dalal, Adele Goldberg, and an anonymous, but artistic, technical editor for their numerous and helpful comments.

REFERENCES

ABRA70   ABRAMSON, N. "The ALOHA system—another alternative for computer communications," in *Proc. 1970 Fall Jt. Computer Conf.,* AFIPS Press, Arlington, Va., pp. 281–285.

ABRA73   ABRAMSON, N. "The ALOHA system," in *Computer-communication networks,* N. Abramson and F. Kuo (Eds.), Prentice-Hall, Englewood Cliffs, N.J., 1973.

BARA64   BARAN, P. "On distributed communication networks," *IEEE Trans. Commun. Syst.* CS-12 (March 1964), 1–9.

BERT80   BERTINE, H. V. "Physical level protocols," *IEEE Trans. Commun.* COM-28 (April 1980), 433–444.

BOGG80   BOGGS, D. R., SHOCH, J. F., TAFT, E. A., AND METCALF, R. M. "Pup: An Internet architecture," *IEEE Trans. Commun.* COM-28 (April 1980), 612–624.

CAPE79a   CAPETANAKIS, J. I. "Generalized TDMA: The multi-accessing tree protocol," *IEEE Trans. Commun.* COM-27 (Oct. 1979), 1476–1484.

CAPE79b   CAPETANAKIS, J. I. "Tree algorithms for packet broadcast channels," *IEEE Trans. Inf. Theory* IT-25 (Sept. 1979), 505–515.

CHLA76   CHLAMTAC, I. "Radio packet broadcasted computer network—the broadcast recognition access method," M.S. thesis, Dep. Mathematical Sciences, Tel Aviv Univ., Tel Aviv, Israel, 1976.

CHLA79   CHLAMTAC, I., FRANTA, W. R., AND LEVIN, D. "BRAM: The broadcast recognizing access method," *IEEE Trans. Commun.* COM-27 (Aug. 1979), 1183–1190.

CHU78   CHU, K. "A distributed protocol for updating network topology information," Rep. RC 7235, IBM Thomas J. Watson Res. Cent., Yorktown Heights, N.Y., 1978.

CLAR78   CLARK, D. D., POGRAN, K. T., AND REED, D. P. "An introduction to local area networks," *Proc. IEEE* 66 (Nov. 1978), 1497–1517.

COMP79   *Computing Surveys* 11, 4 (Dec. 1979).

CROW73   CROWTHER, W., RETTBERG, R., WALDEN, D., ORNSTEIN, S., AND HEART, F. "A system for broadcast communication: Reservation-Aloha," in *Proc. 6th Hawaii Int. Conf. Systems Science,* 1973, pp. 371–374.

DAVA79   DAVIDA, G. I. "Hellman's scheme breaks DES in its basic form," *IEEE Spectrum* 16 (July 1979), 39.

DAVD77   DAVIDSON, J., HATHAWAY, W., POSTEL, J., MIMNO, N., THOMAS, R., AND WALDEN, D. "The ARPANET Telnet protocol: Its purpose, principles, implementation, and impact on host operating system design," in *Proc. 5th Data Communication Symp.* (ACM/IEEE) (1977), pp. 4.10–4.18.

DAVI72   DAVIES, D. W. "The control of congestion in packet-switching networks," *IEEE Trans. Commun.* COM-20 (June 1972), 546–550.

DAVI73   DAVIES, D. W., AND BARBER, D. L. A. *Communication networks for computers,* Wiley, New York, 1973.

DAVI79   DAVIES, D. W., BARBER, D. L. A., PRICE, W. L., AND SOLOMONIDES, C. M. *Computer networks and their protocols,* Wiley, New York, 1979.

DAVS76   DAVISSON, L., AND GRAY, R. (Eds.). *Data compression,* Dowden, Hutchinson & Ross, Stroudsburg, Pa., 1976.

DAY80   DAY, J. "Terminal protocols," *IEEE Trans. Commun.* COM-28 (April 1980), 585–593.

DEPA76   DEPARIS, M., DUENKI, A., GLEN, M., LAWS, J., LEMOLI, G., AND WEAVING, K. "The implementation of an end-to-end protocol by EIN centers: A survey and comparison," in *Proc. 3rd Int. Conf. Computer Communication* (ICCC) (Aug. 1976), pp. 351–360.

DIFF76a   DIFFIE, W., AND HELLMAN, M. E. "A critique of the proposed data encryption standard," *Commun. ACM* 19 (March 1976), 164–165.

DIFF76b   DIFFIE, W., AND HELLMAN, M. E. "New directions in cryptography," *IEEE Trans. Inf. Theory* IT-22 (Nov. 1976), 644–654.

DIFF77   DIFFIE, W., AND HELLMAN, M. E. "Exhaustive cryptanalysis of the NBS data encryption standard," *Computer* 10 (June 1977), 74–84.

DOLL78   DOLL, D. R. *Data communications.* Wiley, New York, 1978.

FARB72   FARBER, D. J., AND LARSON, K. C. "The system architecture of the distributed computer system—the communications system," in *Symp. Computer Networks,* Polytechnic Institute of Brooklyn, Brooklyn, N.Y., April 1972.

FOLT80   FOLTS, H. C. "Procedures for circuit-switched service in synchronous public data networks," *IEEE Trans. Commun.* COM-28 (April 1980), 489–496.

FRAS75   FRASER, A. G. "A virtual channel network," *Datamation* 21 (Feb. 1975), 51–56.

FRAT73   FRATTA, L., GERLA, M., AND KLEINROCK, L. "The flow deviation method: An approach to store-and-forward communication networks," *Networks* **3** (1973), 97–133.

FREE80   FREEMAN, H. A., AND THURBER, K. J. "Updated bibliography on local computer networks," *Comput. Arch. News* **8** (April 1980), 20–28.

GELE78   GELENBE, E., LABETOULLE, J., AND PUJOLLE, G. "Performance evaluation of the HDLC protocol," *Comput. Networks* **2** (Sept.–Oct. 1978), 409–415.

GERL77   GERLA, M., AND KLEINROCK, L. "Closed loop stability controls for S-ALOHA satellite communications," in *Proc. 5th Data Communication Symp.* (ACM/IEEE), (1977), pp. 2-10-2-19.

GIEN78   GIEN, M. "A file transfer protocol (FTP)," *Computer Networks* **2** (Sept.–Oct. 1978), 312–319.

GUNT81   GUNTHER, K. D. "Prevention of deadlocks in packet-switched data transport systems," *IEEE Trans. Commun.* **COM-29** (April 1981), 512–524.

HELL79   HELLMAN, M. E. "DES will be totally insecure within ten years," *IEEE Spectrum* **16** (July 1979), 32–39.

HELL80   HELLMAN, M. E. "A cryptanalytic time–memory tradeoff," *IEEE Trans. Inf. Theory* **IT-26** (July 1980), 401–406.

INWG78   "A proposal of an Internetwork end to end protocol," in *Proc. Symp. Computer Network Protocols*, University of Liege, Belgium, Feb. 1978, pp. H:5–25.

IRLA78   IRLAND, M. I. "Buffer management in a packet switch," *IEEE Trans. Commun.* **COM-26** (March 1978), 328–337.

KAMO81   KAMOUN, F. "A drop and throttle flow control policy for computer networks," *IEEE Trans. Commun.* **COM-29** (April 1981), 444–452.

KLEI78   KLEINROCK, L., AND YEMINI, Y. "An optimal adaptive scheme for multiple access broadcast communication," in *Proc. ICC* (IEEE), 1978, pp. 7.2.1–7.2.5.

KUO81   KUO, F. F. (Ed.) *Protocols and techniques for data communication networks*, Prentice-Hall, Englewood Cliffs, N.J., 1981.

LIU78   LIU, M. T. "Distributed loop computer networks," in *Advances in Computers*, M. C. Yovits (Ed.), Academic Press, New York, 1978, pp. 163–221.

MANN78   MANNING, E. G. "On datagram service in public packet-switched networks," *Comput. Networks* **2** (May 1978), 79–83.

MART78   MARTIN, J. *Communications satellite systems*, Prentice-Hall, Englewood Cliffs, N.J., 1978.

McQu74   McQUILLAN, J. M. "Adaptive routing algorithms for distributed computer networks," Ph.D. dissertation, Div. Engineering and Applied Sciences, Harvard Univ., 1974.

McQu77   McQUILLAN, J. M., AND WALDEN, D. C. "The ARPA network design deci-

sions," *Comput. Networks* **1** (Aug. 1977), 243–289.

MERK78a   MERKLE, R. C. "Secure communications over insecure channels," *Commun. ACM* **21** (April 1978), 294–299.

MERK78b   MERKLE, R. C., AND HELLMAN, M. E. "Hiding information and receipts in trapdoor knapsacks," *IEEE Trans. Inf. Theory* **IT-24** (Sept. 1978), 525–530.

MERL80a   MERLIN, P. M., AND SCHWEITZER, P. J. "Deadlock avoidance in store-and-forward networks—I: Store-and-forward deadlock," *IEEE Trans. Commun.* **COM-28** (March 1980), 345–354.

MERL80b   MERLIN, P. M., AND SCHWEITZER, P. J. "Deadlock avoidance in store-and-forward networks—II: Other deadlock types," *IEEE Trans. Commun.* **COM-28** (March 1980), 355–360.

METC76   METCALFE, R. M., AND BOGGS, D. R. "Ethernet: Distributed packet switching for local computer networks," *Commun. ACM* **19** (July 1976), 395–404.

NEED78   NEEDHAM, R. M., AND SCHROEDER, M. D. "Using encryption for authentication in large networks of computers," *Commun. ACM* **21** (Dec. 1978), 993–999.

NEED79   NEEDHAM, R.M. "System aspects of the Cambridge ring," in *Proc. 7th Symp. Operating Systems, Principles* (ACM), 1979, pp. 82–85.

PETE61   PETERSON, W. W., AND BROWN, D. T. "Cyclic codes for error detection," *Proc. IRE* **49** (Jan. 1961), 228–235.

POPE79   POPEK, G. J., AND KLINE, C. S. "Encryption and secure computer networks," *Comput. Surveys* **11** (Dec. 1979), 331–356.

POST80   POSTEL, J. B. "Internetwork protocol approaches," *IEEE Trans. Commun.* **COM-28** (April 1980), 604–611.

RIVE78   RIVEST, R. L., SHAMIR, A., AND ADLEMAN, L. "A method for obtaining digital signatures and public key cryptosystems," *Commun. ACM* **21** (Feb. 1978), 120–126.

ROBE73   ROBERTS, L. G. "Dynamic allocation of satellite capacity through packet reservation," in *1973 Nat. Computer Conf.*, AFIPS Press, Arlington, Va., pp. 711–716.

ROTH77   ROTHAUSER, E. H., AND WILD, D. "MLMA—a collision-free multi-access method," *Proc. IFIP Congr. 77*, (IFIP) (1977), 431–436.

RUDI76   RUDIN, H. "On routing and delta routing: A taxonomy and performance comparison of techniques for packet-switched networks" *IEEE Trans. Commun.* **COM-24** (Jan. 1976), 43–59.

RYBC80   RYBCZYNSKI, A. "X.25 interface and end-to-end virtual circuit service characteristics," *IEEE Trans. Commun.* **COM-28** (April 1980), 500–510.

SALT78   SALTZER, J. H. "On digital signatures," *Oper. Syst. Rev.* **12** (April 1978), 12–14.

SCHI78   SCHICKER, P., AND DUENKI, A. "The virtual terminal definition," *Comput. Networks* **2** (Dec. 1978), 429–441.

ScHo76   SCHOLL, M. "Multiplexing techniques for data transmission over packet switched radio systems," Ph.D. dissertation, Computer Science Dep., UCLA, 1976.

ScHW80   SCHWARTZ, M., AND STERN, T. E. "Routing techniques used in computer communication networks," *IEEE Trans. Commun.* **COM-28** (April 1980), 539–552.

SEGA81   SEGALL, A. "Advances in verifiable fail-safe routing procedures," *IEEE Trans. Commun.* **COM-29** (April 1981), 491–497.

SHAM79   SHAMIR, A. "How to share a secret," *Commun. ACM* **22** (Nov. 1979), 612–613.

SHAM80   SHAMIR, A., AND ZIPPEL, R. "On the security of the Merkle–Hellman cryptographic scheme," *IEEE Trans. Inf. Theory* **IT-26** (May 1980), 339–340.

SHAP77   SHAPLEY, D., AND KOLATA, G. B. "Cryptology: Scientists puzzle over threat to open research, publication," *Science* **197** (Sept. 30, 1977), 1345–1349.

SHOC81   SHOCH, J. "An annotated bibliography on local compuer networks," Xerox Tech. Rep., Xerox PARC, April 1980.

SLOA75   SLOANE, N. J. A. *A short course on error correcting codes,* Springer-Verlag, Berlin and New York, 1975.

SUGA79   SUGARMAN, R. M. "On foiling computer crime," *IEEE Spectrum* **16** (July 1979), 31–32.

SUNS78   SUNSHINE, C. A., AND DALAL, Y. K. "Connection management in transport protocols," *Comput. Networks* **2** (Dec. 1978), 454–473.

TANE81   TANENBAUM, A. S. *Computer networks,* Prentice-Hall, Englewood Cliffs, N.J., 1981.

TOML75   TOMLINSON, R. S. "Selecting sequence numbers," in *Proc. ACM SIGCOMM/ SIGOPS Interprocess Communication Workshop* (ACM) (1975), pp. 11–23.

WILK79   WILKES, M. V., AND WHEELER, D. J. "The Cambridge digital communication ring," in *Proc. Local Area Communication Network Symp.*, Mitre Corp and NBS (1979), pp. 47–61.

YEMI79   YEMINI, Y., AND COHEN, D. "Some issues in distributed process communication," in *Proc. 1st Int. Conf. Distributed Computer Systems* (IEEE), 1979, pp. 199–203.

ZIMM80   ZIMMERMANN, H. "OSI reference model—the ISO model of architecture for open systems interconnection," *IEEE Trans. Commun.* **COM-28** (April 1980), 425–432.

Received January 1981; final revision accepted September 1981.

Reprinted from *The Proceedings of COMPCON F'83*, 1983, pages 479-487.

A CHECKLIST OF COMMUNICATIONS PROTOCOL FUNCTIONS ORGANIZED USING THE
OPEN SYSTEM INTERCONNECTION SEVEN-LAYER REFERENCE MODEL

Albert W. Bowers

The MITRE Corporation
1820 Dolly Madison Boulevard
McLean, Virginia 22102

Edward B. Connell

Data Systems Technology Office
NASA/Goddard Space Flight Center
Greenbelt, Maryland 20771

ABSTRACT

The International Standards Organization's (ISO's) Open System Interconnection (OSI) Seven-Layer Reference Model is beginning to receive wide acceptance. This paper identifies most major communications protocol functions and subfunctions and assigns them to the Reference Model layers using the ISO guidelines. Particular attention is given to protocol functions that span more than one layer. The partitioning of these multilayer functions among the affected layers is discussed to identify the specific subfunctions assigned to each layer and the engineering principles employed for making these allocation decisions.

The recommended use of the checklist is addressed to emphasize that the checklist and layering principles are primarily a convenient means for describing a complex protocol. Whether or not the software and hardware reflect the layered approach, the layered approach represents a simple straightforward method for describing the protocol. This fact is illustrated through the use of an example of an actual communications protocol that was documented using the checklist approach.

The checklist provides a useful function in helping to identify the principle engineering considerations involved in the interconnection of two or more system modules that employ an electrical interface for passing digitally encoded data. It helps to ensure that the engineer gives consideration to each function, weighing the true need for the function, instead of omitting functions, or underestimating requirements, principally through oversight. The checklist is intended for use as a guide to determining requirements rather than a detailed treatise on all aspects of communications protocols. More emphasis is given to the treatment of functions in layers four and above than to those below four because the layers below four either now have standards or have committees formed to develop standards. The checklist is intended as a method for identifying which standards to reference rather than as an outline for reiterating the standard where a standard exists.

INTRODUCTION

The National Aeronautics and Space Administration (NASA) is continually investigating better ways to define the interfaces between the many elements of its space mission support system. The ability to ensure that all aspects of each interface are adequately treated in a consistent manner is of vital concern. This paper illustrates the complexity of the system interfaces and presents an approach to identifying the interface requirements that ensures specification and consideration of the full range of needs at the design level. The approach allows the designer to select the subset of specification elements that applies to the particular interface of concern.

This paper then examines NASA's efforts to implement this concept and provides initial results of that activity. A brief description of the implementation methodology (a communications checklist) is given, and the application of this checklist to an actual interface description is shown.

BACKGROUND

The system that supports NASA's space missions has evolved over a period of time to support a broad range of widely differing mission requirements. As might be expected, the resulting system is large and complex and comprises a number of different organizations. Figure 1 is a block diagram representation of part of that system—the portion that supports near-Earth missions that use the services of the Tracking and Data Relay Satellite System (TDRSS). The major functions, and the interfaces between those functions, are identified; each of the major functions is managed by a separate organization within the Goddard Space Flight Center (GSFC).

This system has several important characteristics. First, it is a large system managed by a number of organizational elements; second, it is very complex, comprising many elements with many interfaces; third, it is a distributed system, both geographically and

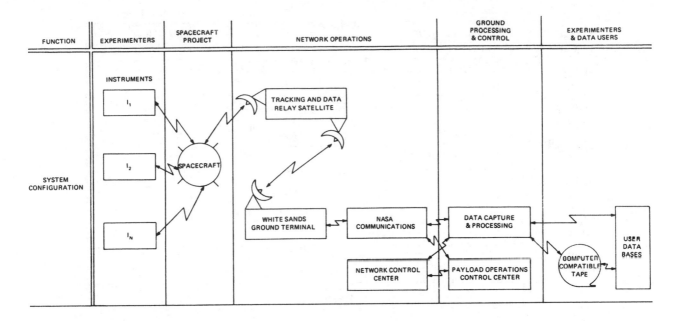

Figure 1. NASA Near-Earth Data System

in space; and fourth, it must be capable of evolutionary, modular growth, since replacement of the total system, whether to meet new requirements or to accommodate new technology, would be too expensive to contemplate. Clearly, some systematic approach is needed to adequately describe and document such a system.

The technique of "layering" is a systems engineering tool that can provide such a systematic approach. Layering is the partitioning of a large, complex task into smaller, simpler tasks, each performing some well-defined function using only a well-defined set of services provided by the layer immediately below. Layering has been developed and refined to assist in solving problems that result from characteristics such as the four identified for the GSFC near-Earth system. Layering allows a system to be partitioned so that development and operational responsibilities can be assigned to the management elements best equipped to deal with them; it helps master complexity by dividing a large task into several smaller tasks; it can be used to define the system in a way that conforms to the natural spatial distribution of the system; and it provides a methodology for defining the system so that evolution and growth can take place in an incremental fashion. Thus, layering is a natural first step in defining and documenting a large, complex system.

If a group of engineers were assigned to the task of defining the layers of a complex system each engineer would probably develop a different system description. Since one goal of describing a system using a layered approach is to develop a common definition and terminology, it is desirable to have a reference model that is globally interpretable. Since about 1977, the OSI subcommittee of the ISO has worked to standardize the rules of interaction between interconnected systems. This effort led to the definition of an interconnection architecture called the "Reference Model for Open Systems Interconnection." This seven-layer model is now generally accepted by ISO, the International Telegraph and Telephone Consultative Committee (CCITT), the European Com-

puter Manufacturers Association (ECMA), and a number of national standards bodies, including the American National Standards Institute (ANSI). Briefly, the functions of the seven layers (Figure 2) are:

- Application Layer—Supports an application process in the application environment (remote-job entry, process selection, recovery).

- Presentation Layer—Provides format translations/transformations between application processes.

- Session Layer—Supports the interaction between communicating application processes by establishing and maintaining a session connection.

- Transport Layer—Provides reliable end-to-end transport of messages across one network or several interconnected networks.

- Network Layer—Provides a logical channel between two end points of a communications network.

- Data Link Layer—Provides for reliable exchange of logical sequences of data blocks across one communications channel.

- Physical Layer—Provides physical characteristics necessary for transmissions between equipments.

Because this model is being accepted worldwide, both in standards organizations and in commercial groups, it was felt to be a reasonable choice to use in documenting portions of the NASA system. In particular, it seemed appropriate as a descriptive tool in a set of interface control documents that were being developed to document major changes in many interfaces within NASA's

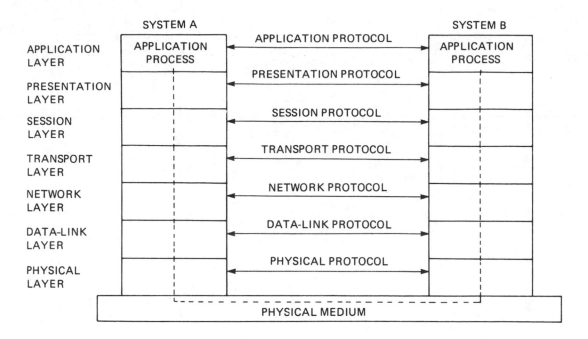

Figure 2. Protocol Layers of Reference Model for Open Systems Interconnection

Spaceflight Tracking and Data Network System. That system, which is composed of a number of distributed tracking and receiving stations interconnected by a worldwide network, is being replaced by the TDRSS—a satellite-based tracking and data-relay system. When this transition is made, interfaces that have been in place for years will either change drastically or be eliminated, and new interfaces will appear. It was decided to attempt to cast the new interface definitions in terms of the reference model.

After several months of effort, it became clear that the reference model, while providing elegant and impressive descriptions of the layers, services, and relationships between the layers, is disappointingly vague in defining where in the model to place certain specific protocol services. The result of this lack of firm definition was a general inconsistency in the interface descriptions, which were prepared by different people. Furthermore, it was not possible to find an "authority" on the reference model who could arbitrate disagreements. Therefore, it was decided to create a "checklist" for use by personnel involved in developing the interface control documents. This checklist would be the referee and final judge in determining in which layer specific services were placed. To gain insights into the experiences of others and to perhaps help others take advantage of NASA's experiences, it was further decided to publish the checklist and distribute it as widely as possible for review and comment.

WHAT IS THE CHECKLIST AND WHO NEEDS IT?

The engineers responsible for designing large distributed computer-based systems that are connected by a communications network are seldom communications experts. They are probably experts in specific subfunctions of the overall system with only limited knowledge of communications. Defining the interfaces between each distributed component requires more knowledge of

the information to be exchanged than of the media over which it will be transported. Therefore, what does the systems engineer do to determine the interface requirements? Looking at what was done in the past and trying to extrapolate for the new requirements is one well-worn method. But this method is frought with problems of subtle omissions.

A good reference manual containing "all you wanted to know but were afraid to ask" data would be very useful. The checklist is meant to address such occasional needs. Although it is not meant as a "how-to" guide for the true communications engineer, it is a good start toward a reference manual for the systems engineer who needs to review his "shopping list" to decide what he needs from the "local communications network grocery store." Used as a reminder of what is or could be made available, it can reduce the probability that a useful service will be forgotten.

If the checklist is to continue to fulfill its intended function, it must be revised periodically to incorporate new ideas and improved services. At the same time, a compromise must be made between explicit functional detail and gross generic services. If the technical content is excessive, it may not be used. Likewise, if there is too little information, it will provide no useful service.

Now that the intended audience for the checklist has been identified and put in proper perspective, the checklist itself can be discussed.

CHECKLIST DESCRIPTION

Table 1 shows a generic list of protocol services on the left and indicates the OSI Reference Model layers (columns) associated with each service. It is immediately obvious that numerous services support multiple layers. In some instances, these generic

Table 1. Summary of Association of Services with the OSI Reference Model Layers

Services \ Layer	Physical 1	Data Link 2	Network 3	Transport 4	Session 5	Presentation 6	Application 7
Electrical	—						
Mechanical	—						
Logical	—	—					
Address Management		—	—	—	—	—	—
Connection Life		—	—	—	—	—	—
Routing/Switching			—	—	—		
Expedited Data		—	—	—	—	—	—
Peer-to-Peer Layer Coordination		—	—	—	—	—	—
Service Quality		—	—	—	—	—	
Flow Control		—	—	—	—	—	
Restart/Reset		—	—	—	—	—	
Management Reporting			—		—		—
Multiplexing		—	—	—	—	—	
Sequencing		—	—	—	—		
Segmenting/Blocking		—	—				
Format		—	—	—	—	—	—
Gateway				—			
Data Compression/Decompression						—	
Encryption/Decryption	—					—	
Code Conversion						—	
Virtual Device						—	
Virtual Program						—	
Syntax						—	
Security			—				—
Cost Accounting			—				—
Priority				—			—
Scheduling				—			—
Semantics						—	

names clearly define the kind of support provided in each layer. Most of the Reference Model services are not discussed in the literature or ISO documents in sufficient detail to determine their complete list of subfunctions. Much of our effort was therefore devoted to researching NASA's needs in each area, as well as the needs of the general communications community. The determination of the specific functions within each service and how these functions should be allocated to each layer was based on a concept that placed essential functions at the lowest layer and assigned the remainder to higher layers. This is obviously good engineering practice. The task was one of determining the best way to define the functions within each service so that optimal layer assignments could be made.

The purpose of the checklist is to provide a means for a system designer to identify logical protocol functions and ensure that a new system design will not accidently omit a desired capability. There was no intention of providing information concerning specific implementation techniques. Because each service can have many alternative implementations, the checklist is certainly not a protocol specification. However, it can serve as a reasonable outline for writing a digital communications interface specification.

A future enhancement of the checklist is intended to indicate references to existing standards for each service. The systems engineer can then refer to the referenced standards, eliminating duplication of effort in writing a specification while reducing the potential for conflicting descriptions of requirements at each end of the interface.

IDENTIFICATION OF FEATURE FUNCTIONS

Table 2 represents a small segment of the checklist and shows the breakdown of several protocol services into their individual functional elements. It also shows that each function does not necessarily appear in each layer where its parent service is listed. Such omissions may not be completely correct. In a few cases, when the checklist was being generated, omissions of this type were challenged and often eliminated when a valid service in the layer was identified.

The subject of protocols for digital communications is continuing to evolve and, with it, new ideas, requirements, and implementation techniques. For these reasons, one should not expect any checklist or standard to cover all cases. The checklist must be a living document that is updated as systems become more complex.

The information in Table 2 is still too generic to ensure that the proper functional partitioning will be accomplished uniformly and consistently by all users of the checklist. Additional levels of refinement are required to achieve useful understanding.

BRIEF DESCRIPTION OF SUBFUNCTIONS

Table 3 is an example of the services expanded into functions and subfunctions for the Reference Model's Application layer.

This table illustrates the current level of detail used in the checklist for describing subfunctions. The application layer descriptions contain more explanation of individual features than those in the lower layers because the Application layer has not received as much attention within the communications community as the other layers. The treatment of access and resource security is particularly emphasized in this example. By employing the network protocol and a network administrator (a person) to maintain centralized access control, a communications system can operate like a Data-Base Management System, using an integrated data-base directory and security system. No access to the network (or data-base) or its nodes would be possible without going through the network security manager (data-base directory manager). This approach provides security, and it can also make the network user-friendly because network resource access can be based on the original security check and does not have to be repeated for each new access.

TREATMENT OF MULTILAYER FEATURES

Table 4 illustrates one of ten major services that span multiple layers. This table briefly indicates the subfunctions assigned to each layer. It also illustrates the allocation of essential subfunctions to the lowest layers.

If complex subfunction definitions are limited to the few words, as illustrated in Table 4, ambiguity can result. Therefore, the checklist provides further amplification for these functions. This amplification gives the reasons for the subdivision and defines or implies the interfaces between layers. The additional level of detail given to these services was necessary to fill the void in treatment by the OSI Reference Model.

The service allocations employed have been reviewed formally by NASA and informally by the National Bureau of Standards (NBS); neither review can be said to represent the views of the ISO or the communications community in general. Until the checklist is subjected to detailed reviews relative to a specific protocol implementation, it is unlikely that significant controversy will surface. This review requirement is true for all levels of the OSI Reference Model above layer 4 or 5, since few commercial systems provide services in these layers that follow the Reference Model guidelines.

The checklist is one more source of material for supporting and amplifying the OSI Reference Model. As such, it needs wide visibility and critical review.

STATUS OF THE CHECKLIST

The current version of the checklist has been reviewed at NASA and at NBS. At NASA, it has also been used as the guide for documenting a local area network communications protocol. These reviews and use by NASA are preliminary steps toward the potential goal of establishing the checklist as a formal NASA system designer's reference. The results of the initial reviews have indicated that the document does merit such use.

Table 2. Communications Model Checklist Generic Services and Subfunctions

Services \ Layer	1	2	3	4	5	6	7
Connection Life							
Establishment		X	X	X	X	X	X
Release		X	X	X	X	X	X
Abort			X		X		X
Multiplex operation.			X	X			
Initiation procedures.		X	X	X	X	X	X
Service quality matching. . .			X		X		
Synchronization		X	X				
Routing/Switching							
Strategy.				X			
Implementation.			X				
Control node(s).			X				
Tables			X	X			
Cost.				X			
Delay.				X			
Congestion			X				
Scheduled/dynamic usage . .				X			
Priority				X			
Fail-safe/fail-soft			X		X		
Bandwidth allocation				X			

69

Table 3. Applications Layer Checklist

Security: Identify logon and password requirements for:

a) Access to the network
b) Access to a remote host on the network

- Identify multilevel security requirements and procedures for partitioning of resource access based on security level and passwords.
- Identify methods for initially entering logon ID and password into system tables and means for changing these entries by user and by system administrator.
- Identify means for reporting multiple attempts to enter passwords.
- Identify procedures for terminating connections that cannot satisfy password within reasonable number of tries.

Cost Accounting:

- Cost-account per connection for host and network separately.
- Ability to change cost-accounts within a connection period.
- Verification of valid cost-account and permission to use cost-account.
- Reporting of cost-account use.

Priority:

- Priority for queue position, bandwidth allocation, minimum delay in use of network services, and ability to specify priority for host services.

Scheduling:

- Identify means for scheduling of host services, network routing, bandwidth, delay requirements, priority, security level during transmission, physical devices on hosts in support of application, and application program use.

Address Management:

- Application layer address is its legal cost account, logon ID, and password in each node or host.

Connection Establishment, Release, Abort:

- Establishment requirements based on logon ID, password, cost account, application program access password, and file(s) access password.
- Release at normal program termination or programs error termination.
- Abort from programs at end or on receipt of manual abort signal from user.

Expedited Data:

- Ability of application program to generate a message having expedited priority.

Peer-to-Peer Layer Coordination:

- Coordination to ensure that sending and receiving devices and programs are available to send and receive data.
- All files are open and on-line and all supporting devices are operational and properly attached to required programs.
- Sufficient CPU, RAM, and other resources have been allocated.
- Any special parameter settings of the operating system or the application program have been made.

Communications Mode:

- Identification of interactive or batch requirement and initiation of programs in proper mode.
- Identification of any security requirements for encryption of fields and files or during actual transmission.

Quality of Service:

- Identification of specific generic parameters that can be employed by the Presentation layer to define bit-error rates, delay, lost data, restarts, bandwidth, and error reporting requirements.

Format Transformation:

- Hardcopy and softcopy format giving physical location of data fields, field sizes in lines and characters, color, shading, line drawing characteristics, font types, font sizes, hardcopy physical dimensions, interactive operator control fields (touch, lightpen, trackball, function key) relationships.

Semantics:

- Cause and effect relationships for interactive operations, error conditions in terms of programs to be initiated or services to be requested.

Management Reporting:

- Reporting of security monitor functions pertaining to password penetration, unauthorized access, cost-account use, proper security level for access, logon penetration.
- Reporting of availability versus need; service quality received versus requested.

Table 4. Address Management

Application Address: Corresponds to the cost account and security identification used to verify the users legitimate use of the facilities.

Presentation Address: Corresponds to the file or physical device to be employed that may need format and syntax transformations for compatibility.

Session Address: To tie two software programs together. The duration of the session is independent of the duration of any other lower level support provided. The source and destination addresses appear as a specific bit string in a message for networks employing virtual circuits or datagrams. Normally equivalent to a port address or a virtual machine address.

Transport Address: To define a virtual circuit or communications channel between hosts or source and destination nodes on a network. This is independent of the number of physical devices at each host or node and independent of the number of intermediate nodes that support the communications link between hosts or the number of alternate or parallel paths between nodes and hosts. The address appears as a specific bit string in a message for networks using virtual circuits or datagrams (i.e., non-designated or unscheduled links). Normally equated to an end-node address (source or destination).

Network Address: To define a specific routing along one or more physical communication links between nodes within a single network having its own address structure. This address may be transparent to all layers above the network layer. It may or may not be required as a specific bit string by the network. For example, it is used to identify a table entry for the virtual circuit established between two or more nodes (source, intermediates, destination).

Internet Address: To define a specific connection spanning two or more networks, having their own address structure, within a larger national, international, or global network system. Employed only when communicating across several independent networks.

Data Link Address: To define a single physical connection between two nodes in a network. Parallel connections between the same two nodes have separate data-link addresses. Probably not a specific bit string in the message. Normally handled by flow control logic and circuit selection dynamics, and is known only to Network and Data-Link layers.

NASA views the checklist as a living document, worth updating to reflect new concepts and refinements in protocol services, functional allocations, and definition. Copies of the checklist document may be obtained from either the MITRE Corporation or NASA/GSFC at the following addresses:

The MITRE Corporation
Mr. Albert W. Bowers
1820 Dolly Madison Boulevard
McLean, Virginia 22102

NASA/Goddard Space Flight Center
Mr. Edward B. Connell, Code 502
Greenbelt, Maryland 20771

An Introduction to Network Architectures

V. KONANGI AND **C. R. DHAS**

Protocols and interfaces between interconnected systems.

THE successful integration and cross fertilization of communications and geographically-dispersed computing facilities is fast leading to an information era where information has to be extracted from large distributed databases. In addition to their present computing features, computing systems organized into a network would also be required to gather, process, and distribute information from these distributed databases. In trying to manipulate information in a collection of heterogeneous systems and databases that are all accessible via a common communications network, the user is faced with a series of obstacles. The initial obstacle involves connectivity. The user has to be aware of the physical location of the database(s) of interest and then initiate appropriate procedures to get connected to the system(s). The user must also be familiar with the idiosyncrasies of the communications facility, database(s), and computer system(s) which add substantially to the complexity of the information management process.

Clearly, the user should be shielded from the internal complexities of individual systems by creating and presenting a virtual uniprocessor to the user. The characteristics of a multiplicity of resource components, both physical and logical, should be transparent to the user.

The basic function performed by the communications subsystem is the provision of an access path by which a user can access services or connect another user. An access path is a sequence of functions that make it possible for one user to be physically connected to others, and in addition, to communicate with them in spite of errors of various types and differences in the choice of speed and format of the messages exchanged.

The existence of a physical connection, via the communications subsystem, between any two entities does not guarantee communication between them. Intelligent or meaningful communication requires the exchange of information in an orderly way, using a well defined and structured set of rules and conventions. These sets of rules are called protocols. Though protocols may be *ad hoc*, they are generally standardized specifications. The presence of well defined protocols and interfaces between interconnected systems enables them to work in cooperation to achieve a

common purpose. The careful design of protocols and their standardization provides resource independence and a uniform interface to all services. This functional view of the network is called the network architecture. The view is independent of implementation, in order to take advantage of technology/cost tradeoffs. The architecture of a network consists of the precise definition of the functions the network and its components should perform and the protocols to be used. The contemporary approach is to express architectures using layered, peer architectural techniques. The set of agreements for each of the pairwise interactions may be termed protocols; thus, the network architecture is specified in terms of protocols for communication between pairs of peer-level layers. The peer-layer communication concept is critical to network design.

The basic issues in a distributed environment are the open interworking and the general communicability of distributed systems. Clearly, the basic function of communication is necessary in order to accomplish this. In a distributed environment, the nature of the communication function should be such that the transmission management is not limited to a particular technology. It should also be flexible enough to interface with different technology and at the same time have enough modularity to provide only minimal functional capabilities, when that mode of operation is appropriate. Thus, the transport layer which implements the transmission management functions provides a transparent path for the data throughout the network, independently of the contents of the data.

Once the transport mechanism is set up, the next issue is function management, which in our environment is the exchange of user information to accomplish a task or a set of tasks.

The above two functions, communication and function management, relieve the application from the burden of establishing a path and managing information. This also serves to hide the idiosyncrasies of the above two functions from the application.

Alternative Approaches

A protocol is a procedure for the exchange of information

Reprinted from *IEEE Communications Magazine*, Volume 21, Number 7, October 1983, pages 44-50. Copyright © 1983 by The Institute of Electrical and Electronics Engineers, Inc.

between processes, not only in a network environment but also in multiprocessor systems for controlling the interaction of parallel processes [5], in real-time applications for controlling a number of different devices, and in other systems where there is no fixed time relationship between the occurrence of an event and the action implied by the event. Protocol functions are accomplished by an exchange of messages between processes. The format and meaning of these messages comprise the logical definition of the protocol; rules of procedure determine the actions of the processes cooperating in the protocol. The set of these rules constitutes the procedural definition of the protocol. The logical definition is the syntax of the protocol, while the procedural definition is the semantics of the protocol. The actual functions performed by a protocol are determined by the task that needs to be executed and the environment in which it must function.

In most architectures, three levels of protocol function can be easily identified, even though they may not be explicitly visible as such; these are the user, process, and communication levels. The user is interested in accessing and processing information which may be stored either locally or at a distance. This can be viewed as an exchange of command and data between a set of processes. Without an inter-process communications facility, cooperation between various processes may not be possible at all. To illustrate the basic idea of the interprocess communication involved, consider a Process P in System A accessing a database D in System B.

The following steps can be identified:

- Systems A and B recognize that Process P needs to access Database D;
- Creation and/or activation of access process at System B;
- System A recognizes the command to System B and transmits the command to System B;
- The process in System B executes the command and transmits the desired data from database D to System A;
- Deactivation of the access process at System B after completion of the task.

The ease with which the above steps can be carried out is dependent on the inter-process communications facilities and the associated protocols [12, 14, 11]. Thus, it is possible to provide an inter-process communications system between the processes and allow communication to take place through the inter-process communications (IPC) system, as shown in Fig. 1. The set of functions available in the IPC is a function of the process requirement. But some of the functions required by processes in an inter-process communication environment are common to all processes. The most common among these is the error-free transport of data between processes. The design of inter-process communications systems has evolved from *ad hoc* methods to highly structured techniques. Modular design techniques are used to reduce the complexity of the system. Network architectures are designed hierarchically, consisting of a number of layers. Even though formal

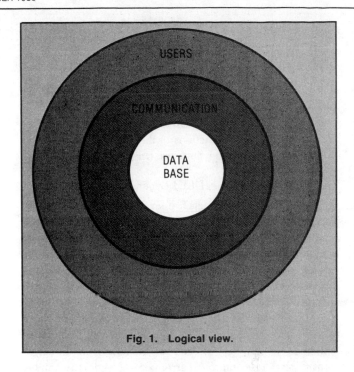

Fig. 1. Logical view.

procedures do not exist for arrival at a unique layered structure, a good architecture should be flexible, efficient, easy to implement, and should enhance the understanding of the system. The modularity of this approach minimizes the interdependency between various components of the network structure. The definition of the structure should be independent of the implementation of the network. This layered structure is referred to as onion skin or peer architecture [7, 8, 6, 9, 13, 15]. Layering of protocols is one of the most effective means for structuring a network architecture. Each level utilizes the functions of the lower level and adds some functionality of its own for possible use by the next higher level. This permits an implementation at one level to be modified without affecting the overall structure, as long as the interfaces with the adjacent levels are unchanged. Therefore, the layered approach simplifies both the design and the implementation.

Systems Network Architecture

Systems Network Architecture (SNA) [4, 7, 2] is IBM's view of network architecture for distributed processing. Figure 2 shows the logical model of the network architecture. These layers model the logical architecture; physically, the layers at one end need not reside in a single hardware.

In the world of IBM, all the functions represented by the layers of the architecture may reside in the host system (System 370). Functions approximately corresponding to the link and path controls could be resident in the software of a separate communications controller, with the remaining functions in the host. It is also possible to move almost all the access path functions out to a front-end communications processor. The allocation of logical functions to hardware resources depends upon the functional capability of the hardware unit. The end users of an SNA network are presented with a highly transparent, sequential, bit-serial path which is independent of the topology, route selection, or transmission media of the network. In SNA, logical connection between network addressable units is called a session. The functions required for establishing and managing these sessions are contained in various layers of the network architecture.

A layered hierarchical peer-process approach has been used to distribute the functions in the network architecture. The layers and their functions are briefly discussed below.

The Data Link Control (DLC) Layer

The DLC layer constructs frames from the raw bit stream. The detection and correction of transmission errors is done in a manner that makes it transparent to the higher layers. The number of stations on the link may be two (point-to-point) or more (multipoint). The physical connection may be switched or nonswitched. The structure of the protocol at this layer has the characteristics of being code-independent and fully transparent to the bit pattern being handled, and uses a single format for a combination of the data and control. It efficiently combines a number of control functions in a single transmission, uses improved error control techniques, and is independent of both the application and the path control layer. The protocol used is the Synchronous Data Link Control (SDLC).

The Path Control (PC) Layer

The PC layer routes messages between sources and destinations. Congestion in the communications subnet, due to the presence of too many packets, is controlled by this layer. To improve transmission efficiency, this layer can packetize outgoing messages and depacketize incoming messages.

The Transmission Control (TC) Layer

Transmission control creates, manages, and deletes transport connections called sessions. It manages the flow of data on these sessions.

The Data Flow Control (DFC) Layer

This layer controls the user request/response flow and ensures flow integrity at the user level. It has the function of accommodating the idiosyncrasies of message direction and the intermittency demanded by the end user. Such idiosyncrasies include the choice of full-duplex or half-duplex, the mode of user interaction, and grouping of messages, to name a few.

The Presentation Services (PS) Layer

This layer provides services which include data transformations (such as data and text compression), additions (such as column headings for displays), and editing and translations (such as program commands into local terminal languages).

The End User (EU) Layer

The network addressable unit (NAU) services provide the user interface. Within each SNA network, and even within individual sessions, the functions within the layers may be subset and tailored to the requirements of the application. Some functional options are statistically chosen when creating a system, while others are dynamically selected at session establishment time. The control of SNA networks is achieved through a hierarchy of control domains. A network may consist of multiple domains, with each domain controlled by a Systems Services Control Point (SSCP). In a network with multiple domains, the SSCP's communicate with each other in the overall management of the network.

The ARPANET

The ARPANET is a highly successful experimental packet switching network with about 100 nodes. In addition to terrestrial communications media, it also uses satellite channels. The ARPANET differs from other networks in that the communications network is both physically and logically separate from the host network. In the communications subnetwork, a communication mechanism is created for the attached host through the interface message processor (IMP).

Figure 3 shows the structure of the ARPANET communications protocol hierarchy. A brief description of the functions of the various layers is presented below.

IMP-IMP Layer

The interface message processor is part of the communications subnetwork, and supports interconnection of a host to the packet switched network. The IMP also performs a store-and-forward function of the packets. The IMP to IMP protocol creates a virtual communication path between the hosts. The protocol is responsible for detecting and correcting transmission error, avoiding congestion of packets within the subnetwork, and routing packets to their destinations. The functions in this layer are analogous to the link and path control layers of SNA.

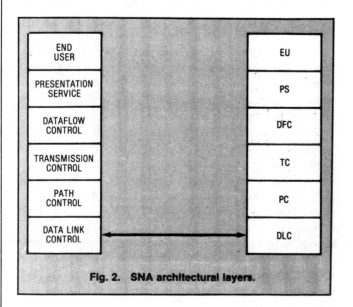

Fig. 2. SNA architectural layers.

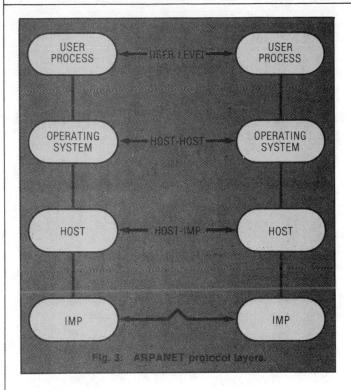

Fig. 3. ARPANET protocol layers.

user programs and some may perform packet switching; others may do both. The communications interface of the logical link is realized using a layered architectural design. The network architecture is divided into five functional layers: the physical link layer, the data link control layer, the transport layer, the network service layer, and the application layer. The functions performed by each of these layers are distributed among the nodes and reflected in protocols that are used to communicate between and synchronize the peer layers in the nodes. A functional description of the layers follows.

The Physical Link Layer

This layer manages the physical transmission of information over a data channel. It is concerned with the physical and electrical characteristics of the media, such as signaling techniques, clocking on the channel, and interfaces to the computer system and communications carrier services. It creates an interface, which is independent of the channel, across which data blocks may be transmitted and received. Protocols applicable to this layer are interface standards such as RS-232C.

The Data Link Control Layer

The purpose of this layer is to create a sequential error-free communications path between adjacent nodes over which data blocks may be transferred. It also manages the transmission and reception of multi-access and half-duplex channels, and offers a channel independent error-free sequential interface. The standard protocol for this layer is the digital data communications message protocol (DDCMP).

The Transport Layer

The transport of messages from source to destination nodes is the function of this layer. It provides switching functions to establish an end-to-end path through intermediate nodes created by the data link control layer. A node route table is used to route messages. The creation and update of the routing table is independent of the actual switching and is performed by the routing algorithm. An adaptive, low cost, and changing path-when-channels-fail criterion is used in selecting end-to-end paths. The routing algorithm is a part of the transport layer.

The Network Services Layer

The creation and management of the logical link paths for the users of the network is the responsibility of this layer. It uses the transport layer to move messages from the source node to the destination node. Within a node, it delivers messages to the proper logical link and performs such functions as flow control and buffer management. In DNA, each packet is routed independently of its predecessors. The interface to this layer is the communications service by which programs communicate independent of their physical location in the network. The protocol for this layer is the network service protocol (NSP).

Host-IMP Layer

This protocol is path-independent and provides a mechanism to transfer data between the host and the communications network, that is, the IMP. This layer aids the host in sending messages composed of packets to other specified destination hosts. By means of acknowledgments from the destination to the source, the source host is informed about the status of the messages forwarded by it.

Host-Host Layer

The hosts use the host-to-host protocol to manage the user communications channels. This layer links the host operating systems for initiating user jobs in a remote host and maintaining communications between jobs in different hosts.

User Process-User Process Layer

The purpose of this layer is to facilitate the transfer of information between user processes. These functions coordinate networking functions that operate at the application or the privileged application-subsystem level.

Digital Network Architecture (DNA)

DNA [7, 13] is the definition of interfaces, structures, and protocols which create a communications environment among the many heterogeneous products of the Digital Equipment Corporation. The basic mechanism provided by DNA is an object-to-object or process-to-process communications logical link, where a logical link is a sequential error-free path connecting the system resources over which data may be exchanged. The path created is full duplex and flow controlled using a request count scheme in which messages are transmitted only when requested by the receiver.

Unlike ARPANET, DNA makes no distinction between hosts and IMP's. In DNA, some systems (nodes) may run

The Application Layer

This layer exchanges data, through independent logical links, for the fulfillment of application functions. Such exchanges may include remote file access, file transfer, terminal control, database transaction request, and application program-to-application program data transfers.

In general, layer functions are realized by protocols implemented within layer modules, used to synchronize and transfer data between the corresponding layers within the DNA structure hierarchy. Figure 4 shows this peer layer communications structure.

Open System Interconnection (OSI) Reference Model

The objective of the International Standards Organization's OSI [6, 9, 15] is to define a set of standards which allow systems to cooperate. A system which obeys applicable OSI standards in its communications with other systems is termed an open system. "Openness" does not imply any particular systems implementation, technology, or interconnection means, but rather refers to the mutual recognition and support of the applicable standards. The Reference Model allows sufficient flexibility so that it can accommodate expanding technology and user demands. This flexibility is also intended to allow the phased transition from existing implementations to OSI standards.

The Reference Model has been approached with the thought of four basic elements. These are:

- the application-processes which exist within the OSI environment,
- the connections which join the application-processes and permit them to exchange information,
- systems, and
- the physical media for Open Systems Interconnection.

The internal organization and functioning of each individual open system is outside the scope of OSI standards, and these are not visible to other systems with which it is interconnected. The OSI architecture consists of seven layers, and standard protocols have been developed for the three bottom layers. The seven-layered OSI architecture is briefly described below.

The Physical Layer

The Physical Layer provides mechanical, electrical, functional, and procedural characteristics to activate, maintain, and deactivate physical connections for bit transmission between data-link entities, possibly through intermediate systems, each relaying bit transmission within the Physical Layer. The present standard protocols for the Physical Layer are: X.21, V.24, and V.35.

The Data Link Layer

The Data Link Layer provides functional and procedural means to establish, maintain, and release data-link connections among network entities. A data-link connection is built upon one or several physical connections.

The objective of this layer is to detect and possibly correct errors which may occur in the physical layer. In addition, the

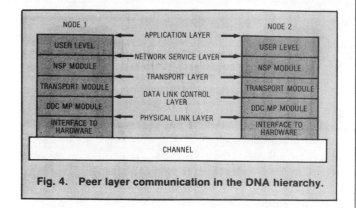

Fig. 4. Peer layer communication in the DNA hierarchy.

Data Link Layer enables the Network Layer to control interconnection of data-circuits within the Physical Layer. The most popular data link protocol is the High Level Data Link Control (HDLC).

The Network Layer

In the open systems architecture, some systems are the destination for data, while others may function as intermediate nodes only; they forward data to other intermediate nodes or to the destination. The routing of data and network connection are examples of functions in this layer. Thus, this layer provides functional and procedural means to exchange network service data units between two transport entities over a network connection. It provides transport entities with independence from routing and switching considerations associated with the establishment and operation of a given network connection. The network layer determines the chief characteristics of the host-IMP interface. Congestion in the communication subnet, due to the presence of too much data, is normally controlled by this layer. An important basis for protocols in the network layer is Level 3 of the X.25 interface.

The Transport Layer

Over and above the services provided by the network layer, there is a need to control data transmission from source-end system to destination-end system. Therefore, the transport layer exists to provide a universal transport service in association with the services provided by the underlying layers. The transport layer provides transparent transfer of data between session entities and relieves the session entities of the details involved in reliable (error-free) communication. The transport layer optimizes the use of the available communications services by the session entities and provides cost effective means for data transfer. The transport layer also determines the type of service provided to the session layer and, ultimately, to the network users. The most popular type of transport connection is an error-free virtual point-to-point channel that delivers messages in the same order in which they were sent.

The transport layer is an end-to-end layer; a process on the source-end system converses with a peer process on a destination-end system. In contrast, each system and its neighbors which may not be the source and destination systems carry out the protocols of the lower layers. At present, national/international standards do not exist for the network layer and the layers above it.

The Session Layer

The purpose of this layer is to provide the means for cooperating presentation-entities (processes) to organize and synchronize their dialog and manage their data exchange. The session layer is the user's interface into the network. The functions provided by the session layer can be classified into two categories: 1) a session administration service which binds two presentation entities into a relationship and unbinds them when the session is over; and 2) a session dialog service which controls the data exchanged by delimiting and synchronizing the data operations between two presentation entities. To enable the transfer of data between presentation entities, the session layer may utilize the services provided by the lower layers. Thus, the session layer adds application-oriented functions to the basic communications service provided by the transport layer. Accepted standards for the session layer do not exist at present. In most networks, the functions of the session layer are considered to be part of the higher level functions, such as virtual terminal and file transfer.

The Presentation Layer

The purpose of the presentation layer is to represent information to communicating application-entities in a way that preserves meaning while resolving syntax differences. The presentation layer is concerned only with the syntactic view of the data and not with its semantics, that is, its meaning to the application layer, which is only known by the application-entities. Hence, the presentation layer provides a set of services which may be selected by the application layer to enable it to interpret the meaning of the data exchanged. These services are for the management of the entry, exchange, display, and control of structured data. The presentation layer is location-independent and provides an environment for applications to communicate without undue concern about interface variability and application modification.

The Application Layer

As the highest layer in the OSI architecture, the application layer provides a means for the application processes to access the OSI environment. The purpose of the layer is to serve as the window between communicating application-processes using the OSI environment to exchange meaningful information. As the only layer that directly provides services to the application-processes, the application layer necessarily provides all services directly usable by application-processes.

The protocols of this layer serve the end user by providing the distributed information service appropriate to an application, its management, and to system management. Management of open systems interconnection comprises those functions required to initiate, maintain, terminate, and

record data concerning the establishment of connection for data transfer among application-processes. The function of all lower layers is to support the application layer.

An application is made up of autonomous application-processes which cooperate and intercommunicate according to application layer protocols. Application-processes are the ultimate source and sink for the data exchanged. Applications or application-processes may be of any kind—manual, computerized, industrial, or physical. Figure 5 shows the layers of the OSI architecture.

In addition to the above, there are other network architectures, such as UNIVAC's Distributed Communications Architecture, Honeywell, Control Data, Hewlett-Packard, and NCR. All of them use different variations of the layered architecture concept.

Conclusions

A broad spectrum of transmission methods and media can be used, which include public and private transmission media and distributed as well as local networks. Techniques such as packet, message, and circuit switching may be used in conjunction with local broadcast networks, satellite channels, multi-drop, and point-to-point circuits. Each of these transmission services has its own distinguishing characteristics. This implies that processes which connect via a multitude of transmission media or networks will have to implement different procedures for each of these media.

The contemporary approach is to design a standard communication service, called the "transport service," which offers a number of facilities accessible via primitives at the transport interface. This interface is standard throughout the network, and provides the facility for processes to establish connections with each other and to exchange messages. The motivation for providing the transport interface as a networkwide facility is to relieve each process from the burden of managing its communication requirements. Above this layer, other protocol layers can be formed if desired.

The processes above the transport service will use protocols to accomplish user tasks. The function of these

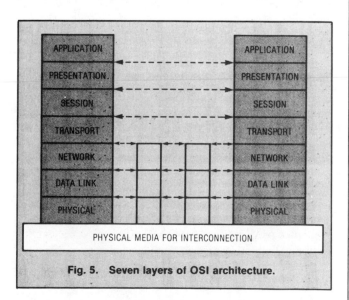

Fig. 5. Seven layers of OSI architecture.

protocols will be a command structure to synchronize and execute these tasks. Whereas the levels up to the transport level are concerned with data transmission, the layers above the transport level perform task management functions. These are defined by the users and are specific to the task. Some of the functions common to layers above the transport protocol are terminal handling and file transfer. The higher level layer, above the transport layer, can be partitioned to correspond to the three layers of the International Standards Organization's Levels 5, 6, and 7.

The higher level layers, in addition to providing connection ports to processes, manage sessions between a pair of local processes as well as between a local and a remote process. In the latter case, the services of the transport service are called on to establish a path with the remote session control. This layer will manage a number of distributed sessions, local or remote, for the execution of total tasks. It is achieved via a protocol in which a number of distributed session control layers participate.

Although the functions that are part of the network architecture have been identified, this by itself does not produce a complete network architecture. The other components required are the "formats" and "protocols" that relate these distributed functions to each other. This needs further research in the area of network architecture. In any case, the resulting architecture must be flexible enough so that its evolution into the International Standard Organization's architecture is easily feasible.

References

[1] G. V. Bochmann and J. Gecsei, "Towards Videotex Standards," *Proc. Viewdata 80 Conf.*, (Online), London, 1980.
[2] M. L. Burke, "X.25/systems network architecture compatibility," *International Conference on Communications*, June 1979.
[3] "X.25," CCITT, *Orange Book*, vol. VII-2, pp. 70-108, 1977.
[4] R. Cypser, *Communications Architecture for Distributed Systems*, Reading, MA: Addison Wesley, 1979.
[5] D. W. Davies et al, *Computer Networks and Their Protocols*, New York: John Wiley & Sons, 1979.
[6] M. Gien and H. Zimmerman, "Design principles for interconnection," *Proc. Sixth Data Communications Symposium*, November 1979.
[7] P. E. Green, "An introduction to network architectures and protocols," *IBM Syst. J.*, vol. 18, no. 2, 1979.
[8] J. M. McQuillan and V. G. Cerf, *Tutorial: A Practical View of Computer Communications Protocols*, IEEE Computer Society.
[9] L. Pouzin and J. B. Zimmerman, "A tutorial on protocols," *Proc. IEEE*, November 1978.
[10] R. Rosenthal, *Accessing Online Network Resources with a Network Access Machine*, National Bureau of Standards.
[11] K. J. Thurber, *Tutorial: A Pragmatic View of Distributed Processing Systems*, IEEE Computer Society.
[12] T. A. Unger, R. A. McBride, J. Slonim, and F. J. Maryanski, "Design for integration of a DBMS into a network environment," *Proc. Sixth Data Communications Symposium*, pp. 26-34, November 1979.
[13] S. Wecker, "Computer network architecture," *Computer*, vol. 12, no. 9, September 1979.
[14] R. C. White, "NETCOM: A real-time message routing capability for a maxi/mini computer network," *Proc. Computer Networking Symposium*, 1978.
[15] H. Zimmerman, "OSI reference model—the ISO model of architecture for open systems interconnections," *IEEE Trans. Commun.*, COM-28, no. 4, April 1980.
[16] A. S. Tanenbaum, *Computer Networks*, Englewood Cliffs, NJ: Prentice Hall, 1981.
[17] ISO/TC 97/SC16N719, August 1981.

Vijaya K. Konangi is a faculty member in electrical engineering at Cleveland State University. His research interests include computer architecture, computer networks, and distributed processing. He is a Member of the IEEE and the ACM. He received the B.E. and M.Sc. degrees from the University of Madras, India and the Ph.D. degree from Iowa State University.

C. R. Dhas received his Ph.D. from Iowa State University, Ames, Iowa. He is a Member of the ACM and IEEE, and his areas of interest include computer architecture, computer networks, and distributed processing. ∎

The DoD Internet Architecture Model

Vinton G. Cerf

Director, Systems Development, MCI Telecommunications, 1133 19th Street N.W., Washington, DC 20036, USA

and

Edward Cain

Defense Communications Engineering Center, 1860 Wiehle Ave., Reston, VA 22090, USA

This paper outlines the principles on which the U.S. Department of Defense packet internet architecture is based and characterizes some of the protocols which implement the architecture. Major factors which influenced the development of this architectural model include experimental and operational experience with a large number of interconnected packet networks, assessments and evaluations of military requirements for national and international interoperability and multiple jurisdiction operation, and specific concerns regarding security, survivability and operation under crisis conditions.

Keywords: DoD, Internet, Protocol, Military Requirements, Interoperability, Security, Survivability, Crisis conditions, Packet Communications, Protocol Architectures, Standards.

Dr. Vinton G. Cerf is presently Director of Systems Development, MCI Telecommunications, Inc. From 1976 to 1982, Dr. Cerf was Program Manager and Principal Scientist at the Defense Advanced Research Projects Agency. During this period he was responsible for technical oversight of research programs in packet switching technology. He has made innovative contributions in the technologies of internetworking and packet switching protocol development. Earlier in his career, Dr. Cerf was an assistant professor at Stanford University, held a position on the Staff of the Computer Science Department at UCLA, and did consulting work in networking. Dr. Cerf has published many papers and has chaired numerous technical sessions in his field. His memberships include ACM, Sigma Xi, IEEE and IFIP.

1. Introduction

The DoD Internet Architecture Model, referred to in the remainder of this paper as the Internet Model, has evolved over a period of seven or eight years, in concert with increasing DoD experience with packet switched computer communications technology. The model has its roots in work sponsored by the Defense Advanced Research Projects Agency in the late 1960's which led to the development and deployment of the ARPANET [1,2]. This initial packet network technology development was soon followed by a number of others involving a variety of transmission media, such as mobile packet radio [4,5], packet satellite [6,10], local area networks [11,12], and an increasing number of private and public data networks. Historical views of the development of many of these packet communications systems can be found in [13–15].

Networking architectures revolve around the protocols which are used to control the transport of data among the systems which must communicate with one another. The services available from various networks which are considered to be part of the overall system play an important role in determining the kinds of protocols which are needed, as do the types of services which are to be supported. The actual implementation of the protocols, their placement in "boxes" and the nature of the operating systems all contribute intimately to the design of the protocol architecture and its ultimate performance.

Among the fundamental assumptions which have influenced the organization of the Internet

Ed Cain is the Chairman of the Protocol Standards Technical Panel, a DoD-wide forum for debate on the technical aspects of DoD standards for host-to-host and higher level protocols. His work at the Defense Communications Engineering Center includes the testing of protocols for performance and functional correctness, and the design of packet switching networks for secure, robust data communications for tactical and strategic military applications. He holds a BEE degree from Georgia Tech, and has done graduate work at VPI&SU.

North-Holland
Computer Networks 7 (1983) 307-318.

Model, perhaps the most basic is that it is both feasible and useful to segregate the various functions which must be performed to achieve the set of services desired into separate components which ultimately take the form of layers of protocols. The notion of protocol layering is not new. It was an important organizational principle in the development of the ARPANET protocols [16–19] and has influenced the protocol models of various computer vendors such as Digital Equipment Corporation (DECNET) and International Business Machines (SNA), to name two, and also the models of the various national and international data communications standards-making bodies such as the CCITT and ISO [23].

It is perhaps a subtle point, but an important one, that the concept of protocol layering should lead to the notion that a particular function or service may be viewed as achieved by means of a series of protocols, each depending upon the lower ones for service. It should not be concluded, however, either that only one protocol exists at each layer or even that the functionality of protocols in the same layer is necessarily the same or even similar. This is a controversial view, but it stems from the observation that protocols often are adjacent to one another in the same layer because they share the *same set of support protocols* and for no other reason that that. This views leads to a protocol model, illustrated in Fig. 1, in which the ensemble of protocols in the model form a de-pendency *hierarchy*. It should be noted that many protocols may occupy the same *layer* in the hierarchy.

Another point which seems important to make about layering is that there is often an implicit assumption that one can easily substitute one protocol for another in a particular layer without affecting the functionality of the protocols which depend on it. This assumption (or goal) is sometimes unwarranted, although it seemingly makes life easier for the protocol architecture designer. The problem lies in the nature of the functionality of the protocols in a particular layer and the nature of the services they can easily offer.

For example, broadcast service or multiaddress service [11,12,20,21] is more easily achieved by networks whose natural medium is broadcast in nature, such as the Ethernet or broadcast packet satellite. Substitution of the ARPANET or a public data network which provides an X.25 [22] interface, may fail to provide the service needed by higher level protocols which ASSUMED the existence of a broadcast or multicast feature in a lower *layer*.

This observation leads to the view that a particular model and especially the protocols fitting that model, may form a self-consistent *protocol suite* (to use Padlipsky's terminology [18]), but arbitrary substitution of a new protocol within the hierarchy may violate these implicit assumptions. This observation is not to say that no substitutions can

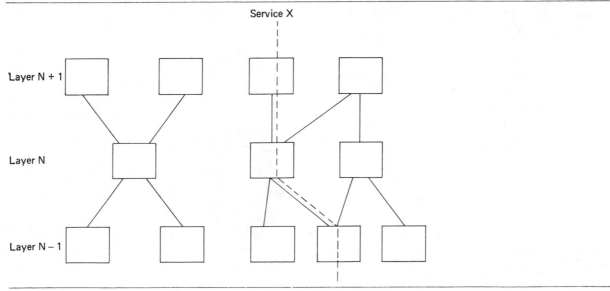

Fig. 1. Protocol Hierarchy Model.

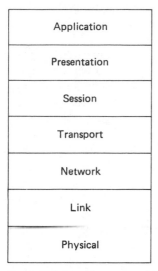

Fig. 2. ISO Open Systems Architecture.

work, but only that it is probably too much to assume that any layer N protocol (to use the ISO terminology) may replace any other layer N protocol without impact on layer N + 1 and above. Furthermore, it is the view of the authors that the goal of total interchangeability of layer N protocols is unnecessary. It is reasonable to expect that distinct types of service may be offered at a given layer in the hierarchy (e.g. transaction/connectionless and virtual circuit).

The most widely publicized protocol architecture is the ISO Open Systems Architecture or Open Systems Interconnection Model. Fig. 2 illustrates its structure, according to the current Draft International Standard [23]. The view portrayed in Figure 2 is, of course, overly simplified. For example, it does not reflect current study of connectionless modes of service, nor does it reflect the internal structure of the Network layer which has a "global network" sublayer under consideration [44]. Furthermore, consideration of network interfaces for local nets (e.g. Ethernet [11]) in addition to the CCITT recommendation X.25 [22] at the Network, Link and Physical layers is also underway.

One conclusion from the foregoing is that the ISO model is still undergoing development and is likely to incorporate new concepts, some of which are considered by the authors to be critically important for military applications.

The next section offers a summary of the DoD Internet Model along with some views on assumptions and requirements which are specific to military systems.

2. The Internet Model

The basic Internet Model is illustrated in two forms in Figs. 3 and 4. Figure 3 emphasizes the basic expectation that multiple networks of widely differing internal characteristics will be a natural and necessary part of military networking. This view has been expressed in many publications, some of which are listed in the Reference section of this paper [24–36]. This conclusion is a consequence of the fact that there are many different packet networking technologies [14], each of which can play a role in military systems. Local networks are well suited to intra-platform (vehicle, building,...) applications. Long-haul nets (e.g. ARPANET, SATNET, Defense Data Net,...) will be needed for wide-area communication. Packet radio or other mobile digital communication systems will be needed in tactical applications involving battlefield automation [33]. No single technology is ideal for all applications, yet the full collection of systems must interoperate.

The principal method for achieving interoperability in the DoD Internet Model is the use of a standard Gateway which can route internet traffic from one net to another and the use of a standard set of protocols operating above the internetwork layer (see Figure 4). Gateways are specifically intended to support the interconnection of heterogeneous packet nets [25-29,33,35,37,39]. This is in contrast to the existing CCITT view that all public packet nets will conform to the X.25 recommendation [22] and will utilize a common procedure, X.75, for exchange of packets between networks [38]. The principal difference between the CCITT/ISO view and the DoD view revolves around the question of network interfaces. The DoD view is that different packet nets may reasonably employ very different network interfaces (e.g. ARPANET vs. Ethernet) as a consequence of differences in service functionality while the CCITT/ISO view tends to assume more homogeneity. The introduction into the ISO model of a "global network" sublayer (Fig. 4) suggests, however, that this view is being reconsidered at least by ISO.

Fig. 4 also illustrates a difference between the ISO and DoD models at the higher layers, ISO

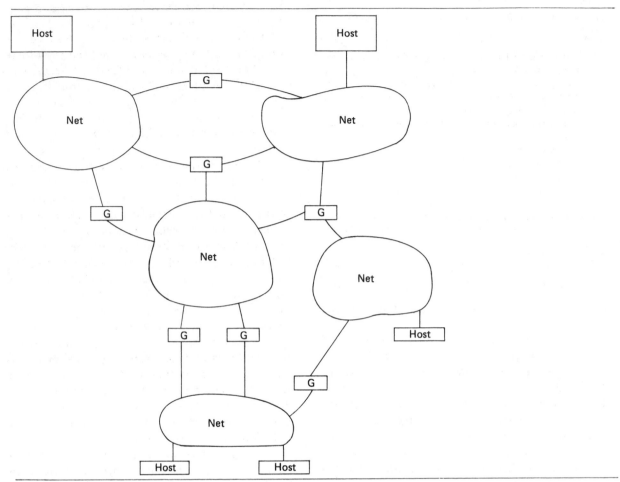

Fig. 3. Basic Internet-system Architecture.

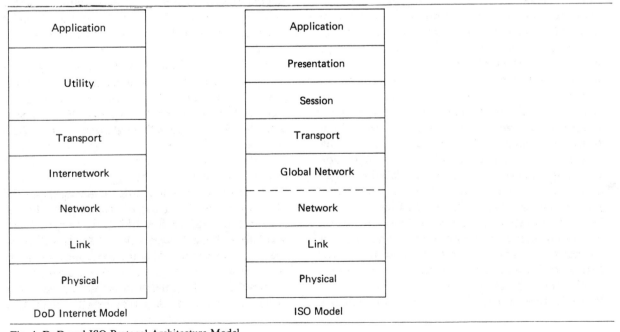

Fig. 4. DoD and ISO Protocol Architecture Model.

Table 1
Assumptions and Requirements Influencing DoD Internet Model

---

1. Heterogeneous Packet Networks (i.e. Physical, Link, Network Layers differ).
2. Datagram (connectionless) Service at Internet Layer.
3. Architectural Provision for Interoperable Tactical and Strategic Communication.
4. High Reliability and Survivability Under Hostile Conditions.
5. Combined Voice and Data Services.
6. Interactive, Real-Time, Transaction, and Bulk Data Transport Services.
7. Precedence and Security at Several Layers.
8. Broadcast/Multicast Services.
9. Host-Host File Transfers and File Access.
10. Widely Varying Terminal Types Using Remote Service Hosts.
11. Electronic Message Switching Services Utilizing Different Transport Protocols.
12. Multimedia (Text, Fax, Graphics, Voice) Electronic Messaging.
13. Distributed, redundant Name-to-Address Translation Services.

---

defines Session and Presentation layers as distinct. In the DoD model, protocols accomplishing these functions are combined into a single "utility" layer. This difference stems mostly from the experience DoD has had with specific protocols serving a variety of applications. The DoD protocols implemented thus far have not lended themselves to a single protocol for dealing with presentation issues (formats, conversions, etc.), nor has there yet been a specific need for many of the functions ascribed by ISO to the session layer. System Development Corporation, in its study of protocol architecture for DoD [28], did identify functions which might reasonably be incorporated into a general protocol above the transport layer but below the application layers and below the layer DoD uses to "house" its utility protocols. These functions related to the management of multiple transport protocol services (e.g. virtual circuit, real-time, transaction) on behalf of a single application, and multiple connections in support of multiparty, distributed applications, and multiple connections in support of multiparty, distributed applications. Although this remains an area for further study, it is possible that the DoD Internet Model will eventually include a layer between Utility and Transport.

Table 1 illustrates a list of basic assumptions,

and requirements which have guided the development of the Internet Model and its associated protocols. In the next section, specific protocols which have been incorporated into the DoD Internet Protocol Hierarchy are discussed, in the context of the elements of Table 1.

3. The Internet Protocol Hierarchy

The relationship among the protocols which are in use by DoD, or are under development, are illustrated in Figure 5. Their functionality and relationship to requirements in Table 1 are discussed in the following sections. Documentation for most of these protocols may be found in references [40,41]; others are referenced explicitly.

3.1. Physical Layer

At this layer, a wide range of standard and unique interfaces are used to support the connection of hosts to their supporting networks. BBN 1822 [42] is the specification for a unique, 25-wire, bit serial asynchronous interface which permits a host or a packet switch to control the flow of data on a bit-by-bit basis. Typical data rates for this interface run between 100–400 kb/s.

Physical interfaces suitable for the support and use of modem connections between hosts and packet switches typically use CCITT V.24, V.35, or the more recent EIA RS-449 standards. MIL-STD-188C is a U.S. military standard which specifies signal levels somewhat different from EIA RS-232C.

Local network hardware interfaces range from designs which are specific to computer vendor bus standards (e.g. DEC UNIBUS or Q BUS) to standards such as the Xerox-Intel-DEC Ethernet and the plural IEEE 802 local network standard.

3.2. Link Layer

At this level, one finds unique standards such as the BBN "HDLC Distant Host" (HDH) and "Very Distant Host" (VDH) or the more widely used CCITT/ISO High Level Data Link Control (HDLC) procedure. The latter is also referred to as Advanced Data Communication Control Protocol (ADCCP) as standardized by the American National Standards Institute (ANSI). The IBM

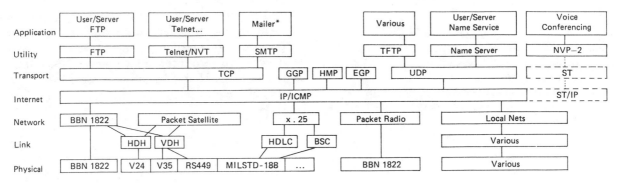

Fig. 5. DoD Internet Protocol Hierarchy.

binary synchronous link procedure (BSC) is also found, along with a HDLC as link level support for the CCITT X.25 recommendation.

Local networks may or may not provide a link level protocol interface, depending on vendor and network type.

3.3. Network Layer

For U.S. military nets such as the ARPANET, MINET, Defense Data Net (DDN), World Wide Military Command and Control System Intercomputer Net (WIN), Community Intelligence Network (COINS) and others based on the Bolt Beranek and Newman C/30 packet switch, BBN specification 1822 [42] spells out the specifics of the procedures for exchange of packets between hosts and the packet net. The DARPA packet satellite net (SATNET) [6–8], Navy Mobile Access Terminal Net (MATNET) [93], and DARPA/DCA Wideband Net (WBNET or EISN) all use a unique procedure for accessing stream, datagram and broadcast conferencing services supported by packet satellite technology.

The DARPA Packet Radio Net uses another unique interface for packet exchange, including special "type of service" indicators for support of real-time voice or normal interactive/bulk data transfer services.

Local networks such as Ethernet [Xerox, ACC Inc.], CHAOSNET (MIT), Ungermann-Bass Net/One, Proteon Pronet, Mitre's Mitrebus, MIT-Lincoln Laboratory LEXNET, BBN's Fibernet (optical), SRI International's SRINET, etc. all use various network level formats and procedures to support point-to-point, broadcast and multicast services.

3.4. Internet Layer

At this level, all network services are unified and viewed by hosts as an internet datagram service. Global internet addressing, internet routing and error handling are defined as part of the service. A special "type of service" field in each internet datagram can be used to select appropriate lower level network services.

The principal protocols at this level are the Internet Protocol (IP) and Internet Control Message Protocol (ICMP) which are used to coordinate host/internet interactions including routing advice from gateways to hosts (e.g. redirection of traffic to alternate gateways) and warning messages related to congestion or unrecoverable failures (e.g. destination host or network not reachable).

At this layer, gateways can compensate for variations in maximum packet size in each net by fragmenting internet datagrams to fit. The fragments can be routed independently and are assembled at the destination host, rather than at each intermediate gateway. This strategy minimizes delay through the system and makes it more feasible to support real-time services such as packetized speech, target tracking and fire control.

An experimental extension to the IP protocol, called "ST" for "stream" protocol has been implemented to support exploration of voice conferencing or mixed voice/data services in the context of multiple, interconnected packet nets.

3.5. Transport Level

There are three primary host support protocols at this level. These are the Transmission Control

Protocol (TCP), User Datagram Protocol (UDP) and ST Protocol. TCP is a highly reliable, end-to-end, sequenced byte stream protocol which uses retransmission and positive acknowledgment to assure data delivery. An end-to-end, window-based flow control strategy is used. This protocol provides "virtual circuit" service to higher level protocols and applications. It is external to the IP so that other protocols and applications can be supported which do not require this level of service.

The User Datagram Protocol (UDP) provides support for transaction-like protocols which do not require the same type of sequencing and controls as that provided by TCP.

The experimental ST protocol supports broadcast, multicast and conferencing services, particularly those which do not require guaranteed delivery of all data (e.g. packet voice, target tracks), but do have very stringent real-time requirements.

The remaining protocols at this level include the Gateway-Gateway Protocol (GGP), External Gateway Protocol (EGP) [45], and Host Monitoring Protocol (HMP). GGP is specifically designed for the support of gateway routing, status and congestion control information and forms the heart of the internetwork control system. The EGP is a variation of GGP which does not rely as heavily on tight coupling of the GGP protocol, especially to cater to local nets connected as "stubs" on an existing long-haul internet system. The long-haul system, for example, might use GGP (carefully tuned) to support EGP-based local net interconnection.

The Host Monitoring Protocol (HMP) is a protocol for general purpose monitoring of any internet host. This protocol provides a basis for central (and redundant) monitoring of host status (including gateways themselves). This information is essential for the isolation and repair of failures and detection of performance anomalies in a large internet system.

3.6. Utility Layer

At this layer, the protocols become much more application-specific. The File Transfer Protocol is used to identify, access and move files from one host to another. It has several modes of operation depending on file type and includes provision for transparent transfer ("image" mode) between hosts using identical operating systems.

TELNET is a protocol which allows serving hosts to treat all remote terminals as if they were standard "Network Virtual Terminals" (NVT). This protocol incorporates a basic model of a terminal as a scroll-mode, ASCII TTY, but also has provisions for complex negotiations of special features (e.g. local or remote echo, page mode, CRT width and length, etc.). The primary benefit of this protocol has been to simplify the software necessary in service hosts to isolate them from knowledge of specific features of remote terminals. In this sense, it is similar to the CCITT X.28/X.29 protocols which operate directly above CCITT X.25 service.

Simple Mail Transfer Protocol (SMTP) supports the transfer of electronic messages among arbitrary hosts in the internet. It has provision for acting in store-and-forward as well as end/end delivery mode, allowing distinct transport level protocols to be used to actually transport the electronic messages. It also supports batching of messages destined for the same destination or mail forwarder so that only a single message copy needs to be sent even though there are multiple recipients.

Trivial File Transport Protocol is a very simple, block-at-a-time transport procedure which is often used to support file and message transport to small personal computers or to systems just beginning to bring up the protocol set. Its advantage is simplicity, but is not a high bandwidth protocol owing to its single-block-at-a-time nature. On very low delay nets, it can achieve respectable transfer rates.

The Name Server Protocol supports the translation of string names for hosts and servers into their total internet addresses. This becomes a critical part of the system architecture as the size of the internet environment grows beyond the capacity of central name assignment and management to cope. It also allow hosts to move from one address to another, and to keep only currently-used name/address pairs in local storage rather than tables for all possible destination names and addresses.

NVP-2 is the Network Voice Protocol, version 2. It incorporates support for negotiating various types of voice compression to be used and to support the passing of the "floor" during a conference in a smooth and controlled manner. It includes the concept of a closed user group, multicasting (multiple-destination addressing) and dynamic joining and leaving of conference members. The protocol is able to accept and use (play back) packets received in error and is able to use time-stamp information as well as sequence numbering to determine whether a voice packet should be played out, retained for later output or discarded. NVP 2 relies on the special features of the ST and ST/IP protocols to support its unique requirements for low delay and multicasting.

3.7. Application level

At this level, we find actual programs which use the lower level protocols to accomplish specific applications such as electronic mail service, remote terminal access to service programs, etc.

4. Loose Ends

There are a number of issues and concepts which should be mentioned, including security concepts, front-ends, bit map displays, mobile hosts, network partition resolution, and a generic observation about the incompleteness of all protocol architectures developed to date (as far as the authors can determine).

4.1. Architectural Incompleteness

Aside from all the various developments, services and protocols which the authors cannot predict, and therefore have left out, there is one glaring omission in the Internet Model, which is also missing from the OSI model. Most of these models tend to describe the relationship of protocols as seen by host computers connecting to networks. What is missing from the architectural model is the hierarchy of protocols present within each packet network and within the internetwork system. Each of the various types of networks mentioned has very different internal operation. A complete model would include some representation of the various protocols (e.g. routing, flow and congestion control, monitoring) used to support network and internetwork operation. For simplicity they have been ignored in this paper, but it seems appropriate to acknowledge this fact.

4.2. Front-ends

The models as shown in Figs. 2, 4 and 5, although consistent with the concept, do not ex-

plicitly indicate where and how front-end systems can be incorporated into the architecture. The DoD Internet Model can be extended, as shown in Fig. 6 to accommodate one form of front-ending. Since the possibilities are endless, the example in Fig. 6 is taken for concreteness from actual DoD implementations. Note that the host has access both to the transport layer and internet layer protocols via the front-end protocol. This permits some flexibility in placing the transport layer protocols in the host or the front-end and also supports operation of such protocols as the Host Monitoring Protocol in the Host even though its support protocol (IP) is implemented in the front-end.

4.3. Network Partitioning

The internet system architecture contemplates the interconnection of many nets by means of gateways. It may happen, under hostile conditions, that one or more of the subnets may partition into a collection of disjoint pieces. It may still be the case, however, that full connectivity among all hosts may be achieved by judicious routing of traffic through the gateway system from one partition to another (see Fig. 7). The existing protocols for gateway operation must be extended to detect such partitioning and adjust the routing tables in the gateways (and hosts) to achieve recovery where this is possible. It is not a trivial problem.

4.4. Mobile Hosts

The addressing structure of the Internet Protocol assigns host addresses on a hierarchical (i.e. relative) basis, as a function of the network to which the host is attached. The TCP protocol depends upon the IP network and host addresses for part of its connection identifiers; the full identifiers include port numbers assigned by the TCP level and carried in its header. If a host were to move from one net to another (e.g. via an airborne packet radio), its network (and host) addresses would change and this would affect the connection identifiers used by the TCP to maintain state information. In effect, roving hosts require some means of dynamically re-defining TCP connection identifiers. This is rather like a problem called "dynamic reconnection" which has plagued net-

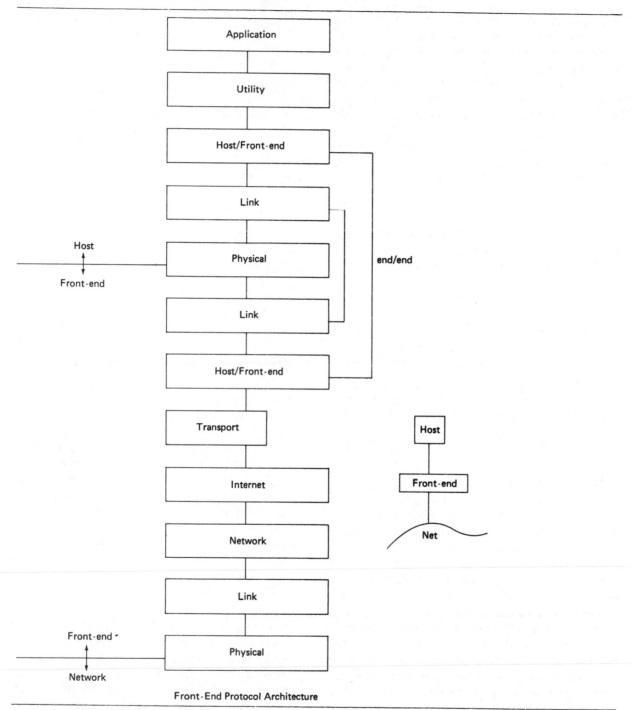

Fig. 6. Front-End Protocol Architecture.

work designers since the inception of the AR-PANET project in 1968.

The crux of the problem lies in the use of the IP network and host addresses by the TCP level of protocol. The DoD Internet Model accommodates the re-binding of host names to internetwork addresses through the use of the distributed name server protocol, however use of this mechanism

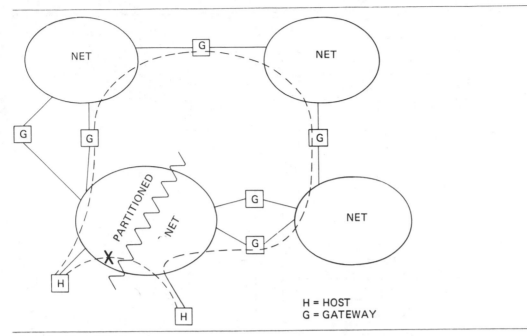

Fig. 7. Partitioned Net Recovery.

requires that the TCP connections be broken and re-established. One strategy for dealing with this problem is to create logical addresses for hosts at the TCP level which are bound to internet addresses at the IP level by means of name server mapping sorts of mechanisms. While this adds overhead to the TCP header, it creates an opportunity for dynamically re-binding the TCP level connection identifiers to the IP level addresses. Detailed consideration of this concept is beyond the scope of the paper.

Xerox Corporation's Network System protocols attempt to solve this problem by assigning each host a unique 48 bit identifier [43]. The binding of host name and identifier need never change. However, it is still necessary to find out to which net the host is now connected. The Xerox architecture provides a 16 bit "hint" to help the Xerox gateways route packets to the right destination net. The question of keeping track of the "hint" leads back to name server concepts, such as those currently incorporated in the DoD Internet Model.

4.5. Bit-Map Displays

With the increasing availability of higher resolution, bit-map displays, many of the issues in Network Virtual Terminal and message/file for-

mat became substantially more complex. Multiple font representations are needed, as well as treatment of variable size and placement of "windows" through which different applications outputs can be viewed by a user. The DoD Network Virtual Terminal Protocol does not address this important area and will have to do so soon simply because there are already in use thousands of personal computers and fancy bit-map displays in military applications. For example, there are approximately 30 Three-Rivers PERQ personal computers aboard the U.S. CVN Carl Vinson, an operational vessel in the fleet.

4.6. Security

Finally, it is essential that the DoD Internet Model incorporate a provision for the latest concepts in end-to-end and multilevel security. The model has been modified to take this into account so that end/end security methods, such as the one illustrated in Figure 8 can be supported.

Classification restrictions prevent a full discussion of this topic in an unclassified paper. Figure 8 shows that the type of security which can be supported includes the insertion of devices between hosts and networks (rather like front-ends) so that cryptographic measures may be taken to

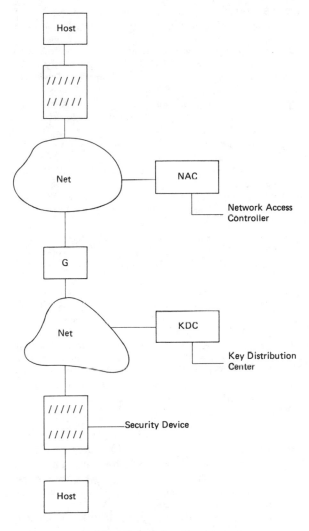

Fig. 8. End/End Network Recovery.

system has potential limits to the satisfactory functioning of its gateway routing, flow and congestion control algorithms. Concepts such as area routing are typically introduced to increase the dynamic range of network control, at the cost of reduced optimality in the performance of the control algorithms. Introduction of EGP into the DoD internet system represents a first step along the path towards a solution to managing a large-scale internet system.

4.8. Summary

This paper has addressed the organization of the DoD Internet Model and compared it to the ISO open systems Interconnection Model. A review of the actual protocols which populate the DoD Internet Protocol Hierarchy was provided and the paper concluded with a discussion of several areas requiring further attention.

It is opinion of the authors that the DoD Internet Model is the most fully developed, military-oriented networking architecture in existence. It is based on over 10 years of field experience with the most advanced packet switching systems in the world. We do not believe, however that the model can remain static. The many loose ends are proof that the model and its protocols must evolve. It is our hope that this evolution can be accomplished in cooperation with our NATO allies and generally within the framework of the national and international protocol standardization initiatives now underway.

secure the communication between source and destination hosts. Automatic, electronic re-keying, using a key distribution center (KDC) which distributes keys according to policy set by a network access controller (NAC) is a part of the architecture. Of course, conventional link level encryption within each net can be supported simultaneously.

4.7. Growth

Just as conventional packet networks reach limits to the ability of network routing, flow and congestion control algorithms to work satisfactorily beyond certain network sizes, the internet

References

[1] L.G. Roberts, and B.D. Wessler, "Computer Network Development to Achieve Resource Sharing," proc. AFIPS SJCC, V.36 543-549, 1970.

[2] F.E. Heart, RE "The Interface Message Processor for the ARPA Computer Network," proc. AFIPS SJCC V.36, pp. 551-567, 1970.

[3] R.E. Kahn, "Resource-Sharing Communication Networks," proc. IEEE, V.60(11), pp. 1347-1407, November 1972.

[5] R.E. Kahn, "The Organization of Computer Resources into a Packet Radio Network," IEEE Trans. Commun., Vol. COM-25(1), January 1977.

[6] R.E. Kahn, "The Introduction of Packet Satellite Communications," National Telecommunications Conference, November 1979, pp. 45.1.1–45.1.8.

[7] I.M. Jacobs, et al., "General Purpose Satellite Networks," proc. IEEE, Vol. 66 (11), November 1978, pp. 1448–1467.

[8] I.M. Jacobs, et al., "Packet Satellite Network Design Issues," proc. Nat'l Telecommunications Conf., November 1979.

[9] L.N. Evenchik, D.A. McNeill, et al., "MATNET, An Experimental Navy Shipboard Satellite Communications Network," proc. INFOCOM 82, March 1982, p. 2–11.

[10] L. Palmer, et al, "SATNET Packet Data Transmissions," COMSAT Technical Review, vol. 12(1), Spring 1982, pp. 181–212.

[11] R.M. Metcalfe and D.R. Boggs, "Ethernet: Distributed Packet Switching for Local Computer Networks," Comm. ACM, Vol. 19(7), July 1976, pp. 395–404.

[12] D. Clark, K. Pogran and D. Reed, "An Introduction to Local Area Networks," IEEE proc. Vol. 66 (11), November 1978, pp. 1497–1517.

[13] L.G. Roberts, "The Evolution of Packet Switching", proc. IEEE, V.66(11), November 1978, p. 1307.

[14] V.G. Cerf, "Packet Communication Technology," Protocols and Techniques for Data Communication Networks (F. Kuo, ed.), Prentice Hall, New York, 1980, Chapter I.

[15] Defense Advanced Research Projects Agency, "A History of the ARPANET: The First Decade," prepared by Bolt Beranek and Newman, April 1981 (Defense Tech. Info. Center AD A1 15440).

[16] S. Carr, S. Crocker and V. Cerf, "HOST-HOST Communication Protocol in the ARPA Network," proc. AFIPS Spring Joint Computer Conference, V. 36, 1970.

[17] S.D. Crocker, J.F. Heafner, R.M. Metcalfe and J.B. Postel, "Function-oriented Protocols for the ARPA Computer Network," proc. AFIPS SJCC Vol. 90, pp. 271–279, 1972.

[18] M. Padlipsky, "A Perspective on the ARPANET Reference Model," proc. INFOCOM 83, April 1983.

[19] ARPANET Protocols Handbook, (Feinler, E. and Postel, J., Editors) Network Information Center, SRI International, NIC 7104.

[20] Y.K. Dalal, "Broadcast Protocols in Packet Switched Computer Networks," Ph. D. Thesis, Stanford Univ., CSL Technical Report 28, 1977.

[21] Carl Sunshine, "Addressing Problems in Packet Network Interconnection," proc. INFOCOM 82, Las Vegas, IEEE Press, March 1982, pp. 12–18.

[22] "Recommendation X.25/Interface Between Data Terminal Equipment (DTE) and Data Circuit Terminating Equipment (DCE) for Terminals Operating in the Packet Mode on Public Data Networks," in CCITT Orange Book, Vol. 7, Int. Telephony and Telegraphy Consultative Committee, Geneva, Switzerland, 1980.

[23] International Organization for Standardization, "Reference Model of Open Systems Interconnection," ISO/TC97/SC16, Draft International Standard ISO/DIS/7498, 1982.

[24] J.F. Shoch, D. Cohen and E. Taft, "Mutual Encapsulation of Internetwork Protocols," Computer Networks, May 1981, pp. 287–300.

[25] V. Cerf, "The CATENET Model for Internetworking," Internet Experiment Note No. 48, available from SRI International, Network Information Center, Menlo Park, California.

[26] V. Cerf, and P.T. Kirstein, "Issues in Packet Network Interconnection," IEEE, V. 66(11), November 1978, pp. 1386–1408.

[27] J.B. Postel, "Internetwork Protocol Approaches," IEEE Trans. or Communications, Vol. COM-28, No. 4, April 1980, pp. 604–611.

[28] System Development Corporation, "DoD Protocol Reference Model," (Draft), TM-7172/201/00, February 1982.

[29] C. Sunshine, "Interconnection of Computer Networks," Computer Networks, 1977, pp. 175–195.

[30] Y.K. Dalal, "Use of Multiple Networks in Xerox' Network System," proc. 24th IEEE Computer Society International Conference (COMPCON), February 1982.

[31] V. Cerf, and R.E. Lyons, "Military Requirements for Packet-Switched Networks and Their Implications for Protocol Standardization," Proceedings of EASCON Conference, 1982.

[32] B.H. Davies and A.S. Bates, "Internetworking in the Military Environment," Proc. INFOCOM 82, IEEE Press, 1982, pp. 19–29.

[33] Tactical Information Exchange (TIE) Working Group, "Tactical Information Exchange (TIE) Framework Development," edited by R&D Associates, RDA-TR-117100-001, October 1981.

[34] Lavean E. Gilbert and Ronald E. Sonderegger, "A Communication System Architecture for Interoperable Systems," International Telemetering Conference," San Diego, CA, 28–30 September 1982.

[35] J. Postel, C. Sunshine and D. Cohen, "Recent Developments in the DARPA Internet Program," Proceedings of ICCC, London 1982.

[36] J. Shoch, "Internetwork Naming, Addressing and Routing," COMPCON Fall 1978 Proceedings, September 1978.

[37] V.G. Cerf and R.E. Kahn, "A Protocol for Packet Network Intercommunication," IEEE Trans. on Communications, Vol. COM-22, No. 5, May 1974.

[38] "Proposal for Provisional Recommendation X.25 on International Interworking Between Packet Switched Data Networks," in CCITT Study Group VII Contribution No. 207, Int'l Telephony and Telegraphy Consultative Committee, Geneva, Switzerland, May 1978.

[39] A. Sheltzer, R. Hinden and M. Brescia, "Connecting Different Types of networks With Gateways," Data Communications, Vol. 12, No. 8, August 1982, pp. 111–122.

[40] Internet Protocols Transition Workbook (J. Postel and E. Feinler, Eds.), SRI International, Network Information Center, Menlo Park CA, 1982.

[41] Internet Protocols Implementor's Guide (J. Postel and E. Feinler, Eds.), SRI International, Network Information Center, Menlo Park, CA, 1982.

[42] Bolt Beranek and Newman, "Specification for the Interconnection of a Host and an IMP," Report No. 1822, 1982 Revision.

[43] Y.K. Dalal and R.S. Printis, "48-Bit Absolute Internet and Ethernet Host Numbers," Seventh Data Communications Symposium, October 1981.

[44] B.M. Wood, "Open Systems Interconnection – Basic Concepts and Current Status," proc. ICCC 82, London, September 1982, pp. 775–780.

[45] E. Rosen, "Exterior Gateway Protocol (EGP)", RFC 827, Bolt Beranek and Newman Inc., Cambridge, MA, October 1982.

A PERSPECTIVE ON THE ARPANET REFERENCE MODEL

M. A. Padlipsky

MITRE Corp., Bedford, MA

Abstract

This paper discusses the "Reference Model" of the ARPANET protocol suite. Although the "ARM" has been in existence for some time, it has not previously been addressed explicitly in the open literature. Given the recent wide-spread publicizing of the ISO's "Reference Model", however, as a proposed advance, it is particularly appropriate, even belatedly, to attempt to document what, in the author's view, stands as the current state of the art.

Introduction

Despite the fact that "the ARPANET" stands as the proof-of-concept of intercomputer networking and, as discussed in more detail below, introduced such fundamental notions as Layering and Virtualizing to the literature, the wide availability of material which appeals to the International Standards Organization's Reference Model for Open System Interconnection (ISORM) has prompted many newcomers to the field to overlook the fact that, even though it was largely tacit, the designers of the ARPANET protocol suite have had a reference model of their own all the long. That is, since well before ISO even took an interest in "networking", workers in the ARPA-sponsored research community have been going about their business of doing research and development in intercomputer networking with a particular frame of reference in mind. They have, unfortunately, either been so busy with their work or were perhaps somehow unsuited temperamentally to do learned papers on abstract topics when there are interesting things to be said on specific topics, that it is only in very recent times that there has been much awareness in the research community of the impact of the ISORM on the lay mind. When the author is asked to review solemn memoranda comparing such things as the ARPANET treatment of "internetting" with that of CCITT employing the ISORM "as the frame of reference," however, the time has clearly come to attempt to enunciate the ARPANET Reference Model (ARM) publicly—for such comparisons are painfully close to comparing an orange with an apple using redness and smoothness as the dominant criteria, given the philosophical closeness of the CCITT and ISO models and their mutual disparities from the ARPANET model.

This paper, then, is primarily intended as <u>a</u> perspective on the ARM. (Secondarily, it is intended to point out some of the differences between the ARM and the ISORM. For a perspective on this subtheme, please see Note [1]) It can't be "the official" version because the ARPANET Network Working Group (NWG), which was the collective source of the ARM, hasn't had an official general meeting since October, 1971, and can scarcely be resurrected to haggle over it. It does, at least, represent with some degree of fidelity the views of a number of NWG members as those views were expressed in NWG general meetings, NWG protocol design committee meetings, and private conversations over the intervening years. (Members of the current ARPA Internet Working Group, which applied and adapted the original model to a broader arena than had initially been contemplated, were also consulted.) That might not sound so impressive as a pronunciamento from an international standards organization, but the reader should be somewhat consoled by the consideration that not only are the views expressed here purported to be those of the primary workers in the field, but also at least one Englishman helped out in the review process.

Historical/Philosophical Context

Although rigorous historians of science might quibble as to whether they were "invented" by a particular group, it is an historical fact that many now widely-accepted, fundamental concepts of intercomputer networking were original to the ARPANET Network Working Group. [2] Before attempting to appreciate the implications of that assertion, let's attempt to define its two key terms and then cite the concepts it alludes to:

By "<u>intercomputer</u> <u>networking</u>" we mean the attachment of multiple, usually general-purpose computer systems--in the sense of Operating Systems of potentially different manufacture (i.e., "Heterogeneous Operating Systems")—to some communications network, or communications networks somehow interconnected, for the purpose of achieving resource sharing amongst the participating operating systems, usually called Hosts. (By "<u>resource sharing</u>" we mean the potential ability for programs on each of the Hosts to interoperate with programs on the other Hosts and for data housed on each of the Hosts to be made available to the other Hosts in a more general and flexible fashion than merely enabling users on each of the Hosts to be able to login to the other Hosts as if they were local; that is, we expect to do more than mere "remote

The paper also will appear in *The Elements of Networking Style* by Michael A. Padlipsky. It will be published by Prentice-Hall, Inc., 1985.

access" to intercomputer networked Hosts.) By "the ARPANET Network Working Group," we mean those system programmers and computer scientists from numerous Defense Advanced Research Projects Agency-sponsored installations whose home operating systems were intended to become early Hosts on the ARPANET. (By "the ARPANET" we mean, depending on context, either that communications network sponsored by DARPA which served as proof-of-concept for the communications technology known as "packet switching," or, consistent with common usage, the intercomputer network which was evolved by the NWG that uses that communications network—or "comm subnet"—as its inter-Host data transmission medium.)

The concepts of particular interest are as follows: By analogy to the use of the term in traditional communications, the NWG decided that the key to the mechanization of the resource-sharing goal (which in turn had been posited in their informal charter) would be "protocols" that Hosts would interpret both in communicating with the comm subnet and in communicating with each other. Because the active entities in Hosts (the programs in execution) were widely referred to in Computer Science as "processes," it seemed clear that the mechanization of resource sharing had to involve interprocess communication; protocols that enabled and employed interprocess communication became, almost axiomatically, the path to the goal. Perhaps because the limitations of mere remote access were perceived early on, or perhaps simply by analogy to the similar usage with regard to distinguishing between physical tape drives and tape drives associated with some conventionally-defined function like the System Input stream or the System Output stream in batch operating systems, the discernible communications paths (or "channels") through the desired interprocess communication mechanism became known as "logical connections"— the intent of the term being to indicate that the physical path didn't matter but the designator (number) of the logical connection could have an assigned meaning, just like logical tape drive numbers. Because "modularity" was an important issue in Computer Science at the time, and because the separation of Hosts and Interface Message Processors (IMP's) was a given, the NWG realized that the protocols it designed should be "layered," in the sense that a given set of related functions (e.g., the interprocess communication mechanism, or "primitives," as realized in a Host-to-Host protocol) should not take special cognizance of the detailed internal mechanics of another set of related functions (e.g., the comm subnet attachment mechanism, as realized in a Host-Comm Subnet Processor protocol), and that, indeed, protocols may be viewed as existing in a hierarchy.

With the notion of achieving resource sharing via layered protocols for interprocess communication over logical connections fairly firmly in place, the NWG turned to how best to achieve the first step of intercomputer networking: allowing a distant user to login to a Host as if local—but with the clear understanding that the mechanisms employed were to be generalizable to other types of resource sharing. Here we come to the final fun-

damental concept contributed by the NWG, for it was observed that if n different types of Host (i.e., different operating systems) had to be made aware of the physical characteristics of m different types of terminal in order to exercise physical control over them—or even if n different kinds of Host had to become aware of the native terminals supported by m other kinds of Hosts if physical control were to remain local—there would be an administratively intractable "n x m problem." So the notion of creating a "virtual terminal" arose, probably by analogy to "virtual memory" in the sense of something that "wasn't really there" but could be used as if it were; that is, a common intermediate representation (CIR) of terminal characteristics was defined in order to allow the Host to which a terminal was physically attached to map the particular characteristics of the terminal into a CIR, so that the Host being logged into, knowing the CIR as part of the relevant protocol, could map out of it into a form already acceptable to the native operating system. And when it came time to develop a File Transfer Protocol, the same virtualizing or CIR trick was clearly just as useful as for a terminal oriented protocol, so virtualizing became part of the axiom set too.

The NWG, then, at least pioneered and probably invented the notion of doing intercomputer networking/resource sharing via hierarchical, layered protocols for interprocess communication over logical connections of common intermediate representations/virtualizations. Meanwhile, outside of the ARPA research community, "the ARPANET" was perceived to be a major technological advance. "Networking" became the "in" thing. And along with popular success came the call for standards; in particular, standards based on a widely-publicized "Reference Model for Open System Interconnection" promulgated by the International Standards Organization. Not too surprisingly, Open System Interconnection looks a lot like resource sharing, the ISORM posits a layered protocol hierarchy, "connections" occur frequently, and emerging higher level protocols tend to virtualize; after all, one expects standards to reflect the state of the art in question. But even if the ISORM, suitably refined, does prove to be the wave of the future, this author feels that the ARM is by no means a whitecap, and deserves explication—both in its role as the ISORM's "roots" and as the basis of a still-viable alternative protocol suite.

Axiomatization

Let's begin with the axioms of the ARPANET Reference Model. Indeed, let's begin by recalling what an axiom is, in common usage: a principle the truth of which is deemed self-evident. Given that definition, it's not too surprising that axioms rarely get stated or examined in non-mathematical discourse. It turns out, however, that the axiomatization of the ARM—as best we can recall and reconstruct it—is not only germane to the enunciation of the ARM, but is also a source of instructive contrasts with our view of the axiomatization of the ISORM. (See [1] again.)

Resource Sharing

The fundamental axiom of the ARM is that intercomputer networking protocols (as distinct from communications network protocols) are to enable heterogeneous computer operating systems ("Hosts") to achieve resource sharing. Indeed, the session at the 1970 SJCC in which the ARPANET entered the open literature was entitled "Resource Sharing Computer Networks".

Of course, as self-evident truths, axioms rarely receive much scrutiny. Just what resource sharing is isn't easy to pin down-- nor, for that matter, is just what Open System Interconnection is. But it must have something to do with the ability of the programs and data of the several Hosts to be used by and with programs and data on other of the Hosts in some sort of cooperative fashion. It must, that is, confer more functionality upon the human user than merely the ability to log in/on to a Host miles away ("remote access").

A striking property of this axiom is that it renders protocol suites such as "X.25"/"X.28"/ "X.29" rather uninteresting for our purposes, for they appear to have as their fundamental axiom the ability to achieve remote access only. (It might even be a valid rule of thumb that any "network" which physically interfaces to Hosts via devices that resemble milking machines--that is, which attach as if they were just a group of locally-known types of terminals--isn't a resource sharing network.)

Reference [3] addresses the resource sharing vs. remote access topic in more detail.

Interprocess Communication

The second axiom of the ARM is that resource sharing will be achieved via an interprocess communication mechanism of some sort. Again, the concept isn't particularly well-defined in the "networking" literature. Here, however, there's some justification, for the concept is fairly well known in the Operating Systems branch of the Computer Science literature, which was the field most of the NWG members came from. Unfortunately, because intercomputer networking involves communications devices of several sorts, many whose primary field is Communications became involved with "networking" but were not in a position to appreciate the implications of the axiom.

A process may be viewed as the active element of a Host, or as an address space in execution, or as a "job", or as a "task", or as a "control point"--or, actually, as any one (or more) of at least 29 definitions from at least 28 reputable computer scientists. What's important for present purposes isn't the precise definition (even if there were one), but the fact that the axiom's presence dictates the absence of at least one other axiom at the same level of abstraction. That is, we might have chosen to attempt to achieve resource sharing through an explicitly interprocedure communication oriented mechanism of some sort--wherein the entities being enabled to communicate were subroutines, or pieces of address spaces--but we didn't. Whether this was because somebody realized that you could do interprocedure communication (or achieve a "virtual address space" or "distributed operating system" or some such formulation) on top of an interprocess communication mechanism (IPC), or whether "it just seemed obvious" to do IPC doesn't matter very much. What matters is that the axiom was chosen, assumes a fair degree of familiarity with Operating Systems, doesn't assume extremely close coupling of Hosts, and has led to a working protocol suite which does achieve resource sharing--and certainly does appear to be an axiom the ISORM tacitly accepted, along with resource sharing.

Logical Connections

The next axiom has to do with whether and how to demultiplex IPC "channels", "routes", "paths", "ports", or "sockets". That is, if you're doing interprocess communication (IPC), you still have to decide whether a process can communicate with more than one other process, and, if so, how to distinguish between the bit streams. (Indeed, even choosing streams rather than blocks is a decision.) Although it isn't treated particularly explicitly in the literature, it seems clear that the ARM axiom is to do IPC over logical connections, in the following sense: Just as batch oriented operating systems found it useful to allow processes (usually thought of as jobs--or even "programs") to be insulated from the details of which particular physical tape drives were working well enough at a particular moment to spin the System Input and Output reels, and created the view that a reference to a "logical tape number" would always get to the right physical tape drive for the defined purpose, so too the ARM's IPC mechanism creates logical connections between processes. That is, the IPC addressing mechanism has semantics as well as syntax.

"Socket" underline{n} on any participating Host will be defined as the "Well-Known Socket" (W-KS) where a particular service (as mechanized by a program which follows, or "interprets", a particular protocol [4]) is found. (Note that the W-KS is defined for the "side" of a connection where a given service resides; the user side will, in order to be able to demultiplex its network-using processes, of course assign different numbers to its "sides" of connections to a given W-KS. Also, the serving side takes cognizance of the using side's Host designation as well as the preferred socket, so it too can demultiplex.) Clearly, you want free sockets as well as Well-Known ones, and we have them. Indeed, at each level of the ARM hierarchy the addressing entities are divided into assigned and unassigned sets, and the distinction has proven to be quite useful to networking researchers in that it confers upon them the ability to experiment with new functions without interfering with running mechanisms.

On this axiom, the ISORM differs from the ARM. ISORM "peer-peer" connections (or "associations") appear to be used only for demultiplexing, with the number assigned by the <u>receive</u> side rather than the send side. That is, a separate protocol is introduced to establish that a particular "transport" connection will be used in the present "session" for some particular service. At the risk of editorializing, logical connections seem much cleaner than "virtual" connections (using virtual in the sense of something that "isn´t really there" but can be used as if it were, by analogy to virtual memory, as noted above, and in deference to the X.25 term "virtual circuit", which appears to have dictated the receiver-assigned posture the ISORM takes at its higher levels.) Although the ISORM view "works", the W-KS approach avoids the introduction of an extra protocol.

Layering

The next axiom is perhaps the best-known, and almost certainly the worst-understood. As best we can reconstruct things, the NWG was much taken with the Computer Science buzzword of the times, "modularity". "Everybody knew" modularity was a Good Thing. In addition, we were given a head start because the IMP´s weren´t under our direct control anyway, but could possibly change at some future date, and we didn´t want to be "locked in" to the then-current IMP-Host protocol. So it was enunciated that protocols which were to be members of the ARM suite (ARMS, for future reference, although at the time nobody used "ARM", much less "ARMS") were to be <u>layered</u>. It was widely agreed that this meant a given protocol´s control information (i.e., the control information exchanged by counterpart protocol interpreters, or "peer entities" in ISORM terms) should be treated strictly as data by a protocol "below" it, so that you could invoke a protocol interpreter (PI) through a known interface, but if either protocol changed there would not be any dependencies in the other on the former details of the one, and as long as the interface didn´t change you wouldn´t have to change the PI of the protocol which hadn´t changed.

All well and good, if somewhat cryptic. The important point for present purposes, however, isn´t a seemingly-rigorous definition of Layering, but an appreciation of what the axiom meant in the evolution of the ARM. What it meant was that we tried to come up with protocols that represented reasonable "packagings" of functionality. For reasons that are probably unknowable, but about which some conjectures will be offered subsequently, the ARM and the ISORM agree strongly on the presence of Layering in their respective axiomatizations but differ strikingly as to what packagings of functionality are considered appropriate. To anticipate a bit, the ARM concerns itself with three layers and only one of them is mandatorily traversed; whereas the ISORM, again as everybody knows, has, because of emerging "sub-layers", what must be viewed as at least seven layers, and many who have studied it believe that all of the layers must be traversed on each transmission/reception of data.

Perhaps the most significant point of all about Layering is that the most frequently-voiced charge at NWG protocol committee design meetings was, "That violates Layering!" even though nobody had an appreciably-clearer view of what Layering meant than has been presented here, yet the ARMS exists. We can only guess what goes on in the design meetings for protocols to become members of the ISORM suite (ISORMS), but it doesn´t seem likely that having more layers could possibly decrease the number of arguments....

Indeed, it´s probably fair to say that the ARM view of Layering is to treat layers as quite broad functional groupings (Network Interface, Host-Host, and Process-Level, or Applications), the <u>consti-tuents</u> of which are to be modular. E.g., in the Host-Host layer of the current ARMS, the Internet Protocol, IP, packages internet addressing--among other things--for both the Transmission Control Protocol, TCP, which packages reliable interprocess communication, and UDP--the less well-known User Datagram Protocol--which packages only demultiplexable interprocess communication ... and for any other IPC packaging which should prove desirable. The ISORM view, on the other hand, fundamentally treats layers as rather narrow functional groupings, attempting to <u>force</u> modularity by requiring additional layers for additional functions (although the "classes" view of the proposed ECMA-sponsored ISORM Transport protocol tends to mimic the relations between TCP, UDP, and IP).

It is, by the way, forcing this view of modularity by multiplying layers rather than by trusting the designers of a given protocol to make it usable by other protocols within its own layer that we suspect to be a major cause of the divergence between the ISORM and the ARM, but, as indicated, the issue almost certainly is not susceptible of proof. (The less structured view of modularity will be returned to in the next major section.) At any rate, the notion that "N-entities" <u>must</u> communicate with one another by means of "N-1 entities" does seem to us to take the ISORM out of its intended sphere of description into the realm of prescription, where we believe it should not be, if for no other reason than that for a reference model to serve a prescriptive role levies unrealizable requirements of precision, and of familiarity with all styles of operating systems, on its expositors. In other words, as it is currently presented, the ISORM hierarchy of protocols turns out to be a rather strict hierarchy, with required, "chain of command" implications akin to the Elizabethan World Picture´s Great Chain of Being some readers might recall if they´ve studied Shakespeare, whereas in the ARM a cat can even invoke a king, much less look at one.

Common Intermediate Representations

The next axiom to be considered might well not be an axiom in a strict sense of the term, for it is susceptible of "proof" in some sense. That is, when it came time to design the first Process-Level (roughly equivalent to ISORM Level 5.3 [5] through 7) ARMS protocol, it did seem self-evident that a "virtual terminal" was a sound conceptual model-- but it can also be demonstrated that it is. The argument, customarily shorthanded as "the N X M

Problem", was sketched above; it goes as follows: If you want to let users at remote terminals log in/on to Hosts (and you do—resource sharing doesn't preclude remote access, it subsumes it), you have a problem with Hosts' native terminal control software or "access methods", which only "know about" certain kinds/brands/types of terminals, but there are many more terminals out there than any Host has internalized (even those whose operating systems take a generic view of I/O and don't allow applications programs to "expect" particular terminals). You don't want to make N different types of Host/Operating System have to become aware of M different types of terminal. You don't want to limit access to users who are at one particular type of terminal even if all your Hosts happen to have one in common. Therefore, you define a common intermediate representation (CIR) of the properties of terminals—or create a Network Virtual Terminal (NVT), where "virtual" is used by analogy to "virtual memory" in the sense of something that isn't necessarily really present physically but can be used as if it were. Each Host adds one terminal to its set of supported types, the NVT—where adding means translating/mapping from the CIR to something acceptable to the rest of the programs on your system when receiving terminal-oriented traffic "from the net", and translating/mapping to the CIR from whatever your acceptable native representation was when sending terminal-oriented traffic "to the net". (And the system to which the terminal is physically attached does the same things.)

"Virtualizing" worked so well for the protocol in question ("Telnet", for TELetypewriter NETwork) that when it came time to design a File Transfer Protocol (FTP), it was employed again—in two ways, as it happens. (It also worked so well that in some circles, "Telnet" is used as a generic term for "Virtual Terminal Protocol", just like "Kleenex" for "disposable handkerchief".) The second way in which FTP (another generic-specific) used Common Intermediate Representations is well-known: you can make your FTP protocol interpreters (PI's) use certain "virtual" file types in ARMS FTP's and in proposed ISORMS FTP's. The first way a CIR was used deserved more publicity, though: We decided to have a command-oriented FTP, in the sense of making it possible for users to cause files to be deleted from remote directories, for example, as well as simply getting a file added to a remote directory. (We also wanted to be able to designate some files to be treated as input to the receiving Hosts' native "mail" system, if it had one.) Therefore, we needed an agreed-upon representation of the commands—not only spelling the names, but also defining the character set, indicating the ends of lines, and so on. In less time than it takes to write about, we realized we already had such a CIR: "Telnet".

So we "used Telnet", or at any rate the NVT aspects of that protocol, as the "Presentation" protocol for the control aspects of FTP—but we didn't conclude from that that Telnet was a lower layer than FTP. Rather, we applied the principles of modularity to make use of a mechanism for more than one purpose—and we didn't presume to know

enough about the internals of everybody else's Host to dictate how the program(s) that conferred the FTP functionality interfaced with the program(s) that conferred the Telnet functionality. That is, on some operating systems it makes sense to let FTP get at the NVT CIR by means of closed subroutine calls, on others through native IPC, and on still others by open subroutine calls (in the sense of replicating the code that does the NVT mapping within the FTP PI). Such decisions are best left to the system programmers of the several Hosts. Although the ISORM takes a similar view in principle, in practice many ISORM advocates take the model prescriptively rather than descriptively and construe it to require that PI's at a given level must communicate with each other via an "N-1 entity" even within the same Host. (Still other ISORMites construe the model as dictating "monolithic" layers—i.e., single protocols per level—but this view seems to be abating.)

One other consideration about virtualizing bears mention: it's a good servant but a bad master. That is, when you're dealing with the amount of traffic that traverses a terminal-oriented logical (or even virtual) connection, you don't worry much about how many CPU cycles you're "wasting" on mapping into and out of the NVT CIR; but when you're dealing with files that can be millions of bits long, you probably should worry—for those CPU cycles are in a fairly real sense the resources you're making sharable. Therefore, when it comes to (generic) FTP's, even though we've seen it in one or two ISORM L6 proposals, having only a virtual file conceptual model is not wise. You'd rather let one side or the other map directly between native representations where possible, to eliminate the overhead for going into and out of the CIR—for long enough files, anyway, and provided one side or the other is both willing and able to do the mapping to the intended recipient's native representation.

Efficiency

The last point leads nicely into an axiom that is rarely acknowledged explicitly, but does belong in the ARM list of axioms: Efficiency is a concern, in several ways. In the first place, protocol mechanisms are meant to follow the design principle of Parsimony, or Least Mechanism; witness the argument immediately above about making FTP's be able to avoid the double mapping of a Virtual File approach when they can. In the second place, witness the argument further above about leaving implementation decisions to implementers. In the author's opinion, the worst mistake in the ISORM isn't defining seven (or more) layers, but decreeing that "N-entities" must communicate via "N-1 entities" in a fashion which supports the interpretation that it applies intra-Host as well as inter-Host. If you picture the ISORM as a high-rise apartment building, you are constrained to climb down the stairs and then back up to visit a neighbor whose apartment is on your own floor. This might be good exercise, but CPU's don't need aerobics as far as we know.

Recalling that this paper is only secondarily about ARM "vs." ISORM, let's duly note that in the ARM there is a concern for efficiency from the perspective of participating Hosts' resources (e.g., CPU cycles and, it shouldn't be overlooked, "core") expended on interpreting protocols, and pass on to the final axiom without digressing to one or two proposed specific ISORM mechanisms which seem to be extremely inefficient.

Equity

The least known of the ARM axioms has to do with a concern over whether particular protocol mechanisms would _entail_ _undue_ _perturbation_ _of_ _native_ _mechanisms_ if implemented in particular Hosts. That is, however reluctantly, the ARMS designers were willing to listen to claims that "you can't implement that in my system" when particular tactics were proposed and, however grudgingly, retreat from a mechanism that seemed perfectly natural on their home systems to one which didn't seriously discommode a colleague's home system. A tacit design principle based on equity was employed. The classic example had to do with "electronic mail", where a desire to avoid charging for incoming mail led some FTP designers to think that the optionally mandatory "login" commands of the protocol shouldn't be mandatory after all. But the commands were needed by some operating systems to actuate not only accounting mechanisms but authentication mechanisms as well, and the process which "fielded" FTP connections was too privileged (and too busy) to contain the FTP PI as well. So (to make a complex story cryptic), a common name and password were advertised for a "free" account for incoming mail, and the login commands remained mandatory (in the sense that any Host could require their issuance before it participated in FTP).

Rather than attempt to clarify the example, let's get to its moral: The point is that how well protocol mechanisms integrate with particular operating systems can be extremely subtle, so in order to be equitable to participating systems, you must either have your designers be sophisticated implementers or subject your designs to review by sophisticated implementers (and grant veto power to them in some sense).

It is important to note that, in the author's view, the ISORM not only does not reflect application of the Principle of Equity, but it also fails to take any explicit cognizance of the necessity of properly integrating its protocol interpreters into continuing operating systems. Probably motivated by Equity considerations, ARMS protocols, on the other hand, represent the result of intense implementation discussion and testing.

Articulation

Given the foregoing discussion of its axioms, and a reminder that we find it impossible in light of the existence of dozens of definitions of so fundamental a notion as "process" to believe in rigorous definitions, the ARPANET Reference Model is not going to require much space to articulate.

Indeed, given further the observation that we believe reference models are supposed to be descriptive rather than prescriptive, the articulation of the ARM can be almost terse.

In order to achieve efficient, equitable resource sharing among dissimilar operating systems, a layered set of interprocess communication oriented protocols is posited which typically employ common intermediate representations over logical connections. Three layers are distinguished, each of which may contain a number of protocols.

The Network Interface layer contains those protocols which are presented as interfaces by communications subnetwork processors ("CSNP"; e.g., packet switches, bus interface units, etc.) The CSNP's are assumed to have their own protocol or protocols among themselves, which are not directly germane to the model. In particular, no assumption is made that CSNP's of different types can be directly interfaced to one another; that is, "internetting" will be accomplished by Gateways, which are special purpose systems that attach to CSNP's as if they were Hosts (see also "Gateways" below). The most significant property of the Network Interface layer is that bits presented to it by an attached Host will _probably_ be transported by the underlying CSNP's to an addressed Host (or Hosts) (i.e., "reliable" comm subnets are not posited--although they are, of course, allowed). A Network layer protocol interpreter ("module") is normally invoked by a Host-Host protocol PI, but may be invoked by a Process Level/Applications protocol PI, or even by a Host process interpreting no formal protocol whatsoever.

The Host-Host layer contains those protocols which confer interprocess communication functionality. In the current "internet" version of the ARM, the most significant property of such protocols is the ability to direct such IPC to processes on Hosts attached to "proximate networks" (i.e., to CSNP's of various autonomous communications subnetworks) other than that of the Host at hand, in addition to those on a given proximate net. (You can, by the way, get into some marvelous technicoaesthetic arguments over whether there should be a separate Internet layer; for present purposes, we assume that the Principle of Parsimony dominates.) Another significant property of Host-Host protocols, although not a required one, is the ability to do such IPC over logical connections. Reliability, flow control, and the ability to deal with "out-of-band signals" are other properties of Host-Host protocols which may be present. (See also "TCP/IP Design Goals and Constraints", below.) A Host-Host PI is normally invoked by a Process Level/Applications PI, but may also be invoked by a Host process interpreting no formal protocol whatsoever. Also, a Host need not support more than a single, possibly notional, process (that is, the code running in an "intelligent terminal" might not be viewed by its user--or even its creator--as a formal "process", but it stands as a de facto one).

The Process Level/Applications layer contains those protocols which perform specific resource sharing and remote access functions such as allowing users to log in/on to foreign Hosts, transferring files, exchanging messages, and the like. Protocols in this layer will often employ common intermediate representations, or "virtualizations", to perform their functions, but this is not a necessary condition. They are also at liberty to use the functions performed by other protocols within the same layer, invoked in whatever fashion is appropriate within a given operating system context.

Orthogonal to the layering, but consistent with it, is the notion that a "Host-Front End" protocol (H-FP), or "Host-Outboard Processing Environment" protocol, may be employed to offload Network and Host-Host layer PI's from Hosts, to Outboard Processing Environments (e.g., to "Network Front Ends", or to BIU's, where the actual PI's reside, to be invoked by the H-FP as a distributed processing mechanism), as well as portions of Process Level/Applications protocols' functionality. The most significant property of an H-FP attached Host is that it be functionally identical to a Host with inboard PI's in operation, when viewed from another Host. (That is, Hosts which outboard PI's will be attached to in a flexible fashion via an explicit protocol, rather than in a rigid fashion via the emulation of devices already known to the operating system in question.)

Whether inboard or outboard of the Host, it is explicitly assumed that PI's will be appropriately integrated into the containing operating systems. The Network and Host-Host layers are, that is, effectively system programs (although this observation should not be construed as implying that any of their PI's must of necessity be implemented in a particular operating system's "hard-core supervisor" or equivalent) and their PI's must be able to behave as such.

Visualization

Figures 1 and 2 (adapted from [6]) present, respectively, an abstract rendition of the ARPANET Reference Model and a particular version of a protocol suite designed to that model. Just as one learns in Geometry that one cannot "prove" anything from the figures in the text, they are intended only to supplement the prose description above. (At least they bear no resemblance to highrise apartment houses.)

TCP/IP Design Goals and Constraints

The foregoing description of the ARM, in the interests of conciseness, deferred detailed discussion of two rather relevant topics: just what TCP and IP (the Transmission Control Protocol and the Internet Protocol) are "about", and just what role Gateways are expected to play in the model. We turn to those topics now, under separate headings.

As has been stated, with the success of the ARPANET [7] as both a proof-of-concept of inter-computer resource sharing via a packet-switched communications subnetwork and a (still) functional resource sharing network, a number of other bodies, research and commercial, developed "their own networks." Often just the communications subnetwork was intended, with the goal being to achieve remote access to attached Hosts rather than resource sharing among them, but nonetheless new networks abounded. Hosts attached to the original ARPANET or to DoD nets meant to be transferences of ARPANET technology should, it was perceived in the research community, be able to do resource sharing (i.e., interpret common high level protocols) with Hosts attached to these other networks. Thus, the first discernible goal of what was to become TCP/IP was to develop a protocol to achieve "internetting".

At roughly the same time—actually probably chronologically prior, but not logically prior—the research community came to understand that the original ARPANET Host-Host Protocol or AH-HP (often miscalled NCP because it was the most visible component of the Network Control Program of the early literature) was somewhat flawed, particularly in the area of "robustness." The comm subnet was not only relied upon to deliver messages accurately and in order, but it was even expected to manage the transfer of bits from Hosts to and from its nodal processors over a hardware interface and "link protocol" that did no error checking. So, although the ARPANET-as-subnet has proven to be quite good in managing those sorts of things, surely if internetting were to be achieved over subnets potentially much less robust than the ARPANET subnet, the second discernible goal must be the reliability of the Host-to-Host protocol. That is, irrespective of the properties of the communications subnetworks involved in internetting, TCP is to furnish its users—whether they be processes interpreting formal protocols or simply processes communicating in an ad hoc fashion—with the ability to communicate as if their respective containing Hosts were attached to the best comm subnet possible (e.g., a hardwired connection).

The mechanizations considered to achieve reliability and even those for internetting were alien enough to AH-HP's style, though, and the efficiency of several of AH-HP's native mechanisms (particularly Flow Control and the notion of a Control Link) had been questioned often enough, that a good Host-Host protocol could not be a simple extension of AH-HP. Thus, along with the desire for reliability came a necessity to furnish a good Host-Host protocol, a design goal easy to overlook. This is a rather subtle issue in that it brings into play a wealth of prior art. For present purposes, in practical terms it means that the "good" ideas (according to the technical intuition of the designers) of AH-HP—such as sockets, logical connections, Well-Known Sockets, and in general the interprocess communication premise—are retained in TCP without much discussion, while the "bad" ideas are equally tacitly jettisoned in favor of ones deemed either more appropriate in their own right or more consistent with the other two goals.

It could be argued that other goals are discernible, but the three cited--which may be restated and compressed as a desire to offer a good Host-Host protocol to achieve reliable internetting--are challenging enough, when thought about hard for a few years, to justify a document of even more than this one's length. What of the implied and/or accepted design constraints, though?

The first discernible design constraint borders on the obvious: Just as the original ARPANET popularized packet-switching (and, unfortunately to a lesser extent, resource sharing), its literature popularized the notion of "Layering." Mechanistically, layering is easy to describe: the control information of a given protocol must be treated strictly as data by the next "lower" protocol (with processes "at the top," and the/a transmission medium "at the bottom"), as discussed earlier. Philosophically, the notion is sufficiently subtle that even today researchers of good will still argue over what "proper" layering implies, also as discussed earlier. For present purposes, however, it suffices to observe the following: Layering is a useful concept. The precise set of functions offered by a given layer is open to debate, as is the precise number of layers necessary for a complete protocol suite to achieve resource sharing. (Most researchers from the ARPANET "world" tend to think of only three layers--the process, applications, or user level; the Host-Host level; and the network level--though if pressed they acknowledge that "the IMPs must have a protocol too." Adherents of the International Standards Organization's "Open System Interconnection" program--which appears to be how they spell resource sharing--claim that seven is the right number of levels--though if pressed they acknowledge that "one or two of them have sublevels." And adherents of the Consultative Committee for International Telephony and Telegraphy don't seem particularly concerned with resource sharing to begin with.) At any rate, TCP and IP are constrained to operate in a (or possibly in more than one) layered protocol hierarchy. Indeed, although it is not the sole reason, this fact is the primary rationale for separating the internetting mechanization into a discrete protocol (the Internet Protocol: IP). In other words, although designed "for" the ARM, TCP and IP are actually so layered as to be useful even outside the ARM.

It should be noted that as a direct consequence of the Layering constraint, TCP must be capable of operating "above" a functionally-equivalent protocol other than IP (e.g., an interface protocol directly into a proximate comm subnet, if internetting is not being done), and IP must be capable of supporting user protocols other than TCP (e.g., a non-reliable "Real-Time" protocol).

Resisting the temptation to attempt to do justice to the complexities of Layering, we move on to a second design constraint, which also borders on the obvious: Only minimal assumptions can be made about the properties of the various communications subnetworks in play. (The "network" composed of the concatenation of such subnets is sometimes called "a catenet," though more often--and less picturesquely--merely "an internet.") After all, the main goal is to let processes on Hosts attached to, essentially, "any old (or new) net" communicate, and to limit that communication to processes on Hosts attached to comm subnets that, say, do positive acknowledgments of message delivery would be remiss. [8]

Given this constraint, by the way, it is quite natural to see the more clearly Host-to-Host functions vested in TCP and the more clearly Host-to-catenet functions vested in IP. It is, however, a misconception to believe that IP was designed in the expectation that comm subnets "should" present only the "lowest common denominator" of functionality; rather, IP furnishes TCP with what amounts to an abstraction (some would say a virtualization--in the ARPANET Telnet Protocol sense of virtualizing as meaning mapping from/to a common intermediate representation to/from a given native representation) of the properties of "any" comm subnet including, it should be noted, even one which presents an X.25 interface. That is, IP allows for the application to a given transmission of whatever generic properties its proximate subnet offers equivalents for; its design neither depends upon nor ignores the presence of any property other than the ability to try to get some packet of bits to some destination, which surely is an irreducible minimum for the functionality of anything one would be willing to call a network.

Finally, we take note of a design constraint rarely enunciated in the literature, but still a potent factor in the design process: Probably again stemming from the popularity of the original ARPANET, as manifested in the number of types of Hosts (i.e., operating systems) attached to it, minimal assumptions are made about the nature or even the "power" of the Hosts which could implement TCP/IP. Clearly, some notion of process is necessary if there is to be interprocess communication, but even here the entire Host might constitute a single process from the perspective of the catenet. Less clearly, but rather importantly, Hosts must either "be able to tell time" or at least be able to "fake" that ability; this is in order to achieve the reliability goal, which leads to a necessity for Hosts to retransmit messages (which may have gotten lost or damaged in the catenet), which in turn leads to a necessity to know when to retransmit. It should be noted, however, that this does not preclude a (presumably quite modestly endowed) Host's simply going into a controlled loop between transmissions and retransmitting after enough megapasses through the loop have been made--if, of course, the acknowledgment of receipt of the transmission in question has not already arrived "in the meantime."

To conclude with a formulation somewhere between the concise and the terse, TCP/IP are to constitute a means for processes on Hosts about which minimal assumptions are made to do reliable interprocess communication in a layered protocol suite over a catenet consisting of communications subnetworks about which minimal assumptions are made. Though it nearly goes without saying, we would probably be remiss not to conclude by observing that that's a lot harder to do than to say.

Gateways

One other aspect of the ARPANET Reference Model bears separate mention. Even though it is an exceedingly fine point as to whether it's actually "part" of the Model or merely a sine qua non contextual assumption, the role of Gateways is of considerable importance to the functioning of the Internet Protocol, IP.

As noted, the defining characteristic of a Gateway is that it attaches to two or more proximate comm subnets as if it were a Host. That is, from "the network's" point of view, Gateways are not distinguished from Hosts; rather, "normal" traffic will go to them, addressed according to the proximate net's interface protocol. However, the most important property of Gateways is that they interpret a full version of IP which deals with internet routing (Host IP interpreters are permitted to take a static view of routing, sending datagrams which are destined for Hosts not directly attached to the proximate net to a known Gateway, or Gateways, addressed on the proximate net), as well of course, as with fragmentation of datagrams which, although of permissible size on one of their proximate nets, are too large for the next proximate net (which contains either the target Host or still another Gateway).

Aside from their role in routing, another property of Gateways is also of significance: Gateways do not deal with protocols above IP. That is, it is an explicit assumption of the ARM that the catenet will be "protocol compatible", in the sense that no attempt will be made to translate or map between dissimilar Host-Host protocols (e.g., TCP and AH-HP) or dissimilar Process-level protocols (e.g., ARPANET FTP and EDN FTP) at the Gateways. The justifications for this position are somewhat complex; the interested reader is encouraged to see Reference [10]. For present purposes, however, it should suffice to note that the case against translating/mapping Gateways is a sound one, and that, as with the ARMS protocols, the great practical virtue of what are sometimes called "IP Gateways" is that they are in place and running.

"Architectural" Highlights

As was implied earlier, one of the problems with viewing a reference model prescriptively rather than descriptively is that the articulation of the model must be more precise than appears to be humanly possible. That the ISORM, in striving for superhuman precision, fails to achieve it is not grounds for censure. However, by reaching a degree of apparent precision that has enticed at least some of its readers to attempt to use it in a prescriptive fashion, the ISORM has introduced a

number of ambiguities which have been attributed as well to the ARM by relative laymen in intercomputer networking whose initial exposure to the field was the ISORM. Therefore, we conclude this not-very-rigorous paper with a highly informal treatment of various points of confusion stemming from attempting to apply the ISORM to the ARM.

(It should be noted, by the way, that one of the most striking ambiguities about the ISORM is just what role X.25 plays in it: We have been informed by a few ISORMites that X.25 "is" Levels 1-3, and we accepted that as factual until we were told during the review process of the present paper that "that's not what we believe in the U.K." What follows, then, is predicated on the assumption that the earlier reports were probably but not definitely accurate--and if it turns out to be in time to help prevent ISO from embracing X.25 exclusively by pointing out some of the problems entailed, so much the better.)

"Customized Parking Garages"

The typical picture of the ISORM shows what looks like two highrises with what looks like two parking garages between them. (That is, seven layers of protocol per "Data Terminal Equipment", three layers per "Data Circuit Terminating Equipment".) The problem is that only one "style" of parking garage--i.e., one which presents an X.25 interface--is commonly understood to be available to stand beside an ISORM DTE by those who believe that ISO has adopted X.25 as its L1-3. In the ARM, on the other hand, no constraints are levied on the Communications Subnetwork Processors. Thus, satellite communications, "Packet Radios", "Ethernets" and the like are all accommodated by the ARM.

Also, the sort of Outboard Processing Environment mentioned earlier in which networking protocols are interpreted on behalf of the Host in a distributed processing fashion is quite comfortably accommodated by the ARM. This is not to say that one couldn't develop an OPE for/to the ISORM, but rather that doing so does not appear to us to be natural to it, for at least two reasons: 1. The Session Level associates sockets with processes, hence it belongs "inboard". The Presentation Level involves considerable bit-diddling, hence it belongs "outboard". The Presentation Level is, unfortunately, above the Session Level. This seems to indicate that outboard processing wasn't taken into account by the formulators of the ISORM. 2. Although some ISORMites have claimed that "X.25 can be used as a Host-Front End Protocol", it doesn't look like one to us, even if the ability to do end-to-end things via what is nominally the Network interface is somewhat suggestive. (Those who believe that you need a protocol as strong as TCP below X.25 to support the virtual circuit illusion might argue that you've actually outboarded the Host-Host layer, but both the X.25 spec and the ISORM appeal to protocols above X.25 for full L II functionality.) Perhaps, with sufficient ingenuity, one might use X.25 to convey an H-FP, but it seems clear it isn't meant to be one in and of itself.

"Plenty of Roads"

Based upon several pictures presented at conferences and in articles, DCE's in the X.25-based ISORM appear to many to be required to present X.25 interfaces to each other as well as to their DTE's. Metaphorically, the parking garages have single bridges between them. In the ARM, the CSNP-CSNP protocol is explicitly outside the model, thus there can be as many "roads" as needed between the ARM equivalent to ISORM parking garages. This also allays fears about the ability to take advantage of alternate routing in X.25 subnets or in X.75 internets (because both X.25 and X.75 are "hop-by-hop" oriented, and would not seem to allow for alternate routing without revision).

"Multiple Apartments Per Floor"

As noted, the ISORM's strictures on inter-entity communication within each "highrise" are equivalent to having to climb downstairs and then back up to visit another apartment on your own floor. The ARM explicitly expects PI's within a layer to interface directly with one another when appropriate, metaphorically giving the effect of multiple apartments on each floor oft a common hallway. (Also, for those who believe the ISORM implies only one protocol/apartment per layer/story, again the ARM is more flexible.)

"Elevators"

The ISORM is widely construed as requiring each layer to be traversed on every transmission (although there are rumors of the forthcoming introduction of "null layers"), giving the effect of having to climb all seven stories' worth of stairs every time you enter the highrise. In the ARM, only Layer I, the Network Interface layer, must be traversed; protocols in Layers II and/or III need not come into play, giving the effect of being able to take an elevator rather than climb the stairs.

"Straight Clotheslines"

Because they appear to have to go down to L3 for their initiation, the ISORM's Session and Transport connections are, to us, metaphorically tangled clotheslines; the ARM's logical connections are straight (and go from the second floor to the second floor without needing a pole that gets in the way of the folks on the third floor--if that doesn't make a weak metaphor totally feeble.)

"Townhouse Styles Available"

Should ISORM Level 6 and 7 protocols eventuate which are desirable, the "two-story townhouse style apartments" they represent can be erected on an ARM L I - L II (Network Interface and Host-Host Layers) "foundation". With some clever carpentry, even ISORM L5 might be cobbled in.

"Manned Customs Sheds"

Although it's straining the architectural metaphor quite hard, one of the unfortunate implications of the ISORM's failure to address operating system integration issues is that the notion of "Expedited Data" exchanges between "peer entities" might only amount to an SST flight to a foreign land where there's no one on duty at the Customs Shed (and the door to the rest of the airport is locked from the other side). By clearly designating the Host-Host (L II) mechanism(s) which are to be used by Layer III (Process-Level/ Applications) protocols to convey "out-of-band signals", the ARM gives the effect of keeping the Customs Sheds manned at all times. (It should be noted, by the way, that we acknowledge the difficulty of addressing system integration issues without biasing the discussion toward particular systems; we feel, however, that not trying to do so is far worse than trying and failing to avoid all parochialism.)

"Ready For Immediate Occupancy"

The ARM protocol suite has been implemented on a number of different operating systems. The ISORM protocol suite "officially" offers at most (and not in the U.K., it should be recalled) only the highly constraining functionality of X.25 as L1-L3; L4-L7 are still in the design and agreement processes, after which they must presumably be subjected to stringent checkout in multiple implementations before becoming useful standards. The metaphorical highrises, then, are years away from being fit for occupancy, even if one is willing to accept the taste of the interior decorators who seem to insist on building in numerous features of dubious utility and making you take fully furnished apartments whether you like it or not; the ARM buildings, on the other hand, offer stoves and refrigerators, but there's plenty of room for your own furniture--and they're ready for immediate occupancy.

Conclusion

The architectural metaphor might have been overly extended as it was, but it could have been drawn out even further to point up more issues on which the ARM appears to us to be superior to the ISORM, if our primary concern were which is "better". In fairness, the one issue it omitted which many would take to be in the ISORM's favor is that "vendor support" of interpreters of the ISORM protocols will eventually amount to a desirable "prefabrication", while the building of the ARM PI's is believed to be labor-intensive. That would indeed be a good point, if it were well-founded. Unfortunately for its proponents, however, close scrutiny of the vendor support idea suggests that it is largely illusory (vide [11]), especially in light of the amount of time it will take for the international standardization process to run its course, and the likelihood that specification ambiguities and optional features will handicap interoperability. Rather than extend the present paper even further, then, it seems fair to conclude that with the possible exception of "vendor support" (with which exception we take exception, for it should be noted that a number of vendors are already offering support for TCP/IP), the ARPANET Reference Model and the protocols designed in conformance with it are at least worthy of consideration by anybody who's planning to do real intercomputer networking in the next several years-- especially if they have operating systems with counterparts on the present ARPANET, so that most if not all of the labor intensive part has been taken care of already--irrespective of one's views on how good the ISORM protocols eventually will be.

Acknowledgments

Although it has seldom been more germane to observe that "any remaining shortcomings are the author's responsibility", this paper has benefited tremendously from the close scrutiny and constructive comments of several distinguished members of both the research community and the (DoD) Protocol Standards Technical Panel. The author is not only extremely grateful to, but is also extremely pleased to acknowledge his indebtedness to the following individuals (cited in alphabetical order): Mr. Trevor Benjamin, Royal Signals and Radar Establishment (U.K.); Mr. Edward Cain, Chairman of the PSTP; Dr. Vinton Cerf, DARPA/IPTO (at the time this was written); Dr. David Clark, M.I.T. Laboratory for Computer Science (formerly Project MAC); and Dr. Jonathan Postel, U.S.C. Information Sciences Institute. Posterity may or may not thank them for their role in turning an act of personal catharsis into a fair semblance of a "real" paper, but the author emphatically does.

Notes and References

[1] It almost goes without saying that the subtheme is certainly not intended to be a definitive statement of the relative merits of the two approaches, although, as will be seen, the ARM comes out ahead, in our view. But then, the reader might well say, what else should I expect from a paper written by one of the developers of the ARM? To attempt to dispel thoughts of prejudgment, the author would observe that although he is indeed an Old Network Boy of the ARPANET, he was not a member of the TCP/IP (the keystone of the current ARM) design team, and that he began looking into ARM "vs." ISORM from the position of "a plague on both your houses". That he has concluded that the differences between TCP/IP-based ARM intercomputer networking and X.25-based ISORM intercomputer networking are like day and night may be taken as indicative of something, but that he also holds that the day is at least partly cloudy and the night is not altogether moonless should at least meliorate fears of prejudice. That is, of course the ISORM has its merits and the ARM its demerits neither of which are dealt with here. But "A Perspective" really means "My Perspective", and the author really is more concerned in this context with exposition of the ARM than with twitting the ISORM, even if he couldn't resist including the comparisons subtheme because of the one-sidedness of the ISORM publicity he has perceived of late.

[2] Source material for this section was primarily drawn from the author's personal experience as a member the NWG and from numerous conversations with Dr. Jonathan B. Postel, long-time Chairman of the NWG and participant in the design meetings prior to the author's involvement. (See also Acknowledgments.)

[3] Padlipsky, M. A. "The Elements of Networking Style", M81-41, The MITRE Corporation, Bedford, MA, October 1981. [*]

[4] Yes, the notion of using "protocols" might well count as an axiom in its own right, but, no, we're not going to pretend to be that rigorous.

[5] That is, about three tenths of the possible span of "Session" functionality, which has to do with making up for the lack of Well-Known Sockets, isn't subsumed by the ARM Process-Level protocols, but the rest is, or could be.

[6] Davidson, J., et al., "The ARPANET Telnet Protocol: Its Purpose, Principles, Implementation, and Impact on Host Operating System Design," Proc Fifth Data Communications Symposium, ACM/IEEE, Snowbird, Utah, September, 1977.

[7] See Proceedings of the 1970 SJCC, "Resource Sharing Computer Networks" session, and Proceedings of the 1972 SJCC, "The ARPA Network" session for the standard open literature references to the early ARPANET. Other source material for this chapter is drawn from the author's personal conversations with TCP/IP's principal developers; see also Acknowledgments.

[8] A strong case can be made for desiring that the comm subnets make a "datagram" (or "connectionless") mode of interface available, based upon the desire to support such functionality as Packetized Speech, broadcast addressing, and mobile subscribers, among other things. For a more complete description of this point of view, see [9]. For present purposes, we do not cite the presentation of a datagram mode interface as a design constraint because it is possible--albeit undesirable--to operate IP "on top of" a comm subnet which does not present such an interface.

[9] Cerf, V. G. and R. E. Lyons, "Military Requirements for Packet-Switched Networks and for Their Protocol Standardization" Proc EASCON 1982.

[10] Padlipsky, M. A., "Gateways, Architectures and Heffalumps", M82-51, The MITRE Corporation, Bedford, MA, September 1982. [*]

[11] ---------- "The Illusion of Vendor Support", M82-49, The MITRE Corporation, Bedford, MA, September 1982. [*]

([*] Public release pending.)

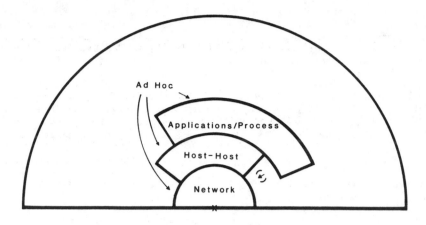

Notes

    A. X marks the egress (and the ingress)
    B. The whole picture either lives in or is flexibly attached
        to a Host
    C. (↓) indicates it's at least imaginable to use the network
        layer without/in-lieu-of a Host-Host protocol in some
        circumstances
    D. (And if comm subnet processors are present, there will
        doubtless be a CSNP-CNSP protocol in play - which
        is rendered uninteresting for present purposes by
        Note B.)

Figure 1. ARM in the Abstract

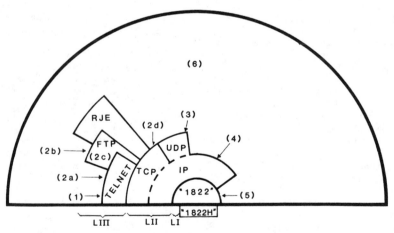

Legend
(1) Where Terminal-Terminal Protocol would go*
(2a)... (2d) Where Mail Protocol could go*
(3) Where muxed packetized speech goes
(4) Where unmuxed packetized speech could go
(5) Where you could "pump bits at a peripheral" on a LAN
(6) Still ad hoc Land
    ● "1822" for concreteness only (need not be taken literally)
    ● RJE not endorsed, merely suggestive of using two PLP's
        in-support-of/doing-virtualization for a third
_____

* Found via well-known socket

Figure 2. ARMS, Somewhat Particularized

SECTION 2 PHYSICAL AND DATA LINK PROTOCOLS

2.1 PHYSICAL PROTOCOLS

Most digital data processing devices are possessed of limited data transmission capability. Typically, they generate only simple digital signals using two voltage levels to encode binary data. The distance across which they can transmit data is generally limited. Consequently, it is rare for such a device to attach directly to a long-distance transmission medium. The more common situation is depicted in Figure 2.1. The devices we are discussing, which include terminals and computers, are generically referred to as *data terminal equipment* (DTE). A DTE makes use of the transmission system through the mediation of *data circuit-terminating equipment* (DCE). An example of the latter is a modem used to connect digital devices to voice-grade lines.

On one side, the DCE is responsible for transmitting and receiving bits, one at a time, over a transmission medium. On the other side, the DCE must interact with the DTE. In general, this requires both data and control information to be exchanged. This is done over a set of wires referred to as *interchange circuits*. For this scheme to work, a high degree of cooperation is required. The two DCEs must understand each other. That is, the receiver of each must use the same encoding scheme as the transmitter of the other. In addition, each DTE-DCE pair must be designed to have complementary interfaces and must be able to interact effectively. To ease the burden on data processing equipment manufacturers and users, standards have been developed that specify the exact nature of the interface between the DTE and the DCE. In contemporary parlance, these standards are known as physical layer protocols.

Most but not all physical protocol standards employ the model depicted in Figure 2.1. More generally, a physical protocol refers to the interface through which a device transmits and receives data signals. For example, in the context of local networks, a physical protocol defines the interface between an attached device and the local network transmission medium; there is no model of DTE/DCE employed.

The interface has four important characteristics [BERT80]:

- Mechanical.
- Electrical.
- Functional.
- Procedural.

The *mechanical* characteristics pertain to the actual physical connection of the DTE and DCE. Typically, the signal and control leads are bundled into a cable with a terminator plug, male or female, at each end. The DTE and DCE must each present a plug of opposite gender at one end of the cable, effecting the physical connection. This is analogous to the situation for residential electrical power. Power is provided via a socket or wall outlet, and the device to be attached must have the appropriate plug (two-pronged, two-pronged polarized, three-pronged).

The *electrical* characteristics have to do with the voltage levels and timing of voltage changes. Both DTE and DCE must use the same coding scheme for representing data, must use the same voltage levels to mean the same thing, and must use the same duration of signal elements. These characteristics determine the data rates and distances that can be achieved.

Functional characteristics specify the functions that are performed, by assigning meaning to the various interchange circuits. Functions can be classified into the broad categories of data, control, timing, and ground.

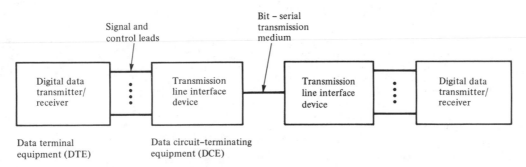

Figure 2-1: Generic Interface to Transmission Medium

Procedural characteristics specify the sequence of events for transmitting data, based on the functional characteristics of the interface.

The most widely used physical protocol is RS-232-C. Although now considered obsolete, this standard has survived because of the huge base of existing equipment that uses it. An improved interface is defined by a set of standards: RS-449, RS422-A, and RS-423-A. This set of standards has achieved considerable acceptance. However, it too is being supplanted by standards that exploit the advances in electronic technology of recent years. Portions of both X.21 and the forthcoming ISDN standard are in this category.

2.2 DATA LINK PROTOCOLS

A physical interface or protocol provides only a raw bit stream service, which is subject to error. A data link protocol is used to manage the communication between two connected devices and to transform an unreliable transmission path into a reliable one. The key elements of a data link protocol are:

- *Frame synchronization:* Data are sent in blocks called frames. The beginning and end of each frame must be clearly identifiable.

- *Use of a variety of line configurations:* Devices may be connected by a point-to-point link or a multipoint link. Examples of the latter are (1) a multidrop line that connects multiple terminals to a single computer port, and (2) a local network.

- *Flow control:* The sending station must not send frames at a rate faster than the receiving station can absorb them.

- *Error control:* The bit errors introduced by the transmission system must be corrected.

- *Addressing:* On a multipoint line, the identity of the two stations involved in a transmission must be known.

- *Control and data on same link:* It is usually not desirable to have a separate communications path for control signals. Accordingly, the receiver must be able to distinguish control information from the data being transmitted.

- *Link management:* The initiation, maintenance, and termination of a sustained data exchange require a fair amount of coordination and cooperation among stations. Procedures for the management of this exchange are required.

With the use of a data link protocol, the next higher layer may assume virtually error-free transmission over the link. However, if communication is between two systems that are connected via a network, the connection will comprise a number of data links in tandem, each functioning independently. Thus the higher layers are not relieved of an error control responsibility.

The most widely used data link standard is HDLC and two very similar standards, LAP-B and ADCCP.

2.3 ARTICLE SUMMARY

Bertine provides a detailed discussion, with examples, of physical level protocols. One of the more common standards at this level, RS-449, is discussed by Folts. Conard surveys data link protocols. The most common modern link protocols are bit oriented, and these are described by Weissberger. The final article discusses the IEEE 802 local network standards, which encompasses both physical and link layers.

Reprinted from *Data Communications Network Interfacing and Protocols*, 1981, pages 2-1—2-18. Copyright 1981 by The Institute of Electrical and Electronics Engineers, Inc.

PHYSICAL LEVEL INTERFACES AND PROTOCOLS

H. V. BERTINE

Abstract - The physical level is the most basic protocol level in the hierarchy of data communication protocols. This level covers the physical interface between devices and the rules by which bits are passed from one to another. These devices may be, for example, a data terminal equipment (DTE) and a data circuit-terminating equipment (DCE, e.g., a modem). This paper describes the physical level and the national and international standards that have been developed for this level. Included are insights into the development of recently adopted physical level standards.

I. INTRODUCTION

The CCITT* Recommendation X.25 protocol for access to packet switched data networks is probably the first internationally recognized data communication protocol to use the concept of levels or layers. The 1976 version of Recommendation X.25 [1] defined the first level, which it designated level 1, as

"The physical, electrical, functional, and procedural characteristics to establish, maintain and disconnect the physical link between the DTE and the DCE."

CCITT, in its work on a layered model for public data network (PDN) applications, states [2]

"The physical layer represents the most basic level of the Model and describes transparent transmission of a bit stream over a circuit built in some physical communications medium."

"The physical layer provides mechanical, electrical, functional, and procedural characteristics to activate, maintain, and deactivate physical connections, referred to as data circuits for bit transmission between link functional units."

ISO,** in its work on open system interconnection, has developed a seven layer architectural model [3]. This model defines the physical layer as

"The physical layer provides mechanical, electrical, functional and procedural characteristics to activate, maintain and deactivate physical connections for bit transmission between data link entities possibly through intermediate systems, each relaying bit transmission within the physical layer."

"A physical connection may allow duplex or half-duplex transmission of bit streams."
ISO also introduces the concept of a physical service data unit

"A physical service data unit consists of one bit in serial transmission and of "n" bits in parallel transmission."

"The transmission of physical service data units (i.e., bits) can be performed by synchronous or asynchronous transmission."

---

* International Telegraph and Telephone Consultative Committee. CCITT is a committee of the International Telecommunications Union (ITU), a specialized agency of the United Nations Organization. The CCITT work on data communications is focused in two study groups. CCITT Study Group XVII is responsible for data communications over telephone facilities. Its work is contained in V-series recommendations. CCITT Study Group VII is responsible for data communications over data networks. Its work is contained in X-series recommendations.

** International Organization for Standardization. ISO is a voluntary nontreaty group made up of the principal standardization body of each represented nation. The U.S. member body is the American National Standards Institute (ANSI). The ISO work on data communications is focused in two subcommittees of Technical Committee 97 (Computers and Information Processing). ISO/TC97/SC6 is responsible for data communications. ISO/TC97/SC16 is responsible for open systems interconnection.

These definitions are being reviewed. For example, an internal working document [4] within ISO proposes to modify the definition of the physical layer to read

> "The physical layer provides the functional and procedural means to activate, maintain and deactivate physical connections for bit transmission between data link entities. Physical layer entities are interconnected by means of a physical media. Mechanical and electrical characteristics are defined at one or more points of interest (e.g., point of demarcation) along the physical media."

Several observations can be made from the above quotations. First, the two international sources of the quotations reflect the widespread interest in this subject. Second, at the present time, there is no precise consensus of what the physical level includes. However, it is clear that the physical level has four important characteristics which will be designated here as

- mechanical,
- electrical,
- functional, and
- procedural.

In Section II, each of these characteristics will be discussed in detail.

The physical level exists at a variety of places. A very important and widely standardized interface is the one between the DTE and the DCE as depicted in Figure 1. The most familiar DTE/DCE interface in the U.S. is that described by EIA* RS-232-C [5]. There are other serial data DTE/DCE interfaces, such as EIA RS-449 [6], CCITT X.20 [7], and X.21 [7]. There are also what are known as parallel data DTE/DCE interfaces, such as CCITT V.19 [8] and V.20 [8]. Other types of data communication interfaces are important, such as EIA RS-366-A [9] which covers the DTE interface to automatic calling equipment (ACE). There is also a physical interface between the DCE (e.g., a modem) and the transmission facility (e.g., telephone line) as specified in CCITT V-series modem recommendations [8]. Another important interface is the signaling interface between networks such as that specified by CCITT Recommendation X.75 [7].

Space does not permit a description of the physical level characteristics of each of the interfaces in this chapter. However, two specific interfaces, EIA RS-449 and CCITT X.21, will be discussed in detail in Section III to provide a flavor for the considerations which go into the development of the physical level.

Parameters associated with the physical level also have been standardized. For example, EIA RS-269-B [10], ANSI**X3.1 [11] and X3.36 [12], and CCITT V.5 [8], V.6 [8] and X.1 [7] set forth the signaling rates (i.e., bits/s) for the physical level of the DTE/DCE interface. The alignment of data and timing signals for synchronous operation are specified in EIA RS-334 [13]. Signal quality for asynchronous operation is specified in EIA RS-363 [14] and RS-404 [15] and ISO 7480 [16]. Space does not permit further discussion of these standards.

Work is continuing to further the standardization of the physical level. Section IV provides a look at this effort.

II. CHARACTERISTICS OF THE PHYSICAL LEVEL

As mentioned previously, the four principal characteristics making up the physical level are: mechanical, electrical, functional, and procedural. Each is briefly described in this section.

---

* Electronic Industries Association. EIA is a national body that represents manufacturers in the U. S. electronics industry. The EIA work on data communications is carried out by Technical Committee TR30. EIA standards on data communications are published in the RS-series. In addition, EIA publishes supplementary material in Industrial Electronics Bulletins.

** American National Standards Institute. ANSI is a non-profit, non-governmental organization. It serves as the national clearing house and coordinating activity for voluntary standards in the U.S. The ANSI work on data communications is focused in two technical committees of Standards Committee X3 (Computers and Information Processing). Technical Committee X3S3 is responsible for data communications and Technical Committee X3T5 is responsible for open systems interconnection. American National Standards resulting from the work of these committees are contained in the X3.-series.

A. Mechanical Characteristics

The mechanical aspects pertain to the point of demarcation. Typically, this is a pluggable connector but other arrangements, such as screw terminals, are sometimes used. Included are the specifics of the connector, the assignment of interchange circuits (see Section II-C) to pins, the connector latching arrangement, mounting arrangements, etc. The location of the interface connector (e.g., close to or on the DCE) is often specified as well as the provision of cabling (e.g., interface cabling is generally considered part of the DTE).

The following are the various mechanical interfaces that have been standardized by ISO.

- ISO 2110 [17]: 25-pin connector used for serial and parallel voice-band modems, public data network interfaces, telegraph (including Telex) interfaces, and automatic calling equipment. EIA RS-232-C and EIA RS-366-A are compatible with ISO 2110.
- ISO 2593 [18]: 34-pin connector used for the CCITT Recommendation V.35 [8] wide-band modem. Although there is no equivalent EIA standard, this interface is used within the U. S.
- ISO 4902 [19]: 37/9-pin connectors used for serial voice-band and wide-band modems. EIA RS-449 is compatible with ISO 4902.
- ISO 4903 [20]: 15-pin connector used for public data network interfaces specified by CCITT Recommendations X.20, X.21, and X.22 [7]. There are no equivalent standards in the U. S.

The various connectors and their relative sizes are illustrated in Figure 2. All connectors, except for the 34-pin connector, belong to the same connector family.

The newest standards (37/9-pin and 15-pin) contain additional specifications to solve many of the mechanical interface problems experienced with implementations of the earlier standards. A key provision is the specification of an inexpensive DCE latching block (see Figure 2) which enables latching and unlatching to be done either with or without a tool. This innovation should eliminate the incompatibilities associated with the wide variety of latching devices in use today. Another improvement is the placing of limitations on the size of the DTE connector including cover, cable clamp, and latching arrangement. This permits compact mounting arrangements involving multiple DCE connectors while assuring adequate clearances.

The EIA RS-449 and CCITT X.21 interfaces discussed in Section III use these new connector specifications.

B. Electrical Characteristics

In the early standards (EIA RS-232-C, CCITT Recommendation V.28 [8]), the electrical characteristics were defined at the point of demarcation. More recent standards (EIA RS-422-A [21] and RS-423-A [22], CCITT Recommendations V.10 [8]/X.26 [7] and V.11 [8]/X.27 [7]) specify the electrical characteristics of the generators and receivers and give guidance with respect to the interconnecting cable. The latter situation, while simplifying the job of the integrated circuit manufacturer, has been criticized because there is no specification at the point of demarcation. The absence of this specification hampers sectionalization of trouble.

The following are the various electrical characteristics that have been standardized by CCITT.

- V.10/X.26: New unbalanced electrical characteristics. EIA RS-423-A, FED-STD 1030 [23], and MIL-STD 188-114 [24] are compatible with V.10/X.26.
- V.11/X.27: New balanced electrical characteristics. EIA RS-422-A, FED-STD 1020 [25], and MIL-STD 188-114 are compatible with V.11/X.27.
- V.28: Unbalanced electrical characteristics. EIA RS-232-C is compatible with V.28.
- V.31 [8]: Electrical characteristics for interchange circuits controlled by contact closure. Used in parallel modem (CCITT V.20 [8]). EIA RS-410 [26] is a similar standard.
- V.35 [8]: Balanced electrical characteristics used on the data and timing circuits of the CCITT V.35 modem. Although there is no equivalent EIA standard, this interface is used within the U. S.

The use of the latter two electrical characteristics is limited and, therefore, they will not be discussed further. Figure 3 provides a comparison of V.28, V.10 and V.11. The key item to note is that V.10 provides a transitional mechanism since it is interoperable with both V.28 and V.11.

The new unbalanced and balanced electrical characteristics were developed to provide improved performance in terms of supporting higher bit rates and longer cable distances compared with V.28 and RS-232-C. Integrated circuit manufacturers were active in the development of these new electrical characteristics to insure their practical realization in state-of-the-art technology.

The electrical characteristics of V.28/RS-232-C specify a single-ended generator that produces a 5-15 V signal (negative for binary 1, positive for binary 0) with respect to signal ground (common return). A single common return lead is used for all interchange circuits. Generator risetime is relatively fast such that the time for the signal to pass through the ± 3 V transition region does not exceed 1 ms and, for data and timing interchange circuits, also does not exceed 3% (for V.28; 4% for RS-232-C) of the nominal signal element duration. A single-ended receiver is specified having a dc resistance between 3 k and 7 $k\,\Omega$. These electrical characteristics are generally limited to data signaling rates below 20 kbit/s and cable distances shorter than 15 m.

The new unbalanced electrical characteristics specify a low-impedance ($\leq 50\Omega$) single-ended generator that produces a 4-6 V signal (negative for binary 1, positive for binary 0) with respect to the common return. A single common return lead for each direction of transmission can be used across the interface. Waveshaping of the generator output signal is used to control the level of near-end crosstalk to adjacent circuits in the interconnection. Data signaling rates up to 3 kbits/s can be used over cable distances up to 1000 m. For data signaling rates above 3 kbits/s, the cable distance decreases with increasing signaling rate to 10 m at 300 kbits/s.

The new balanced electrical characteristics specify a low-impedance ($\leq 100\ \Omega$) balanced generator that produces a 2-6 V differential signal (A terminal negative with respect to the B terminal for binary 1, opposite polarity for binary 0). Each interchange circuit requires a pair of wires for balanced operation. Data signaling rates up to 100 kbits/s can be used over cable distances up to 1000 m. For data signaling rates above 100 kbits/s, the cable distance decreases with increasing signaling rate to 10 m at 10 Mbits/s.

The new balanced and unbalanced electrical characteristics are identical for the receiver. They specify a differential receiver which has a high input impedance (≥ 4 k Ω) and a small transition region (± 0.2 V).

The correlation between the binary 1 and 0 states given above for each of the electrical characteristics and the states of the interchange circuits is shown in Figure 4.

A key feature built into the new electrical characteristics is an evolution path from the existing V.28/RS-232-C electrical characteristics. The V.10/RS-423-A specifications were specifically designed to permit interoperation with both V.28/RS-232-C and V.11/RS-422-A. The EIA RS-449 and CCITT X.21 interfaces discussed in Section III make use of this capability.

C. Functional Characteristics

Interchange circuit functions are typically classified into the following broad categories: data, control, timing, and grounds. Further classification into primary and secondary channel functions are made for those DTE/DCE interfaces employing a secondary channel.

The following are the two CCITT recommendations which define the functions of interchange circuits.

- V.24 [8]: DTE/DCE and DTE/ACE interchange circuits. Originally developed for use with modems and automatic calling equipment associated with modems, they may also be used with digital networks. EIA RS-232-C and RS-449 are compatible with V.24 for DTE/DCE interchange circuits and EIA RS-366-A is compatible with V.24 for DTE/ACE interchange circuits.
- X.24 [7]: DTE/DCE interchange circuits. Developed for use with public data networks (CCITT Recommendations X.20, X.21, and X.22). There is no equivalent standard in the U. S.

The V.24 interchange circuits have been used for several decades. They employ the concept of one function per interchange circuit. Over the years, the list of interchange circuits has grown steadily. The 1980 version of Recommendation V.24 defines 43 interchange circuits for use in various DTE/DCE interfaces and 12 interchange circuits for the DTE/ACE interface.

In the 1968-1972 CCITT study period, work started on interface standards (X.20 and X.21) specifically designed for the emerging duplex data networks. The technology to be employed in these networks favored a "compact" interface where the ACE functions, DCE control functions, and data were multiplexed over a single "data" interchange circuit in each direction. The result of this work was Recommendation X.24 which defines a small set of interchange circuits. This set includes a data and a control circuit in each direction plus a single bit timing circuit from the DCE. An optional byte timing circuit from the DCE is also defined. The 1980 version of X.24 also defines a framing circuit from the DCE which is used in the new X.22 interface.

The EIA RS-449 interface described in Section III-A uses V.24 interchange circuits and the CCITT X.21 interface described in Section III-B uses X.24 interchange circuits.

D. Procedural Characteristics

The final aspect of the physical level is the set of procedures for using the interchange circuits. These procedures are the ones that need to be performed to enable the transmission of bits so that the higher level functions can take place. The exact division between which procedures are part of the physical level and which procedures are higher level procedures is an area of considerable debate.

The following are the various CCITT recommendations which define procedures at the physical level.

- V.24: Procedures affecting the interrelationships between certain interchange circuits. EIA RS-232-C and RS-449 contain equivalent procedures.
- V.25 [8]: Procedures for use with automatic calling equipment. EIA RS-366-A contains equivalent procedures.
- V.54 [8]: Procedures regarding maintenance test loops. EIA RS-449 contains equivalent procedures.
- V-series modems [8]: Modem specific procedures for the use of interchange circuits. Several Federal standards contain equivalent procedures.
- X.20: Procedures for asynchronous operation on a public data network. There is no equivalent standard in the U. S.
- X.20 bis [7]: Procedures for asynchronous operation on a public data network for DTEs designed to interface with V-series asynchronous modems. EIA RS-232-C contains equivalent procedures.
- X.21: Procedures for synchronous operation on a public data network. There is no equivalent standard in the U. S.
- X.21 bis [7]: Procedures for synchronous operation on a public data network for DTEs designed to interface with V-series synchronous modems. EIA RS-232-C and RS-449 contains equivalent procedures.
- X.22: Procedures for synchronous operation on a public data network whereby several circuits are time division multiplexed. There is no equivalent standard in the U. S.
- X.150 [7]: Procedures regarding maintenance test loops for public data networks.

Two examples of these procedures are given in Section III.

You may have wondered what happened to CCITT Recommendation X.25 [7] which was discussed. X.25, which specifies the packet mode interface to packet switched public data networks, does contain a section on the physical level. This section, however, simply references the appropriate sections of X.21 and X.21 bis.

III. EXAMPLES OF THE PHYSICAL LEVEL

In this section two examples are given of the physical level for DTE/DCE interfaces. The first is EIA RS-449 which was developed to replace EIA RS-232-C. The second is CCITT Recommendation X.21 which was developed specifically as a synchronous interface to public data networks. In each example, the four characterists of the physical level - mechanical, electrical, functional, and procedural - are clearly evident.

Before taking up these new interfaces, it is appropriate to briefly review EIA RS-232-C, the dominant DTE/DCE interface in use today. The first version of this standard, RS-232, was adopted in May, 1960. It was revised three times - in October, 1963 as RS-232-A, in October, 1965 as RS-232-B, and in August, 1969 as RS-232-C.

RS-232-C defines 21 interchange circuits. Each circuit provides a single function as summarized in Figure 5. Not all circuits are needed in every application. For example, the timing circuits are omitted for non-synchronous applications, certain control circuits are omitted for non-switched applications, and the five secondary channel circuits are omitted when secondary channel operation is not employed.

The interchange circuit procedures contained in RS-232-C are more fully described in a separate Application Notes document [27]. Included is a series of charts giving control circuit state diagrams for a number of applications. An example illustration of these procedures is given in Figure 6. This figure, covering half duplex operation over the switched network, shows the major states and transitions for the six principal RS-232-C control circuits.

RS-232-C includes the specification of electrical characteristics for the interchange circuits. These unbalanced characteristics were described above in Section II-B. They apply at the point of demarcation between the DTE and DCE (i.e., at the 25-pin connector). Interface operation is generally limited to data signaling rates below 20 kbit/s and cable distances shorter than 15 m.

A. EIA RS-449

RS-232-C was recognized by EIA in 1973 to be a limiting factor in many user environments. The principal new capabilities and benefits desired were

- improved performance, longer interface cable distances, and a significantly higher maximum data rate (to be achieved with the new electrical characteristics);
- additional interface functions, such as loopback testing; and
- resolution of the mechanical interface problems which had lead to a proliferation of designs, many of which were incompatible with one another.

The first approach examined was to update RS-232-C. Creating an RS-232-D would require a degree of compatibility with RS-232-C which would have severely compromised the desired new capabilities and benefits.* Therefore, the decision was made to develop a new interface. Two major approaches for this new interface were studied at the outset and were reviewed many times thereafter. One was to follow the basic concepts of RS-232-C. The other was to seek alignment with the developing CCITT work on Recommendation X.21. (See Section III-B.)

The principal advantage of the first approach is the ability to interoperate with RS-232-C. This would not be possible with the X.21 approach. The principal advantage of the X.21 approach is a lower cost interface achieved through a substantial reduction in the number of interchange circuits. However, as discussed in Section IV, there are significant technical and performance problems associated with the adoption of X.21 for the modem interface. Therefore, the first approach was taken with two principal objectives:

- the ability to interoperate the new equipment with the presently existing RS-232-C equipment (no modifications to RS-232-C equipment permitted), and
- to obtain the new capabilities cited earlier when two new equipments are interfaced.

These objectives were satisfied (as described below) and RS-449 was published by EIA in November, 1977, after international agreement was reached in CCITT and ISO. To simplify the following discussion, the EIA terminology will be used. The listings given in Section II can be used for reference to the equivalent international standards.

---

* The opposite was true for the automatic calling equipment interface, RS-366. It has been updated as RS-366-A.

1) Functional:

One of the problems with RS-232-C was that many equipments included interface circuits in addition to those defined in RS-232-C. New Sync (now known as New Signal) is one example. More importantly, there was a strong need to incorporate additional capabilities in the interface for loopback testing and other functions. These problems were solved in RS-449 by the addition of new interchange circuits following the philosophy used in RS-232-C of one function per interchange circuit. Figure 7 provides a complete listing of the thirty RS-449 interchange circuits and gives the equivalent interchange circuits in RS-232-C and CCITT Recommendation V.24.**

A new set of interface circuit names and mnemonics is used in RS-449. The names were chosen to more accurately describe the function performed and to eliminate the term "data set," which is no longer appropriate. The mnemonics were chosen to be easily related to the circuit names and to be unique from those used in RS-232-C to avoid confusion.

Briefly, the new circuits are

- Send Common (SC) - provides a signal common return path for all unbalanced interchange circuits employing one wire used in the direction toward the DCE.
- Receive Common (RC) - provides a signal common return path for all unbalanced interchange circuits employing one wire used in the direction toward the DTE.
- Terminal In Service (IS) - indicates to the DCE whether or not the DTE is operational. A major use is to make an associated port on a line hunting group busy if the DTE is out-of-service.
- New Signal (NS) - indicates to the DCE when the DCE receiver should be prepared to acquire a new line signal. A major use is to improve the overall response time of multipoint polling systems.
- Select Frequency (SF) - controls the DCE transmit and receive operation with respect to two frequency bands. Its purpose is to allow selection of the frequency mode of the DCE in multipoint circuits where all stations have equal status.
- Local Loopback (LL) - requests the DCE to initiate a loopback of signals in the local DCE toward the local DTE. Its purpose is to allow checking of the functioning of the DTE and the local DCE.
- Remote Loopback (RL) - requests the DCE to initiate a loopback of signals in the remote DCE toward the local DTE. Its purpose is to allow checking of the functioning of the DTE, local DCE, transmission channel, and the remote DCE.
- Test Mode (TM) - indicates to the DTE when a test condition has been established involving the local DCE. Its purpose is to distinguish test conditions from other nondata mode conditions of the DCE.
- Select Standby (SS) - requests the DCE to replace regular facilities with predetermined standby facilities. Its purpose is to facilitate the rapid restoration of service when a failure has occurred.
- Standby Indicator (SB) - indicates to the DTE whether regular facilities or standby facilities are in use. This may be in response to activation by circuit SS or by other means.

2) Procedural:

The text of RS-449 contains the procedures for using the interchange circuits. The basic RS-232-C procedures were carried over into RS-449. The state diagrams prepared in an application note to RS-232-C [27] (e.g., see Figure 6) can be applied to RS-449.

The procedures for the new test and standby interchange circuits are principally based on action-reaction pairs. For example, the Local Loopback circuit is turned ON by the DTE (the action) to request a local loopback. The DTE now waits. When the DCE has established the loopback, it turns the Test Mode circuit ON (the reaction) indicating that the loop has been established and any data sent by the DTE on the Send Data circuit should be returned to the

---

** CCITT is studying the addition to Recommendation V.24 of the one RS-449 interchange circuit (Terminal In Service) presently not included.

DTE on the Receive Data circuit. The DTE can now begin sending test data. A similar action-reaction sequence is followed when deactivating the loopback.

3) Electrical:

As stated earlier, interoperability with EIA RS-232-C was a principal objective in the design of EIA RS-449. This is achieved by permitting the use of the unbalanced RS-423-A electrical characteristics on interchange circuits when the data rate is less than 20 kbits/s, the upper limit for RS-232-C. Unlike X.21 (see Section III-B1), this flexibility to use the unbalanced electrical characteristics is allowed for both the DTE and DCE. To provide good performance for data rates above 20 kbits/s (where interoperability with EIA RS-232-C does not apply), EIA RS-449 designates certain circuits which must be operated with the balanced RS-422-A electrical characteristics. This enables EIA RS-449 to be used for data rates up to 2 Mbits/s.

The key to obtaining this flexibility is the use of two wires for each of the following ten interchange circuits (designated by RS-449 as Category I circuits):

SD - Send Data	RS - Request to Send
RD - Receive Data	CS - Clear to Send
TT - Terminal Timing	RR - Receiver Ready
ST - Send Timing	TR - Terminal Ready
RT - Receive Timing	DM - Data Mode

Either RS-422-A or RS-423-A generators can be used on these circuits for data rates below 20 kbits/s. For data rates above 20 kbits/s, these circuits are RS-422-A. All other interchange circuits (designated by RS-449 as Category II circuits) always use RS-423-A and thus have one wire per interchange circuit with a common signal return lead. Figure 8 summarizes this arrangement.

Two important benefits are achieved. For DTEs or DCEs designed for operation at speeds of 20 kbits/s or less, a manufacturer may choose to implement the unbalanced RS-423-A electrical characteristics on all interchange circuits. With this design, a single RS-449 implementation can operate with another RS-449 device or interoperate with an RS-232-C device (see Section III-A5). Alternatively, a manufacturer may choose to implement the balanced RS-422-A electrical characteristics on the Category I interchange circuits. With this design, a single RS-449 implementation can operate with another RS-449 device at all bit rates up to 2 Mbits/s with maximum performance. This is contrasted with the variety of different interfaces (RS-232-C, V.35, etc.) required in the past, each applying to a narrow range of data rates.

4) Mechanical:

The RS-449 connectors come from the same connector family as the familiar 25-pin connector used with RS-232-C. This selection was made because of the favorable experience associated with the use of the 25-pin connector. In order to satisfy the requirements of some foreign administrations, two connectors are used. A 37-pin connector is used for the basic interface. If secondary channel operation is used, these leads appear on a separate 9-pin connector. An important side benefit of the 9-pin and 37-pin connectors is that they are different from the present 25-pin and 34-pin connectors. This prevents the accidental interconnection of incompatible electrical characteristics which may result in physical damage to interface generators and terminators.

The mechanical enhancements described in Section II-A involving standardization of the DCE latching block and maximum DTE connector envelope size are incorporated in RS-449. The pin assignment plan was carefully chosen to minimize crosstalk in multipair cable (i.e., one Category I circuit or two Category II circuits in the same direction are assigned to a pair) and to facilitate the design of an adapter when interworking with RS-232-C is desired.

Finally, provision was made for the use of shielded interface cable. Pin 1 of the interface connector is used to insure continuity of the shields between tandem connections of shielded interface cable.

5) Interoperability:

Interoperability with RS-232-C, when desired, may be accomplished by means of a simple passive adapter and a few additional design criteria for the RS-449 interchange circuits. The adapter specification and the detailed design criteria are contained in [19] and [28]. No modifications are needed for the RS-232-C equipment. Performance for interoperability is that associated with RS-232-C interfaces.

B. CCITT Recommendation X.21

CCITT Recommendation X.21 will be used in this section as a second illustration of the four characteristics of the physical level. To simplify the presentation, references, when made, will be to CCITT and ISO standards.

The 1980 version of CCITT Recommendation X.21 contains two distinct parts. One part specifies a "general purpose" DTE/DCE interface for synchronous operation on public data networks. This is the physical level part of Recommendation X.21. The second part of Recommendation X.21 specifies the call control procedures for circuit switched services. There is still debate in the standards arena about whether these are also part of the physical level. The emerging consensus is that the call control elements of X.21 involve link level (e.g., for character alignment and parity) and network level (e.g., for addressing and call progress signals) functions. This viewpoint is taken here and thus these functions are not discussed further.

1) Electrical:

One of the objectives for Recommendation X.21 was to permit interface operation over distances considerably greater than that available with Recommendation V.28. To achieve this objective at the synchronous data rates given in X.1,* the new balanced electrical characteristics (Recommendation X.27) were specified for the DCE side of the interface. To allow flexibility in DTE design at the four lower data rates, the DTE is permitted to use either the new balanced or the new unbalanced (Recommendation X.26) electrical characteristics. For the 48 kbit/s rate, only the balanced electrical characteristics are permitted to insure good performance.

2) Mechanical:

The mechanical interface for X.21 is specified by ISO 4903. The mechanical enhancements described earlier for RS-449 involving standardization of the DCE latching block, maximum DTE connector envelope size, and the use of pin 1 for shield also apply to ISO 4903. Similarly, the 15-pin interface connector comes from the same family of connectors as the familiar 25-pin connector.

Another major enhancement is the result of careful assignment of interchange circuits to connector pin numbers. The pin assignments provide for the connection of interchange circuits to multipaired interconnecting cable so that each interchange circuit operates over a pair. Of particular importance is the use of two wires for each interchange circuit even when interworking between a DTE using X.26 electrical characteristics and a DCE using X.27 electrical characteristics. This eliminates the need for either options inside the equipment or a special interface cord which connects certain pins together. Also, this provides a performance level when interworking which approximates the performance level when X.27 is used by both equipments.

3) Functional:

Another objective in the design of Recommendation X.21 was to considerably reduce the number of interchange circuits while at the same time folding into the interface the automatic calling function. Thus, as illustrated pictorially in Figure 9, X.21 contains five basic interchange circuits. A transmit (T) circuit and a receive (R) circuit are used to convey both user data and network control information depending on the state of the control (C) circuit and the indication (I) circuit. Bit timing is continuously provided by a signal element timing (S) circuit. A sixth interchange circuit which provides byte timing information is optional. A signal ground circuit is also provided. Detailed definitions of these interchange circuits are contained in CCITT Recommendation X.24.

---

* CCITT Recommendation X.1 specifies data rates of 600, 2400, 4800, 9600, and 48,000 bits/s for Recommendation X.21.

4) Procedural:

As mentioned earlier, some of the procedures in X.21 may be considered above the physical level. However, the procedures associated with the quiescent phase of X.21 are generally agreed to be within the physical level. Two quiescent signals are defined for the DCE: *DCE not ready* and *DCE ready*.

- *DCE not ready* indicates that no service is available. It is signaled whenever possible during network fault conditions and when network test loops are activated. *DCE not ready* is signaled with continuous binary 0 on circuit R and the OFF condition on circuit I.
- *DCE ready* indicates that the DCE (network) is ready to enter operational phases. *DCE ready* is signaled with continuous binary 1 on circuit R and the OFF condition on circuit I.

A major feature incorporated into X.21 is the definition of three quiescent signals for the DTE. Two DTE not ready signals are defined to distinguish between a nonoperational DTE and a condition in which the DTE is operational but is temporarily out of service.

- *DTE uncontrolled not ready* indicates that the DTE is unable to enter operational phases because of an abnormal condition. *DTE uncontrolled not ready* is signaled with continuous binary 0 on circuit T and the OFF condition on circuit C.

- *DTE controlled not ready* indicates that, although the DTE is operational, the DTE is temporarily unable to enter operational phases. *DTE controlled not ready* is signaled with a continuous bit stream of alternate binary 0 and binary 1 bits (i.e., 0101...) on circuit T and the OFF condition on circuit C.

- *DTE ready* indicates that the DTE is ready to enter operational phases. *DTE ready* is signaled with continuous binary 1 on circuit T and the OFF condition on circuit C.

To insure proper detection of these signals, X.21 requires that the DTE and DCE be prepared to send these signals for a period of at least 24 bit intervals. Detection of these signals for 16 contiguous bit intervals is required.

The various combinations of the two DCE quiescent signals and the three DTE quiescent signals provide for the six quiescent states of the X.21 interface as shown in Figure 10. The implementations of X.21 by some networks do not allow all the possible transitions between these states. Therefore, Figure 10 only shows those transitions that are valid for all networks.

X.21 also contains provisions to insure proper interpretation of the interface under fault conditions (e.g., power off, disconnection of the interface cable, failure of an interchange circuit, and loss of incoming line signal to the DCE). Finally, X.21 (and X.150) defines the interface state for each of the various maintenance test loops.

IV. THE FUTURE

The preceding sections have reviewed the basic characteristics of the physical level and have described two recently standardized DTE/DCE interfaces. However, one should not assume that the physical level work is complete. In fact, three major activities are presently underway:

- direct DTE-to-DTE operation,
- tandem DCE-to-DCE operation, and
- "universal" DTE/DCE interface and the "mini" interface.

The first activity is being pursued with both EIA RS-449 and with CCITT Recommendations X.20 and X.21. Present thinking for synchronous interfaces is to use a data, timing, and control circuit in each direction with a simple crossover adapter between the two DTEs. Asynchronous interfaces would omit the timing circuits and, for X.20, also omit the control circuits. This arrangement is straightforward for EIA RS-449 and CCITT X.20 but requires the addition of a new timing interchange circuit for the X.21 DTE. A draft standard based on this thinking is presently being voted on by the ISO [29].

The second activity is being spurred by the multiplexing capability provided by the 9600 bits/s modem specified in CCITT Recommendation V.29 [8]. Tandem DCE-to-DCE operation would allow any number of the derived channels from the V.29 modem to be extended to a distant location by means of a pair of modems. The principal issue is which interchange circuits need to be interconnected through a simple crossover adapter and the proper slaving of the timing circuits in the DCEs. These issues are presently being addressed in CCITT Study Group XVII. The third activity is the most ambitious of the three. The objective is to define a single "universal" DTE/DCE interface suitable for use on both public data networks and on telephone networks. This interface would include the automatic calling capability and utilize only a small number of interchange circuits.

The major driving force for the "mini" interface for modems is to reduce the cost of the interface by reducing the number of interchange circuits. This translates to the elimination of the separate ACE interface, fewer wires in the interface cable, a smaller connector, and fewer generators/receivers. The X.21 interface has been proposed as a candidate for the "mini" interface but there are several significant problems. One major problem is the significant reduction in throughput for half-duplex operation and for multipoint polling systems [30]. This occurs since X.21 does not provide immediate recognition of a specific control signal. That is, X.21 requires the recognition of a bit pattern in contrast to the instant recognition of a signal level on a individual control lead.

A second problem with using X.21 is the loss of functionality because there is no means to pass control information during data transfer. Two examples concerning signaling to the DTE while the receive direction is in the data transfer phase illustrate this problem. In this situation, X.21 circuit I is ON (indicating data transfer phase) and circuit R carries user data. Thus, there is no way to convey to the DTE information about the receive direction, such as Signal Quality (RS-232-C circuit CG, RS-449 circuit SQ and V.24 circuit 110). In addition, there is no way to convey to the DTE information about the transmit direction, such as Clear to Send (RS-232-C circuit CA, RS-449 circuit CS and V.24 circuit 105). The impact of this latter problem is illustrated by a centralized multipoint system operating with the use of continuous carrier from the master station. After the remote DTE detects its poll, it responds by turning circuit C ON (a function equivalent to Request to Send in present day modems). However, as discussed above, there is no means to convey to the DTE when the DCE is prepared to accept data (i.e., the Clear to Send function). Since this time interval varies with modem type, this loss of capability is significant.

Other flexibilities of the EIA RS-232-C and RS-449 interfaces, such as separate send and receive timing circuits, would be lost if X.21 were used without change. Also, quite a few RS-232-C, RS-449 and V.24 interchange circuit functions that apply outside of the data transfer phase are not presently accommodated by X.21. Examples include data signaling rate selection, selection and indication of standby facilities, select frequency and loopback testing. Either these functions will be lost or X.21 must be modified to accommodate them. In addition, a way must be provided for handling a secondary channel. A separate connector for the secondary channel will probably be needed.

An alternative proposal for the "mini" interface, called the encoded control approach, was introduced by the U. S. in June, 1981 [31]. This proposal reduces the number of interchange circuits to two in each direction plus signal ground. Only customer data appears on the two data circuits and all control information is exchanged on the two control circuits via time division multiplexing techniques. Time-critical control functions are serviced more often to avoid throughput penalties. All present control functions, including the auto calling functions, are accommodated along with spare capacity for expanded functions. Timing information is imbedded in the data and control circuits in each direction via differential Manchester encoding. Balanced electrical characteristics (V.11) and a 9-pin interface connector are used in a manner which facilitates DTE-DCE, DTE-DTE and DCE-DCE operation.

While this alternative approach has many attractive attributes, it also has draw-backs. Differential Manchester encoding doubles the signalling rate across the interface and the control circuits need to operate at eight times the rate of the data circuits to avoid a throughput penalty. This reduces the interface cable distance at the higher data rates and reduces the maximum interface data rate. Also, it is a completely new interface - it is not compatible with any existing equipment.

The debate is continuing both nationally (EIA, ANSI) and internationally (ISO, CCITT). Some favor the immediate adoption of a modified version of X.21 for the "mini" interface so as to achieve the "universal" interface objective. Modifications to X.21 are proposed to reduce or eliminate some of the drawbacks cited above but a fully "universal" interface is not achieved since an X.21 "mini" interface used for asynchronous operation does not align with the public data network asynchronous interface (X.20). Others feel that the encoded control approach offers a quantum step forward and is flexible to accommodate future needs as they become identified. Still others prefer to retain the status quo pending development of the interface requirements for the Integrated Services Digital Network by CCITT. They are concerned about standardizing a "mini" interface which may have a short life.

At this point in time, the only certainty is that the debate will continue. However, it is hoped that the strong desire that has been expressed for the "universal" interface will lead to the necessary agreements in the 1980's.

V. REFERENCES

[1] CCITT Recommendation X.25, in CCITT Orange Book, vol. VIII. 2 (Public data networks), 1977.

[2] CCITT COM VII No. R6, Appendix 1 to Annex 4, "Proposed draft recommendation - Reference model for public data network applications," May, 1981.

[3] ISO Draft Proposal 7498, "Data processing - Open systems interconnection - Basic reference model," December, 1980.

[4] ISO/TC97/SC6 N2132, "Physical layer and physical media for OSI," October, 1980.

[5] EIA Standard RS-232-C. "Interface between data terminal equipment and data communication equipment employing serial binary data interchange," August, 1969.

[6] EIA Standard RS-449. "General purpose 37-position and 9-position interface for data terminal equipment and data circuit-terminating equipment employing serial binary data interchange," November, 1977, and Addendum 1 to RS-449, February, 1980.

[7] CCITT X-Series Recommendations, in CCITT Yellow Book, vols. VIII.2 and VIII.3, (Data Communication networks), 1981.

[8] CCITT V-Series Recommendations, in CCITT Yellow Book, vol. VIII.1 (Data communication over the telephone networks), 1981.

[9] EIA Standard RS-366-A, "Interface between data terminal equipment and automatic calling equipment for data communication," March, 1979.

[10] EIA Standard RS-269-B, "Synchronous signaling rates for data transmission," January, 1976.

[11] ANSI X3.1, "Synchronous signaling rates for data transmission," 1976.

[12] ANSI X3.36, "Synchronous high-speed data signaling rates between data terminal equipment and data communication equipment," 1975.

[13] EIA Standard RS-334, "Signal quality at interface between data processing terminal equipment and synchronous data communication equipment for serial data transmission," March, 1967.

[14] EIA Standard RS-363, "Standard for specifying signal quality for transmitting and receiving data processing terminal equipments using serial data transmission at the interface with non-synchronous data communication equipment, May, 1969.

[15] EIA Standard RS-404, "Standard for start-stop signal quality between data terminal equipment and non-synchronous data communication equipment," March, 1973.

[16] ISO Draft International Standard 7480, "Start-stop transmission signal quality at DTE/DCE interfaces," October, 1980.

[17] ISO International Standard 2110, "Data communication - 25-pin DTE/DCE interface connector and pin assignments" (Revision of ISO 2110-1972), 1980.

[18] ISO International Standard 2593, "Connector pin allocations for use with high-speed terminal equipment," 1973 (being revised as "Data communication - 34-pin DTE/DCE interface connector and pin assignments, DIS 2593, October, 1980).

[19] ISO International Standard 4902, "Data communication - 37-pin and 9-pin DTE/DCE interface connectors and pin assignments," 1980.

[20] ISO International Standard 4903, "Data communication - 15-pin DTE/DCE interface connector and pin assignments," 1980.

[21] EIA Standard RS-422-A, "Electrical characteristics of balanced voltage digital interface circuits," December, 1978.

[22] EIA Standard RS-423-A, "Electrical characteristics of unbalanced voltage digital interface circuits," December, 1978.

[23] FED-STD 1030, "Electrical characteristics of unbalanced voltage digital interface circuits," September, 1975.

[24] MIL-STD 188-114, "Electrical characteristics of digital interface circuits," March, 1976.

[25] FED-STD 1020, "Electrical characteristics of balanced voltage digital interface circuits," September, 1975.

[26] EIA Standard RS-410, "Standard for the electrical characteristics of Class A closure interchange circuits," April, 1974.

[27] EIA Industrial Electronics Bulletin No. 9, "Application notes for EIA Standard RS-232-C," May, 1971.

[28] EIA Industrial Electronics Bulletin No. 12, "Application notes on interconnection between interface circuits using RS-449 and RS-232-C," November, 1977.

[29] ISO Draft International Standard 7477, "Requirements for DTE to DTE physical connection," October, 1980.

[30] CCITT COM XVII No. 214, U.S. contribution, "Methods of control information interchange for the mini-interface," October, 1979.

[31] U.S. working paper to ISO/TC97/SC6/WG3 "Approaches to the DTE/DCE physical interface," June, 1981.

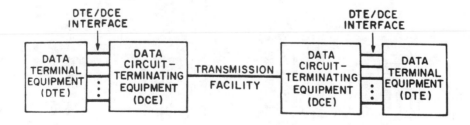

FIGURE 1   DTE/DCE INTERFACE

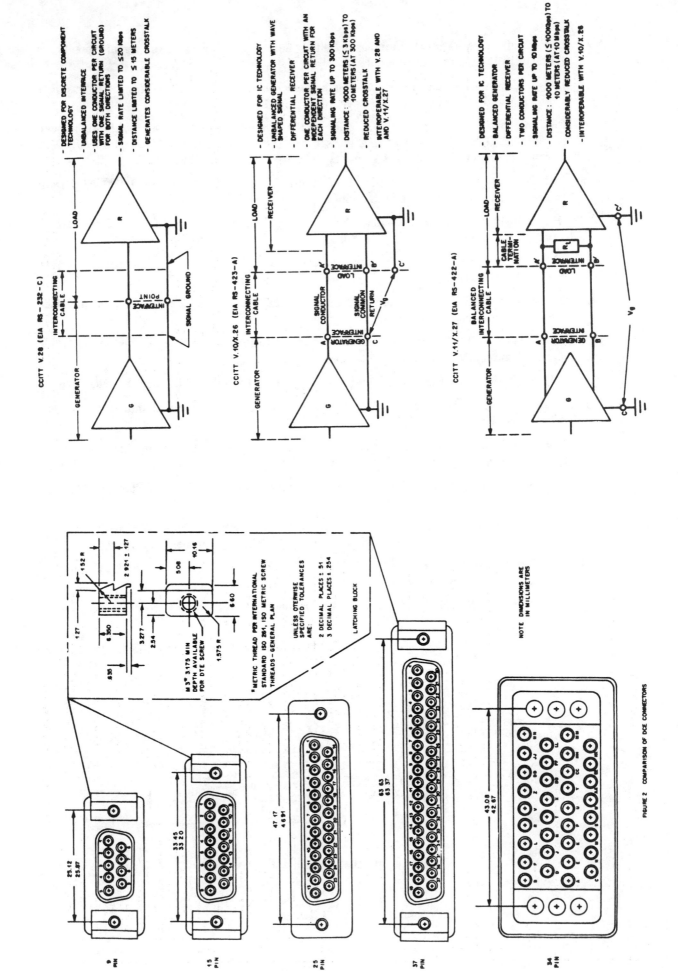

FIGURE 2   COMPARISON OF DCE CONNECTORS

NOTE DIMENSIONS ARE IN MILLIMETERS

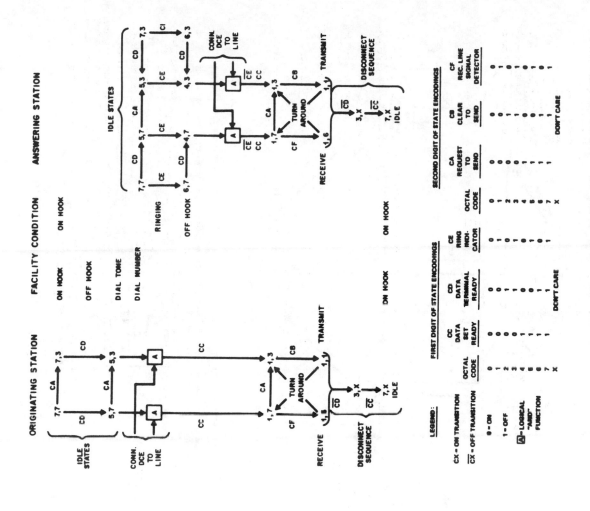

FIGURE 6 EIA RS-232-C CONTROL LEAD SEQUENCES FOR HALF DUPLEX OPERATION ON SWITCHED SERVICE

FIGURE 4
SIGNAL STATE CORRELATION TABLE

BINARY	1	0
DATA	MARK	SPACE
CONTROL	OFF	ON

CIRCUIT		NAME	DIRECTION	DESCRIPTION
GROUND	AA	PROTECTIVE GROUND		ELECTRICALLY BONDS TOGETHER THE EQUIPMENT FRAMES
	AB	SIGNAL GROUND OR COMMON RETURN		ESTABLISHES THE COMMON GROUND REFERENCE POTENTIAL FOR ALL INTERCHANGE CIRCUITS
DATA	BA	TRANSMITTED DATA	TO DCE	CONVEYS DATA SIGNALS FOR TRANSMISSION TO THE COMMUNICATIONS CHANNEL
	BB	RECEIVED DATA	TO DTE	CONVEYS DATA SIGNALS RECEIVED FROM THE COMMUNICATIONS CHANNEL
CONTROL	CA	REQUEST TO SEND	TO DCE	REQUESTS ABILITY TO TRANSMIT DATA TO THE COMMUNICATIONS CHANNEL
	CB	CLEAR TO SEND	TO DTE	INDICATES WHETHER OR NOT THE DCE IS READY TO TRANSMIT DATA TO THE COMMUNICATIONS CHANNEL
	CC	DATA SET READY	TO DTE	INDICATES WHETHER OR NOT THE DCE IS IN THE DATA MODE
	CD	DATA TERMINAL READY	TO DCE	CONTROLS THE SWITCHING OF THE DCE TO AND FROM THE COMMUNICATIONS CHANNEL
	CE	RING INDICATOR	TO DTE	INDICATES WHETHER OR NOT A "RINGING SIGNAL" IS BEING RECEIVED BY THE DCE
	CF	RECEIVED LINE SIGNAL DETECTOR	TO DTE	INDICATES WHETHER OR NOT THE DCE IS RECEIVING A LINE SIGNAL FROM THE COMMUNICATIONS CHANNEL
	CG	SIGNAL QUALITY DETECTOR	TO DTE	INDICATES WHETHER OR NOT THERE IS A HIGH PROBABILITY OF ERROR IN THE RECEIVED DATA
	CH	DATA SIGNAL RATE SELECTOR (DTE SOURCE)	TO DCE	SELECTS BETWEEN TWO DATA SIGNALING RATES OR RANGES OF RATES
	CI	DATA SIGNAL RATE SELECTOR (DCE SOURCE)	TO DTE	INDICATES ONE OF TWO DATA SIGNALING RATES OR RANGES OF RATES
TIMING	DA	TRANSMITTER SIGNAL ELEMENT TIMING (DTE SOURCE)	TO DCE	PROVIDES TIMING SIGNALS FOR TRANSMITTED DATA
	DB	TRANSMITTER SIGNAL ELEMENT TIMING (DCE SOURCE)	TO DTE	PROVIDES TIMING SIGNALS FOR TRANSMITTED DATA
	DD	RECEIVER SIGNAL ELEMENT TIMING (DCE SOURCE)	TO DTE	PROVIDES TIMING SIGNALS FOR RECEIVED DATA
SECONDARY	SBA	SECONDARY TRANSMITTED DATA	TO DCE	EQUIVALENT TO CIRCUIT BA EXCEPT IT APPLIES TO THE SECONDARY CHANNEL
	SBB	SECONDARY RECEIVED DATA	TO DTE	EQUIVALENT TO CIRCUIT BB EXCEPT IT APPLIES TO THE SECONDARY CHANNEL
	SCA	SECONDARY REQUEST TO SEND	TO DCE	EQUIVALENT TO CIRCUIT CA EXCEPT IT APPLIES TO THE SECONDARY CHANNEL
	SCB	SECONDARY CLEAR TO SEND	TO DTE	EQUIVALENT TO CIRCUIT CB EXCEPT IT APPLIES TO THE SECONDARY CHANNEL
	SCF	SECONDARY RECEIVED LINE SIGNAL DETECTOR	TO DTE	EQUIVALENT TO CIRCUIT CF EXCEPT IT APPLIES TO THE SECONDARY CHANNEL

FIGURE 5 EIA RS-232-C INTERCHANGE CIRCUITS

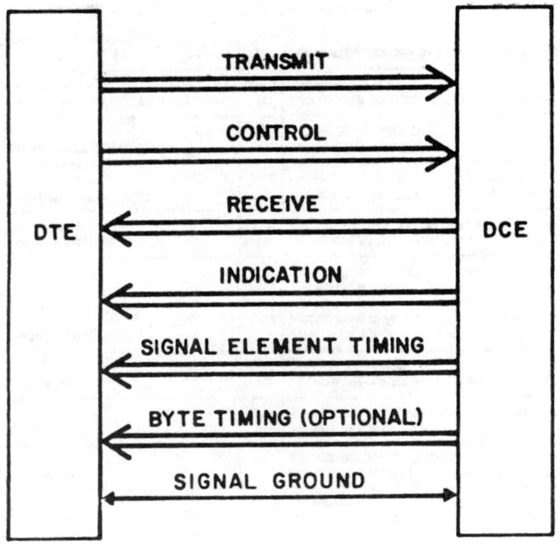

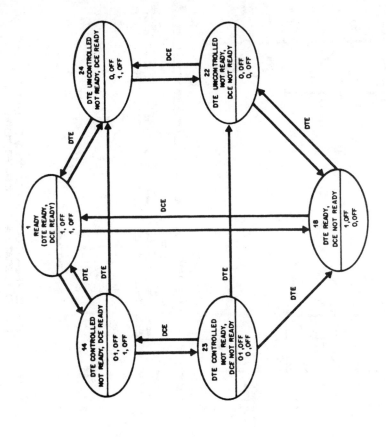

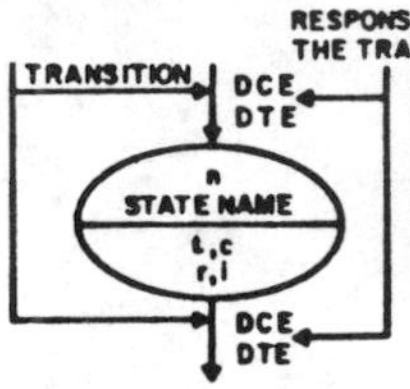

RESPONSIBLE FOR
THE TRANSITION

t = SIGNAL ON T CIRCUIT
c = SIGNAL ON C CIRCUIT
r = SIGNAL ON R CIRCUIT
i = SIGNAL ON I CIRCUIT
n = STATE NUMBER
T = TRANSMIT INTERCHANGE CIRCUIT
C = CONTROL INTERCHANGE CIRCUIT
R = RECEIVE INTERCHANGE CIRCUIT
I = INDICATION INTERCHANGE CIRCUIT

0 AND 1 = REFER TO STEADY BINARY CONDITIONS
01 = REFERS TO ALTERNATE BINARY 0 AND BINARY 1 CONDITIONS
OFF AND ON = RESPECTIVELY REFER TO CONTINUOUS OFF (BINARY 1) AND ON (BINARY 0) CONDITIONS

FIGURE 10 CCITT RECOMMENDATION X.21 QUIESCENT STATES

FIGURE 9 CCITT RECOMMENDATION X.21 DTE/DCE INTERFACE

DCE

TRANSMIT
CONTROL
RECEIVE
INDICATION
SIGNAL ELEMENT TIMING
BYTE TIMING (OPTIONAL)
SIGNAL GROUND

DTE

120

CATEGORY I CIRCUITS – DATA SIGNALING RATE ≤ 20,000 BITS PER SECOND

CATEGORY I CIRCUITS – DATA SIGNALING RATE > 20,000 BITS PER SECOND

CATEGORY II CIRCUITS

NOTE: THE A, A', B, B', C AND C' DESIGNATIONS ARE THOSE SPECIFIED IN RS-422-A AND RS-423-A

* OPTIONAL CABLE TERMINATION RESISTANCE

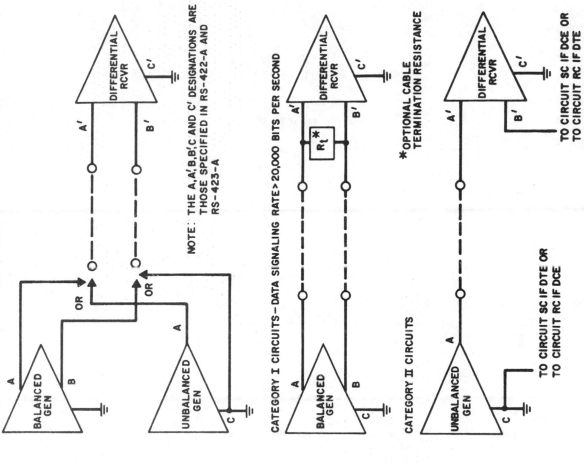

FIGURE 8 EIA RS-449 INTERFACE CONNECTIONS OF GENERATORS AND RECEIVERS

	EIA RS-449		EIA RS-232-C		CCITT RECOMMENDATION V-24
SG	SIGNAL GROUND	AB	SIGNAL GROUND OR COMMON RET.	102	SIGNAL GROUND OR COMMON RET.
SC	SEND COMMON			102a	DTE COMMON RETURN
RC	RECEIVE COMMON			102b	DCE COMMON RETURN
IS	TERMINAL IN SERVICE				
IC	INCOMING CALL	CE	RING INDICATOR	125	CALLING INDICATOR
TR	TERMINAL READY	CD	DATA TERMINAL READY	108/2	DATA TERMINAL READY
DM	DATA MODE	CC	DATA SET READY	107	DATA SET READY
SD	SEND DATA	BA	TRANSMITTED DATA	103	TRANSMITTED DATA
RD	RECEIVE DATA	BB	RECEIVED DATA	104	RECEIVED DATA
TT	TERMINAL TIMING	DA	TRANSMITTER SIGNAL ELEMENT TIMING (DTE SOURCE)	113	TRANSMITTER SIGNAL ELEMENT TIMING (DTE SOURCE)
ST	SEND TIMING	DB	TRANSMITTER SIGNAL ELEMENT TIMING (DCE SOURCE)	114	TRANSMITTER SIGNAL ELEMENT TIMING (DCE SOURCE)
RT	RECEIVE TIMING	DD	RECEIVER SIGNAL ELEMENT TIMING	115	RECEIVER SIGNAL ELEMENT TIMING (DCE SOURCE)
RS	REQUEST TO SEND	CA	REQUEST TO SEND	105	REQUEST TO SEND
CS	CLEAR TO SEND	CB	CLEAR TO SEND	106	READY FOR SENDING
RR	RECEIVER READY	CF	RECEIVED LINE SIGNAL DETECTOR	109	DATA CHANNEL RECEIVED LINE SIGNAL DETECTOR
SQ	SIGNAL QUALITY	CG	SIGNAL QUALITY DETECTOR	110	DATA SIGNAL QUALITY DETECTOR
NS	NEW SIGNAL			136	NEW SIGNAL
SF	SELECT FREQUENCY			126	SELECT TRANSMIT FREQUENCY
SR	SIGNALING RATE SELECTOR	CH	DATA SIGNAL RATE SELECTOR (DTE SOURCE)	111	DATA SIGNALING RATE SELECTOR (DTE SOURCE)
SI	SIGNALING RATE INDICATOR	CI	DATA SIGNAL RATE SELECTOR (DCE SOURCE)	112	DATA SIGNALING RATE SELECTOR (DCE SOURCE)
SSD	SECONDARY SEND DATA	SBA	SECONDARY TRANSMITTED DATA	118	TRANSMITTED BACKWARD CHANNEL DATA
SRD	SECONDARY RECEIVE DATA	SBB	SECONDARY RECEIVED DATA	119	RECEIVED BACKWARD CHANNEL DATA
SRS	SECONDARY REQUEST TO SEND	SCA	SECONDARY REQUEST TO SEND	120	TRANSMIT BACKWARD CHANNEL LINE SIGNAL
SCS	SECONDARY CLEAR TO SEND	SCB	SECONDARY CLEAR TO SEND	121	BACKWARD CHANNEL READY
SRR	SECONDARY RECEIVER READY	SCF	SECONDARY RECEIVED LINE SIGNAL DETECTOR	122	BACKWARD CHANNEL RECEIVED LINE SIGNAL DETECTOR
LL	LOCAL LOOPBACK			141	LOCAL LOOPBACK
RL	REMOTE LOOPBACK			140	LOOPBACK/MAINTENANCE TEST
TM	TEST MODE			142	TEST INDICATOR
SS	SELECT STANDBY			116	SELECT STANDBY
SB	STANDBY INDICATOR			117	STANDBY INDICATOR

FIGURE 7 EQUIVALENCY OF INTERCHANGE CIRCUITS

ERRATA FOR
PHYSICAL LEVEL INTERFACES AND PROTOCOLS

H. V. BERTINE

p2, 5 lines from bottom:
   Chapter. ---> paper.

p3, 3rd bullet:
   37/9-pin connectors ---> 37-pin and 9-pin connectors

p6, 3rd line before Section III:
   discussed. ---> discussed in the Introduction.

p6, last line:
   lead ---> led

Figure 7:
   add in the CCITT Recommendation V.24 column in the same row as NS NEW SIGNAL : 136 NEW
   SIGNAL

A powerful standard replaces the old interface standby

Harold C. Folts, National Communications System, Arlington, Va.

Emphasizing evolution not revolution, the EIA developed RS-449 to supplant RS-232-C. The newer standard enables higher data rates, greater cable lengths, and more interface functions.

The Electronic Industries Association (EIA) RS-232-C standard has served long and well as the physical interface for data communications applications. However, advancing technology and users' demands have exceeded its capacity to meet current operational requirements effectively, so the EIA has devised the more powerful RS-449.

Why is the RS-449 standard needed? When the EIA began to develop a new series of interface standards in 1972, it recognized a number of serious limiting factors in RS-232-C. These problems include:

- An upper data-rate limit of only 20 kbit/s
- A cable-length limit of only 15 meters (50 feet)
- A proliferation of mechanical interface designs with many incompatibilities
- Inclusion by many manufacturers of nonstandard interface circuits with arbitrary pin assignments
- Inconsistent uses of functional control circuits (for example, CA, CB, CC, and CF—described in Table 2)
- Insufficient capacity to control additional loop-test functions for fault isolation.

As a result of these limitations, users are unable to realize expanded operational performance, with, say, increased data rate and cable length. Also, they are not assured that one manufacturer's device will work properly with one from another manufacturer through an RS-232-C interface.

RS-449, like RS-232-C, specifies the interface between data terminal equipment (DTE) and data circuit-terminating equipment (DCE). The DCE is essentially a modem for data transmission over an analog, or telephone, circuit, while the DTE can be anything from a simple keyboard terminal to a sophisticated host computer or a subnetwork.

RS-449—at one time called RS-XYZ—has been carefully structured to support higher data rates (up to 2 Mbit/s) and increased interface cable distances (60 to 1,200 meters or 200 to 4,000 feet). Most important, the new standard provides an economical, orderly transition from the vast inventory of RS-232-C equipment in current operation to the evolving products of the future. Existing equipment can remain operational, giving it a more cost-effective lifetime, as the RS-449 equipment is phased into operation. RS-232-C gear will not suddenly be obsolete.

An interesting dichotomy of feeling exists regarding the introduction of RS-449. On one hand, some manufacturers are reluctant to implement it because many applications will still be able to be supported effectively by RS-232-C. Some people maintain that a more dramatic future advancement in interface characteristics, based on new standards work presently under way, is better justification for incorporating product changes. The utility of an *evolutionary* philosophy to accommodate an advancing technology is not nearly as appealing to some interests as the introduction of a *revolutionary,* streamlined interface that would compel users to retrofit or replace equipment.

On the other hand, there is strong sentiment, particularly from the user community, that significant improvements in operating capability must be specified now for the data communications interfaces. But an interface standard must continue to facilitate efficient transmission of data over telephone and voice-grade lines—which will remain in use for quite some time in the future. A transition to new technology is most welcome if it neither forces existing equipment into disuse nor reduces transmission efficiency.

Another feeling, in the middle, is one of "wait and see." Although possibly a nuisance for some manufacturers, if several companies adopt RS-449, the rest will follow suit. There is yet not enough user interest in the marketplace to motivate manufacturers, creating the typical "chicken and egg" dilemma. Until users are aware of RS-449 and its benefits, they won't demand equipment that is compatible with it.

Implementations of RS-449 are now starting to appear, however, as exemplified by the Bell System's Dataphone II modems and a few other announcements in the trade journals. On the user side, the Government has adopted RS-449 as Federal Standard 1031, which becomes mandatory for all procurements by federal agencies starting June 1, 1980. The orderly evolution is now gaining momentum with RS-449, so a painful revolution can be avoided in the future.

New compatibilities

While RS-232-C is complete in itself—containing the electrical, functional, and mechanical characteristics—the new series combines greatly expanded specifications in three standards: RS-422-A, RS-423-A, and RS-449. The latter serves as the basic interface document, referring to the electrical characteristics of RS-422-A and RS-423-A, as appropriate, for each type of interface circuit and its associated data rate. The functional characteristics follow the same philosophy as RS-232-C, which uses a separate circuit for each interface function. Eight new functions have been added to RS-449 to meet new operational requirements. These functions, together with extra wires for balanced electrical operation, have made it necessary to specify different connectors with increased pin capacity.

The CCITT achieved international compatibility by adopting recommendations equivalent to RS-449 and

1. Balancing act. *The balanced configuration uses differential signaling over a wire pair. The unbalanced one signals over one wire per circuit, with a shared return.*

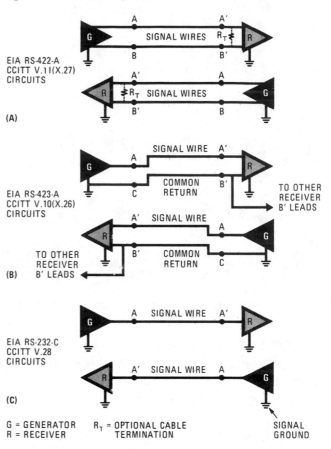

G = GENERATOR   R_T = OPTIONAL CABLE
R = RECEIVER   TERMINATION   SIGNAL GROUND

to a standard in the International Organization for Standardization (ISO). The relationships of equivalent EIA, federal, and CCITT/ISO standards are shown in Table 1. RS-232-C also has international equivalents, but incompatibilities similar to those already mentioned exist here as well.

The electrical characteristics specified by RS-422-A and RS-423-A are intended to provide both better transmission performance than RS-232-C's and features for economical implementation in integrated-circuit technology. The new standards deal with the traditional serial-binary switch-signals of the two d.c. voltage levels across the interface.

Balanced and unbalanced

In order to facilitate the evolution to the next generation of equipment, the EIA developed interface characteristics for both balanced and unbalanced circuitry. RS-422-A specifies electrically balanced receivers and generators that tolerate more—and produce less—noise to provide superior performance up to 10 Mbit/s and to meet even more-demanding requirements in the future. RS-423-A stipulates unbalanced operation with a transmission capability of up to 100 kbit/s and is operable with both RS-232-C and RS-422-A, thus facilitating evolution.

The various configurations are illustrated in Figure

Table 1   Standards counterparts

EIA	FEDERAL	CCITT RECOMMENDATIONS (ELECTRICAL/ FUNCTIONAL)	+ ISO (MECHANICAL)
RS-423-A	1030A	V.10(X.26)	---
RS-422-A	1020A	V.11(X.27)	---
RS-449	1031	V.24/V.10/V.11	4902
RS-232-C	NONE	V.24/V.28	2110

1. The balanced one employs differential signaling over a pair of wires for each circuit. The unbalanced configuration signals over one wire for each circuit and uses a common return circuit. There is a noteworthy difference between the unbalanced operation of RS-232-C and RS-423-A. RS-232-C uses a single-ended receiver with the signal ground providing the common return path. RS-423-A uses a balanced differential receiver with the common return connected to signal ground at the generator end only. This gives improved performance in the presence of noise. Effectively, the longer the circuit, the more balanced it becomes.

One problem associated with unbalanced circuits is noise due to signal transitions. RS-232-C requires that signal rise time not exceed 3 percent of the bit duration. Such a sharp signal produces considerable noise problems. RS-423-A, on the other hand, allows a rise-time figure up to 30 percent slower.

The plots of cable length versus data rate for RS-423-A (Fig. 2) are based on a rise-time characteristic that allows a maximum generator-end crosstalk (noise coupled between adjacent circuits) of a 1-volt peak. Two rise-time forms are indicated: exponential and linear. The linear form—Implemented within the chips—is expected to be more commonly employed.

The 10 percent (rise-time/bit-duration) exponential curve is the same as that described in the original issue of RS-423. The 30 percent exponential curve has been translated from the standard's "A" revision. The 30 percent linear curve is a further translation, a 2.3 improvement factor over the exponential one. Although an upper limit of 100 kbit/s is shown, higher signaling rates are possible; the only limiting factor is the operating speed of particular integrated circuits.

The balanced electrical characteristics of RS-422-A provide even better performance, as shown in Figure 2. Top performance is realized with an optional cable termination of approximately 120 ohms in the receiver load (Fig. 1A). The other balanced curve depicts the equivalent specification in CCITT Recommendation V.11, without the cable termination in the load. Performance is reduced because of reflections from the load and consequent signal degradation. These curves, however, are very conservative for RS-422-A balanced operation. Actually, *kilometers* (miles) of cable distances for the lower data rates can be realized with good engineering practice.

Another significant feature of RS-422-A and RS-423-A is that both specify the same balanced differential receiver, although transmission originates from different types of generators. This provides an essential commonality to facilitate the evolution from RS-232-C. RS-449 exploits this common feature by specifying two categories of circuit configurations.

Implementing the transition

Category I circuits connect the A′ and B′ terminations (Fig. 1) of each receiver with a pair of wires to the generator. As shown in Figure 3A, either a balanced or unbalanced generator can be directly connected in a Category I circuit for data rates of 20 kbit/s and below. When operability with RS-232-C is desired, RS-423-A generators should be implemented; otherwise, RS-422-A generators can be used. Note that even with RS-423-A generators, the operating performance approaches that of fully balanced circuits.

Category II circuits apply only to RS-423-A. They employ a shared common-return circuit from the B′

---

2. Performing better. *The highest data rate is realized with RS-422-A balanced transmission and a cable termination of 120 ohms (Fig 1A). The RS-423-A plots are* *based on a rise-time characteristic that allows a maximum generator-end crosstalk of 1-volt peak. The linear rise-time form is expected to be more commonly employed.*

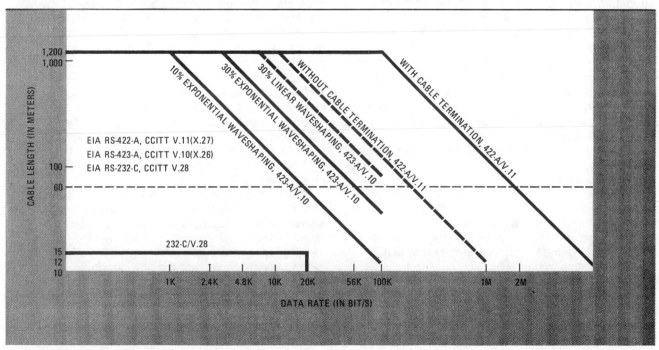

3. Categorizing the circuits. *For Category I, either a balanced or unbalanced generator can be directly connected. For Category II, only unbalanced apply.*

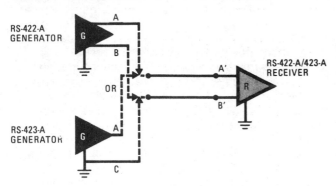

(A) CATEGORY I CIRCUIT

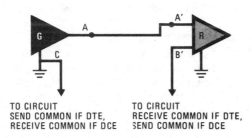

TO CIRCUIT
SEND COMMON IF DTE,
RECEIVE COMMON IF DCE

TO CIRCUIT
RECEIVE COMMON IF DTE,
SEND COMMON IF DCE

(B) CATEGORY II CIRCUIT

lead of each receiver on one side of the interface to signal ground on the interface's generator side (Fig. 3B). There is one common return for each direction of transmission, as detailed in Figure 1B.

The Category I configuration applies to circuits that carry the data signals or the control functions that must respond rapidly. Category II circuits, which minimize the number of wires in the interface, are used for all other control functions that are not sensitive to fast response times.

All but one functional circuit of the earlier standard were retained by RS-449. Some circuit names, however, were revised, and mnemonics were devised to easily identify them. Table 2 lists the RS-449 circuits plus the equivalent RS-232-C and CCITT circuits.

Circuit AA (protective ground) of RS-232-C was omitted because of a conflict in National Electric Code requirements. In its place, RS-449 provides for a cable-shield connection, when used.

Several circuits were added to enrich the functionality of the interface and to accommodate the new common-return circuits for RS-423:

■ Send Common (SC) provides the signal-common-return path from the B′ receiver leads in the DCE to the signal ground in the DTE.

■ Receiver Common (RC) enables the signal-common-return path from the B′ receiver leads in the DTE to the signal ground in the DCE.

■ Terminal in Service (IS) indicates to the DCE that the DTE is operational. This can make busy a port on

a trunk's hunting group when the DTE is out of service.

■ New Signal (NS) tells the DCE when to prepare to acquire a new incoming signal from a remote station. This improves the overall response time in multipoint polling networks. (The function of this circuit was revised from the original RS-449 because of a subsequent agreement in CCITT. An addendum, RS-449-1, was issued with this change in February 1980.)

■ Select Frequency (SF) indicates to the DCE which receive and transmit frequencies to employ in a multipoint circuit where all stations have equal status.

■ Local Loopback (LL) requests loopback initiation of transmitted signals to the receive circuit within the local DCE. This checks the functioning of the local interface and DCE.

■ Remote Loopback (RL) requests loopback initiation of signals in the remote DCE, which tests the operation of the transmission channel and remote DCE.

■ Test Mode (TM) relays to the DTE that a test condition has been established involving the local DCE.

■ Select Standby (SS) requests the DCE to transfer to alternate standby communications facilities. This assists rapid restoral of service failures.

■ Standby Indicator (SB) indicates to the DTE that standby facilities are in use.

The procedures for circuit operation are essentially action-reaction types and are described in RS-449. For example, circuit CS (clear to send) turns on, after the modem is initialized, in response to RS (request to send) turning on. Circuit TM (test mode) turns on after the loop in the DCE is established in response to LL (local loopback) turning on. No state diagrams are presented in RS-449 to further describe the procedures, but reference to EIA Industrial Electronics Bulletin No. 9 for RS-232-C provides a useful guide.

Mechanical expansion

The additional functional circuits and wires for Category I expand the requirements beyond the capacity of the 25-pin RS-232-C connector. After careful research, EIA decided to stay with the style of connector that has proved quite satisfactory. Therefore, it selected the 37-pin connector—the same type as the 25-pin—for the primary channel interchange circuits.

If secondary channel operation is to be used for acknowledgments or as a low-speed TTY channel, a separate nine-pin connector is also needed. However, the use of secondary channels is expected to diminish considerably in the future, and the inclusion of the second connector was one result of an international compromise in CCITT.

Most applications will use only the 37-pin connector. The thought of this connector's probable size has overstimulated the imaginations of many. To visualize the relative sizes of the 25-pin "mouse" and the 37-pin "elephant," consider the following: the widths and depths are the same, and the new connector is about ⅝-inch longer than the 2-⅛-inch older one. As well as supplying additional pin capacity, the bigger connector prevents accidental connection to RS-232-C equipment without proper protection.

The pin assignments shown in Table 2 for the inter-

Table 2 RS-449 circuits

MNEMONIC	CIRCUIT NAME	CATEGORY	PIN NUMBER	RS-232-C CIRCUIT	CODE	CCITT NUMBER
37-PIN PRIMARY-CHANNEL CONNECTOR						
—	NONE	—	—	PROTECTIVE GROUND	AA	NONE
—	(SHIELD)	—	1	—	—	(SHIELD)
SG	SIGNAL GROUND	—	19	SIGNAL GROUND	AB	102
SC	SEND COMMON	II	37	—	—	102A
RC	RECEIVE COMMON	II	20	—	—	102B
IS	TERMINAL IN SERVICE	II	28	—	—	135
IC	INCOMING CALL	II	15	RING INDICATOR	CE	125
TR	TERMINAL READY	I	12, 30	DATA TERMINAL READY	CD	108
DM	DATA MODE	I	11, 29	DATA SET READY	CC	107
SD	SEND DATA	I	4, 22	TRANSMITTED DATA	BA	103
RD	RECEIVE DATA	I	6, 24	RECEIVED DATA	BB	104
TT	TERMINAL TIMING	I	17, 35	TRANSMITTER-SIGNAL-ELEMENT TIMING (DTE)	DA	113
ST	SEND TIMING	I	5, 23	TRANSMITTER-SIGNAL-ELEMENT TIMING (DCE)	DB	114
RT	RECEIVE TIMING	I	8, 26	RECEIVER-SIGNAL-ELEMENT TIMING	DD	115
RS	REQUEST TO SEND	I	7, 25	REQUEST TO SEND	CA	105
CS	CLEAR TO SEND	I	9, 27	CLEAR TO SEND	CB	106
RR	RECEIVER READY	I	13, 31	RECEIVED-LINE SIGNAL DETECTOR	CF	109
SQ	SIGNAL QUALITY	II	33	SIGNAL-QUALITY DETECTOR	CG	110
NS	NEW SIGNAL	II	34	—	—	136
SF	SELECT FREQUENCY	II	16	—	—	126
SR	SIGNALING-RATE SELECTOR	II	16	DATA-SIGNAL-RATE SELECTOR (DTE)	CH	111
SI	SIGNALING-RATE INDICATOR	II	2	DATA-SIGNAL-RATE SELECTOR (DCE)	CI	112
LL	LOCAL LOOPBACK	II	10	—	—	141
RL	REMOTE LOOPBACK	II	14	—	—	140
TM	TEST MODE	II	18	—	—	142
SS	SELECT STANDBY	II	32	—	—	116
SB	STANDBY INDICATOR	II	36	—	—	117
—	(SPARES)	—	3, 21	—	—	—
9-PIN SECONDARY-CHANNEL CONNECTOR						
—	(SHIELD)	—	1	—	—	(SHIELD)
SG	SIGNAL GROUND	—	5	SIGNAL GROUND	AB	102
SC	SEND COMMON	II	9	—	—	102A
RC	RECEIVE COMMON	II	6	—	—	102B
SSD	SECONDARY SEND DATA	II	3	SECONDARY TRANSMITTED DATA	SBA	118
SRD	SECONDARY RECEIVE DATA	II	4	SECONDARY RECEIVED DATA	SBB	119
SRS	SECONDARY REQUEST TO SEND	II	7	SECONDARY REQUEST TO SEND	SCA	120
SCS	SECONDARY CLEAR TO SEND	II	8	SECONDARY CLEAR TO SEND	SCF	121
SRR	SECONDARY RECEIVER READY	II	2	SECONDARY-RECEIVED-LINE SIGNAL DETECTOR	SCF	122

face circuits were carefully chosen so that a pair of wires share diagonally adjacent terminations. Each Category I circuit (Fig. 3A) is assigned to a pair, while two Category II circuits (Fig. 3B) with the same signaling direction share a pair to reduce the effects of generator-end crosstalk on other circuits. Pin 1 connects to the cable shield to provide continuity for tandem connection of shield cables.

Another significant addition to the mechanical arrangement is a standardized latching stud. Minimum clearances around the connector and maximum envelope size are specified in RS-449. This enables the use of a latching device without a separate tool (such as a screwdriver), although the latching block allows for screw attachment, if desired. Only the latching stud and threaded screw hole are standardized to allow freedom in design of the latching device.

As already indicated, RS-449 enables the transition from large inventories of existing equipment to future generations of products. By adhering to the provisions of EIA Industrial Electronics Bulletin No. 12, RS-449 equipment on one side of an interface can readily operate with RS-232-C equipment on the other side. In addition, RS-449 equipment can evolve to a simplified 15-pin X.21 "mini-interface" in the distant future.

New gear's responsibility

The onus for adaptation rests solely with the new RS-449 equipment so that existing RS-232-C equipment must not be changed or retrofitted. A simple 37-to-25-pin mechanical adapter (see Gallery, p. 54) is needed. Additionally, the Category I circuits require RS-423-A unbalanced generators and a few other specifications indicated in Bulletin No. 12.

Several manufacturers are either offering, or planning to offer, inexpensive adapters. When the new circuits operate with RS-232-C equipment, the old limitations of 15 meters (50 feet) and 20 kbit/s apply, since the performance can be no better than that imposed by the worst component. The true operational superiority will be realized when RS-449 equipment is connected to both sides of the interface.

Work is also under way to further streamline the mechanical aspects of the DTE/DCE interface by greatly reducing the number of wires across it. This work is based upon CCITT Recommendation X.21, which contains two parts: (1) a general-purpose physical interface for all public data networks and (2) call-establishment procedures for circuit-switched data networks.

The physical level provides six functional circuits using the RS-422-A or RS-423-A (Category I) electrical characteristics with a similar 15-pin connector. These characteristics are suitable at this time only for full-duplex digital circuits. There are no known plans in the United States for X.21 circuit-switched data networks. However, the packet networks will use RS-232-C and RS-449 at the physical level.

The national and international standards organizations also continue to develop further special procedures, taking advantage of microprocessor technology, to use an X.21 interface with modems for data transmission over analog circuits. This work is in its very

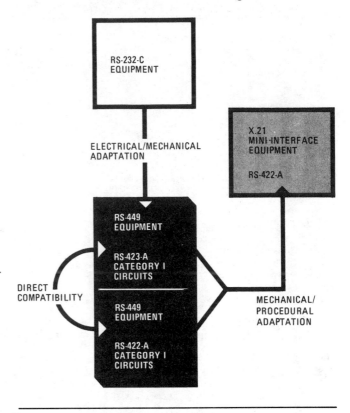

4. Comes the evolution. *This is the clear path for the graceful evolving of future interface technology. The X.21 mini-interface is considered the ultimate goal.*

early stages, and there are many formidable problems to overcome before a practical, efficient protocol can be realized. An acceptable interface must be efficient for all modes of operation. Even when a sufficient solution is found, the mini-interface will not be compatible with RS-232-C equipment. A direct step to such an interface will automatically force costly retrofits and the obsolescence of existing RS-232-C equipment.

However, RS-449 provides a further bridge to the X.21 mini-interface of the future. The appendix in RS-449 has established a direct mapping of the functional circuits with X.21. The electrical characteristics are the same with Category I circuits, which will provide direct interoperability. Only a simple 37-to-15-pin adapter and a new protocol—probably through software additions—will be needed.

Figure 4 shows the clear evolutionary path for interface technology. One need not abandon RS-232-C equipment in order to convert to the X.21 mini-interface. Considerable foresight, planning, and competent work of international scope went into building the RS-449 bridge to the future. Unless users wish to take a financial bath in the river, RS-449 should be phased into application in a timely manner. This planned evolution will preclude a painful revolution. ■

Note: For information on the conception of the new interface standards and their place in network protocols, refer to "Interfaces: new standards catch up with technology," DATA COMMUNICATIONS, June 1977, p. 31.

Reprinted from *Proceedings of the IEEE*, Volume 71, Number 12, December 1983, pages 1378-1393. Copyright © 1983 by The Institute of Electrical and Electronics Engineers, Inc.

Services and Protocols of the Data Link Layer

JAMES W. CONARD

Invited Paper

Abstract—Data Link control protocols are among the oldest recognized communication protocols. The protocol provides a well-defined set of rules which govern the interchange of supervisory information and user data over the interconnecting communication link. Such rules are essential to successful and efficient operation.

Data Link protocols have evolved continuously from the early free-wheeling protocols, through the widely implemented character-oriented protocols, to the increasingly popular bit-oriented protocols. Data Link protocols play a vital role in the drive toward Open Systems Interconnection (OSI). Constituting Layer 2 of the International Standards Organization (ISO) Reference Model, these procedures, and the services that they offer, are directed at assuring successful and reliable transfer of information over point-to-point or multipoint data links.

This paper reviews the role of link protocols in the open systems environment. It discusses the objectives and functions of these protocols and delineates the services provided to the higher layers. A review, with examples, of the protocols suitable for use within the framework of OSI is included. The paper concludes with a look at some of the current Data Link issues.

INTRODUCTION

A DATA LINK protocol consists of a set of very specific rules governing the interchange of information over an interconnecting communications link between devices which are executing a set of well-defined functions on behalf of cooperating users.

The devices may be terminals, computers, message or packet switches, concentrators, or any of a broad range of equipment generically identified as data terminal equipment. The users may be application software running in an information processor or human operators interacting with a system through a terminal device. The interconnecting links may be any of several arrangements configured from private or public point-to-point, multipoint, switched, or nonswitched facilities using a variety of media such as twisted-pair, cable, land line, microwave, or satellite channels. The information being interchanged can be supervisory data related to link control or user data in many forms serving inquiry/response, batch, time sharing, job entry, and other such applications.

Data Link protocols reside at Layer 2—the Data Link Layer of the International Standards Organization's (ISO) Reference Model for Open Systems Interconnection (OSI) [1]. The OSI Reference Model is illustrated in Fig. 1 with the Data Link Layer highlighted. In terms of the architectural concepts of OSI, the Data Link builds on, or "adds value" to, the services provided by the underlying Physical Layer. The combined capability is then offered upward to the Network Layer. The primary objective of the Data Link Layer is to assure the reliable transfer of user data over a Data Link.

Manuscript received June 10, 1983; revised August 1, 1983.
The author is with Conard Associates, Costa Mesa, CA 92626.

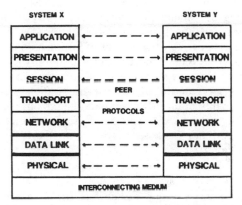

Fig. 1. The Data Link Layer in the OSI architecture.

DATA LINK LAYER FUNCTIONS

In achieving the fundamental objective of Data Link control, the Data Link Layer entity must cope with both the requirements of the communications medium and the requirements of the user. Together, these sometimes conflicting requirements define the functions which must be accomplished by the Data Link logic. Over the years, a set of general Data Link functions has emerged. These functions are common to all Data Link protocols. The way the functions are accomplished varies with type and sophistication of the actual protocol being used. The set of required functions is delineated below.

Initialization

The initialization function deals with the establishment of an active Data Link connection over an already existing physical path. The physical path may be built on one or more physical circuits. The acquisition of the path and the movement of bits over the path are the responsibility of the underlying physical layer processes. Initialization usually involves the exchange of supervisory sequences establishing readiness to receive or transmit and, if necessary, identification of the parties.

Identification

Identification processes are necessary to identify a particular receiver or sender among the many that may be present on a multipoint facility or among the huge number that may be accessible through the switched network. Data Link Layer identification is usually accomplished through an exchange of, or the *a priori* assignment of, Data Link addresses. The identification process may also require the exchange of parameters describing the capability of the communicating stations.

Synchronization

The underlying Physical Layer provides a stream of synchronized bits. A function of the Data Link Layer is to determine where in this stream of bits the intelligence being transferred lies. The synchronization process accomplishes this by providing functions to acquire, maintain, and, if necessary, reestablish character synchronization, that is, bringing the receiver's decoding mechanisms into alignment with the transmitter's encoding mechanisms.

Segmenting and Delimiting

A blocking or framing mechanism is necessary to divide the users' information into segments suitable for transmission through the Data Link. Extremely long blocks of information are unlikely to survive transmission through a noisy medium without error. On the other hand, very short blocks may be inefficient. Blocking and framing mechanisms aid the synchronization process and provide the ability to identify when data should, but may not, be present. They also provide convenient segments on which to apply error-detection processes.

Transparency

The transparency function is one which permits the Data Link control to be totally "transparent" to the format or structure of the users information. Transparency permits the user to send information in any code set, in any length, and in any format with the assurance that Data Link mechanisms will not "trip over it," that is, will not interpret any user data as link control information. Data Link protocols vary widely in the techniques used to provide transparency.

Flow Control

Receivers need to be able to regulate the flow of information into their systems in order to prevent being overwhelmed by incoming data in cases where the input rate exceeds the station's capacity to accept and process the data. Flow control functions accomplish this regulation.

Error and Sequence Control

Error-control processes provide for the detection of errors induced by the transmission medium, the acknowledgment of correctly received segments, and requests for retransmission of segments containing errors. Vertical, longitudinal, and cyclic redundancy checks are the most commonly used error-detection techniques. Some Data Link protocols also employ sequence control, which numbers and verifies individual segments of data, to guarantee the detection of missing segments.

Abnormal Condition Recovery

This function includes the processes required to detect and recover from abnormal occurrences such as loss of response, illegal or invalid sequences, severed links, and the many other unpleasant things that can happen to information as it moves over the link. Timeout processes are a common method of detecting such occurrences.

Termination

Following the transfer of the user's information, the link, which was logically established by the initialization process, is terminated. Termination functions involve "tidying up" the link by assuring that all data sent have been received and then gracefully clearing the logical connection. Link termination does not necessarily involve disconnection of the physical path.

Link Management

Additional Data Link Layer functionality is needed, in the OSI environment, to interface with local management of the Data Link Layer. This includes activating and deactivating the functions as well as monitoring and statistical processes.

Summary

The listed functions taken together comprise the set of services that the Data Link Layer makes available across the boundary with the Network Layer. A set or subset of these services, called an entity, is then invoked by the Network Layer to support a particular instance of intersystem communication.

SERVICES OF THE DATA LINK LAYER

In terms of OSI, the fundamental purpose of the Data Link Layer is to provide a set of services to the Network Layer. These services are those associated with overcoming the inherent limitations in the interconnecting medium. They represent the composite of the services of the underlying Physical Layer and the "value-added" services of the Data Link Layer.

Data Link services may be divided into three functional groups each associated with one of the phases of Data Link control. As illustrated in Fig. 2, the connect and disconnect phases are the responsibility of the Physical Layer. Establishment services are those concerned with the establishment of a logical connection between two network entities. Data transfer services are responsible for the reliable exchange of user information over the Data Links. Termination services deal with the clearing of the logical connection following data transfer.

As described in [1], Data Link services are invoked or indicated by the use of a set of service primitives exchanged across the layer boundary with the Network Layer (Fig. 3). It should be remembered that the primitives described are abstract in nature, that is, they are used to illustrate and describe the Data Link service and are not an implementation specification. The four standard types of OSI primitives used to interact between the Data Link and Network Layers are:

Request—issued by the Network Layer (the service user) to invoke a specific link layer procedure.

Indication—issued by the Data Link Layer (the service provider) to advise the Network Layer that a service has been invoked either by the peer Network Layer in a connected system or by the Data Link Layer in the local system.

Response—issued by the Network Layer to complete a procedure previously indicated.

Confirm—issued by the Data Link Layer to complete a previously requested procedure.

A complete service request or indication is composed of one of the primitive types plus the specific name of the service being requested or indicated, as for example, CONNECT REQUEST used to initiate a connection to another OSI system or ABORT

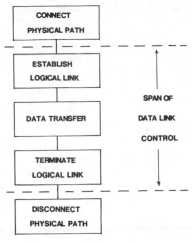

Fig. 2. Communication phases.

SERVICES	PRIMITIVE TYPES			
	REQUEST	INDICATE	RESPONSE	CONFIRM
ESTABLISH PHASE				
CONNECT	●	●	●	●
ACTIVATE	●			●
ACQUIRE	●			●
IDENTIFY	●	●	●	●
NEGOTIATE	●	●	●	●
TRANSFER PHASE				
DATA	●	●	●	●
EXPEDITED DATA	●	●	●	●
FLOW CONTROL	●	●		
RESET	●	●	●	
NOTIFY	●	●		●
ABORT	●	●		
TERMINATE PHASE				
DISCONNECT	●	●		●
DEACTIVATE	●			●

Fig. 3. Data Link service primitives.

INDICATION indicating that an abort has occurred. In addition, a service request or indication may (and usually is) accompanied by parameters listing further information about the service. Parameters could include addresses, the data to be transferred, quality requirements, reason codes for some action, and so on.

Establishment Services

The first phase of Data Link control is concerned, for a connection-oriented service, with establishing a logical connection with another system. The Data Link establishment services, which may be invoked by the Network Layer using the primitives just defined, might include the following:

CONNECT: This service provides one or more Data Link connections between two cooperating Network Layer entities. The CONNECT service uses all four primitive types, that is:

CONNECT REQUEST   CONNECT INDICATE
CONNECT RESPONSE   CONNECT CONFIRM

CONNECT primitives are normally accompanied by parameters answering such questions as: To whom should the connection be established (Addresses)? What quality of service is required (Throughput, Response Time)?

Other establishment services being considered for OSI include:

ACTIVATE: This service would originate with a link layer management function: Its intent is to initialize a previously idle Data Link Layer entity. Both request and confirm primitives would be used.

ACQUIRE: Request and confirm ACQUIRE primitives would be used to select a particular physical path from a group of available paths.

IDENTIFY: A Data Link Layer identification service provides the Network Layer with endpoint identifiers which can be used to identify another network entity. An example is the need to specifically identify connections built on multipoint physical connections. IDENTIFY service would use all four primitive types.

NEGOTIATE: A service of this type would provide the basis for negotiation of quality of service parameters in an attempt to satisfy the requirements of the user.

Termination Service

Data Link connection termination service is used to clear or release the connection established by the connection service. The defined terminate primitives are:

DISCONNECT: This service causes the Data Link Layer to release, or indicates that the Data Link Layer has released, the logical connection between two Network Layer entities. A connection could be cleared by either the local or remote peer Network Layer or by either of the Data Link Layer entities. DISCONNECT is accompanied by both request and indicate primitive types.

Another candidate for a termination service is DEACTIVATE which would be invoked by a link layer management function to turn off the Data Link Layer function.

Data-Transfer Services

The data-transfer services provide for the exchange of user data in either direction, or in both directions simultaneously, over an established Data Link connection. The Data Link Layer maintains the integrity and sequence of the user data. Data-transfer services include the following:

DATA TRANSFER: This service permits the exchange of units of user data across a Data Link connection. The size of the data unit may be constrained by the error rate of the physical path and the Data Link Layer error-detection capability. This Data Link Layer service assures that, if required, the sequence integrity of the user's information will be maintained. Typical parameters accompanying this primitive would include address, the data to be sent or their location, and quality of service parameters. All four primitive types would be used with the data service, i.e.,

DATA REQUEST   DATA INDICATE
DATA RESPONSE   DATA CONFIRM

EXPEDITED DATA: This service, when available, permits the Network Layer to send a unit of data which will be given transmission precedence over normal data on the same logical connection.

FLOW CONTROL: This service provides for the regulation of the rate of transfer of incoming data.

RESET: The Data Link reset service provides the Network Layer with the means to cause the Data Link to discard data units associated with a connection and to notify the remote Network Layer that a reset has occurred.

NOTIFY: This service provides the means by which the Network Layer could request the current status of the link layer and by which the Data Link Layer notifies the Network Layer of any error condition or abnormal occurrence which is not recoverable at the Data Link Layer.

ABORT: An abort service is one which would be either requested by the network or indicated by the Data Link Layer to indicate the destructive termination of a transmission unit in process.

Fig. 3 summarizes the Data Link Layer service primitives by communications phase and primitive type. It must be noted that the preceding description of the Data Link service primitives is not intended to be an implementation specification. The use of primitives as descriptive tools does not preclude any specific implementation approach. They are conceptual in nature and should not be viewed as associated with any particular access method. The formal specification of the services to be provided by the Data Link Layer is now underway. The completion of this effort will provide the framework leading to the definition of the protocols which are or may be required to provide those services.

PROTOCOLS OF THE DATA LINK LAYER

The services of the Data Link Layer are made available at the boundary between the Network and the Data Link Layer entities. The primitives are used to invoke these services. The Data Link Layer must execute these services in cooperation with its peer Data Link entity in the connected system. This cooperation is accomplished through the use of a Data Link control protocol.

Data Link protocols have a long and colorful history. They are among the earliest of recognized communication protocols. Link protocols evolved with the growth of communications from the early free-wheeling, asynchronous, terminal protocols, through the synchronous, character-oriented device protocols, to the bit-oriented link protocols that are on their way to dominating the Data Link control arena.

Modern Data Link protocols fall into two major classes, both of which are suitable for use in the OSI environment. The class known as character-oriented protocols are characterized by their use of a defined subset of a code set such as ASCII or EBCDIC to execute communication control functions. Typical of the character-oriented protocols are the American National Standards Institute's (ANSI)X3.28 and the International Standards Organization's ISO 1745. The best known manufacturer's version of this protocol class is undoubtedly IBM's Binary Synchronous Communication (BSC) protocol but there are many other versions from different manufacturers.

Bit-oriented Data Link protocols form a separate class. They are based on the use of positionally located fields to execute the communications control functions. Having been developed specifically to overcome the deficiencies of the character-oriented class, they are much more flexible and efficient than the older protocols. Bit-oriented protocols are expected to become predominant as the older character-oriented equipment is replaced. The standard bit-oriented protocols are ANSI X3.66 (ADCCP) and ISO HDLC (ISO 3309, 4335). Most major vendors have their own version—IBM's, for example is known as Synchronous Data Link Control (SDLC). Many popular networking applications also use bit-oriented link control. Data Link access to an X.25 public data network, as an example, is based on a particular class of HDLC procedure known to CCITT as Link Access procedure, Balanced (LAP B).

The intention here is to overview these protocols as they relate

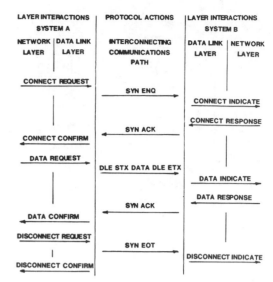

Fig. 4. An example of character-oriented services and protocol.

to open systems applications. There are many excellent references which provide detailed descriptions of the protocols [2], [3]. For complete specification of the protocol operation, the reader is referred to the actual standard protocol documents [4], [5].

A Character-Oriented Protocol Example

There is considerable variety in the detailed procedure used by character-oriented protocols. A simple but typical character-oriented Data Link procedure will be described here to show the interaction between the services and the protocol operation. This procedure is illustrated in Fig. 4.

Establishing the Data Link: In response to a CONNECT REQUEST primitive from the Network Layer, the character-oriented Data Link Layer entity will attempt to establish a logical link connection with the addressed station described in the parameter which accompanied the request. This attempt will begin with the transmission of a link establishment character ENQ (Enquiry). If the peer Data Link entity in the requested system is prepared, it will inform its Network Layer via a CONNECT INDICATION. After receiving a CONNECT RESPONSE, the remote peer Data Link will respond to the ENQ with the character ACK (Acknowledge). In this character-oriented protocol, these exchanges would be preceded with synchronizing characters (SYN). This action will result in a CONNECT CONFIRM primitive being issued by the local Data Link to the local Network Layer. At this point, the Data Link connection is established and the data-transfer phase is entered. Were the requested system not available, the response to the ENQ would have been a NAK (Negative Acknowledge) indicating not ready, or unwilling, to receive.

Character-Oriented Data Transfer: The next logical normal event would be for the Network Layer to issue a DATA REQUEST primitive accompanied by parameters which point to the data to be transmitted. This would cause Data Link to generate a block containing the user data and bounded by the delimiting characters DLE STX at the beginning and DLE ETX at the end, as illustrated in Fig. 5. The leading synchronizing characters (SYN) serve to bring the receiving Data Link entity into character synchronization with the transmitter. The trailing BCC characters are the error-detection sequence used to detect transmission errors.

The correct reception of this block causes the receiving Data

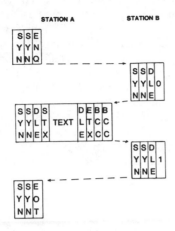

Fig. 5.   Character-oriented block format for synchronous operation.

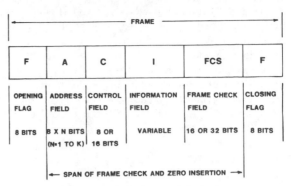

Fig. 6.   Bit-oriented frame structure.

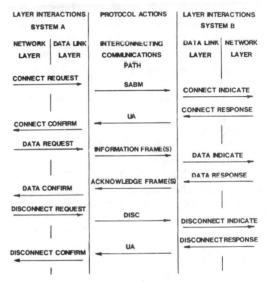

Fig. 7.   An example of bit-oriented services and protocol.

Link Layer to issue a DATA INDICATION primitive to its higher Network Layer and, as a result of the subsequent DATA RESPONSE primitive from the Network Layer, to transmit an ACK. The reception of the ACK causes the local link entity to issue a DATA CONFIRM primitive to the higher layer thus completing this instance of data transfer. This procedure continues as subsequent blocks of information are transferred. Should a block be received in error, the receiving Data Link entity issues a NAK calling for the retransmission of a particular block of data. This retransmission does not involve the higher layer entities.

Terminating the Data Link: When all of the data have been transferred, the Network Layer would iusse a DISCONNECT REQUEST. This would cause Data Link Layer to transmit an EOT (End of Transmission) which would cause an DISCONNECT INDICATION at the remote network layer and a DISCONNECT CONFIRM locally.

A Bit-Oriented Protocol Example

The newer bit-oriented protocols such as HDLC and ADCCP provide a much better "fit" with the formal OSI service specifications. All bit-oriented protocols use a common, standard structure for the link transmission unit. This structure is called a frame and is illustrated in Fig. 6. The format is fixed. Each frame must contain address, control, and check fields. The only variable is the presence or absence of the information field containing user data. A simple example of a bit-oriented protocol executing the Data Link service is illustrated in Fig. 7 and described below.

Establishment of the Data Link: The Network Layer's CONNECT REQUEST causes the Data Link entity to transmit a link establishment command. The exact command used would depend on the particular mode of operation called a Class of Procedure. For the case of a point-to-point link, the choice would most probably be a Set Asynchronous Balanced Mode (SABM) command. Correct reception of this command frame would cause the receiving peer Data Link Layer to reset all variables, issue a CONNECT INDICATION upward, and, in response to the CONNECT RESPONSE, transmit an Unnumbered Acknowledge (UA) frame to the originating Data Link entity. As a result of receiving the UA, the originating Data Link will issue a CONNECT CONFIRM to its Network Layer thus completing link establishment. Failure to establish the connection under the rules of the protocol would result in a DISCONNECT INDICATION primitive.

Information Transfer: Following the establishment phase, the local Network Layer would normally initiate transfer of one or more user data units over the established link. Each of these would involve a DATA REQUEST primitive to the local Data Link Layer. In response, Data Link Layer would package the data unit in an information frame. In the bit-oriented protocols, each information frame is protected, not only by the error-detection mechanism, but also by a sequence numbering scheme by which the protocol can assure the correct sequencing of the data.

The arrival of each correctly sequenced, nonerrored frame at the remote Data Link entity results in DATA INDICATION and DATA RESPONSE exchange with the Network Layer and in an acknowledgment, in the form of a next-expected sequence number, being returned over the Data Link to the originator. Receipt of the acknowledgment causes the local Data Link Layer to issue a DATA CONFIRM locally to complete the transaction.

During the data transfer phase, an ABORT primitive causes the Data Link Layer to abort the in-process transfer. A RESET primitive causes a resetting of sequence numbers at the Data Link Layer. Unrecoverable errors cause the NOTIFY INDICATION primitive to be issued to the respective Network Layer entities. The bit-oriented protocols contain procedural elements to convey these events across the data links.

Data Link Termination: Following data transfer, the Data Link logical connection can be cleared by the issuance of a DISCONNECT REQUEST primitive. This would cause the Data Link entity to issue a disconnect command frame (DISC) to its peer. This would be acknowledged with a UA and confirmed to the Network Layer with a DISCONNECT CONFIRM primitive. Note that the clearing of the logical link need not necessarily result in releasing the physical circuit.

These simple examples and illustrations of the interaction between services and between peer protocols are by no means exhaustive. They serve merely to indicate the tremendous progress that is being made by the industry in creating formal descriptions of the logical activity underlying Data Link Layer operation.

DATA LINK LAYER ISSUES

Despite the progress being made, there remain a number of significant issues to be resolved. These relate to the techniques and actual complete specification of Data Link services, to the application of existing older protocols, and to the need for new protocols to accommodate the rapidly evolving technology.

One major issue that must be resolved is the establishment of techniques to unambiguously specify protocols. Traditionally, protocol operation has been specified in descriptive text. This is unsatisfactory since it leads to possible misinterpretation of the requirements. This is especially evident when translation into different languages is required. Efforts are now under way to develop techniques by which protocol behavior may be specified in high-level language form. These methods have, however, not yet been widely applied at the Data Link Layer.

Further work remains to be done to complete the formal, standard specification of the complete set of services required of a Data Link Layer. This must be done in conjunction with the service descriptions of the using Network Layer and the underlying Physical Layer. Again, work is under way in the national and international standards arena and can be expected to be completed soon.

If true OSI is to be achieved, methods of accommodating and integrating the older Data Link protocols into the open systems environment must be found. Although an example of a character-oriented protocol operation in the OSI environment was given earlier, these older protocols are not really well adapted to this environment. Their structures are generally too rigid. Most do not offer enough capability to provide the desired level of service. There is, however, a tremendous investment in these protocols and an accommodation must be reached. Protocol emulation and conversion is the current solution.

Finally, as technology evolves and new applications and network services become available, Data Link protocols will have to evolve to accommodate them. The need for modification to existing protocols to efficiently handle satellite operation is already evident. Another example is the need for protocols for the new Integrated Services Digital Networks (ISDN) which are expected to grow rapidly over the next decade.

CONCLUSION

After several years of work on the part of dedicated individuals representing the worldwide communications industry, the services and protocols of the Data Link Layer are finally being molded into a cohesive whole which will provide the means to achieve successful interconnection at the Data Link Layer regardless of the particular manufacturer's logo appearing on the interconnected equipment. When combined with the services and protocols of the underlying Physical Layer and the higher Network and Transport Layers, the industry will have reached a significant milestone—true Open Systems Interconnection with enormous benefits in responsive, efficient, and cost-effective intersystem connectibility.

REFERENCES

[1] J. Day and H. Zimmermann, "The OSI Reference Model," this issue, pp. 1334–1340.
[2] J. W. Conard, "Character-oriented data link control protocols," *IEEE Trans. Commun.*, vol. COM-28, pp. 445–454, Apr. 1980.
[3] D. E. Carlson, "Bit-oriented data link control procedures," *IEEE Trans. Commun.*, vol. COM-28, pp. 455–467, Apr. 1980.
[4] ANSI Stand. X3.28-1976, "American national standard procedure for the use of communication control characters of the American National Standard Code for information interchange in specified data communication links," Amer. Nat. Stand. Inst., New York, NY, 1976.
[5] ANSI Stand. X3.66-1979, "Advanced data communication control procedures," Amer. Nat. Stand. Inst., New York, NY, 1979.

BIT ORIENTED DATA LINK CONTROLS

A bit oriented approach to network control is finding increased acceptance among many national and international standards organizations. The simplicity of the single-frame format is just one reason.

by Alan J. Weissberger

The International Standards Organization's Open Systems Interconnection/Reference Model lays the foundation for data communications architecture. As a result, in an open systems environment, end-user hardware such as terminals, workstations, cluster controllers, and computers communicate via a 7-layer peer to peer protocol. The data link layer is the second layer in the model. It provides one of the lowest levels of interconnect, provides services to the network layer above, and uses the services of the physical layer below.

As defined by the International Standards Organization (ISO), a data link control (DLC) is simply a set of rules for orderly information interchange between physically connected stations. Further, there can be one or more data link stations per data terminal equipment. Frontend processors, multiplexers, and remote data concentrators often handle several data links and thus contain many data link stations. Among the most popular DLCs are high level data link control (HDLC), advanced data communications control procedure (ADCCP), X.25 and X.75 link levels, IBM synchronous data link control (SDLC), DEC digital data communications message protocol (DDCMP), and IBM binary synchronous (bisync) communications.

Alan J. Weissberger is technical director of advanced technology at Memorex Corp, 18922 Forge Dr, Cupertino, CA 95014. Mr Weissberger is responsible for planning, systems architecture, and systems integration of data communications products. He is a participating member of ANSI X353.7 and a senior member of the IEEE.

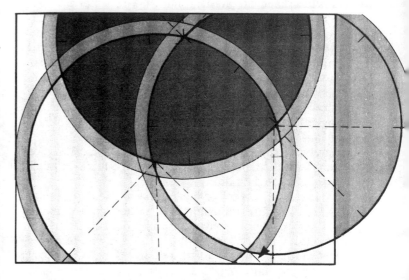

The three categories of DLCs appear in Table 1; Table 2 compares their features. Standards organizations and the U.S. Government have adopted bit oriented procedures as the preferred method of data link control. Similarly, computer manufacturers have adopted bit oriented DLCs for the link layer of their proprietary network architectures. Bit oriented procedures are distinguished from character oriented procedures by the absence of American National Standard Code for Information Interchange (ASCII), extended binary coded decimal interchange (EBCDIC), or other information coded characters for link control. Unlike character oriented DLCs, the attributes of bit oriented DLCs—single-frame format, unrestricted information field length, use of any character code, and only three reserved bit sequences—simplify software design and maintenance.

135

TABLE 1
Three Categories of DLCs

Character Oriented		Character Count	Bit Oriented	
ANSI	X3.28	DEC DDCMP	ANSI	X.3.66 (ADCCP)
ISO	1745, 2111, 2628 2629 (Basic mode)	Statistical Multiplexers	ISO	3309, 4335, 6159, 6256 (HDLC)
ECMA	16, 24, 26, 27, 28, 29, 37	Satellite Communications	CCITT	X.25 LAP, LAPB X.75 link level
IATA	SLC		ECMA	40, 49, 60, 61, 72 (HDLC)
			Federal Government	Fed Std 1003A FIPS 71
IBM	BISYNC		IBM	SDLC
			Burroughs	BDLC
			Univac	UDLC

Operating across the spectrum

HDLC covers many applications including 2-way alternate and 2-way simultaneous data communications. Communications can occur between computers, cluster controllers, concentrators, and buffered terminals, and a wide range of physical data link schemes including point to point, multipoint, switched, and nonswitched. Various HDLC functions are specified in terms of logical DLC stations. A given physical station (computer, multiplexer, cluster controller, or frontend processor) can be composed of one or more logical stations. This is accomplished by HDLC mode setting commands. A physical station may provide simultaneous multiple logical station capability on different links. Typical of this is a multiplexer that serves several links. Alternately, a station may house multiple logical stations such as a cluster controller supporting several terminals over a single data link.

Of the three types of logical stations, only a primary station has link control ability. It transmits command frames to, and receives response frames from, the secondary station on the link. There is one secondary station on a point to point link and one or more on a multipoint link. A primary station maintains separate information transmitting/receiving ability with the primary station. It can be employed on a point to point or multipoint line. A combined station has a balanced link control capable of transmitting both command and response frames to and from another combined station and is therefore restricted to a point to point line. The three types of logical data link control stations, used in different logical link configurations, are shown in Fig 1.

In HDLC there are two basic logical data link configurations: unbalanced and balanced. An unbalanced configuration features one primary station and one or more secondary stations connected to a link (ie, point to point or multipoint, 2-way alternate or 2-way simultaneous, switched or nonswitched). The configuration is unbalanced because the primary station is in control of each secondary station and initiates link level error recovery functions. A balanced configuration consists of two combined stations connected point to point, 2-way alternate or 2-way simultaneous, switched or nonswitched. Both combined stations have equal data transfer and link control ability. The balanced configuration is used in X.25 linked access procedure balanced (LAPB) and X.75 link level.

Two independent point to point unbalanced logical station configurations can be connected in a symmetric manner and multiplexed on a single physical data link. This configuration may be 2-way alternate or 2-way

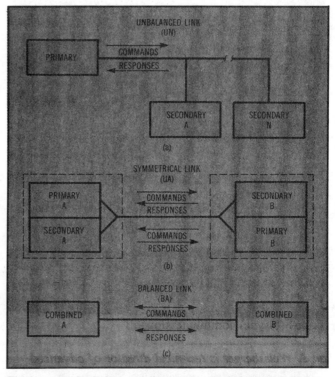

Fig 1 HDLC logic link configurations. Unbalanced system (a) has primary station and one or more secondary stations. Symmetrical configuration (b) features two unbalanced multiplexed links. Balanced system (c) uses two combined stations.

TABLE 2

Feature Comparison of DLCs

Feature	Character Controlled (Bisync)	Character Count (DDCMP)	Bit Oriented (ADCCP/HDLC)
Transmission format	Sync	Async/sync	Sync
Transmission mode	Half duplex	Half/full duplex	Half/full duplex
Framing: Start end	2 SYNs Terminating characters	2 SYNs Character count	Flag Flag
Frame formats	Numerous	1 (3 types)	1 (3 types)
Link control information	Optional header	Required header	1 or 2 octet control field
Station addressing	Contention (point to point) of polling sequence (multipoint)	Address in header	Single or extended address field
Error checking	Text messages only	Header and info field separately	All frames between flags
Error detection/ generation	VRC/LRC-8 VRC/CRC-16 CRC-16 CRC-12	CRC-16	CRC-CCITT V.41 CRC-32
Requests for retransmission	Stop and wait	Go back n frames	Go back n or Selected Reject
Maximum outstanding frames	1	255	7 or 127
Flow control	Control characters: write acknowledge, no acknowledge	None: data discarded	RNR frame, window mechanism
Character codes	ASCII, EBCDIC, SBT	ASCII for SOH, DLE, ENQ only	Any
Information field length	n x 6 (SBT) n x 8 (ASCII/ EBCDIC)	n x 8	Unrestricted
Transparency	Transparent mode escape mechanism	Character count	Zero insertion/ deletion
Control characters/ bit patterns	Numerous 1- and 2-character sequences	SYN, SOH DLE, ENQ	Lag, abort, idle

simultaneous, switched or nonswitched. In this configuration there are two primary to secondary station logical channels with primary stations having responsibility for mode setting. Each of the four stations has an information transmitting line, one information receiving line, or both. This configuration is used in X.25 link access procedure (LAP).

Logical states and modes

Communication between any two stations is conducted in one of three logical states: information transfer state (ITS), initialization state, or logically disconnected state. While in the ITS, the secondary/combined station transmits and receives information frames. This state is entered after the logical link is set up in one of three possible modes: normal response mode (NRM), asynchronous response mode (ARM), or asynchronous balanced mode (ABM).

NRM is used in an unbalanced configuration in which the secondary station initiates transmission of frames only as the result of receiving explicit permission to do so from the primary station. Permission is obtained when a frame with the poll bit set is received. After the secondary station receives permission, it initiates a response transmission consisting of one or more frames, while maintaining an active channel state. The last frame of the response transmission is explicitly indicated by the secondary station setting the final bit. Following the indication of the last frame, the secondary station stops transmitting until explicit permission is again received from the primary station.

ARM is used in an unbalanced configuration in which the secondary station initiates transmission without receiving explicit permission from the primary station. Such an asynchronous transmission, containing single or multiple frames, transfers information or indicates status changes in the secondary station (eg, the number of the next expected frame, transition from a ready to a busy condition or vice versa, or occurrence of an exception condition). ABM is used in a balanced configuration in which a combined station initiates transmission without receiving permission from the other combined station. Otherwise, it is identical to ARM.

While in the initialization state, communications are under control of a system defined procedure outside the scope of HDLC. The system defined procedure causes the secondary/combined station to be initialized by receiving parameters from the remote primary/combined station. The logically disconnected state (LDS) prevents the secondary/combined station from receiving or transmitting information. Communications observe the constraints of one of two disconnected modes: normal disconnected mode (NDM) or asynchronous disconnected mode (ADM).

NDM is used in an unbalanced configuration in which the secondary station is logically disconnected from the link and not permitted to initiate or receive information. The secondary station can initiate transmission only as the result of receiving explicit permission to do so from the primary station. After receiving permission, the secondary station initiates a single-frame transmission indicating its status. ADM is used in an unbalanced or balanced configuration in which the secondary/combined station is logically disconnected from the link and not permitted to initiate or receive information. A station in ADM initiates transmission without receiving explicit permission from the primary/combined station and transmits a single frame indicating the station status.

Classes of procedures

There are three classes of HDLC procedures: unbalanced asynchronous response mode (UA), unbalanced normal response mode (UN), and balanced asynchronous response mode (BA). Each class has a basic repertoire of commands and responses, plus functional extensions that can be selected as options. Classes UA and UN can be used on either unbalanced or symmetric configurations, although only UN can be used with a multipoint data link. Class BA is used on a balanced point to point configuration and generally operates with equal or better link efficiency than the UA class (ie, CCITT X.75 link level and X.25 LAPB).

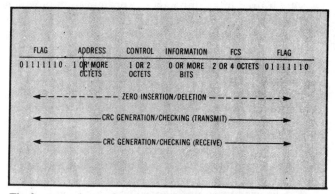

Fig 2 HDLC frame formats. Each frame consists of opening flag octets and sequence of additional address and information octets. All frames must be enclosed by flag octets.

Because of the equal link control nature of combined stations, BA makes for more uniform equipment design. A station conforms to a given class of procedures if the receiving station can decode and respond to the control field in the received command/response: a primary station receives all responses in the class of procedures, a secondary station receives all commands, and a combined station receives both.

In HDLC operations all stations use the same basic frame format (see Fig 2). This format is independent of their mode, class of procedure, and link configuration. Each frame contains an opening flag, address field, control field, frame check sequence (FCS) field, a closing flag, and depending upon the frame type, an information field. Information frames and some unnumbered frames contain an information field; supervisory frames do not.

The flag is a fixed 8-bit pattern, also known as an octet. One flag can be shared between contiguous frames such that the ending flag and opening flag are the same. Address fields can be one or more octets and can be recursively extended, by prior agreement, to accommodate addressing of any number of stations. A 1 in the least significant bit (LSB) of an extended address octet terminates the address field; a 0 extends it. The control field consists of one or two octets depending on whether basic or extended mode is specified. Depending on the frame type, the information consists of either user data or specially formatted data. An FCS field is the result of a 16-bit CRC that is generated by the transmitting station and checked at the receiving station, using the CCITT V.41 polynomial: $X^{16} + X^{12} + X^5 + 1$. A 32-bit CRC is being included in the next version of ISO 3309 and is already included in FED-STD-1003A and FIPS 71-1. Address and control fields transmit and receive with the LSB first. FCS transmits and receives with the highest order polynomial coefficient first. The order of bit transmission for the information field is application dependent.

Besides the flag there are two reserved bit patterns: abort = 01111111 and idle = 111111111111111. An abort terminates a frame prematurely. It is sent when the transmitting station has a problem, such as an underrun, or is required to take recovery action based on a frame received during transmission. Flags following an abort keep the link active so transmission can continue. The idle pattern identifies an inactive or idle link state. When a half-duplex station detects the idle pattern, it can reverse the direction of transmission (turn the line around) and then transmit. The idle may be an indication of physical level failure if flags are expected in the quiescent state when the transmitter has nothing to send.

A link is in an active link state when a primary station, secondary station, or combined station is actively transmitting a frame, an abort sequence, or interframe time fill. When the link is in the active state, the transmitting station may continue transmission at its discretion. Interframe time fill is accomplished by

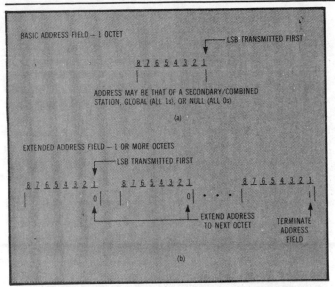

Fig 3 HDLC address field format. Basic address field (a) is one octet in length. Extended address field (b) is established by prior agreement of DLC stations. Zero in LSB position extends address field; 1 terminates it.

transmitting continuous flags between frames. An invalid frame is one that is not properly bound by two flags (thus, an aborted frame is an invalid frame) or one that is too short (ie, shorter than 32 bits between flags or address, control, and FCS fields not completed). A secondary station or combined station will ignore any invalid frame.

Transparency enables a DLC to treat all transmitted and received data, including normally restricted control characters, as a pure data stream. HDLC provides transparency for all data between opening and closing flags. The occurrence of the flag, abort, or idle sequences within a frame is prevented via a 0-bit insertion/deletion technique (sometimes called bit stuffing). The transmitter inserts a 0 bit following five contiguous 1 bits anywhere between the opening flag and the closing flag of the frame. Inserting the 0 bit thus applies to the contents of the address, control, information, and FCS fields (including the last five bits of the FCS). The receiver continuously monitors the received bit stream; upon receiving a 0 bit followed by five contiguous 1 bits, the receiver inspects the following bit. If it is a 0, the five contiguous 1 bits are passed as data and the 0 bit is deleted; if the sixth bit is a 1, the receiver inspects the seventh bit; if it is 0, a flag sequence has been received; if it is a 1, an abort has been received. The inserted and deleted zeros are not subject to the FCS calculation.

Address field formats

A unique address is associated with every secondary or combined station on a link. When a secondary or combined station responds, it will always utilize its own unique address. Additionally, a secondary or combined station may be capable of accepting frames that use a group or global address. An example of this might be a broadcast message to all secondary stations on a multipoint line. The address field in a command frame transmitted by a primary or combined station contains the address of the (remote) secondary or combined station. The address field in a response frame transmitted by a secondary or combined station contains the address of that station.

Two address encoding formats are defined for the address field: basic and extended (see Fig 3). These formats are mutually exclusive for any given secondary station or combined station on a link, and the addressing format must be explicitly specified. In basic address format, the address field contains one address octet, which may be a single secondary/combined station address. In extended address format, the address field is a sequence of octets that make up one address. This field may be a single secondary/combined station address, or a group or global secondary/combined station address. When the first (least significant) bit of an address octet is 0, the subsequent octet is an extension of the address field (except for null address). The address field is terminated by an octet having a 1 in the first bit position. Thus, the address field is recursively extendable.

A single octet address of eight 1 bits is reserved as the global address in both basic and extended addressing. The global address is used if a specific secondary/combined station address is not known (eg, switched connection) or is not relevant to the situation (eg, broadcast transmission). When the first octet of the address field appears as eight 0 bits, the address is considered to be a null (no station) address and the frame will be ignored. The null address frame might be used as an initialization or diagnostic procedure to verify that a DLC station is online.

Three types of HDLC frames are information, supervisory, and unnumbered. The frame type is specified by the first two (least significant) bits of the control field. Information (I) frames may contain an arbitrary number of bits of user data in the information field. (Some bit oriented DLCs such as SDLC and X.25 require an integral number of octets in the information field.) I frames are sequentially numbered with a send sequence number $N(S)$ and allow piggybacking of acknowledgments of received frames through a receive sequence number $N(R)$. They also carry a P or F bit. Supervisory (S) frames are used to acknowledge correctly received I frames by their receive sequence number $N(R)$. S frames can also request transmission of I frames in the event of transmission errors, or request a temporary suspension of the transmission of I frames. S frames also carry a P/F bit. Unnumbered (U) frames are used during link initialization or disconnection for additional link control functions. There are no sequence numbers; consequently, 5 modifier bits are available that allow definition of up to 32 additional responses. The type and number of these commands and responses depend upon the HDLC class of procedure.

Parameters associated with frames

Each I frame is sequentially numbered and may have the value 0 through modulus − 1, where modulus is the modulo of the sequence numbers. Modulus equals 8 for the basic control field format and 128 for the extended control field format. The sequence numbers cycle through the entire range and recirculate starting from zero. The maximum number of sequentially numbered I frames that a station may have outstanding (ie, unacknowledged) at any given time is called the window size. This number can never exceed one less than the modulus of the sequence numbers. The window size is determined by either the sending or receiving station storage capability; eg, the number of the I frames that

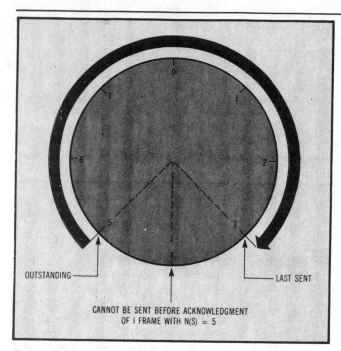

Fig 4 Window operation. Assume basic control field, window size of 7, and I frames with N(S) = 5, 6, 7, 0, 1, 2, 3 have been sent without receiving an acknowledgment. At this point the window has closed; one or more I frames must be acknowledged by received N(R) 6 before the next I frame can be transmitted.

can be stored for transmission or retransmission (in the event of a transmission error). When I frames are acknowledged, the window is rotated and additional I frames can be sent. Fig 4 illustrates window operation.

Every station in the information transfer state maintains a send variable on the I frames it transmits, and a receive variable on the I frames it correctly receives. Each station capable of transmitting I frames has a send variable S that indicates the sequence number of the next I frame to be transmitted. S takes on the value 0 through modulus 1. S is incremented by 1 with each completed I frame transmission. For example, after the I frame with N(S) = 6 is transmitted, S = 7. S will not be incremented when an I frame transmission is aborted. Only I frames contain N(S), the sequence number of the transmitted frame. Prior to transmission of an I frame, N(S) is set equal to S. In the previous example, the next I frame to be transmitted would have N(S) = S = 7.

Each station capable of receiving I frames will have a receive variable R equal to the expected N(S) contained in the next I frame received. R is incremented by 1 upon receipt of an error-free I frame whose N(S) = R. For example, if the modulus is 8 and the I frame with N(S) = 7 is correctly received, then R = 0. All I frames and S frames contain an N(R), the expected sequence number of the next received I frame. Immediately before transmitting or retransmitting an I or S frame, N(R) is set equal to R. N(R) thus indicates that the station transmitting the N(R) has correctly received all I frames numbered up to and including N(R) − 1. In the previous example, N(R) = R = 0.

Poll (P) and final (F) bits are used for various operations. They indicate when a secondary station can begin and has finished a response transmission under NRM. The poll/final (P/F) bit can also aid in determining if error recovery is required or in obtaining a response

from the secondary/combined station. The P bit is set to 1 by the primary/combined station in command frames to solicit (poll) a response or sequence of response frames from a secondary station(s) or a combined station.

The F bit is set to 1 by a secondary station to indicate that the response frame was sent in reply to the receipt of a poll command. Additionally, the F bit indicates in NRM that the final frame has been transmitted as the result of a previous poll command. The F bit is set to 1 by a combined station to indicate, in ABM, the response frame sent in reply to the receipt of a poll command.

Control field formats

The basic control fields consist of the single octet shown in Fig 5. For I frames, the N(S) and N(R) modulus is 8, which allows up to 7 outstanding (unacknowledged) frames. The window size is usually fixed at seven, but may be less in low cost HDLC terminals that do not have sufficient buffer storage to hold seven outstanding frames.

Extended control field consist of two octets. On long propagation delay links (eg, satellite or multiple microwave hop transmission) it is desirable for reasons of efficiency to have more than seven outstanding I frames. Extended control field extends the modulus of the sequence numbers for N(S) and N(R) to 128. The window size may be less than 127 in order to conserve buffer space. For example, if I frame length is 1k bytes, a window size of 127 would require a 128k transmit buffer (current frame plus 127 outstanding frames) and a 127k receive buffer. An HDLC terminal probably would not have that much storage and would therefore select a much smaller window size.

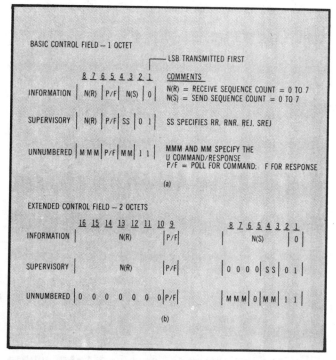

Fig 5 HDLC control field formats. First 2 bits of first octet specify frame type: information, supervisory, or unnumbered. In basic control field (a), up to 7 I frames can be outstanding. In extended control field (b), up to 127 frames can be outstanding. Maximum number of outstanding I frames is determined by user-specified window size.

Increased popularity of bit oriented protocols and HDLC interconnect formats is resulting in a proliferation of bit oriented data link controls.

In extended control field format, an HDLC transmitter sets the P/F bit in bit position 9 (ADCCP sets the P/F bits in positions 5 and 9) for unnumbered format commands and responses. A receiver in extended control field format interprets the P/F bit in bit position 9. A receiver in basic control field format cannot receive an extended control field format frame.

Comparison of bit oriented DLCs

The grandfather of all bit oriented DLCs is ISO HDLC. Subsets of ISO HDLC include the European Computer Manufacturers Association (ECMA) HDLC, the American National Standards Institute (ANSI) ADCCP, the International Consultative Committee for Telephone and Telegraph (CCITT) X.25 and X.75 link levels, the Federal Government's 1003A and FIPS PUB 71 and 78 standards, and IBM's SDLC. Federal standards, ISO ADCCP, and ECMA are basically equivalent. As an option proposed for ISO HDLC (3309) and ADCCP, federal standards allow for a 32-bit cyclic redundancy check (CRC). Note that ISO HDLC differs from ADCCP in that HDLC requires the poll/final (P/F) bit to be set in only the second control octet (8-bit group), rather than both octets of an extended control field. The standard also disallows use of the four nonreserved unnumbered command/response frames in ADCCP, and adds, rather than deletes, a RSET command. ECMA HDLC encompasses ISO HDLC plus the TEST command and response frames. CCITT X.25 LAPB and X.75 link levels are point to point subsets of ISO HDLC. The IEEE 802 logical link control is a bit oriented procedure for local area networks. It has a slightly different frame structure, a 32-bit CRC, and provisions for a mandatory connectionless type of service as well as an optional connection oriented service.

IBM SDLC is roughly equivalent to the ISO HDLC UN class of procedure as specified in DIS 6159 and the NDM as specified in DIS 4335/DAD 1. All IBM SDLC products provide the minimum command/response repertoire of the UN class and particular products provide one or more of the available options.

However, IBM SDLC contains additional commands and responses not found in ISO HDLC. These include the TEST command/response for link testing purposes, the configure (CFGR) command, CFGR response, and binary coded number (BCN) response for SDLC loop mode. ISO HDLC does not include loop operation, which is a major feature of SDLC. In addition, IBM SDLC address and control fields are one octet each (ie, there is no provision for an extended address or extended control field). The SDLC information field is restricted, its length is a multiple of 8 bits, while the HDLC information field length is a system specified parameter. Finally, there is no option for a 32-bit CRC in SDLC.

IBM products implement a subset of SDLC. For example, some IBM products do not allow use of the read (RD) response while the reject (REJ) command and response are used only in SDLC products that provide 2-way simultaneous (TWS) information interchange. Two-way alternate (TWA) products such as the IBM 3274 and 3276 use P/F bit checkpointing and a primary station timer for error recovery.

Increased popularity of bit oriented protocols and HDLC interconnect formats is resulting in a proliferation of bit oriented data link controls. For today's network designer, familiarity with this approach to protocols is becoming increasingly essential. This article is offered to make the minutiae of bit oriented HDLCs slightly less imposing. In Part II, an expanded discussion of the power and flexibility of bit oriented approaches to data communication control will be presented.

IN DEPTH

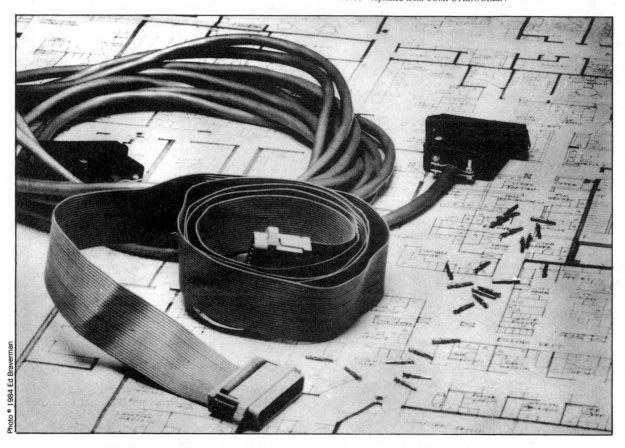

Photo © 1984 Ed Braverman

IEEE Project 802

Setting standards for local-area networks

By William Stallings

Development of the local-area network market depends on the availability of a low-cost interface. The cost to connect equipment to a local network must be much less than the cost of the equipment alone. This requirement as well as the complexity of the local-area network protocols dictate a very large-scale integration (VLSI) solution.

Chip manufacturers will be reluctant to commit the necessary resources without a high-volume market. A local-area network standard would ensure volume and also enable communication among equipment from a variety of manufacturers.

The Institute of Electrical and Electronics Engineers Computer Society established IEEE Project 802 in February 1980 to draft a local-area network standard. The work of the 802 committee has now come to fruition. Several parts of the proposal are now working their way through national and international standards organizations, and the remainder will follow soon.

The task of IEEE 802 was to specify the means by which devices could communicate over a local network. The committee characterized its work as follows:

"A local network is a data communications system that allows a number of independent devices to communicate with each other. This standard defines a set of interfaces and protocols for the local network.

"A local network is distinguished from other types of data networks in that the communication is usually confined to a moderate-size geographic area such as a single office building, a warehouse or a campus. The network can generally depend on a communications channel of moderate to high data rate which has a consistently low error rate. The network is generally owned and used by a single organization, in contrast to long-distance networks which interconnect facilities in different parts of the country or are used as a public utility. The local-area network is also different from networks

The objective of the local-area network standard is to ensure compatibility between equipment made by different manufacturers. The world of local networks will rapidly become an IEEE 802 world. As IEEE 802 products become widely available, nonstandard offerings can be expected to wither away — with two exceptions.

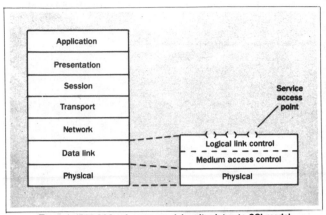

Figure 1. IEEE 802 reference model as it relates to OSI model

that interconnect devices on a desktop or components within a single piece of equipment.

"The objective of the local network standard is to ensure compatibility between equipment made by different manufacturers such that data communications can take place between the devices with a minimum effort on the part of the equipment users or the builders of a system containing the equipment. To accomplish this, the standard will provide specifications that establish common interfaces and protocols for local-area data communications networks."

The committee quickly reached two conclusions. First, the task of communicating across a local network is sufficiently complex that it needs to be broken up into more manageable subtasks. And second, no single technical approach will satisfy all requirements.

The first conclusion is reflected in a "local network reference model," compared in Figure 1 to the better-known open systems interconnection (OSI) model. The local network reference model has three layers:

Physical: This layer is concerned with the nature of the transmission medium and the details of device attachment and electrical signaling.

Medium access control: A local network is characterized by a collection of devices all needing to share a single transmission medium. A means to control access is needed so that only one device attempts to transmit at a time.

Logical link control: This layer is concerned with establishing, maintaining and terminating a logical link between devices.

The committee reluctantly reached the second conclusion when it became apparent that no single standard would satisfy all participants. There was support for both ring and bus topologies. Within the bus topology, there was support for two access methods (carrier-sense multiple access with collision detection [CSMA/CD] and token bus) and two media (baseband and broadband). The response of the committee was to standardize all serious proposals rather than to try to settle on just one. The result is shown in Figure 2.

The work of the IEEE 802 committee is currently organized into the following subcommittees:

■ IEEE 802.1 Higher Layer Interface Standard.
■ IEEE 802.2 Logical Link Control Standard (LLC).
■ IEEE 802.3 CSMA/CD.
■ IEEE 802.4 Token Bus.
■ IEEE 802.5 Token Ring.
■ IEEE 802.6 Metropolitan Area Network (MAN).

The Higher Layer Interface subcommittee is not developing standards, but rather is working on a variety of related issues such as higher layer interfaces, internetworking, addressing and network management.

Work has been completed on LLC, CSMA/CD and token bus for an initial standard. All three are now approved IEEE standards (IEEE Std. 802.2-1983, 802.3-1983 and 802.4-1983 respectively). Work continues on token ring within IEEE 802, with the intention of passing it to the IEEE Standards Board by the middle of this year.

The work on metropolitan area networks has as yet made little progress. The subcommittee is attempting to develop a small number of reasonable alternatives for further study.

The acceptance of the IEEE 802 standards has been remarkably widespread. The National Bureau of Standards, which issues Federal Information Processing Standards (Fips) for U.S. government procurements, has announced the intention of issuing Fips for CSMA/CD and LLC. The others will probably follow. The International Standards Organization (ISO) has decided to adopt the IEEE 802 documents in toto as Draft Proposed Standards. This is the first step in the development of international standards. The influential European Computer Manufacturers Association (Ecma), which had been actively drafting its own local-area network standards, has now officially deferred to IEEE 802.

The marketplace

The acceptance of the IEEE 802 standards in the marketplace is assured. As the preceding discussion suggests, the work of the IEEE 802 committee has no competition for standardization. The standards are being adopted within the U.S. and internationally.

Vendors, too, are lining up behind the standard. Fortunately, the CSMA/CD baseband standard is vir-

tually identical to the Ethernet specification. Thus, many Ethernet vendors have announced IEEE 802.3 products and a number of semiconductor houses have announced IEEE 802.3 chips. Token bus broadband is about to follow the same pattern. At least one local-area network vendor (Concord Data Systems) has announced an IEEE 802.4 product. The token ring standard has yet to blossom, but the expected announcement of an IEEE 802.5 product by IBM would change the picture overnight.

What of nonstandard offerings? Many of these can be expected to wither away as the IEEE 802 products become widely available. Two exceptions are likely. The first is the low-cost, twisted-pair local network intended primarily for personal computers. The Corvus Systems, Inc. Omninet is the most prevalent example. Large numbers of these networks are already installed. With the possible exception of the twisted-pair ring, the IEEE 802 standards do not address this marketplace.

The second exception is from a company called AT&T, which will announce its own local network product shortly. The AT&T offering is totally distinct from all of the various IEEE 802 options and is based on a hybrid circuit and packet-switching technology.

With these exceptions, the world of local networks will rapidly become an IEEE 802 world.

Logical link control

The purpose of any data link control protocol is to provide a reliable communications path between two devices. Typically, data is transmitted in frames, which include control information for error control and flow control.

Because a local network consists of multiple, peer communications stations, the data link control requirement is more complex. The following functions are considered desirable:

Datagram: Some form of connectionless service is needed for efficient support of highly interactive traffic.

Virtual circuit: A connection-oriented service is also usually needed.

Multiplexing: Generally, a single physical link attaches a station to a local-area network; it should be possible to provide data transfer with multiple end points over that link.

Multicast, broadcast: The link layer should provide a service of sending a message to multiple stations or all stations.

Both the virtual circuit and multiplexing capabilities can be supported with the concept of the service access point (SAP). Figure 3 shows three stations attached to a local network. Each station has an address.

Further, the link layer supports multiple SAPs, each with its own address. The link layer provides communications between SAPs.

Assume that a process or application X in station A wishes to send a message to a process in station C. X may be a report generator program in minicomputer A. C may be a printer and a simple printer driver. X attaches itself to SAP 1 and requests a connection to station C, SAP 1 (station C may have only one SAP if

it is a single printer).

Station A's link layer then sends to the local-area network a "connection-request" frame, which includes the source address (A,1), the destination address (C,1) and some control bits indicating that this is a connection request.

The network delivers this frame to C, which, if it is free, returns a "connection-accepted" frame. Henceforth, all data from X will be assembled into a frame by A's LLC, which includes source (A,1) and destination (C,1) addresses.

Incoming frames addressed to (A,1) will be rejected unless they are from (C,1); these might be acknowledgment frames, for example. Similarly, station C's printer is declared busy, and C will only accept frames from (A,1).

Thus a connection-oriented service is provided. At the same time, process Y could attach to (A,2) and exchange data with (B,1). This is an example of multiplexing. In addition, various other processes in A could use (A,3) to send datagrams to various destinations.

IEEE 802 LLC specification

LLC provides two services:

Unacknowledged connectionless service: This is a datagram service that simply allows for sending and receiving frames. It supports point-to-point, multipoint and broadcast.

Connection-oriented service: This provides a virtual-circuit-style connection between service access points. It provides flow control, sequencing and error recovery.

These services are specified in terms of primitives that can be viewed as commands or procedure calls with parameters. Table 1 summarizes the LLC primitives.

The unacknowledged connectionless service provides for only two primitives across the interface between the next highest layer and LLC (not counting management service primitives). L-DATA.request is used to pass a frame to LLC for transmission. L-DATA.indication is used to pass a frame up from LLC upon reception.

The connection-oriented service includes L-DATA-CONNECT.request and L-DATA-CONNECT.indication, with meanings analogous to those above, plus L-DATA-CONNECT.confirm, which conveys the result (acknowledged, failure) of the previous associated L-DATA-CONNECT.re-

---

Unacknowledged connectionless service
  L-DATA.request
  L-DATA.indication

Connection-oriented service
  L-DATA-CONNECT.request
  L-DATA-CONNECT.indication
  L-DATA-CONNECT.confirm
  L-CONNECT.request
  L-CONNECT.indication
  L-CONNECT.confirm
  L-DISCONNECT.request
  L-DISCONNECT.indication
  L-DISCONNECT.confirm
  L-RESET.request
  L-RESET.indication
  L-RESET.confirm
  L-CONNECTION-FLOWCONTROL.request
  L-CONNECTION-FLOWCONTROL.indication

Table 1. Logical link control primitives

IN DEPTH/LOCAL NETWORK STANDARDS

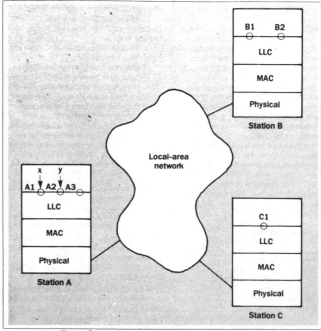

quest. In addition, a station, through an SAP, must be able to establish and tear down a connection and receive an acknowledgment of this action from the remote SAP. Finally, link resetting and flow control are provided.

The LLC frame consists of four fields, as shown in Figure 4. Unlike most link control formats, LLC requires both source and destination addresses to identify the two peer communicating entities. The source and destination are uniquely identified by a (node, SAP) pair. However, the node address is also used by MAC and is included in the outer MAC frame.

The LLC protocol is very similar to High-Level Data Link Control (HDLC). The format of the control field is identical to that of HDLC and the functioning is the same, with three exceptions:

■ LLC makes use only of the asynchronous balanced mode of operation and does not employ HDLC's normal response mode or asynchronous response mode. This mode is used to support connection-oriented service. The set asynchronous balanced mode (SABM) command is used to establish a connection, and disconnect (DISC) is used to terminate the connection.

■ LCC supports a connectionless (datagram) service by using the unnumbered information (UI) frame.

■ LLC permits multiplexing by the use of SAPs.

CSMA/CD

The simplest form of medium access control adopted for IEEE 802 is CSMA/CD. This technique was popularized by Ethernet, which is a baseband local network developed in its original version by Xerox Corp. and then in its second version jointly by Xerox with Digital Equipment Corp. and Intel Corp. A broadband CSMA/CD was pioneered by Mitre Corp.

We begin by looking at a simpler version known as CSMA (carrier sense multiple access). With this scheme, a station wishing to transmit first listens to the medium to determine if another transmission is in progress. If the medium is idle, the station may transmit. Now, it may happen that two or more stations attempt to transmit at about the same time. If this happens, there will be a collision; the data from both transmissions will be garbled and will not be received successfully. To account for this, a station waits a reasonable amount of time after transmitting for an acknowledgment. If there is no acknowledgment, the station assumes that a collision has occurred and retransmits.

With CSMA, an algorithm is needed to specify what a station should do if the medium is found to be busy. Three approaches are shown in Figure 5. One algorithm is nonpersistent CSMA. A station wishing to transmit listens to the medium and obeys the following rules:

1. If the medium is idle, transmit.
2. If the medium is busy, wait an amount of time drawn from a probability distribution (the retransmission delay) and repeat step 1.

The use of random retransmission times reduces the probability of collisions. The drawback is that even if several stations have a frame to send, there is likely to be some wast-

ed idle time following a prior transmission.

To avoid channel idle time, the 1-persistent protocol can be used. A station wishing to transmit listens to the medium and obeys the following rules:

1. If the medium is idle, transmit.
2. If the medium is busy, continue to listen until the channel is sensed idle, then transmit immediately.
3. If there is a collision (determined by a lack of acknowledgment), wait a random amount of time and repeat step 1.

Whereas nonpersistent stations are deferential, 1-persistent stations are selfish. If two or more stations are waiting to transmit, a collision is guaranteed. Things only get sorted out after the collision.

A compromise that attempts to reduce collisions, like nonpersistent, and reduce idle time, like 1-persistent, is p-persistent. The rules are:

1. If the medium is idle, transmit with probability p, and delay one time unit with probability $(1 - p)$. The time unit is typically equal to the maximum propagation delay.
2. If the medium is busy, continue to listen until the channel is idle and repeat step 1.
3. If transmission is delayed one time unit, repeat step 1.

CSMA has one glaring inefficiency. When two frames collide, the medium remains unusable for the duration of transmission of both damaged frames. For long frames, compared with propagation time, the amount of wasted bandwidth can be considerable. This waste can be reduced if a station continues to listen to the medium while it is transmitting. In that case, these rules can be added to the CSMA rules:

1. If a collision is detected during transmission, immediately cease transmitting the frame and transmit a brief jamming signal to ensure that all stations know there has been a collision.

2. After transmitting the jamming signal, wait a random amount of time, then attempt to transmit again using CSMA.

With this addition, the technique is referred to as CSMA/CD. The technique is illustrated in Figure 6. At

time t_o, A begins transmitting a frame addressed to D. At t_1, both B and C are ready to transmit. B senses a transmission and so defers. C, however, is still unaware of A's transmission and begins its own transmission. When A's transmission reaches $C(t_2)$, C detects the collision and ceases transmission. The effect of the collision propagates back to A, where it is detected some time later (t_3), at which time A ceases transmission.

IEEE 802 MAC specification

The IEEE 802 MAC specification follows the general outline described above. One detail worth mentioning is the persistence algorithm. You may be surprised to learn that the IEEE 802 standard specifies the 1-persistent algorithm.

Recall that both nonpersistent and p-persistent have performance prob-

lems. In the nonpersistent case, capacity is wasted because the medium will generally remain idle following the end of a transmission, even if there are stations waiting to send. In the p-persistent case, p must be set low enough to avoid instability, with the result of sometimes atrocious delays under light load.

The 1-persistent algorithm, which after all means $p = 1$, would seem to be even more unstable than p-persistent because of the greed of the stations. What saves the day is that the wasted time resulting from collisions is mercifully short (if the frames are long relative to propagation delay!); and with random back-off, the two stations involved in a collision are unlikely to collide on their next tries. To ensure that back-off maintains stability, a technique known as binary exponential back-off is used. A station will attempt to transmit re-

Figure 2. IEEE 802 local network standards

Figure 3. Local-area network link control scenario

IN DEPTH/LOCAL NETWORK STANDARDS

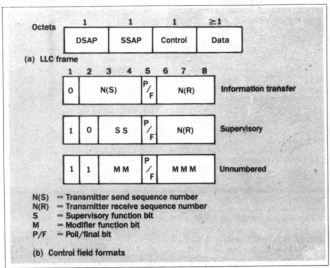

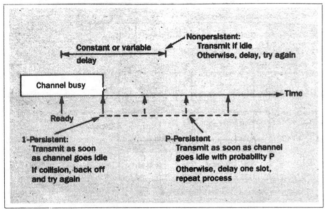

Figure 4. Logical link control format

Figure 5. CSMA persistence and back-off

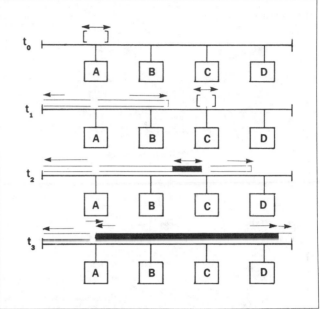

Figure 6. Operation of CSMA/CD on a baseband bus

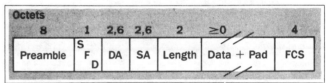

Figure 7. CSMA/CD frame format

peatedly in the face of repeated collisions, but after each collision, the mean value of the random delay is doubled. After 16 unsuccessful attempts, the station gives up and reports an error.

The beauty of the 1-persistent algorithm with binary exponential back-off is that it is efficient over a wide range of loads. At low loads, 1-persistence guarantees that a station can seize the channel as soon as it goes idle, in contrast to the non- and p-persistent schemes. At high loads, it is at least as stable as the other techniques. However, one unfortunate effect of the back-off algorithm is that it has a last-in, first-out effect; stations with no or few collisions will have a chance to transmit before stations that have waited longer.

Figure 7 shows the MAC CSMA/CD frame structure. The individual fields are as follows:

Preamble: an eight-byte pattern used by the receiver to establish bit synchronization and then locate the first bit of the frame.

Start frame delimiter (SFD): indicates the start of a frame.

Destination address (DA): specifies the station(s) for which the frame is intended. It may be a unique physical address (one destination transceiver), a multicast-group address (a group of stations) or a global

address (all stations on the local network).

Source address (SA): specifies the station that sent the frame.

Length: specifies the number of LLC bytes that follow.

LLC data: field prepared at the LLC level.

Pad: a sequence of bytes added to assure that the frame is long enough for proper CD operation.

Frame check sequence (FCS): a 32-bit cyclic redundancy check value. Based on all fields, starting with destination address.

The CSMA/CD physical layer specification calls for a baseband, 50-ohm coaxial cable. In this context, the term baseband refers to the use of digital signaling, as opposed to the use of a modem and analog signaling.

Digital signals are transmitted using Manchester encoding. This is an encoding technique that ensures at least one voltage transmission per bit time. A collision is detected if a larger-than-expected voltage swing is observed.

Several broadband schemes for CSMA/CD are under consideration. Broadband implies the use of analog signals and will allow multiple channels to be carried simultaneously.

Token bus

Token bus is a relatively new

technique for controlling access to a broadcast medium, inspired by the token ring technique discussed later.

For token bus, the stations on the bus or tree form a logical ring; that is, the stations are assigned logical positions in an ordered sequence, with the last member of the sequence followed by the first. Each station knows the identity of the stations preceding and following it. The physical ordering of the stations on the bus is irrelevant and independent of the logical ordering (see Figure 8 on ID/34).

A control packet known as the token regulates the right of access. The token frame contains a destination address. The station receiving the token is granted control of the medium for a specified time. The station may transmit one or more frames and may poll stations and receive responses. When the station is done or time has expired, it passes the token on to the next station in logical sequence. This station now has permission to transmit. Hence, steady-state operation consists of alternating data transfer and token transfer phases. In addition, non-token-using stations are allowed on the bus. These stations can only respond to polls or requests for acknowledgment.

This scheme requires considerable maintenance. The following functions, at a minimum, must be performed by one or more stations on the bus:

Ring initialization: When the network is started up, or after the logical ring has broken down, it must be reinitialized. Some cooperative, decentralized algorithm is needed to

sort out who goes first, who goes second and so on.

Addition to ring: Periodically, nonparticipating stations must be granted the opportunity to insert themselves in the ring.

Deletion from ring: A station can voluntarily remove itself from the ring by splicing together its predecessor and successor.

Fault management: A number of errors can occur. These include duplicate address (two stations think it is their turn) and broken ring (no station thinks that it is its turn).

Token bus specification

The IEEE 802 token bus protocol follows the general principles outlined above. In general, token-passing and data-passing phases alternate.

Figure 9 shows the MAC frame structure for a token bus. The individual fields are as follows:

Preamble: a one-or-more-byte pattern used by receivers to establish bit synchronization and locate the first bit of the frame.

Start delimiter (SD): indicates start of frame.

Frame control (FC): indicates whether this is an LLC data frame. If not, bits in this field control operation of the token bus MAC protocol. An example is a token frame.

Destination address (DA): as with CSMA/CD.

Source address (SA): as with CSMA/CD.

Data unit: field prepared by LLC.

Frame check sequence (FCS): as with CSMA/CD.

End delimiter (ED): indicates end of frame.

IN DEPTH/LOCAL NETWORK STANDARDS

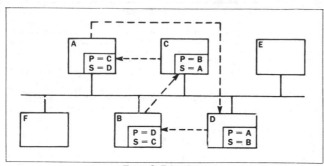

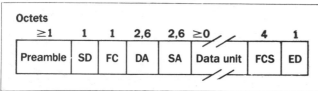

Figure 8. Token bus

Figure 9. Token bus frame format

Octets								
≥1	1	1	2,6	2,6	≥0		4	1
Preamble	SD	FC	DA	SA	Data unit		FCS	ED

The details of the protocol can be grouped into the following categories, which will be considered in turn:

■ Addition of a node.
■ Deletion of a node.
■ Fault management by token holder.
■ Ring initialization.
■ Classes of service.

First, let us consider how a node is added to the ring, using a controlled contention process called *response windows*. Each node in the ring has the responsibility of periodically granting an opportunity for new nodes to enter the ring. While holding the token, the node issues a *solicit-successor* frame, inviting nodes with an address between itself and the next node in logical sequence to demand entrance. The transmitting node then waits for one response window or slot time (equal to twice the end-to-end propagation delay of

the medium). Three events can occur:

1. No response: Nobody wants in. The token holder transfers the token to its successor as usual.

2. One response: One node issues a *set-successor* frame. The token holder sets its successor node to be the requesting node and transmits the token to it. The requester sets its linkages accordingly and proceeds.

3. Multiple responses: The token holder will detect a garbled response if more than one node demands entrance. The conflict is resolved by an address-based contention scheme. The token holder transmits a *resolve-contention* frame and waits four demand windows. Each demander can respond in one of these windows based on the first two bits of its address. If a demander hears anything before its window comes up, it refrains from demanding.

If the token holder receives a val-

id set-successor frame, it is in business. Otherwise, it tries again, and only those nodes that responded the first time are allowed to respond this time, based on the second pair of bits in their address. This process continues until a valid set-successor frame is received, no response is received or a maximum retry count is reached. In the latter two cases, the token holder gives up and passes the token.

Deletion of a node is much simpler. If a node wishes to drop out, it waits until it receives the token, then sends a set-successor frame to its predecessor, instructing it to splice to its successor. If a node fails, it will not pick up the token when the token is passed to it, and this failure will be detected by the token sender, as explained below.

Fault management by the token holder covers a number of contingencies (see Table 2). First, while holding the token, a node may hear a frame indicating that another node has the token. If so, it immediately drops the token by reverting to listener mode. In this way, the number of token holders drops immediately

to one or zero, thus overcoming the multiple-token problem (which could be caused by two nodes having the same address). Upon completion of its turn, the token holder will issue a token frame to its successor. The successor should immediately issue a data or token frame. Therefore, after sending a token, the token issuer will listen for one slot time to make sure that its successor is active. This precipitates a sequence of events:

1. If the successor node is active, the token issuer will hear a valid frame and revert to listener mode.

2. If the issuer does not hear a valid frame, it reissues the token to the same successor one more time.

3. After two failures, the issuer assumes that its successor has failed and issues a *who-follows* frame, asking for the identity of the node that follows the failed node. The issuer should get back a set-successor frame from the second node down the line. If so, the issuer adjusts its linkage and issues a token (back to step 1).

4. If the issuing node gets no response to its who-follows frame, it tries again.

How to contact IEEE 802

The IEEE 802 Project maintained an open-door policy of participation. At any one working group, about 20 to 30 people showed up. Participants came from a variety of backgrounds within communications and marketing. Most worked for a computer vendor or AT&T. The only other major source of participation was the National Bureau of Standards.

Anyone wishing to comment on or question a particular aspect of the proposed standard should write to the chairman of the appropriate working group:

M. Graube, Chairman, IEEE 802
Tektronix
Box 500, MS 50-4473
Beaverton, Ore. 97077

W.T. Lidinsky
Chairman, IEEE 802-1
High-Level Interface Working Group
Bell Laboratories, MS IH6B-309
Naperville-Wheaton Road
Naperville, Ill. 60566

D.E. Carlson
Chairman, IEEE 802-2
Logical Link Control Working Group
AT&T Information Systems
LZ-3E314
307 Middletown-Lincroft Road
Lincroft, N.J. 07738

D.C. Loughry
Chairman, IEEE 802-3
CSMA/CD Working Group
Hewlett-Packard Co.

Building IND-47L
19420 Homestead Road
Cupertino, Calif. 95014

R.H. Douglas
Chairman, IEEE 802-4
Token Bus Working Group
Concord Data Systems
10640 N. 28th Drive
Suite A209
Phoenix, Ariz. 85029

R.A. Donnan
Chairman, IEEE 802-5
Token Ring Working Group
IBM
Department E87/B651
P.O. Box 12195
Research Triangle Park, N.C. 27709

J. Mollenauer
Chairman, IEEE 802-6
Metropolitan Area Network Working Group
Codex
20 Cabot Blvd.
Mansfield, Mass. 02048

M. Stahlman
Chairman, IEEE 802-7
Broadband Technical Advisory Group
General Instruments Corp.
1775 Broadway
New York, N.Y. 10019

W.L. Schumacher
Chairman, IEEE 802-8
Fiber Optics Technical Advisory Group
AMP, Inc.
MS 24-21
P.O. Box 3608
Harrisburg, Pa. 17105

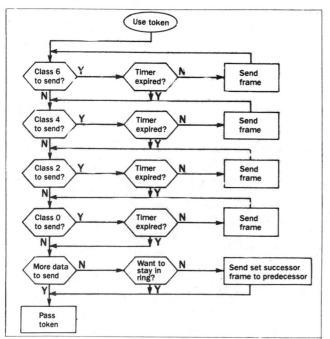

Figure 10. Token bus priority scheme

Condition	Action
Multiple tokens	Defer
Unaccepted token	Retry
Failed station	"Who follows" process
Failed receiver	Drop out of ring
No token	Initialize after time-out

Table 2. Token bus error handling

5. If the who-follows tactic fails, the node issues a solicit-successor frame with the full address range (that is, every node is invited to respond). If this process works, a two-node ring is established, and life goes on.

6. If two attempts of step 5 fail, the node assumes that a catastrophe has occurred; perhaps the node's receiver has failed. In any case, the node ceases activity and listens to the bus.

Logical ring initialization occurs when one or more stations detect a lack of bus activity of duration longer than a time-out value: The token has been lost. This situation can have a number of causes; perhaps the network has just been powered up or a token-holding station fails. Once its time-out expires, a node will issue a *claim-token* frame. Contending claimants are resolved in a manner similar to the response-window process. Each claimant issues a claim-token frame padded by zero, two, four or six slots based on the first two bits of its address.

After transmission, a claimant listens to the medium and if it hears anything, drops its claim. Otherwise, it tries again, using the second pair of its address bits. The process repeats. With each iteration, only those stations that transmitted the longest on the previous iteration try again, using successive pairs of address bits. When all address bits have been used, a node that succeeds on the last iteration considers itself the token holder. The ring can now be rebuilt by the response window process described previously.

As an option, a token bus system can include classes of service that provide a mechanism of prioritizing access to the bus. Four classes of service are defined, in descending order of priority: 6, 4, 2, 0. Any station may have data in one or more of these classes to send. The object is to allocate network bandwidth to the higher priority frames and only send lower priority frames when there is sufficient bandwidth. To explain, let us define the following variables:

■ THT = token holding time: the maximum time that a station can hold the token to transmit class 6 (synchronous) data.

■ TRT4 = token rotation time for class 4: maximum time that a token can take to circulate and still permit class 4 transmission.

■ TRT2 = token rotation time for class 2: as above.

■ TRT0 = token rotation time for class 0: as above.

When a station receives the token, it can transmit classes of data according to the following rules (see Figure 10 on ID/35):

1. It may transmit class 6 data for a time THT. Hence, for an n-station ring, during one circulation of the token, the maximum amount of time available for class 6 transmission is n x THT.

2. After transmitting class 6 data, or if there was no class 6 data to transmit, it may transmit class 4 data only if the amount of time for the last circulation of the token (including any class 6 data just sent) is less than TRT4.

3. The station may next send class 2 data only if the amount of time for the last circulation of the token (including any class 6 and 4 data just sent) is less than TRT2.

4. The station may next send class 0 data only if the amount of time for the last circulation of the token (including any class 6, 4 and 2 data just sent) is less than TRT0.

This scheme, within limits, gives preference to frames of higher priority. More definitively, it guarantees that class 6 data may have a certain portion of the bandwidth.

Two cases are possible. If n x THT is greater than MAX[TRT4, TRT2, TRT0], the maximum possible token circulation time is n x THT, and class 6 data may occupy the entire cycle to the exclusion of other classes. If n x THT is less than MAX[TRT4, TRT2, TRT0], the maximum circulation time is MAX[TRT4, TRT2, TRT0], and class 6 data is guaranteed n x THT amount of that time.

Token bus physical layer specification

For token bus, three physical layer specifications are provided as options. All use 75-ohm CATV coaxial cable, and all use modems and analog signaling. This contrasts with the CSMA/CD baseband specification, which uses digital signaling on a special 50-ohm cable.

The simplest and least expensive option uses a form of frequency-shift keying (FSK) and operates at 1M bit/sec. This scheme is known as "single-channel broadband" to indicate that only one channel of signal can be carried; it is not possible to use frequency-division multiplexing. The second option is also single-channel broadband, using FSK at either 5M or 10M bit/sec. In this case, the electronic specifications are such that this option is easily upgradable to the final and most expensive option.

This final option is a full broadband system, which can carry multiple data channels, as well as video channels, simultaneously. Three data rates are provided: 1M bit/sec, which occupies a 1.5-MHz channel; 5M bit/sec, occupying a 6-MHz channel; and 10M bit/sec, occupying a 12-MHz channel.

Token ring

The token ring technique is the only medium access control protocol specified for the ring topology. The token ring technique is based on the use of a single token that circulates around the ring when all stations are idle (see Figure 11). A station wishing to transmit must wait until it detects a token passing by. It then changes the token from "free token" to "busy token." The station then transmits a frame immediately following the busy token.

There is now no free token on the ring, so other stations wishing to transmit must wait. The frame on the ring will make a round trip and be purged by the transmitting station. The transmitting station will insert a new free token on the ring when the station has completed transmission of its frame and the busy token has returned to the station.

If the bit length of the ring is less than the frame length, the first condition implies the second. If not, a station could release a free token after it has finished transmitting but before it receives its own busy token; the second condition is not strictly necessary.

In any case, the use of a token guarantees that only one station at a time may transmit.

When a transmitting station releases a new free token, the next station downstream with data to send will be able to seize the token and transmit.

Several implications of the token ring technique can be mentioned. Note that under lightly loaded conditions, there is some inefficiency because a station must wait for the token to come around before transmitting. However, under heavy loads, which is where it matters, the ring functions in a round-robin fashion, which is both efficient and fair. To see how this process works, refer to Figure 11.

Note that after station A transmits, it releases a token. The first station with an opportunity to transmit is D.

If D transmits, it then releases a token, and C has the next opportunity and so on. Finally, the ring must be long enough to hold the token. If stations are temporarily bypassed, their delay may need to be supplied artificially.

Token ring specification

The IEEE 802 token ring specification is a refinement of the scheme just outlined. The key elements are as follows:

1. **Single-token protocol:** A station that has completed transmission will not issue a new token until the busy token returns. This procedure is not as efficient, for small frames, as a multiple-token strategy of issuing a free token at the end of a frame. However, the single-token system simplifies priority and error-recovery functions.

2. **Priority bits:** These indicate the priority of a token and, therefore, which stations are allowed to use the token. In a multiple-priority scheme, priorities may be set by station or by message.

3. **Monitor bit:** It may be used if a central ring monitor is employed.

4. **Reservation indicators:** They may be used to allow stations with high-priority messages to indicate in a frame that the next token be issued at the requested priority.

5. **Token-holding timer:** Started at the beginning of data transfer, it controls the length of time a station may occupy the medium before transmitting a token.

6. **Acknowledgment bits:** There are three: error detected (E), address recognized (A) and frame copied (C). These are reset to 0 by the transmitting station. Any station may set the E bit. Addressed stations may set the A and C bits.

Figure 12 shows the two frame formats for token ring. The individual fields are as follows:

Starting delimiter (SD): a unique eight-bit pattern used to start each frame.

Access control (AC): has the format "PPPTMRRR," where PPP and RRR are three-bit priority and reservation variables, M is the monitor bit and T indicates whether this is a token or data frame. In the case of a token frame, the only additional field is ED.

Frame control (FC): indicates whether this is an LLC data frame. If not, bits in this field control operation of the token ring MAC protocol.

Destination address (DA): as in CSMA/CD and token bus.

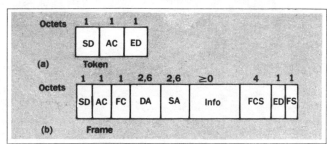

Figure 11. Operation of token ring

Figure 12. Token ring formats

IN DEPTH/LOCAL NETWORK STANDARDS

Source address (SA): as in CSMA/CD and token bus.

LLC: as in CSMA/CD and token bus.

FCS: as in CSMA/CD and token bus.

Ending delimiter (ED): contains the error detection (E) bit and the intermediate frame (I) bit. The I bit is used to indicate that this is a frame other than the final one of a multiple-frame transmission.

Frame status (FS): contains the address recognized (A) and frame copied (C) bits.

Let us first consider the operation of the ring when only a single priority is used. In this case, the priority and reservation bits are not used. A station wishing to transmit waits until a free token goes by, as indicated by a token bit of 0 in the AC field. The station seizes the token by setting the token bit to 1. It then transmits one or more frames, continuing until either its output is exhausted or its token-holding timer expires. After the busy token returns, the station transmits a free token.

Stations in the receive mode listen to the ring. Each station can check passing frames for errors and set the E bit if an error is detected. If a station detects its own address, it sets the A bit to 1; it may also copy the frame, setting the C bit to 1. This allows the originating station to differentiate three conditions: 1) station nonexistent/nonactive, 2) station exists but frame not copied and 3) frame copied.

The foregoing operation can be supplemented by a multiple-priority scheme. For example, bridges could be given higher priority than ordinary stations. The 802 specification provides three bits for eight levels of priority. For clarity, let us designate three values: P_m = priority of message to be transmitted by station; P_r = received priority; and R_r = received reservation. The scheme works as follows:

1. A station wishing to transmit must wait for a free token with $P_r \leq P_m$.

2. While waiting, a station may reserve a token at its priority level (P_m). If a busy token goes by, it may set the reservation field to its priority ($R_r \leftarrow P_m$) if the reservation field is less than its priority ($R_r < P_m$). If a free token goes by, it may set the reservation field to its priority ($R_r \leftarrow P_m$) if $R_r < P_m$ and $P_m < P_r$. This has the effect of preempting any lower priority reservations.

3. When a station seizes a token, it sets the token bit to 1, the reservation field to 0 and leaves the priority field unchanged.

4. Following transmission, a station issues a new token with the priority set to the maximum of P_r, R_r and P_m and a reservation set to the maximum of R_r and P_m.

The effect of the above steps is to sort out competing claims and allow the waiting transmission of highest priority to seize the token as soon as possible. A moment's reflection reveals that, as is, the algorithm has a ratchet effect on priority, driving it to the highest used level and keeping it there.

To avoid this situation, two stacks are maintained, one for reservations and one for priorities. In essence, each station is responsible for assuring that no token circulates indefinitely because its priority is too high. By remembering the priority of earlier transmissions, a station can detect this condition and downgrade the priority to a previous, lower priority or reservation.

Summarizing the priority algorithm

We are now in a position to summarize the priority algorithm. A station having a higher priority than the current busy token can reserve the next free token for its priority level as the busy token passes by. When the current transmitting station is finished, it issues a free token at that higher priority. Stations of lower priority cannot seize the token, so it passes to the requesting station or an intermediate station of equal or higher priority with data to send.

The station that upgraded the priority level is responsible for downgrading it to its former level when all higher priority stations are finished. When the station sees a free token at the higher priority, it can assume that there is no more higher priority traffic waiting, and it downgrades the token before passing it on.

To overcome various error situations, such as no token circulating and persistent busy token, one station is designated as active token monitor. The monitor detects the lost-token condition by using a time-out greater than the time required for the longest frame to completely traverse the ring. To recover, the monitor purges the ring of any residual data and issues a free token. To detect a circulating busy token, the monitor sets the monitor bit to 1 on any passing busy token. If it sees a busy token with a bit already set, it knows that the transmitting station failed to purge its frame. The monitor changes the busy token to a free token.

Other stations on the ring have the role of passive monitor. Their primary job is to detect failure of the active monitor and assume that role. A contention-resolution algorithm is used to determine which station takes over.

The physical layer specification for the token ring remains to be fully worked out. The following options are expected:

- A lower speed (1M to 4M bit/sec) ring will use a 150-ohm shielded twisted pair.
- Higher speed (4M to 40M bit/sec) may be provided with baseband coaxial cable.
- It is expected that a fiber-optic ring will be defined at some later date.

In many ways, the work of the IEEE 802 committee has been a resounding success. The committee has completed or is close to completing a full set of standards, which has received widespread acceptance. If there has been a failure, it is that the group did not come up with a single standard for local networks. This failure, however, reflects the diversity of the technology rather than any inadequacy within the committee.

About the author

Dr. William Stallings lectures and writes on data communications subjects. He is the author of Local Networks: An Introduction *(Macmillan, 1984), upon which this article is based.*

Stallings teaches an IEEE 802 course under the auspices of Omnicom, Inc. of Vienna, Va. He is senior communications consultant with Honeywell Information Systems, Inc. in McLean, Va.

SECTION 3 NETWORK ACCESS PROTOCOLS

3.1 OVERVIEW

The *network layer* is designed to facilitate communication between systems across a communications network. It is at this layer that the concept of a protocol becomes a little fuzzy. This is illustrated in Figure 3.1, which shows two stations that are communicating, not via direct link, but via a packet-switched network. The stations have direct links to the network nodes. The layer 1 and 2 protocols are station-node protocols (local). Layers 4 through 7 are clearly protocols between entities in the two stations (remote). Layer 3 is a little bit of both. Layer 3 is a station-node protocol since it provides a means for the station to gain access to the network and use the services provided by the node to which it attaches. However, to exchange data between stations, there must be some coordination between the two station-node pairs. This gives the layer 3 protocol an "end-to-end" flavor.

The basic service of the network layer is to provide for the transparent transfer of data between transport entities. It relieves the transport layer of the need to know anything about the underlying communications medium. Thus, the layer 3 entity is responsible for invoking routing and relay functions through switched networks.

When a station attaches to a network, not only must a layer 3 protocol be used, but the physical and data link characteristics of the station-node link must be specified. Thus, it is convenient to consider a set of such protocols as a network access protocol. This, in fact, is the way in which most standards have been developed. That is, the standard specifies the protocols of layers 1 through 3 for network access.

The most widely known network access standard is X.25, which defines the protocols for accessing a packet-switched network. For circuit-switched networks, X.21 is common. Finally, standards are now being developed for the forthcoming Integrated Services Digital Network (ISDN).

3.2 CIRCUIT-SWITCHED NETWORK ACCESS

Let us consider what is required, in terms of functions, for two devices to communicate across a circuit-switched network, and relate that to the OSI model. There are two phases of operation that are of interest: the call establishment phase and the data transfer phase.

For the *data transfer phase,* a circuit-switched network provides a transparent data path between communicating stations. To the attached stations, it appears that they have a direct full-duplex link. They are free to use their own formats, protocols, and frame synchronization. This situation is depicted in Figure 3.2a. Each station is attached to a node of the communication network (example: a modem). The dashed line indicates the path of the data and the elements through which it passes. Data from the source station pass through that node, one or more intermediate nodes, and finally through the node to which the destination station is connected. Because the connection is transparent, the protocol from station to node is just at the physical level. Each node acts as a relay, passing on data from input to output. The intermediate nodes perform a switching function but,

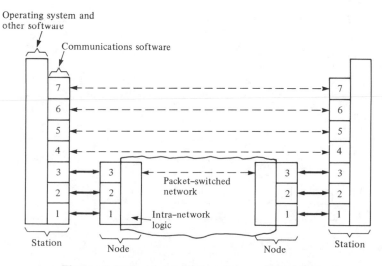

Figure 3-1: Communication across a Network

again, simply relay the data transparently.

The *call establishment phase* is more complex. Both calling and called stations have a dialogue with an element of the network:

- *Calling station:* Sends a call request to the network identifying the called station; receives call progress signals from the network.
- *Called station:* Receives call request from network; sends call acceptance to network.

This dialogue is, in OSI terms, a layer 3 protocol. Figure 3.2b depicts this protocol as taking place between the station and some intermediate node which performs a network exchange function. This node can be considered to represent all of the switching nodes involved in setting up the connection. Note that this node still performs a relay function, but this now occurs at layer 3. Thus, two general types of functions are performed by the network:

- It relays call request and call accepted signals between stations.

- It has a dialogue with each station to establish the call.

Once the call is established, there is no need for an active network role, other than at the physical layer. Thus, the configuration of Figure 3.2a obtains. All protocols, down through layer 2, are end-to-end.

3.3 PACKET-SWITCHED NETWORK ACCESS

Unlike a circuit-switched network, a packet-switched network is not transparent to attached stations, even during the data transfer phase. Stations must break up their data into packets. The station-node protocol must perform the following functions:

- Flow control.
- Error control.
- Multiplexing.

Flow control is needed in both directions. The network must protect itself from congestion, and to do this may need to limit the flow of packets from the attached stations. Simi-

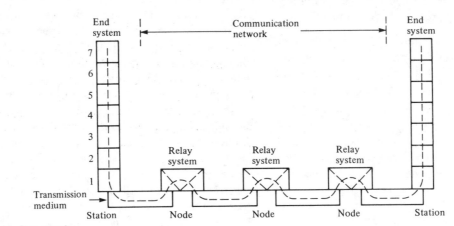

(a) Data transfer

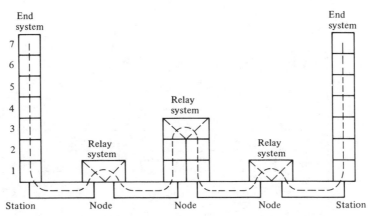

(b) Call establishment

**Figure 3-2: OSI Configurations for Circuit-Switched Communication.
Source: [FOLT83]**

150

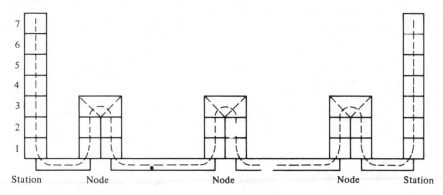

Figure 3-3: OSI Configuration for Packet-Switched Communication

larly, a station needs to be able to control the rate at which the network delivers packets to it. These considerations did not apply in the case of circuit switching. The circuit-switched network provides a transparent path of constant data rate. The network allocates resources to maintain that data rate. The stations may use end-to-end flow control at the data link level to limit data flow.

Since station and node are exchanging control information as well as data, some form of *error control* is needed to assure that all of the control information is received properly.

Finally, most packet-switched networks provide a *multiplexing* service. With this service, a station can establish multiple virtual circuits with other stations at the same time.

Figure 3.3 depicts the protocol architecture implied by the above requirements. Each node, including intermediate nodes, performs functions up through layer 3. The articles reprinted in this section should help clarify this figure.

3.4 ARTICLE SUMMARY

The X.25 standard for access to packet-switched networks is explored by Rybczynski. A practical discussion of the implementation of X.25 is contained in Burg. The X.21 standard for access to circuit-switched networks is discussed by Folts, and Yanoschak provides a practical discussion of its implementation. The final article, by Dècina, describes emerging network access protocols for ISDN.

X.25 Interface and End–to–End Virtual Circuit Service Characteristics

ANTONY RYBCZYNSKI, MEMBER, IEEE

(Invited Paper)

Abstract—Public packet switching networks around the world use CCITT Recommendation X.25, which is the standard device-independent interface between packet networks and user devices operating in the packet-mode. Since its development in 1976 and with four years of network operational experience, the X.25 interface specification has reached a high level of maturity. A revised version of X.25 has been approved by CCITT Study Group VII at its meeting in February 1980. The revised X.25 specification is more complete than its predecessor, eliminates a number of ambiguous areas which lead to network implementation differences, and has been enhanced by the addition of new capabilities both to the X.25 interface and to the end-to-end service.

This paper presents a consolidated view of the end-to-end characteristics of the virtual-circuit-based services accessible through the X.25 interface. It then discusses the characteristics of the revised X.25 interface, with emphasis on areas that have been addressed in the revised Recommendation.

The revised Recommendation leads the way to greater commonality among network implementations. The increased functionality of the end-to-end virtual-circuit services has impact on the relationship of X.25 to system architectures being discussed by international standards bodies.

Manuscript received May 7, 1979; revised December 18, 1979.

The author is with the Computer Communications Group, Trans-Canada Telephone System, Ottawa, Ont., Canada.

I. INTRODUCTION AND GENERAL DESCRIPTION

A. Introduction

THE 1970's heralded the beginning of the development of public networks either in the form of experimental networks (France: RCP, U.K.: EPSS, Japan: DDX) or commercial networks (Canada: Datapac, U.S.A.: Telenet). The basis of all of these networks was the belief that packet-switching was an appropriate technology for public data networks (PDN's). However, in their embryonic stages, the designs of each of these networks incorporated substantially different terminal access procedures for both host computers and slow speed character terminals. It was recognized that the commercial viability of these networks hinged largely on the development and adoption of standard access protocols. These standards would facilitate the connection of varying types of data terminal equipments (DTE's) to the various public networks being developed, as well as facilitate international internetworking. Without these standards, users would almost definitely not be benefiting from the establishment of public data networks on a worldwide basis.

The International Telegraph and Telephone Consultative Committee (CCITT), a permanent organ of the International Telecommunications Union, is responsible for establishing "Recommendations" applicable to various aspects of international communications, including public data networks. A number of recommendations related to PDN services have been approved within the last four years, most notably X.25 [1]-[3].

The year 1980 finds us with PDN's offering packet-mode services being available in the U.S.A., Canada, the U.K., France, and Japan and on the verge of being established in a large number of other countries [4]. All of these networks are based on the support of the aforementioned CCITT Recommendations. Furthermore, international services have already been established among a number of these countries. In order to meet the market need of gaining access to X.25 services, a number of mainframe and terminal manufacturers have announced products supporting X.25.

CCITT Recommendation X.25 was first approved in March 1976. The last formal revision took place in 1977 with the addition of data link control procedures, which are compatible with the high-level data link control (HDLC) procedures standardized by the International Organization of Standardization (ISO). The next formal revision of X.25 will take place in the fall of 1980. This paper conveys the important enhancements to X.25 which have been agreed and are currently contained in the proposed text of the revised Recommendation [5].

B. General Description of the X.25 Interface

The X.25 interface between the DTE and the data circuit-terminating equipment (DCE) consists of three distinct levels of control procedures as illustrated in Fig. 1:

1) the physical level
2) the frame level, and
3) the packet level.

Each of these levels functions independently of the other levels, with the exception that failures at a level may affect the operation of higher levels.

The physical level specifies the use of a duplex, point-to-point synchronous circuit, thus providing a physical transmission path between the DTE and the network. It also specifies the use of the V.24 physical interface (i.e., the EIA RS-232-C standard) between the DTE and a data set or modem. Therefore, no changes to the interface hardware of the DTE are required. The physical level also specifies the use of Recommendation X.21 [6] although this capability is not yet widely available.

The frame level specifies the use of data link control procedures which are compatible with HDLC [7] and with the advanced data communications control procedure (ADCCP) standardized by the U.S. American National Standards Institute (ANSI). The frame level uses the principles of an ISO class of procedures for a point-to-point balanced system; in X.25, these procedures are referred to as the balanced link access procedures (LAPB). The use of this data link control procedure ensures that packets provided by the packet level and contained in HDLC information frames (see Fig. 2) are ac-

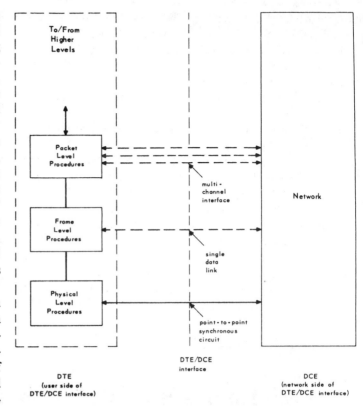

Fig. 1.   Structure of the X.25 interface.

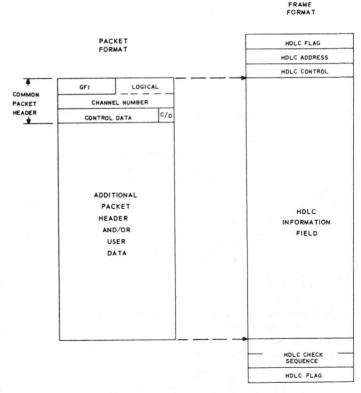

GFI - General Format Identifier
C/D - 0 for user DATA Packet
    - 1 for control packet

Fig. 2.   General X.25 packet and frame formats.

curately exchanged between the DTE and the network. The functions performed by the frame level interface include:

1) the transfer of data in an efficient and timely fashion;

2) the synchronization of the link to ensure that the receiver is in step with the transmitter;

3) the detection of transmission errors and recovery from such errors; and

4) the identification and reporting of procedural errors to higher layers for recovery.

The major significance of the frame level is that it provides the packet level with an error-free, variable delay link between the DTE and the network.

The packet level is the highest level of the X.25 interface and specifies the manner in which control information and user data are structured into packets. The control information, including addressing information, is contained in the packet header field and allows the network to identify the DTE for which the packet is destined. It also allows a single physical circuit to support communications to numerous other DTE's concurrently.

The characteristics of the packet level are further described in Section III.

C. Network Services Available to X.25 DTE's

A distinction must be made between the X.25 interface and the services provided on a PDN operating in the packet-mode and accessed across this interface by the DTE. Recommendation X.25 defines procedures to be used across the interface between the packet-mode DTE and the common-carrier equipment, generally referred to as the DCE. The X.25 interface Recommendation provides access to the following services that may be provided on public data networks:

1) switched virtual circuits (SVC's), also called virtual calls;

2) permanent virtual circuits (PVC's); and

3) datagrams.

A virtual circuit (VC) is a bidirectional transparent, flow-controlled path between a pair of logical or physical ports. A switched virtual circuit is a temporary association between two DTE's and is initiated by a DTE signaling a call request to the network. A permanent virtual circuit is a permanent association existing between two DTE's, which is analogous to a point-to-point private line. Thus, it requires no call set-up or call clearing action by the DTE.

A datagram (DG) is a self-contained entity of data containing sufficient information to be routed to the destination DTE (independently of all other entities) without the need for a call to be established. At this time, the datagram service is not provided on any PDN's. This service is not within the scope of this paper (see, however, [8]).

The characteristics of virtual circuits are now presented.

II. X.25 END-TO-END VIRTUAL CIRCUIT SERVICE CHARACTERISTICS

A. Introduction

The virtual circuit service characteristics are currently specified in a nonsystematic way in various sections of Recom-

mendation X.25. This section attempts to consolidate the specification of VC characteristics. The perspective for this discussion is a view of the DTE-to-DTE services provided by VC's rather than a view of the signaling at either of the two interfaces.

B. Establishment and Clearing of a Virtual Circuit

A switched virtual circuit is established when the call request issued by the calling DTE is accepted by the called DTE. A permanent virtual circuit is always established and therefore, no establishment procedures are required. The call request identifies the called and calling addresses and facilities requested for the call, and may include user data. The user data sent during the call establishment phase is available for use by the higher layers (e.g., system passwords).

During the call establishment phase, the calling DTE may request certain optional user facilities (e.g., reverse charging) to be associated with the VC. In some cases (e.g., throughput class) the called DTE may wish to alter the facility values requested by the caller. Thus, the VC service provides mechanisms for facility negotiations during call setup. Optional user facilities are discussed in Section IV.

If the call is refused by the called DTE, the DTE can signal the reason for call clearing to the calling DTE in a diagnostic code. If the call attempt fails for some other reason, a call progress signal is transmitted across the network indicating one of the causes specified in X.25 and given in Table I. As will be seen in the next section, the diagnostic code is also used by the network to provide extra information to the DTE when it has made a local interface procedure error. This latter use is a characteristic of the X.25 interface rather than of the virtual circuit itself.

Once the call has entered the data transfer phase, either DTE can clear the call using the diagnostic code to signal to the remote DTE the reason for the clearing. If the call is cleared by the network, it will signal this fact and indicate a call progress signal (Table I). When a call is cleared, data may be discarded by the network since the clear is not sequenced in respect to user data. All data generated by the DTE before initiation of a clear procedure will either be delivered to the remote DTE before completion of the clearing procedure at the remote DTE/DCE interface, or be discarded by the network. When a DTE initiates a clear, all data which were generated by the remote DTE before it has received the corresponding indication will be either delivered to the initiating DTE before the clear procedure is completed locally, or discarded by the network.

C. Data Transfer

In the data transfer phase, user data which are conveyed in DATA and INTERRUPT packets are passed transparently through the network. DTE's wishing universal operation on all networks should transmit all packets with data fields containing only an integral number of octets.

Virtual circuit flow control is a mechanism provided to ensure that the transmitting DTE does not generate data at a rate that is faster (on average) than that which the receiving

TABLE I
CLEARING CALL PROGRESS SIGNALS

Call Progress Signal	Explanation
DTE Originated	Called DTE has refused the call or remote DTE has cleared it.
Number busy	The called DTE is engaged in other calls and cannot accept the incoming call.
Out of order	The remote number is out of order. (X.25 Physical and/or Frame levels not in operation).
Remote procedure error	An X.25 procedure error has occurred at the remote DTE/DCE interface.
Reverse charging acceptance not subscribed*	Network has blocked the call because the called DTE does not accept reverse charged calls.
Incompatible destination	The remote DTE/DCE interface does not support a function used or facility requested.
Fast select acceptance not subscribed*	The network has blocked the call because the called DTE does not support fast select calls.
Invalid facility request	Facility request invalid (e.g., a request for a facility which has not been subscribed to or is not available in the local network).
Access barred	The calling DTE is not permitted the connection to the called DTE. (e.g., incompatible closed user group).
Local procedure error	A procedure error is detected at the local DTE/DCE interfaces. (e.g., incorrect format, expiration of a timeout).
Network congestion	Temporary network congestion or a temporary fault condition has occurred within the network.
Not obtainable	The called DTE address does not correspond to any assigned address.
RPOA Out of Order*	The RPOA nominated by the calling DTE is unable to forward the call.

* received only if the corresponding facility is requested by the caller.

DTE can accept. This is achieved by the receiving DTE controlling the rate at which it accepts DATA packets across the DTE/DCE interface, noting that there is an upper limit on the number of DATA packets which may be in the network on a virtual circuit. Thus, flow control has end-to-end significance in that back pressure exerted by a receiving DTE is reflected back to the sending DTE.

A considerable debate has taken place in the past on whether the DTE or the network should determine the maximum number of DATA packets which may be in the network on a virtual circuit. On the one hand, there is a need for the network to assign resources to the VC based on information available to it (e.g., call routing) and on performance, specifically, throughput, characteristics associated with the service. In this case, the network determines the maximum number of DATA packets that can be on a VC and the DTE need not be concerned with this aspect. On the other hand, there is a need to allow DTE's to select the maximum number of DATA packets that can be on a VC and thus be able to ascertain whether certain DATA packets have been delivered to the remote DTE. This information can be used in conjunction with a higher level DTE-to-DTE error control protocol. With the addition of the delivery confirmation procedure in X.25, both objectives can be met simultaneously.

It has been agreed that DTE-to-DTE acknowledgment of delivery be available as a standard characteristic of X.25 virtual circuits. Specifically, if a DTE wishes to receive end-to-end acknowledgment for data it is transmitting across the X.25 interface, it uses an indicator called the delivery confirmation, or D bit, contained in the header of DATA packets. The D bit is always associated with the last octet in the DATA packet in which it is set by the DTE; this relationship is preserved by the network on an end-to-end basis even when the maximum packet lengths used at the DTE/DCE interfaces at each end of a VC are not the same. The acknowledgment is signaled via the packet receive sequence number $P(R)$, discussed in Section III.

Since the network may perform packet-length conversion, X.25 defines a "complete packet sequence" which is a sequence of DATA packets which may be combined by the network. The only DATA packets which can be combined with subsequent DATA packets are those that are full, have the D bit set to zero and have an indication set by the sending DTE that more data is to follow; the D bit has priority over the more data indication in packet combination so that a DATA packet with the D bit set to one is never combined with a subsequent packet. The more data indication may only be set by the DTE in full DATA packets or in partially full DATA packets which also have the D bit set to one. A sequence of DATA packets each carrying a more data indication except fo the last one will be delivered as an equivalent sequence of DATA packets.

Two independent mechanisms are provided to transfer user control information between a pair of DTE's outside the normal flow of data on a VC. The first mechanism transfers user control data within the normal flow control and sequencing procedures on a virtual circuit. This is called the data qualifier procedure and applies to "complete packet sequences."

The second mechanism bypasses the normal DATA packet transmission sequence and provides an out of band (non-sequenced) signaling channel on VC's. The INTERRUPT packet, which is used in this case, may contain one octet of user data and is always delivered at or before the point in the stream of DATA packets at which it was generated, even when DATA packets are being flow controlled.

The maximum attainable throughput on virtual circuits carried at the DTE/DCE interface may vary due to the statistical sharing of transmission and switch resources and is constrained by:

1) the access line speed, local flow control parameters, and traffic on other calls at the local DTE/DCE interface;

2) the access line speed, local flow control parameters, and traffic on other calls at the remote DTE/DCE interface; and

3) the maximum throughput achievable through the network independent of access line characteristics. This limit may differ for national and varying types of international calls.

The above throughput will generally not be reached unless a) the access data links of both ends of the VC are traffic engineered properly, b) the receiving DTE is not flow controlling the DCE, c) the transmitting DTE is sending DATA packets which have the maximum data field length, and d) use of the D bit does not constrain the throughput.

TABLE II
RESETTING CALL PROGRESS SIGNALS

Call Progress Signal	Explanation
DTE Originated	Remote DTE reset the VC
Out of order (PVC only)	The remote DTE is out of order (e.g., X.25 Physical and/or Frame levels not in operation).
Remote procedure error	The call is cleared because of a procedure error at the remote DTE/DCE interface.
Local procedure error	A procedure error is detected at the local DTE/DCE interfaces. (e.g., incorrect format, expiration of a time-out).
Network congestion	Temporary network congestion or temporary fault condition has occurred within the network.
Remote DTE operational (PVC only)	Remote DTE/DCE interface is ready to resume normal operation after a temporary failure or out of order condition.
Network operational (PVC only)	Network is ready to resume normal operation after a temporary failure or congestion.
Incompatible destination	The remote DTE/DCE interface does not support a function used.

D. Error Recovery

The reset procedure is used to reinitialize the virtual circuit and in so doing removes in each direction all user data which may be in the network. When the reset is initiated by the DTE, it may convey to the remote DTE the reason for the resetting via a diagnostic code. If it is a network-generated reset, the reason is conveyed to both DTE's. Table II lists call progress signals associated with resetting in X.25.

All data generated by a DTE before initiation of a reset will either be delivered to the remote DTE before the corresponding indicator, or discarded by the network; all data generated after completion of a reset procedure at the local interface will be delivered after completion of the corresponding reset procedure at the remote interface. When a DTE initiates a reset procedure, all data which was generated by the remote DTE before its receipt of the corresponding indication are either delivered to the initiating DTE before the procedure is completed locally, or discarded by the network. Multiple and simultaneous resets are handled at the local interface as defined by the procedures for single resets.

The maximum number of packets which may be discarded when the clearing or resetting procedure has been invoked is a function of network end-to-end delay and network resources assigned in conjunction with the provided throughput. The maximum number of packets with the D bit set is a parameter of an X.25 interface (i.e., the local DTE transmit window size discussed in Section III-D).

TABLE III
X.25 PACKET FORMATS

Packet Type	Common*	Cause	Diagnostic	Addresses and Address Length	Facilities and Facility Length	Data
CALL REQUEST	REQ	-	-	REQ	REQ	OPT (16)
CALL CONNECTED	REQ	-	-	OPT	OPT	-
DATA	REQ	-	-	-	-	OPT (128)
INTERRUPT	REQ	-	-	-	-	REQ(1)
RR/RNR	REQ	-	-	-	-	-
RESET/CLEAR RESTART REQUEST	REQ	REQ	OPT	-	-	-
INTERRUPT/ RESET/CLEAR/ RESTART CONFIRMATION	REQ	-	-	-	-	-

REQ: required
REQ (X): required, of maximum length X octets
OPT: optional (only if all subsequent optional fields are not present)
OPT (X): optional, of maximum length X octets
- : not applicable
* Three octet Common Packet Header Field

III. X. 25 PACKET LEVEL INTERFACE CHARACTERISTICS

A. Introduction

Recommendation X.25 specifies the procedures to be used by DTE's in establishing, maintaining and clearing virtual circuits. This section now discusses these packet level interface procedures (see, also, [9]).

Packet formats for the various types of packets are summarized in Table III.

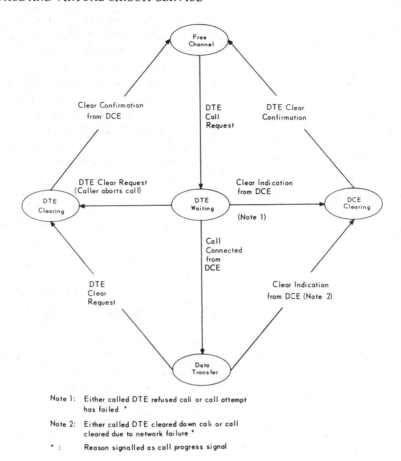

Note 1: Either called DTE refused call or call attempt has failed *

Note 2: Either called DTE cleared down call or call cleared due to network failure *

* : Reason signalled as call progress signal

Fig. 3.   Illustration of call establishment and clearing at the calling DTE/DCE interface.

B. Multiplexing at the X.25 Interface

In order to allow a DTE to establish concurrent virtual circuits with a number of DTE's over a single physical access circuit, the X.25 packet level employs packet-interleaved statistical multiplexing. This multiplexing technique is used to exploit the fact that a typical virtual circuit to a remote DTE may actually be carrying data for only a small percentage of the time. Each packet contains a logical channel number which identifies the packet with a switched or permanent virtual circuit for both directions of transmission.

The range of logical channel numbers that can be used for virtual circuits is established at subscription time by agreement between the DTE and the network. If the DTE can only support a single VC, then logical channel number one will be used. If both PVC's and SVC's are used, then individual PVC's are statically assigned logical channel numbers in a range starting from number one, while logical channels for calls are assigned a range above this. Logical channel numbers for SVC's are dynamically assigned during call establishment and identify all packets (i.e., control and data) associated with the VC. The logical channel numbers are only significant at a particular DTE/DCE interface.

Every packet transferred across an X.25 DTE/DCE interface consists of a three-octet common packet header field as shown in Fig. 2.

C. Establishing and Clearing a Virtual Circuit

A signaling method is provided to allow a DTE to establish switched virtual circuits to other DTE's using logical channel numbers at each end to locally designate these switched virtual circuits.

A DTE initiates a call by sending a CALL REQUEST packet (Fig. 3) to the network. The CALL REQUEST packet includes the logical channel number chosen by the DTE to be used to identify all packets associated with the call. It also includes the network address of the called DTE. A facility field is present only when the DTE wishes to request an optional user facility requiring some indication at call setup. Reverse charging is an example of such a facility. User data may follow the facility field and may contain up to a maximum of 16 octets.

The calling DTE will receive a CALL CONNECTED packet as a response indicating that the called DTE has accepted the call. (Fig. 3.)

If the call is refused by the called DTE, or if the attempt fails, the calling DTE will receive a CLEAR INDICATION indicating the appropriate call progress signal, and a one-octet diagnostic field, generated by the DTE and by the network in the former and latter cases, respectively.

Call clearing, once the call enters the data phase, may be initiated by either DTE (or by the network in case of failure).

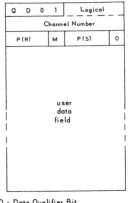

Q - Data Qualifier Bit
D - Delivery Confirmation Bit
M - More Data Bit
P(S) - Packet send sequence Number
P(R) - Packet receive sequence Number

Fig. 4. DATA packet format.

In any event, the logical channel number can be used again for another call when the clearing procedure is completed, normally by the transfer of a CLEAR CONFIRMATION packet.

D. Data Transfer

DATA packets, illustrated in Fig. 4, can only be transferred across a logical channel after the virtual circuit has been established and if flow control constraints are not violated.

$P(S)$ is the packet send sequence number of the packet. Only DATA packets are numbered, the numbering normally being performed modulo 8. The maximum number of sequentially numbered DATA packets that the DTE (or DCE) may be authorized to transmit, without further authorization from the network (or DTE), may never exceed seven. The actual maximum value, called the window size W, is set for the logical channel either at subscription time or at call setup time [using the facility described in Section IV-B2)]. The default value for W is two.

Each DATA packet also carries a packet receive sequence number, $P(R)$, which authorizes the transmission of W DATA packets on this logical channel starting with a send sequence number equal to the value of $P(R)$. If the DTE or the network wishes to authorize the transmission of one or more DATA packets across the interface, but there is no data flow on a given logical channel in the reverse direction on which to piggy-back this information, it can transmit a RECEIVE READY (RR) packet, If, on the other hand, the DTE or the network wishes to confirm the acceptance of a DATA packet with the D bit set to one, but does not wish to authorize the transmission of any more data, it can transmit a RECEIVE NOT READY (RNR) packet. Flow control based on the conveyance of $P(R)$ numbers across a logical channel ensures that a sending DTE does not transmit data at an average rate which is greater than that at which the receiving DTE can accept that data.

The data field of a DATA packet may be any length up to some maximum value. The latter may be established independently at each end of a virtual circuit. Every network will support a maximum value of 128 octets.

When the delivery confirmation or D bit is set to zero, the $P(R)$ number is used to locally convey flow control information. When the D bit in Fig. 4 is used, the corresponding $P(R)$ is used to convey delivery confirmation information and therefore has DTE-to-DTE significance.

In order to allow two communicating DTE's to each operate at their locally selected packet sizes, the user may indicate, in a full DATA packet, or any DATA packet with the D bit set to one, that there is a logical continuation of his data in the next DATA packet on a particular logical channel. This is done with the more data "M" bit contained in the DATA packet header as indicated in Fig. 4. Only a full DATA packet may have a more data indication since a partially full packet is treated as if it had the M bit off.

The procedures used in conjunction with the data qualifier procedure are identical to those that apply to DATA packets. The format used in this procedure is identical to that of the DATA transfer packet except that the "Q" bit is set in the DATA packet header (see Fig. 4).

INTERRUPT packets, on the other hand, may be transmitted across the DTE/DCE interface even when DATA packets are being flow controlled. They may contain neither send nor receive sequence numbers. Only one unconfirmed INTERRUPT may be outstanding at a given time.

E. Error Recovery

1) *Reset Procedure*: The reset procedure is used to reinitialize the flow control procedure on a given logical channel to the state it was in when the virtual circuit was established (i.e., all sequence numbers equal to zero and no data in transit). To reach this state, all DATA and INTERRUPT packets which may be in transit at the time of resetting are discarded. RESET REQUEST and CONFIRMATION packets are used in the reset procedure.

2) *Restart Procedure*: The restart procedure provides a mechanism to recover from major failures. The issuance of a RESTART REQUEST packet is equivalent to sending a CLEAR REQUEST on all logical channels for switched virtual circuits and a RESET REQUEST on all logical channels for permanent virtual circuits. Thus, the restarting procedure will bring the user/network interface to the state it was in when service was initiated.

3) *Error Handling*: Recommendation X.25 (1976) layed the groundwork for further study on how packet level errors were to be handled at the X.25 interface. The following principles were established:

a) procedural errors during call establishment and clearing are reported to the DTE by clearing the call;

b) procedural errors during the data transfer phase are reported to the DTE by resetting the VC;

c) a diagnostic field is included in the reset packet to provide additional information to the DTE;

d) timers are essential in resolving some deadlock conditions;

e) some DTE procedural errors are a result of the DTE and DCE not being aligned as to the subscription options provided at the interface; and

f) rudimentary error tables define the action of the

DCE on receiving various packet types in every various states of the interface.

Several important error conditions were still not covered. Consequently, a major effort was expended to expand the error tables in X.25, to reach agreement on time-out strategies, and to increase the amount of information provided to DTE's via diagnostic codes and via a newly defined DIAGNOSTIC packet mechanism. These will now be briefly discussed.

Error tables were enhanced in two ways. Firstly, the number of error conditions handled was increased significantly. Secondly, the information content was increased by indicating not only the action taken by the DCE on detecting an error condition but also the state which the DCE enters.

A number of special error cases (e.g., packet on unassigned logical channel) have been identified in X.25 for which it is inappropriate to inform a DTE of a procedural error by resetting or clearing the logical channel. In this case it has been agreed that a DIAGNOSTIC packet be used. The DIAGNOSTIC packet is nonprocedural in nature and solely for DTE logging. The DIAGNOSTIC packet identifies the logical channel number on which an error condition has been detected, and includes a diagnostic code.

Two areas associated with time-outs have been addressed. The first area relates to the length of time the DTE has to respond to an incoming call. On one hand, the network wishes to minimize its resources. On the other hand, short time-out values are not reasonable due to the interaction between calls on a single interface, and between the packet and frame levels, and due to user processing within higher layers. A minimum value of three minutes has been agreed.

The second area relates to the action of the DCE when no confirmation has been received to an indication packet (i.e., during resetting, clearing and restarting). In order to avoid long looping conditions, it has been agreed that the DCE will not retransmit indication packets. Instead, the DCE will take the following actions.

1) On expiry of a 60-second timer after issuing a RESET INDICATION, the DCE will clear the call, indicating the reason for clearing via the diagnostic code, and call progress signal. On a PVC, a DIAGNOSTIC packet is sent.

2) On expiry of a 60-second timer after issuing a CLEAR INDICATION, the DCE will issue a DIAGNOSTIC packet and should eventually assume the interface has entered the ready state. In this state, the DCE does not ignore any packets sent by the DTE.

3) On expiry of a 60-second timer after a RESTART INDICATION has been issued, the DCE will issue a DIAGNOSTIC packet. The DCE considers this condition serious and will stay in this state indefinitely.

Diagnostic codes have been defined for reset, clear, and restart packets. The contents of the diagnostic code field provide nonprocedural information which do not alter the meaning of the call progress signal also provided. A DTE is not required to undertake any action on the content of the diagnostic code field. However, the DTE is advised to log the diagnostic to facilitate the correction of the problem.

Network-generated diagnostic codes are hierarchical. That is, for any specific diagnostic code there is always a code which is of a more general nature. The specific codes provide information allowing the DTE implementor to quickly diagnose problems. The more general codes are used when relatively uncommon or unanticipated problems occur. To accelerate trouble resolution, the X.25 error tables have been further enhanced by indicating the diagnostic code generated under each error condition.

F. Interrelationship Between Levels

Changes of the operational states of the physical and frame levels of the DTE/DCE interface do not implicitly change the state of each logical channel at the packet level; such changes when they occur are explicitly indicated by the use of packet level restart, clear, or reset procedures as appropriate.

A failure at the physical and/or frame levels is defined as a condition in which the DCE cannot transmit and receive any frames because of abnormal conditions caused by, for instance, a line fault between the DTE and the DCE. When a failure is detected, the DCE will transmit to the remote end a reset indicating out of order for a permanent virtual circuit and a clear indicating out of order for an existing virtual call. During the failure, the DCE will clear any incoming virtual calls.

When the failure is recovered, the DCE will send a RESTART INDICATION packet indicating network operational to the local DTE; this will result in a reset indicating remote DTE operational to be transmitted to the remote end of each permanent virtual circuit.

IV. OPTIONAL USER FACILITIES

A. Introduction

CCITT Recommendation X.2 defines the availability of various optional user facilities as being universally available or only available in some countries. Recommendation X.25 defines the interface procedures associated with all optional user facilities, irrespective of their availability.

This section describes only those optional user facilities which are proposed to be universally available.

B. Optional User Facilities

1) *Closed User Group Facility*: Closed user group is an optional user facility agreed to for a period of time between the administration and a group of users. This facility permits the users of the group to communicate with each other, but precludes communication with all other users. A DTE may belong to more than one closed user group.

The calling DTE specifies the closed user group selected for a virtual call using the optional user facility parameters in the CALL REQUEST packet. The closed user group selected for a call is indicated to a called DTE using the optional user facility parameters in the INCOMING CALL packet.

2) *Flow Control Parameter Selection*: Flow control parameter selection is an optional user facility agreed to for a period of time which can be used by a DTE for its logical channels. The flow control parameters considered are the packet and window sizes for each logical channel at the DTE/DCE interface for each direction of data transmission.

When the DTE has subscribed to the facility, it may, in a CALL REQUEST packet, separately request packet sizes and window sizes for each direction of data transmission. The maximum packet sizes that may be supported on public data networks are 16, 32, 64, 128, 256, 512, and 1024 octets. If a particular packet or window size is not explicitly requested, the DCE assumes default requests of 128 octets and 2, respectively.

When the DCE transmits a CALL CONNECTED packet, it indicates in the facility field the flow control parameters to be used by the calling DTE. The only valid facility indications in the CALL CONNECTED packet as a function of the facility requests in the CALL REQUEST packet are specified by the following general negotiation rules:

a) window sizes can be changed in the direction of $W = 2$; and

b) packet sizes can be changed in the direction of 128 octets.

When the called DTE subscribes to the facility, the DCE transmits flow control parameter facility indications to be used by the called DTE in selecting the flow control parameters for the call. The called DTE can change the indicated values using the above negotiation rules.

The flow control parameters for logical channels used for PVC's are established at subscription time.

The network may have to constrain the available parameter ranges in order to allow the call to be established.

3) *Throughput Class Negotiation*: Throughput class negotiation is an optional user facility agreed for a period of time which can be used by a DTE for virtual circuits. This facility permits negotiation on a per call basis of the throughput classes. The throughput classes are considered independently for each direction of data transmission.

A throughput class for one direction of transmission is an inherent characteristic of a virtual circuit related to the amount of network resources allocated to it. This characteristic is meaningful when the D bit is set to 0 in DATA packets. It is a measure of the throughput that is not normally exceeded on the VC. However, due to the statistical sharing of transmission and switching resources, it is not guaranteed that the throughput class can be reached 100 percent of the time.

Default values are agreed between the DTE and the network. The default values correspond to the maximum throughput classes which may be associated with any virtual circuit at the DTE/DCE interface.

4) *One-way Outgoing Logical Channel*: The one-way outgoing logical channel is an optional user facility agreed for a period of time. This user facility restricts the use of a range of logical channels to outgoing calls. One-way logical channels retain their full-duplex nature with respect to data transfer.

5) *Incoming or Outgoing Calls Barred*: Incoming or outgoing calls barred are two optional user facilities agreed for a period of time. These facilities apply to all logical channels used at the DTE/DCE interface for switched virtual circuits.

Incoming calls barred prevents incoming calls from being presented to the DTE. The DTE may originate outgoing calls. Outgoing calls barred prevents the DCE from accepting outgoing calls from the DTE. The DTE may receive incoming calls.

V. CONCLUDING REMARKS

A. A Common X.25 DTE

Network implementations of X.25 have come under some criticism in technical papers, such as one from IBM [10], which question whether a sufficient degree of commonality exists in the various X.25 implementations. The revised CCITT Recommendation X.25, which has been approved by Study Group VII in February 1980, resolves a number of key areas which lead to network differences.

From a DTE implementation point of view, a common X.25 interface can be defined [11], which consists of the following universally available features:

1) an ISO-compatible frame level procedure (i.e., LAPB);

2) use of logical channel number one as the starting point for logical channel assignment;

3) modulo 8 packet level numbering;

4) dynamic $P(R)$ significance by use of the delivery confirmation bit;

5) a standard procedure for selecting packet and window sizes, with defaults of 128 octets and 2, respectively;

6) two mechanisms for user control data transfer (i.e., qualified DATA and INTERRUPT packets); and

7) a standard way of specifying required call throughput.

What remains is for various network implementors to announce their implementation plans of the above features.

B. Relationship of X.25 to the Open System Architecture

The set of commonly agreed standards, which make possible meaningful interworking between any combination of communication processing and data processing systems and the relationships among these standards, are collectively known as the Open Systems Architecture (OSA) [12]. The purpose of the OSA is to provide a complete reference structure of standards necessary to achieve system interworking. The reference structure will place existing standards in perspective and facilitate the identification of areas in existing standards requiring additional developments and of areas where standards should be developed.

The CCITT is developing a "layered model of public data network service applications" [13] for the purpose of facilitating DTE interworking or gaining access to network services (e.g., directory assistance, electronic mail). At the same time, ISO is defining a model for open system interconnection [14]. A high degree of compatibility between CCITT's and ISO's Models is desirable; this will be facilitated by the cooperation which already exists between the two organizations.

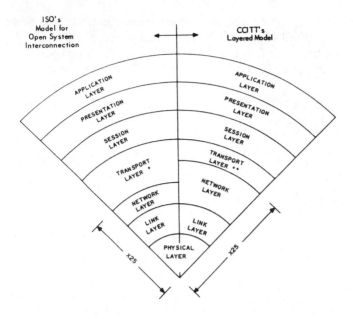

* The Transport Layer is required to provide functions not assumed to be available from X.25 VC's.

**The Transport Layer becomes a null layer if the quality of service provided by X.25 VC's is adequate.

Fig. 5.   Relationship of X.25 to ISO and CCITT models.

It has been generally agreed within ISO and CCITT that the basic structuring technique in OSA is layering, whereby a network of cooperating systems is logically structured into layers. A number of criteria to be applied to the question of how many layers there should be and where layer boundaries should be placed have been defined.

Both ISO and CCITT agree on a seven-layer architecture, as illustrated in Fig. 5. A major difference is in the interpretation of the services provided by the network and transport layers and their relationship to X.25 virtual circuits.

The current view of the CCITT Rapporteur's Group studying OSA is that the services provided by the transport and network layers are identical except perhaps in the quality of service provided, and can be provided by X.25 virtual circuits; these can be provided by packet switching networks, or by using X.25 between DTE's in leased-line and circuit-switching networks. Quality of service becomes an issue since the network layer may vary in its success in reaching the performance level required by the transport layer (e.g., error rates, reliability, cost, throughput). When a transport connection of higher reliability than that provided by the network layer is required, this may be provided by the use of additional procedures within the transport layer. Since these procedures do not add service features, but only increase an aspect of the quality of service, these procedures may be contained in a sublayer within the transport layer.

The current ISO view appears to be that the services provided by the network layer are somewhat primitive, resulting in distinctly different services being provided by the network and transport layers. The services of the network layer can be provided by X.25 virtual circuits. However, in this model,

many of the VC characteristics discussed in Section II are not used; instead, these functions are provided by the transport layer.

The above discussion reflects two views of the relationship of X.25 to OSA. Complete alignment between the two models may yet be achieved.

C. Future Developments

Future activity and further work are required in the following areas:

1) The characteristics of virtual circuits are defined in X.25, though much would be gained by having a separate CCITT Recommendation addressing them.

2) The X.25 interface has become functionally complete after nearly four years of network operational experience. Further work will concentrate on new optional user facilities, and the addition of multilink procedures defined for the frame level.

3) Presently, some networks require the data fields of DATA packets to contain an integral number of octets. The transmission by the DTE of data fields not containing an integral number of octets to the network may cause a loss of data integrity. Further considerations regarding the trends of future requirements and implementations toward either bit-orientation (any number of bits) or octet-orientation (an integral number of octets) for data fields in X.25 packets are under study in CCITT.

4) The evolving Open Systems Architecture provides a basic structure on which future work in ISO and CCITT can be built. The view that X.25 virtual circuits can provide the basic Transport layer services required by the Session layer in OSA must be studied further.

5) There is a real need to select meaningful performance criteria, bearing in mind that the meaningfulness of criteria is viewed differently by network users and by the network providers. Once these criteria have been defined, realistic performance objectives should be set based on user requirements as well as on operating experience. The costs associated with meeting these objectives must also be considered.

ACKNOWLEDGMENT

CCITT relies heavily on contributions submitted by numerous parties including ISO. It has not been practical to reference all of the relevant contributions of the over three hundred which have been submitted to SGVII in this study period. Many of these contributions made proposals, reported on operating experience or more generally discussed areas in X.25 which have been discussed in this paper. Their contribution is acknowledged.

REFERENCES

[1] CCITT Recommendations X.1, X.2, X.25, X.92 and X.96 "Public data networks," *CCITT Orange Book*, vol. VIII.2. Geneva, Switzerland: ITU, 1977.
[2] CCITT Provisional Recommendations X.3, X.25, X.28, and X.29, *CCITT Grey Book*. Geneva, Switzerland: Grey Book. 1978.

[3] CCITT Provisional Recommendations X.75 and X.121, *CCITT Grey Book*. Geneva, Switzerland: ITU, 1979.

[4] P. T. F. Kelly, "Public packet switched data networks, international plans, and standards," *Proc. IEEE*, vol. 66, pp. 1539–1549, Nov. 1978.

[5] CCITT Rapporteur on X.25—Level 3, "Draft revised recommendation X.25," CCITT COM VII-no. 439, as amended, Feb. 1980.

[6] H. Folts, "Procedures for circuit-switched service in synchronous public data networks," in this issue, pp. 489–496.

[7] HDLC, Documents IS3309 and IS4335 plus approved amendments (TC97/SC6/N1300 and 1445) and DP6256, ISO, Geneva, Switzerland.

[8] H. Folts, "X.25 transaction oriented features—Datagram and fast select," in this issue, pp. 496–500.

[9] R. Hovey, "Packet-switched networks agree on standard interface," *Data Commun.* pp. 25, 39, May/June 1976.

[10] M. L. Hess, *et al.*, "A comparison of four X.25 public data networks," in *Proc. Int. Conf. Commun.*, June 1979.

[11] A. M. Rybczynski and J. D. Palframan, "A common X.25 interface to public data networks," to be published, Spring of 1980.

[12] H. Zimmermann, "The ISO model of architecture for open systems interconnection," in this issue, pp. 425–432.

[13] "Report of the 3rd meeting of the CCITT rapporteur on layered models of public data network service applications," CCITT COM VII-no. 393, San Francisco, CA, Sept. 1979.

[14] "Reference model for open systems interconnection, version 4," ISO/TC97/SC16 N227, June 1979.

Antony Rybczynski (S'68–M'72) received the B.Eng. degree from McGill University, Montreal, P.Q., Canada, in 1970, and the M.Sc. degree from the University of Alberta, Edmonston, Alta., Canada, in 1972, both in electrical engineering.

He is Supervising Engineer in Computer Communications Planning, Bell Canada, Ottawa, Canada. After completing his formal education, he joined a multidisciplinary task group formed within Bell Canada to study the marketing, technical, and economic feasibility of a public packet-switching network in Canada. This activity resulted in the development of the Datapac network. He has acted as design authority representing the TransCanada Telephone System in the development of the X.25 interface specification, in close cooperation with members of the staff of the French PTT, the UKPO, the NTT of Japan, and GTE Telenet Corporation of the U.S.A. This activity culminated in the ratification of Recommendation X.25 by the CCITT Plenary in October 1976. He has also been involved in the revised X.25 specification approved by CCITT SG VII in February 1980. In 1978, he was responsible for the establishment of international services between Datapac and Telenet and Tymnet networks. At present, he is responsible for planning the interconnection of Datapac with a number of overseas packet networks, and for the development of the Datapac X.75 internetworking capability.

Mr. Rybczynski is a member of the Association of Professional Engineers of Ontario.

DESIGN CONSIDERATIONS FOR USING
THE X.25 PACKET LAYER IN DATA TERMINAL EQUIPMENT

Fred M. Burg

Bell Laboratories
Holmdel, New Jersey 07733

ABSTRACT

CCITT Recommendation X.25 describes the standard interface for connecting user equipment to packet-switched networks. Looked at from a slightly different perspective, however, X.25 can be viewed as a collection of services that can be molded to provide a wide spectrum of capabilities in Data Terminal Equipment (DTE). The purpose of this paper is to look beyond the somewhat empty words of "X.25 support" and go on to explore several X.25 design choices that need consideration when designing a packet-mode DTE. Although none of these choices affect the ability of a DTE to connect to an X.25 network, they contribute to varying degrees of complexity and flexibility in a DTE.

INTRODUCTION

With the deployment of packet-switched public data networks (PSPDNs) in the mid-70's, a standard network access protocol was needed to promote the production of Data Terminal Equipment (DTE) to connect to these networks. The adoption of Recommendation X.25 by the International Telegraph and Telephone Consultative Committee (CCITT) in 1976 was the first step in the standardization process but left many questions unanswered. This gave rise to a number of incompatibilities among various implementations of X.25.[1] During the ensuing four years, many of these issues were resolved.[2,3] The adoption of the 1980 version of X.25[4] is said to provide a standard interface that will facilitate connection of user equipment to PSPDNs.[5]

X.25 mandates the formats of the packets sent between Data Circuit-terminating Equipment (DCE) and DTEs and the procedures that the DCE will follow in each circumstance. However, CCITT has allowed the manufacturers of X.25 DTEs a degree of freedom in designing a product to connect to a PSPDN. In 1980, the American National Standards Institute (ANSI) task group on Public Data Networks (X3S37) requested that its counterpart in the International Organization for Standardization (ISO) initiate a project to define a standard for a DTE operating within an X.25 environment.[6] As a result, such a project was initiated within ISO in

September, 1980. Since that time, ISO has produced Draft Proposals for the Link Layer and Packet Layer for DTEs operating in the packet mode.[7]

Both X.25 and the ISO X.25-based work cited above describe an *interface* between packet-switched networks and packet-mode DTEs. Looked at from a slightly different perspective, however, X.25 can be viewed as a collection of services that packet-switched networks provide to users (i.e., DTEs). As discussed in the appendix of Reference 3, DTEs connecting to these networks may be "simple," "sophisticated," or somewhere in between, depending on the services utilized. In turn, higher degrees of sophistication require more complexity which tend to increase costs.

The purpose of this paper is to identify some of the issues involved in designing and using the Packet Layer of an X.25 DTE, taking the 1980 version of X.25 as a base. The intent is to stimulate designers and users into looking into the issues involved in using X.25 rather than just accept the somewhat empty statement of "X.25 support." Furthermore, such an analysis should result in an understanding of some of the tradeoffs involved in building an X.25 DTE.

In particular, we will focus on the data needed and provided by a DTE Packet Layer (PL) and the interactions between the PL and some higher level entity such as, in the context of the ISO Reference Model,[8] the Transport Layer (TL). As shown in Figure 1, the TL is directly responsible for issuing instructions (known as *primitives*) to the PL that result in the initiation of X.25 procedures. Likewise, the TL receives information from the PL. By focusing on these interactions and the information surrounding them, we will see that different design philosophies can result in products differing in complexity and flexibility but all capable of connecting to a PSPDN.

A DTE BY ANY OTHER NAME . . .

To illustrate the diversity of DTEs, we take a brief glance at the Bell Operations Systems Network[9,10] (OSN). The Bell Operating Companies (BOC) today use about 100 different types of computer-based systems to automate their operations. Known as *Operations Systems* (OSs), these systems aid BOC personnel with such

Reprinted from *The Proceedings of INFOCOM 83*, 1983, pages 180-188.
Copyright © 1983 by The Institute of Electrical and Electronics Engineers, Inc.

EHO226-1/85/0000/0165$01.00 © 1983 IEEE

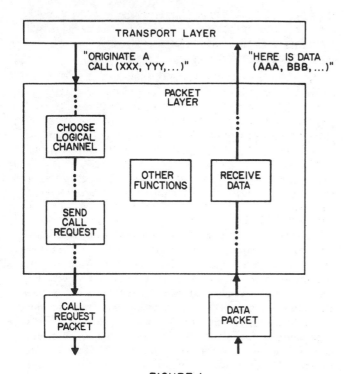

FIGURE 1

PACKET LAYER/TRANSPORT LAYER INTERACTION

functions as marketing, planning, and engineering. OSs communicate with each other as well as with Stored Program Controlled Switching (SPCS) systems. SPCS systems, which control the telephone switching network to accept and route calls, send billing and maintenance data, for example, to appropriate OSs. Still other Transmission Network Terminal Equipment (NTE) also communicate with appropriate OSs to obtain provisioning data, for example, which lists parameters and options to be applied to various types of circuits. The NTE ensures that specified transmission requirements are met for different types of transmission facilities. The data communications elements connecting OSs, SPCS systems, and NTE comprise a major part of the OSN.

The systems mentioned above are implemented on a heterogeneous set of computer hardware and have diverse data communications requirements. For example, several OSs run on the mainframes of IBM, UNIVAC, and other vendors while some OSs run on the minicomputers of DEC and HP, for example. Some of the intelligent NTE use various types of microprocessors.

Just as varied as the range of processors of OSN DTEs is the range of their data communications needs. For example, there is a need to transmit billing data quickly from an SPCS system to an OS. In these cases, unnecessary delay in setting up a connection cannot be tolerated. Other types of data can be safe-stored for some amount of time, allowing it to be retransmitted up

to several times if necessary. In some cases, the amount of data to be exchanged is large; in others, such as a credit-card check, for example, it is quite small.

WHAT X.25 IS AND IS NOT

To fully understand the scope of this paper, it is necessary to understand what X.25 is and is not. We begin by offering the following in the way of an informal definition:

X.25 is a particular set of formats and procedures (i.e., a protocol) that allows access to a public data network operating in the packet mode.

We now turn to the telephone network to illustrate some points about X.25 networks. The primary purpose of the telephone network is to allow the connection of two phones (not people) so that their users (people) can communicate. To allow this, formats and procedures are defined for the several phases of a phone call. For example, the call establishment phase allows the user

a. to signal the network that a call origination is desired;

b. to identify the called station; and

c. to be informed whether the call has been completed and, if not, to receive an indication as to why not (e.g., number busy, unworking number, etc.).

In a broad sense, X.25 specifies analogous procedures and formats which a DTE must follow when operating in a PSPDN environment. For example, while X.25 provides analogous procedures for (a) and (b) above, these two steps are combined into one.

Nothing mentioned above, however, addresses questions such as where the person placing the call obtains the number of the called station, or what the person placing the call does if the call is not completed (this may depend on the network's reason for not completing the call). Likewise, X.25 does not treat these issues. It is the answers to these types of questions that provide for different levels of complexity and flexibility of DTE products and that will be addressed in the subsequent sections of this paper.

LOGICAL THOUGHTS ON LOGICAL CHANNELS

The logical channel (LC) concept in X.25 allows a user to efficiently utilize the bandwidth of the link connecting the DTE to the network while conversing with multiple destinations. A LC exists at the local DTE/DCE interface and identifies the virtual circuit (VC) for which data is being exchanged. These concepts are illustrated in Figure 2.

Several aspects of LCs and VCs need to be

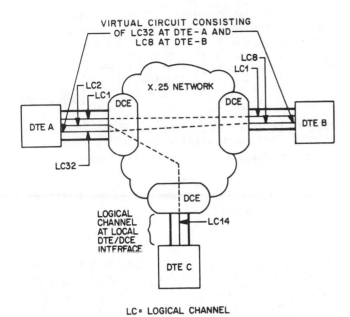

VIRTUAL CIRCUIT CONSISTING
OF LC32 AT DTE-A AND
LC8 AT DTE-B

LC = LOGICAL CHANNEL

FIGURE 2
VIRTUAL CIRCUITS vs LOGICAL CHANNELS

addressed by a DTE implementation. These include:

a. identifying the user(s) of a VC;

b. how many VCs are needed;

c. what type of VCs — Permanent VCs (PVCs) or Switched VCs (SVCs, called Virtual Calls in X.25) — are needed.

The answers to these questions are closely related to one another. We will explore some considerations below.

Identifying Logical Channel Users

A logical channel, as discussed above, is the local portion of a VC which, in turn, connects users (entities, processes) in two DTEs. Therefore, within a DTE, there must be a way to identify the user(s) associated with a particular logical channel. In the simplest case, this association can be a static one for PVCs. That is, this association is made when "gening" the X.25 portion of a DTE by filling in a table, such as that shown in Figure 3, that relates LCs and VCs to users.

On the other hand, the LC/user association can also be made dynamically when establishing an SVC. In this case, one may be able to utilize the Call User Data Field of the CALL REQUEST packet to identify the pair of communicating entities (this is done in the 3270 Display System Protocol[11] which employs X.25 at Levels 1 through 3). In some PSPDNs, for example Telenet,[12]

the DTE is allowed to utilize part of the address fields for the same purpose since network routing does not make use of the entire field (note that this is not presently an X.25 feature).

In a more complex fashion, a VC (either PVC or SVC) can be utilized as a serial or parallel resource connecting two DTEs but not associated with any particular pair of processes (in contrast to the discussion in the preceding paragraphs). When two processes need to communicate, DATA packets are used to "initiate a session" and associate the processes with the VC. As Figure 4-A shows for the serial scenario, the VC is then dedicated to Process #5 and a process in the other DTE (not shown in the figure); all data on the VC flow between these two processes. After the session is terminated (via DATA packets), the VC can be re-used later to connect, for example, Process #14 with a process in the other DTE. In the parallel picture, DATA packets are also employed to initiate sessions and associate users with the VC. This method allows simultaneous communications for pairs of users in the same two DTEs to be multiplexed onto the same VC as shown in Figure 4-B. However, as the figure shows, this strategy necessitates a special header on *all* DATA packets to distinguish between users. The "user circuit" concept discussed in Reference 11 is one example of this.

Number of Logical Channels

Theoretically, X.25 allows any combination of PVCs and SVCs up to 4095 at each DTE/DCE interface. In practice, however, a network provider must determine the number of logical channels to be supported at a DTE/DCE interface[13] to satisfy customer requirements versus the amount of resources needed (e.g., buffer space, processing power, etc.).

Likewise, a DTE implementation may limit the number of allowed LCs for similar reasons. Therefore, one must determine how many logical channels are

LC #	VC TYPE	CALLING USER	CALLED DTE ADDRESS	CALLED USER	
1	PVC	07	04092618	43	
2	PVC	14	04087342	25	
3	PVC	:			

LC = LOGICAL CHANNEL
VC = VIRTUAL CIRCUIT

FIGURE 3
LC/USER ASSOCIATION TABLE

167

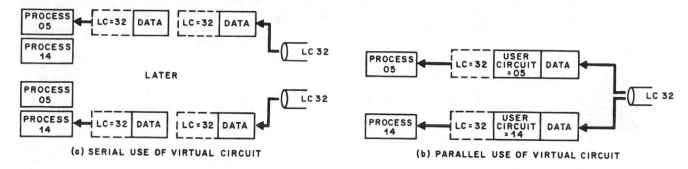

(a) SERIAL USE OF VIRTUAL CIRCUIT   (b) PARALLEL USE OF VIRTUAL CIRCUIT

FIGURE 4

SERIAL vs PARALLEL USE OF VIRTUAL CIRCUIT

needed. As one might suspect, the answer depends on a number of factors, including:

a. whether PVCs or SVCs are used (as discussed below); and
b. the number of simultaneous conversations that must be supported by the DTE.

PVCs vs. SVCs

X.25 allows two virtual circuit services which we have referred to as Permanent (PVC) and Switched (SVC). Depending on the amount of data to be transferred, it may be easier to implement PVCs since the call establishment and termination procedures associated with SVCs are not needed.

SVCs, on the other hand, offer a much wider range of capabilities and may reduce the total number of VCs needed at the DTE/DCE interface. For example, a single SVC using the Fast Select Facility with Restricted Response could be used for a point-of-sale terminal, as opposed to some larger number of PVCs. In this particular case, if the data to be exchanged by the two DTEs is less than 128 octets for each direction, then the data can be sent in the X.25 call setup and call clearing packets, thus obviating the need for many of the X.25 packets and procedures.

Given that more than 128 octets of data is to be exchanged, PVCs may seem to offer two operational advantages. The first one involves *DTE-status reporting.* That is, an X.25 network will inform, in real time, the DTEs at either end of a PVC about changes in the availability of the other DTE. However, as we will see later, extra intelligence is required in the DTE to take full advantage of this information. The second advantage pertains to the call setup delay associated with SVCs. However, SVCs may be no worse than PVCs if higher level entities need to be identified dynamically prior to data transfer. As we have seen, some networks may offer a way to accomplish this during the SVC call setup phase. In this case, identification of higher level entities is accomplished during the call setup packet exchange; with PVCs, an exchange of DATA packets is required.

Putting It All Together—An Example

To see how the preceding discussions fit together, we discuss an example from the Bell Operations Systems Network mentioned earlier. A minicomputer-based data collection (DC) operations system requests three types of time-aggregated data from up to 48 Stored Program Controlled Switching (SPCS) systems. Each data type is handled by a different "process" within the respective system. Logical channels could be set up for the DC system in a number of ways, including the following:

a. Establish 144 LCs, one for each type of data and each SPCS system. With no other information on requirements or costs, PVCs or SVCs would serve equally as well.

b. Set up 48 LCs (PVCs or SVCs), one for each SPCS system. The VC can be used in a parallel fashion by the three pairs of processes.

c. Allow for some maximum number of simultaneous connections the DC system can handle (presumably less than 48). SVCs must then be used to set up connections to each SPCS system as needed.

The three possible LC deployment strategies discussed above vary in their protocol requirements. Using 144 PVCs to realize the first strategy requires a large amount of network and DTE table space for LC information such as window and packet sizes, etc.. Using SVCs in the first or third case requires some type of dynamic process identification, as discussed earlier, during the call establishment phase for the SVC. The third case also requires the DC system to rapidly set up and tear down SVCs to ensure getting all the data. The second strategy requires a process identification, such as the "user circuit" identifier in the 3270 Display System Protocol,[11] to be appended to all data. Obviously, there are tradeoffs involved in choosing the proper strategy.

VENTURING INTO VIRTUAL CALLS

We have previously explored some of the differences between PVCs and SVCs (i.e., Virtual Calls). In this section, we will discuss, from the DTE point of view, some of the procedures associated with the Virtual Call capability that must be considered when designing a PL. A separate section discusses the optional facilities associated with the Virtual Call capability.

Originating Virtual Calls

Given the X.25 formats and procedures for Virtual Call service, interactions must be defined that direct the PL to originate and respond to a Virtual Call.[14] The complexity of this mechanism will depend on a number of factors, including whether multiplexing is performed on top of LCs (as discussed in the previous section), and the optional facilities needed by the user and offered by the X.25 network to which the DTE is to be connected.

To originate a Virtual Call, the PL must transmit a CALL REQUEST packet. Table 1 shows the fields of this packet and some alternatives for supplying the needed information.

As we can see from the table, some of the fields in this packet are under the direct control of the PL or can be determined in a straightforward way. For the remaining fields, a number of alternatives exist for determining the values to be used.

Perhaps of most importance is the Called-DTE Address Field. As suggested, an internal table can be used to map a destination process to a DTE address. However, in environments where processes or entire DTEs can be moved, such tables become quite fallible and may necessitate frequent updating. A network directory service, similar to the 411 Directory Assistance service, may be useful in such cases. On the other hand, such tables can be expanded to provide several addresses to be used in case of failure.

Terminating Calls

Just as the PL must interact with a higher level entity during call setup, it must do the same during call termination. One interaction occurs when higher level entities in both DTEs are satisfied that all data have been delivered to their destination. In addition to this "normal" disconnect procedure, it may be desirable from the higher level entity's perspective to "abort" a call. Again, the higher level entity would instruct the PL to terminate the call. Both interactions produce the same result vis-a-vis the X.25 protocol — transfer of a CLEAR REQUEST packet to the DCE.

A second type of interaction involves the PL informing higher level entities that a call has been cleared. This event can occur for several reasons; we will investigate some in a subsequent section.

TABLE 1
Considerations for Data Needed for X.25 CALL REQUEST Packet

CALL REQUEST Field	Some Considerations
General Format Identifier (GFI)	• if no call-setup D-bit determination is desired, then a constant GFI can be used ("0001" for modulo 8 DATA packet sequence numbering or "0010" for modulo 128 numbering) • in cases where it is desirable to ascertain during call setup whether the D-bit is supported, then the GFI must be modified
Logical Channel Identifier	under PL control
Packet Type Identifier	under PL control
Calling and Called DTE Address Lengths	under PL control but depends on Calling and Called DTE Addresses
Called-DTE Address	• provide an internal table which maps the desired destination "process" to the called-DTE Address • for a keyboard terminal, this may be entered by the operator
Calling-DTE Address	• can be omitted • if it is necessary to reflect the identity of the calling "process" in the digits not used by the network for routing, then this field must be present
Facility Length	under PL control but depends on facilities requested
Facilities	• can be omitted • for facilities requiring a request at call setup time, appropriate X.25 facility procedures are needed. In addition, depending on the facility, additional DTE-internal procedures may be needed (for example, to translate a throughput requirement into a window and packet size negotiation request).
Call User Data	• can be omitted • use data, if any, received from the TL

THREE BITS FOR DATA TRANSFER

In this section, we discuss a few considerations for implementing the data transfer procedure in a DTE. This procedure makes use of the following X.25 elements:

a. the maximum User Data Field length of DATA packets;

b. the Delivery Confirmation Bit (D-bit);

c. the More Data Mark (M-bit);

d. Complete Packet Sequences (CPSs); and

e. the Qualifier Bit (Q-bit).

Although not explicitly mentioned in X.25, we will define an M-bit Sequence (MBS) as the basic unit of data transferred from one PL to another on behalf of the TL (i.e., in terms of the ISO Reference Model, a "packet layer service data unit"). As Figure 5 shows, an MBS is composed of one or more CPSs. In turn, a CPS is the basic unit of data whose integrity is maintained across the network. Note, however, that X.25 does not impose a limit on the maximum number of octets (length) in a CPS nor define how a DTE should use it.

On the other hand, CCITT Recommendation D.12[15] states that charging principles in a PSPDN should be based on CPS.

Packetizing the Data

To transfer a string of data (i.e., an MBS) through a PSPDN to a remote DTE, it must first be broken into DATA packets (i.e., packetized). We will assume that

TABLE 2
Packetizing a 300-Octet M-Bit Sequence

Max User Data Field	Max CPS Length	Resulting Number of:			
		Packets	D-bit=1 Packets*	CPSs	D.12 Segments
128	100	3	2	3	6
128	128	3	2	3	5
128	150	4	1	2	6
128	200	3	1	2	6
128	256	3	1	2	5
128	275	4	1	2	6
128	300	3	0	1	5
256	200	2	1	2	6
256	256	2	1	2	5
256	275	3	1	2	6
256	300	2	0	1	5

* The entries in this column represent the minimum number of packets with the D-bit set to 1. In all cases, the packet carrying the last bit of user data could also have its D-bit set to 1.

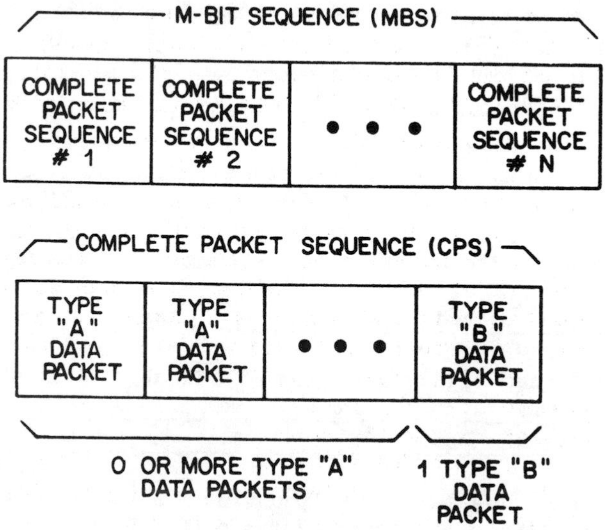

this process is performed by the PL since it must have knowledge of the maximum length allowed for the User Data Field on the virtual circuit. If the MBS requires more than one packet, then the M-bit should be set to one in every DATA packet but the last. For simplicity, each MBS may be sent as one CPS; however, a more sophisticated DTE might, for example, use multiple CPSs per MBS to perform intermediate checkpointing for long MBSs. Table 2 shows the results of packetizing a 300-octet MBS with various combinations of maximum User Data Field lengths and CPS lengths. Where charges are incurred based on the number of transmitted DATA packets or the number of 64-octet segments in each CPS, the choice of CPS length may have a significant effect on costs.

D-BIT	M-BIT	USER DATA FIELD	REMARKS
0	1	FULL	TYPE "A" DATA PACKET
1 1	1 1	< FULL FULL	TYPE "B" DATA PACKET WHICH MARKS THE END OF A CPS BUT NOT THE END OF AN MBS
0 0 0 1 1	0 0 1* 0 0	< FULL FULL < FULL < FULL FULL	TYPE "B" DATA PACKET WHICH SIMULTANEOUSLY MARKS THE END OF A CPS AND AN MBS

＊ AN X.25 NETWORK WILL CHANGE THIS M-BIT TO 0

```
┌──── M-BIT SEQUENCE (MBS) ────┐

COMPLETE    COMPLETE              COMPLETE
PACKET      PACKET      • • •     PACKET
SEQUENCE    SEQUENCE              SEQUENCE
#1          #2                    #N

┌── COMPLETE PACKET SEQUENCE (CPS) ──┐

TYPE       TYPE                  TYPE
"A"        "A"        • • •      "B"
DATA       DATA                  DATA
PACKET     PACKET                PACKET

0 OR MORE TYPE "A"      1 TYPE "B"
DATA PACKETS            DATA PACKET
```

FIGURE 5

RELATIONSHIP BETWEEN DATA PACKETS, COMPLETE PACKET SEQUENCES, AND M-BIT SEQUENCES

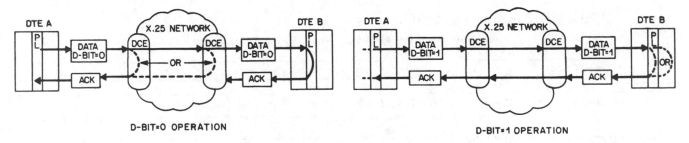

FIGURE 6
TREATMENT OF ACKNOWLEDGEMENTS FOR DATA PACKETS

Setting the D-bit

Through the use of the D-bit, a DTE can instruct the PSPDN as to the type of acknowledgement for each DATA packet. As shown in Figure 6, a DATA packet with a D-bit set to zero is acknowledged by the network without involving the remote DTE ("local" acknowledgment). In the case where the D-bit is set to one, the network may not acknowledge the packet until the destination DTE has received the packet and acknowledged it.

From the above discussion, we see that the interaction between a DTE's PL and TL should include instructions regarding the setting of the D-bit. However, the packetization process, as described earlier, implicitly accounts for the D-bit setting in every DATA packet of an MBS except the last one. Therefore, the instructions from the TL regarding data transfer need only convey information that can be used to set the D-bit in the last DATA packet of an MBS.

Another question to be answered relates to whether the PL or the TL is responsible for initiating the acknowledgement for a DATA packet with a D-bit set to one. From the network's point of view, as shown in Figure 6, it doesn't matter. However, setting the D-bit to one may be used to provide the Receipt Confirmation service between a pair of communicating TLs discussed in Reference 14. In this case, the receiving TL is responsible for triggering an acknowledgement after receiving an MBS from the PL. However, Receipt Confirmation applies only to an MBS in its entirety; DATA packets received with their D-bit set to one that do not terminate an MBS can be acknowledged by the PL without any interaction with the TL. On the transmitting side, additional bookkeeping is needed in the PL to correlate acknowledged DATA packets with MBSs for which Receipt Confirmation was requested by the TL.

Setting the Q-bit

The Q-bit feature of X.25 allows a distinction to be made regarding the flow of the data associated with a given virtual circuit. For example, X.29[16] provides that data to/from a terminal user are carried in DATA packets with their Q-bit set to zero whereas PAD commands and responses regarding this user are carried in packets with their Q-bit set to one.

Similar to the discussion above relating to the D-bit, the interaction between the PL and the TL may allow for instructions regarding the setting of the Q-bit. Since X.25 requires that all DATA packets in a CPS have the same Q-bit setting, these instructions could be in terms of CPSs. To simplify PL design, however, the Q-bit can be set to the same value in all CPSs in an MBS or can always be set to zero if the services provided by it are not needed.

PROBLEMS? CHECK THE CAUSE

The restart, clear, and reset procedures of X.25 allow the DTE or the DCE to signal the occurrence of certain conditions and to provide information which further defines the condition. Although, from the point of view of the DTE PL, these procedures are simple, there is more to them than meets the eye. Below we explore some of the implications of a DTE receiving such a signal (we will not discuss the use of the DCE DIAGNOSTIC packet).

Upon receipt of a RESTART, CLEAR, or RESET INDICATION packet from the network, the PL, at a minimum, is required to transmit the corresponding confirmation packet. The simplest PL implementation need do no more.[3] By way of a few examples, we will see what this implies and what can be gained by having the PL pass an indication of the event (and the associated Cause and Diagnostic Codes) to the TL, as specified in Reference 14. Returning to our phone network analogy again, we note that we are provided with some information when a call is terminated and that our subsequent action may depend on what the problem was (e.g., number busy — try again soon).

Example 1

Suppose that the PL has placed a Virtual Call as requested and that it receives a CLEAR INDICATION packet from the network for the logical channel involved. The PL is obligated by X.25 to return a CLEAR CONFIRMATION packet. If no signal of this event is provided, then the TL may wait (indefinitely?) for a response. However, we saw earlier that the PL should indicate the acceptance or refusal of a call attempt.

TABLE 3
Interpretations of Some of the Clearing Cause Codes

Cause Code	Interpretations and Subsequent Action
Network Congestion	temporary PSPDN problem; after some delay, try again
Number Busy	• all LCs at the called DTE are in use; after some delay, try again • may indicate a need for manual intervention to increase the number of LCs at the called DTE's network interface
Access Barred	the calling DTE is not authorized to communicate with the called DTE; requires manual intervention to adjust network subscription options if communications are to be permitted
DTE Originated	• expected result to Fast Select call with Restricted Response indicated • unexpected — could occur during or after call setup; after some delay, try again

Given that the PL does indicate the occurrence of a clearing procedure to the TL, we need to investigate what the occurrence of a clear may signify. Not every clear is indicative of a problem; we can classify clears into three categories: expected, unexpected but try again soon, and unexpected with other action required to clarify when procedure might be successful. By analyzing the Cause Codes, as defined in X.25 and X.96,[17] the type of clear can be identified and specific action taken by the appropriate higher level entity (e.g., the TL). Table 3 shows a few cases.

Example 2

Suppose that two DTEs have agreed to use a PVC to communicate with one another and that the network detects a Level 1 and/or Level 2 failure in one of the DTEs. The network will transfer, to the active DTE, a RESET INDICATION packet on the appropriate LC with a cause indicating "Out of Order." The PL must respond with a RESET CONFIRMATION. However, without further analysis of the Cause Code, the TL may improperly continue to transfer data to the PL for transmission to the network.

EXAMINING THE OPTIONS

In conjunction with the virtual circuit services, X.25 currently defines 24 optional facilities to which a DTE may subscribe and/or use. We discuss below a few considerations for using these facilities. Note, however, that not all facilities are offered by all X.25 networks — only those classified as *Essential* in X.2[18] must be offered by all PSPDNs (there are six Essential facilities in X.2 for SVCs but none for PVCs) whereas those classified as *Additional* need not.

As mentioned in Reference 3, a DTE may operate with the universal default values supported by the network and need not be concerned with any optional facilities. On the other hand, these facilities extend the services provided by an X.25 network. Some facilities require no additional procedures to be incorporated into the PL (for example, Incoming Calls Barred). Other facilities (for example, Flow Control Parameter Negotiation) require an indication of their use in the Facility Field of the call setup packets — a DTE using them must be able to encode and decode them as prescribed by X.25. Table 4 shows several of the optional facilities available with X.25 and their impact on DTE design.

TABLE 4
Some X.25 Optional Facilities

Facility	Use and Some Design Considerations
Flow Control Parameter Negotiation	• allows PL to negotiate window and/or packet sizes at call setup • need some algorithm to determine what window and/or packet sizes to choose • need to adjust values based on network's response • size of DATA packet buffers may be parameterized to optimize the use of User Data Fields other than 128 octets
Closed User Group (CUG)	• restricts communication to other DTEs within the group • if DTE belongs to more than one CUG, requires table associating DTE addresses with Closed User Group indexes
Incoming Calls Barred; Outgoing Calls Barred	• restricts Virtual Calls from being presented to or originated by the DTE • may simplify design of DTE call setup procedures
One-way Incoming Logical Channel	• restricts use of logical channel to receiving Virtual Calls only • must not be chosen for a Virtual Call originated by the DTE
Reverse Charging Acceptance	• allows DTE to receive calls requesting Reverse Charging • DTE may accept all calls without checking for Reverse Charging or make decision contingent on the caller's identity and/or whether Reverse Charging is requested; in the case of checking for Reverse Charging, the DTE must be able to decode the Facility Field

SUMMARY AND CONCLUSIONS

The 1980 version of X.25 standardizes many aspects of the protocol for accessing a network providing packet-mode service. A spectrum of DTE capabilities can be defined in terms of the utilization of the X.25 procedures and the information derived from them. For example, a point-of-sale terminal would be expected to use less of the X.25 procedures than a minicomputer supporting several concurrent processes. However, both types of DTEs are capable of connecting to an X.25 network.

Although we have restricted ourselves to the Packet Layer of X.25, we have seen that there are many tradeoffs involved in using the X.25 Packet Layer. In particular, we have discussed the need to determine Logical Channel (LC) requirements, showing that one can take a *brute-force* approach which requires extra memory for LC tables, or one can develop extra intelligence for setting up and tearing down LCs as necessary. We have also investigated the use of Clearing Cause codes to show that, depending on the code, it may be possible to retry the call successfully. From these investigations, we conclude that users and designers of X.25 DTEs need to be aware of the various tradeoffs and how they affect the flexibility and complexity of a DTE.

ACKNOWLEDGEMENTS

We would like to acknowledge the efforts of many DTE designers at Bell Laboratories, too numerous to mention, whose probing questions served to initiate the thoughts that provided the foundation for much of this paper.

REFERENCES

[1] "A Comparison of Four X.25 Public Data Networks," M. L. Hess, et al., Proceedings of the International Conference on Communications, June 1979.

[2] "CCITT Recommendation X.25 - 1976 to 1980," H. V. Bertine, Proceedings of the National Telecommunications Conference, November 1980.

[3] "A Common X.25 Interface to Public Data Networks," A. M. Rybczynski and J. D. Palframan, Computer Networks 4 (1980).

[4] "Interface Between Data Terminal Equipment (DTE) and Data Circuit-Terminating Equipment (DCE) for Terminals Operating in the Packet Mode on Public Data Networks," CCITT Recommendation X.25, 1980.

[5] "X.25: The Universal Packet Network Interface," C. Z. Drukarch, et.al., Proceedings of the Fifth International Conference on Computer Communications, October 1980.

[6] "Additional Considerations for DTEs Implementing X.25," ISO paper TC97/SC6 N2060, September 1980.

[7] "Standardizing the User Side of the X.25 Interface," F. M. Burg, Computer Communications, Vol. 5, No. 5, October 1982.

[8] "Data Processing - Open Systems Interconnection - Basic Reference Model," ISO Draft International Standard 7498.

[9] "Planning for the Bell Operations Systems Network," J. J. Amoss, Proceedings of the Fifth International Conference on Computer Communications, October 1980.

[10] "The Bell X.25 Protocol and its Role in the Operations Systems Network," P. F. Wainwright and G. W. Arnold, Proceedings of the Sixth International Conference on Computer Communications, September 1982.

[11] "3270 Display System Protocol," August 1981.

[12] X.25 Documentation Service, Part IV - Packet Level Procedures, GTE Telenet Communications Corporation, June 1980.

[13] X.25 Interface Specifications, Bell System Data Communication Protocol Standards, Technical Reference PUB 54010, August 1981 (Preliminary).

[14] "Data Processing - Open Systems Interconnection - Network Service Definition," ISO paper TC97/SC6 N2610, October 1982.

[15] "Measurement Unit for Charging by Volume in the International Packet-Switched Data Transmission Service," CCITT Recommendation D.12, 1980.

[16] "Procedures for the Exchange of Control Information and User Data Between a Packet Assembly/Disassembly Facility (PAD) and a Packet Mode DTE or Another PAD," CCITT Recommendation X.29, 1980.

[17] "Call Progress Signals in Public Data Networks," CCITT Recommendation X.96, 1980.

[18] "International User Services and Facilities in Public Data Networks," CCITT Recommendation X.2, 1980.

Reprinted from *IEEE Transactions on Communications*, Volume COM-28, Number 4, April 1980, pages 489-496. U.S. Government work. Not protected by U.S. copyright.

Procedures for Circuit-Switched Service in Synchronous Public Data Networks

HAROLD C. FOLTS

(Invited Paper)

Abstract—X.21 specifies a simple character-oriented procedure used to establish a transparent connection through a synchronous Public Data Network. The architecture of call establishment for X.21 is the same as that for call (virtual) establishment of X.25; in this regard, their functionality is nearly identical. This paper describes the background that went into the development of the Recommendation, discusses the architectural relationships, and presents the details of the X.21 circuit-switching protocol.

I. INTRODUCTION

CCITT Recommendation X.21 has been developed as "the General Purpose Interface Between Data Terminal Equipment (DTE) and Data Circuit-Terminating Equipment (DCE) for Synchronous Operation on Public Data Networks" [1]. The only "general purpose" part, however, is the designation of the physical elements which include the electrical (X.26/X.27), functional (X.24), and mechanical (ISO DIS 4903) characteristics [2]. Additionally, the basic family of quiescent signals and states for the interface are specified. These provide the fundamental components of X.21 which will apply to all modes of operation in new data communications applications for circuit-switched, packet-switched, and general-purpose integrated services [3].

The remainder of X.21 includes procedures for leased circuit service (both point-to-point and multipoint) and for circuit-switched services. In relation to the ISO architecture [4], the leased circuit procedures are a specific application at the physical layer, while the circuit-switched procedures involve the link layer and the network layer. The focus of this paper will be on the network layer Call Establishment procedures of Recommendation X.21.

II. BACKGROUND

Extensive activity by telecommunication administrations around the world is taking place in implementing Public Data Networks which will provide tailored data communication services to the user community. In recognition of this new evolution, the International Telegraph and Telephone Consultative Committee (CCITT) established a study program in 1968 by forming a Joint Working Party for New Data Networks (JWP/NRD) to set the basis for international standardization. In 1972, the resulting first X-series of Recommendations, including the original version of X.21, was approved by the Fifth CCITT Plenary Assembly [5]. These Recommendations dealt primarily with circuit-switching technology.

To further refine and expand this work, CCITT then established Study Group VII on Public Data Networks. The main thrust of the work continued toward circuit switching with only a minor question directed toward the emerging packet-switching technology. In 1976, however, a major diversion in direction started to take place with the sudden appearance of the X.25 virtual call packet-switched service [6].

As a result, the emphasis on circuit switching in public data networks has been subsequently overshadowed by the fascination for packet-switching technology. This does not mean, however, that circuit switching has passed into oblivion, but circuit switching is, in fact, being actively pursued by the Nordic Countries (Sweden, Norway, Denmark, and Finland), Japan, the Federal Republic of Germany, Italy, Hungary, and Canada (Infoswitch). Experience and proven technology may very likely lead in the future to an expansion of circuit-switched services in Public Data Networks.

III. ARCHITECTURE

The architecture of Recommendation X.21 has been a subject of considerable misunderstanding and controversy in the ISO and CCITT work developing a standard reference model [4]. While X.21 provides the essential physical components of an interface [2], it also provides the circuit-switched network control procedures. Many have argued that these procedures are also within the physical layer because they result in the establishment of a physical circuit which is then used for data transfer.

By analyzing the X.21 Call Establishment procedures in comparison with the Call Establishment procedures of X.25 [6], it will become clear that the functionality of each is identical. It is technically possible to use the X.21 Call Establishment for a packet-switched virtual circuit as well as to use the X.25 Call Establishment for a circuit-switched physical circuit. Both are network layer control procedures.

The necessity for consistent distribution of functionality among layers for all switched network services was set forth in the United States' contribution to ISO [7]. This consistency is essential if the goal of a universal interface for integrated services is to be realized [3]. ISO/TC 97/SC 6 has endorsed this determination and has submitted a contribution to CCITT stating the revised position on this matter [8].

Manuscript received July 23, 1979; revised December 31, 1979.
The author is with National Communications System, Washington, DC 20305.

IV. CCITT RECOMMENDATION X.21

When work on Recommendation X.21 began in 1969, during the early days of the JWP/NRD, it was recognized that use of any CCITT V-series interfaces (equivalent of RS-232C and RS-366) would not be satisfactory for the new generation of digital Public Data Networks. Therefore, an initial objective was established to develop a new interface that is compatible with advancing technology and tailored for circuit-switched networks providing full transparency (bit sequence and protocol independence) for the transfer of user data.

For call control purposes, use of International Alphabet Number 5 (IA5) was adopted to maintain consistency with the character-oriented Level 2 Basic Mode data link control procedures of ISO 1745 and ANSI X3.28 [9]. At that time, work on the new bit-oriented procedures (ISO HDLC and ANSI ADCCP) was in its infancy [10].

The first version of X.21, approved by the CCITT Fifth Penary Assembly in 1972, was little more than an outline of procedures. It was not complete enough at that time for practical implementation. During 1973-1976, however, substantive work was completed to produce a usable Recommendation [11]. This version was approved by the CCITT Sixth Plenary Assembly in 1976 and appears in the *Orange Book* [1].

Subsequently, work continued to further refine and expand the Recommendation, as well as to include adjustments resulting from implementation experience. The new version of X.21 was completed during the CCITT Study Group VII meeting in April 1979 and was issued as Draft Revision 4 [12]. In addition to significant technical and editorial enhancements, the new revision of X.21 has been completely reorganized to track with the work in developing the standard system architecture [4]. The presentation in this paper will relate to the latest revision.

A. General-Purpose Physical Layer

1) Basic Elements: The physical elements for X.21 [2] include application of the X.26 and X.27 electrical characteristics, together with functional circuits defined by X.24. The mechanical element of the interface is the 15-pin connector specified by ISO DIS 4903 which is from the same family of connectors as the commonly known 25-pin connector. The physical configuration of the DTE/DCE interface for X.21 consists of six circuits as shown in Fig. 1.

The T and R circuits convey data and control information, while the C and I circuits provide control functions similar to "ON/OFF hook" indications. This simple out-of-band control provides an effective mechanism for maintaining full transparency during data transfer. The S circuit provides signal element (bit) timing from the network, and optionally in some networks, the B circuit provides an octet byte alignment with the network.

2) Quiescent Phase Signals: The signals during the quiescent phase indicate the ability of the DTE and the DCE to enter operational phases such as the call control phase. The two

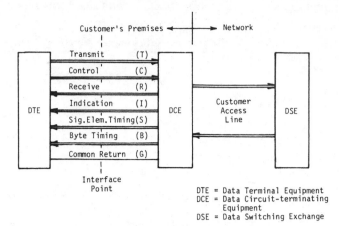

DTE = Data Terminal Equipment
DCE = Data Circuit-terminating Equipment
DSE = Data Switching Exchange

Fig. 1.   X.21 interface.

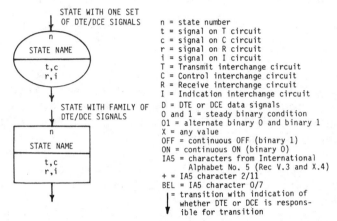

n = state number
t = signal on T circuit
c = signal on C circuit
r = signal on R circuit
i = signal on I circuit
T = Transmit interchange circuit
C = Control interchange circuit
R = Receive interchange circuit
I = Indication interchange circuit
D = DTE or DCE data signals
0 and 1 = steady binary condition
01 = alternate binary 0 and binary 1
X = any value
OFF = continuous OFF (binary 1)
ON = continuous ON (binary 0)
IA5 = characters from International Alphabet No. 5 (Rec V.3 and X.4)
+ = IA5 character 2/11
BEL = IA5 character 0/7
↓ = transition with indication of whether DTE or DCE is responsible for transition

Fig. 2.   Convention for X.21 state.

basic signals used indicate READY and NOT READY. These are further described in more detail by Bertine [2].

B. Circuit-Switching Procedures

For circuit-switched operation, X.21 defines four phases—quiescent, call control, data transfer, and clearing. Within the phases, there are a number of states which are defined by the signals appearing on the T, C, R, and I circuits. Each state is essentially a "snapshot" in time of the interface signals presented by the DTE and the DCE as described in Fig. 2. The interface procedures are then illustrated by state diagrams to present a coherent picture of the operations.

1) Link Layer Elements: As X.21 is intended for synchronous operation, it is necessary to provide for correct alignment of the IA5 character sequences used during the call control phase. This is a link layer function as defined by the architecture [4].

The actual method of achieving character alignment was an issue [11] of intense debate for several years, but was finally resolved in 1976. One proposal was to provide for character alignment as typically used for synchronous character-oriented operation [9]. This provided for use of two or more contiguous SYN characters preceding each sequence of call control characters. The alignment for each direction of transmission would be independent. The other proposal was to use a separate byte alignment interchange circuit

(circuit *B*, Fig. 1) from the DCE to the DTE. Circuit *B* provides the indication of the last bit of an 8-bit byte which represents an IA5 character with parity. The byte alignment information is used both to align characters received on circuit *R* and to align characters transmitted on circuit *T*. Each direction of transmission is then dependent on the byte alignment information provided by the network (DCE).

The compromise which resulted in agreement essentially recognized that either method of operation could be provided, but it requires two or more contiguous SYN characters to be present before each call control sequence in all cases, even when byte timing is provided by circuit *B*. Where byte alignment with the network is required, the DTE must still align transmitted call control characters to the synchronization of either circuit *B*, when used, or received SYN characters from circuit *R*.

This compromise now makes it possible to design a new DTE which can work with all X.21 network implementations where the provision is included in the DTE for alignment of transmitted characters with the synchronization of the received characters. The use of the byte timing circuit *B*, when offered by a network, then becomes a purely optional matter, and operation with a nonbyte aligned network is therefore possible.

Another provision of the compromise agreement allows ready adaptation of existing designs of synchronous character-oriented DTE's to X.21. This requires, for an intermediate period, that all networks accommodate conventional SYN character alignment independent of direction of transmission. The intermediate period is determined by customer demand and other relevant factors as interpreted by the network provider.

Another link layer element of X.21 provides an elementary means of error checking using odd parity according to CCITT Recommendation X.4 [1]. Before the decision was made to employ parity, a thorough study was made as to how powerful an error control was needed. The conclusion showed that with the low error rates expected in Public Data Networks, the use of parity is quite adequate and cost effective.

2) Network Layer Procedures: The character-oriented procedures used during the call control phase establish a connection to one or more distant subscribers through a circuit-switched Public Data Network. To clearly define the procedures, a state diagram, Fig. 3, is used to show the relationship among the various call control phase states which are defined by the text. Only the recognized transitions among the states under normal operation conditions are shown by Fig. 3. As further clarification of the procedures, illustrative time sequence diagrams are also provided in the X.21 documentation. One of these examples is shown in Fig. 4.

Call establishment can only begin from the READY state (state 1). Both the DTE and DCE must be READY before either INCOMING CALL (state 8) or CALL REQUEST (state 2) can be signaled across the interface. It was proposed that the DTE and DCE be allowed to enter call establishment directly either from or toward a NOT READY signal to allow more

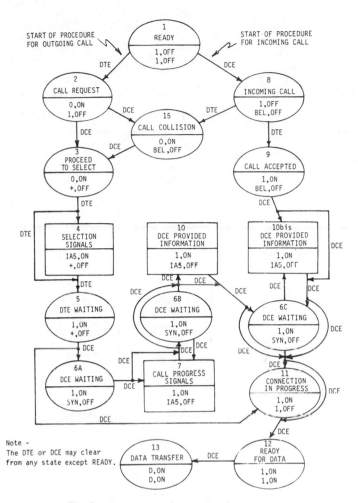

Note –
The DTE or DCE may clear from any state except READY.

Fig. 3.   State diagram for call control phase.

flexibility. Some proposed network designs, however, precluded these other state transitions.

As it is possible for an INCOMING CALL and CALL REQUEST to be inadvertently signaled at the same time, the CALL COLLISION state (state 15) has been included. There was considerable debate as to how a CALL COLLISION should be resolved. In the following the principle of simplicity, only one means of resolution was desired. It was finally agreed that CALL REQUEST should always win because a DTE preparing for an outgoing call may not be able to readily reallocate its internal resources to handle an incoming call.

The process for the calling DTE starts with the signaling of CALL REQUEST with $t = 0$ and $c = $ ON. The simple steady-state signal rather than a character sequence was used to alert the DCE of the request. As a result, only a minimum of intelligence for detection of the signal is needed. Next, in response to CALL REQUEST, the DCE signals PROCEED to SELECT (state 3), $r = +$, $i = $ OFF.

The DTE can then proceed with the SELECTION SIGNAL SEQUENCE for the specific call. During the SELECTION SIGNAL SEQUENCE, the DCE continues to signal $r = +$, $i = $ OFF, while the DTE sends a family of signals containing facility and address information. The formats for these signals are specified in detail in X.21 using the Backus Normal Form

177

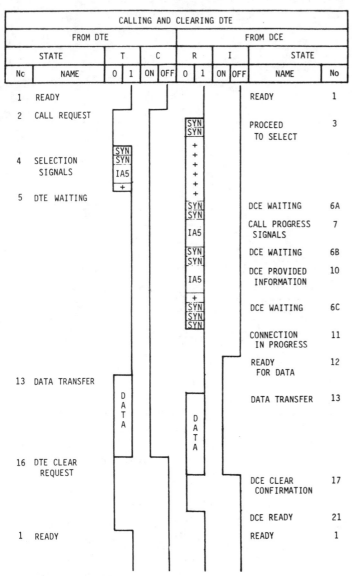

Fig. 4. Example of sequence of events—successful call and clear.

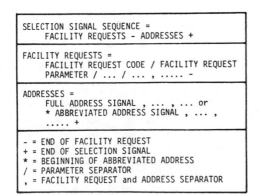

Fig. 5. Simplified example of selection sequence signals.

[13]. For a simplistic description, Fig. 5 presents an example illustration of the format.

The facility request enables selection of special service features for each call, It consists of a Facility Request Code followed by one or more Facility Request Parameters all separated by the "/" character. Multiple Facility Requests are separated by "," characters. The last Facility Request is ended with a "−" character. The definition of facilities is given in CCITT Recommendation X.2, while the actual coding is specified in Annex 7 of X.21. A further discussion on optional user facilities is presented in a later section.

The full address signals are in accordance with the format of the International Numbering Plan for Public Data Networks of CCITT Recommendation X.121 [14]. Abbreviated address signals can be used to represent, with a reduced number of characters, designated full address signals as established by agreement with the specific network. A single abbreviated address code may represent either a single address or a group of multiple addresses. Each abbreviated address signal is preceded by the "." character. Multiple full or abbreviated addresses, which can be intermixed, are separated by "," characters. The last address signal is followed by the "+" character as the "end of selection."

If there is no FACILITY REQUEST in the SELECTION SIGNAL SEQUENCE, the sequence will start immediately with the address signals without any "−" character. If there is no Address signal, but there is a Facility Request, the sequence is ended by the "−" followed by the "+" character.

As shown in Fig. 3, the SELECTION SIGNAL SEQUENCE may be bypassed. This provides for a Direct Calling feature similar to an "OFF-HOOK" or "Hot Line" service which may be used as either a fixed mode of operation or on a dynamic per-call basis. After receiving the PROCEED TO SELECT signal, the DTE signals DTE WAITING (state 5); then the DCE proceeds to establish a connection to a predesignated address or group of addresses. If the choice of direct call or addressed call is allowed dynamically on a per-call basis, the DTE can either enter state 5 or state 4 depending on the service desired.

Once the DCE has the request and necessary information to establish a connection through the network, the DTE signals $t = 1$, $c = $ ON (state 5) as it waits for the network to process the call. If establishment of the call is successful, there will normally not be any CALL PROGRESS SIGNALS (state 7), and in the absence of any special facilities, there will not normally be any DCE PROVIDED INFORMATION (state 10). Depending on how fast the connection is made, the DCE will signal either $r = $ SYN, $i = $ ON (state 6a) or $r = 1$, $i = $ OFF (state 11). The difference will be whether the connection is made to a subscriber within the same switching center, the same network, or through an international connection to another network where the processing time would be greater. The procedure allows a great deal of flexibility in this respect.

The term CALL PROGRESS SIGNALS in state 7 is perhaps a misnomer because they primarily indicate the reasons for nonprogress or unsuccessful completion of the call. The call progress signals are defined by CCITT Recommendation X.96. The new proposed revision of X.96 has now established a

CODE GROUP	CODE	SIGNIFICANCE	CATEGORY
0	00	RESERVED	WITHOUT CLEARING
	01	TERMINAL CALLED	
	02	REDIRECTED CALL	
	03	CONNECT WHEN FREE	
2	20	NO CONNECTION	WITH CLEARING DUE TO SHORT TERM CONDITIONS
	21	NUMBER BUSY	
	22	SELECTION SIGNALS PROCEDURE ERROR	
	23	SELECTION SIGNAL TRANSMISSION ERROR	
4&5	41	ACCESS BARRED	WITH CLEARING DUE TO LONG TERM CONDITIONS
	42	CHANGED NUMBER	
	43	NOT OBTAINABLE	
	44	OUT OF ORDER	
	46	UNCONTROLLED NOT READY	
	47	DCE POWER OFF	
	48	INVALID FACILITY REQUEST	
	49	NETWORK FAULT IN LOCAL LOOP	
	45	CONTROLLED NOT READY	
	51	CALL INFORMATION SERVICE	
	52	INCOMPATIBLE USER CLASS OF SERVICE	
6	61	NETWORK CONGESTION	WITH CLEARING DUE TO NETWORK SHORT TERM CONDITIONS
7	71	LONG TERM NETWORK CONGESTION	WITH CLEARING DUE TO NETWORK LONG TERM CONDITIONS
	72	RPOA OUT OF ORDER	
3	81	REGISTRATION/CANCELLATION CONFIRMED	WITH CLEARING DUE TO DTE-NETWORK PROCEDURE
	82	REDIRECTION ACTIVATED	
	83	REDIRECTION DEACTIVATED	

Fig. 6.   Coding of call progress signals.

great deal of commonality with the call progress signal definition used for packet-switching operation.

Fig. 6 gives a list of the call progress signals applicable to X.21, together with the respective coding. Initially, a two-digit code is applied where the first digit indicates a general category of signal. This enables a relatively simple terminal to just translate the basic category of the call progress signal. The second digit indicates the more specific reason which can be translated by more intelligent terminals. In the future, it will be possible to expand the number of digits if further enrichment is needed. Unfortunately, there is no commonality of coding with the call progress signals for X.25 packet operation. Due to the rapid development of X.25, encoding of general categories of call progress signals were not established as in X.21.

The CALL PROGRESS SIGNAL SEQUENCE must be preceded by at least two "SYN" characters as described earlier for character synchronization. These "SYN" characters will be sent during state 6A. If there is more than one block of signals, the period between them will be filled by additional "SYN" characters during state 6B.

In the 1976 issue [1] of X.21, state 10 was named CALLED LINE IDENTIFICATION. Further study, however, showed that more flexibility will be needed for future enhancements providing a family of signals that may be provided to the DTE from the network. Therefore, the name was changed to DCE PROVIDED INFORMATION. The only signal presently identified for state 10 is the original CALLED LINE IDENTIFI-CATION, but there is an expansion of the companion state 10 bis for the called DTE which will be discussed later. In effect,

CALL PROGRESS SIGNALS are really a subset of the more general DCE PROVIDED INFORMATION. This would logically suggest a possible merger of state 7 and 10 for a simplification of the state diagram. This may be a consideration for the future.

While the above actions have been occurring at the calling DTE/DCE interface, the state diagram also shows the procedures unique at the called DTE/DCE interface in states 8, 9, and 10bis. The INCOMING CALL signal (stage 8) with $r = $ BEL, $i = $ OFF is presented to a READY DTE where $t = 1$, $c = $ OFF. The DTE answers the call by signaling the steady-state conditions of $t = 1$, $c = $ ON for CALL ACCEPTED (state 9).

At this point, the network may wish to provide the Called DTE additional information relating to the call (state 10bis). Similar to state 10 as earlier described, state 10bis was originally named CALLING LINE IDENTIFICATION in the previous version of X.21 [1], but further work has now changed the name to DCE PROVIDED INFORMATION. The new state 10bis includes the original CALLING LINE IDEN-TIFICATION and the new addition of CHARGING INFORMA-TION which will be described later. Consideration in the future will be given to further enhancing state 10bis to include additional capabilities such as subaddressing and a means for acceptance of reverse charging calls.

Another feature under future consideration will be a means for positive and negative acknowledgment of the DCE PROVIDED INFORMATION. As presently defined, negative acknowledgment due to error or rejection is only possible with a complete clearing of the call. It is felt that this may be too drastic where a simple retransmission could solve the problem.

Upon acceptance of the call and any information provided by state 10bis, DCE WAITING state 6c is signaled. At this point, the state diagram does not any longer distinguish between Calling and Called DTE.

The transitions to states 11 and 12 is the process originally known as "connect-through" in the original version of X.21 in 1972. This was an issue of great confusion and debate which resulted in a carefully constructed agreement. The concerns were related to the danger of losing bits of user data and the possible presence of spurious bits during the "connect-through" process.

As the "connect-through" procedure is very complex to describe; the following is the exact test as it appears in X.21 [1] and is presented to assist understanding:

> "All bits sent by a DTE after receiving Ready for data and before sending DTE clear request will be delivered to the corresponding DTE after that corresponding DTE has received Ready for data and before it has received DCE clear indication (provided that the corresponding DTE does not take the initiative of Clearing).
>
> All bits received by a DTE after receiving Ready for data and before receiving DCE clear indication or receiving DCE clear confirmation have been sent by the corresponding DTE. Some of them may have been sent before that corresponding DTE has received Ready for data; those bits are binary 1."

In effect, the result of the process of the transition on circuit R from "SYN" in state 6 (a, b, or c), or from "+" of state 5, to "1" of state 11 and 12 is the completion of the end-to-end connection. The "SYN" (or "+") is generated internally within the network, while the "1" originates from the distant DTE on circuit T and is carried through the network and presented to the local DTE on circuit R. Because the transistion on circuit I may not be concurrent with the transition on circuit R, due to network signaling differences, state 11 has been included but, as shown, may be bypassed. The significant state is READY FOR DATA (state 12) where a guaranteed transparent end-to-end path is established and ready for transfer of user data in state 13.

3) Clearing: In the proposed ISO architecture [4], a disconnection function is defined for each level to terminate operational phases. In the case of X.25, there is a disconnection function at each of the first three levels [6], each of which serves as specific purpose. X.21 being a greatly simplified procedure for circuit-switched applications does not provide for any disconnection function at either the link or the network layers. Instead, the basic level 1 NOT READY functions of $r = 0$, $i = $ OFF, and $t = 0$, $c = $ OFF serve to terminate the operational phases of a call.

Fig. 7 shows the state diagram for clearing of a circuit-switched connection and return to the READY state. Clearing can be initiated at any time by either the DTE or the DCE from any state in Fig. 3 except READY. A DTE initiates clearing by sending DTE CLEAR REQUEST (state 16) and the

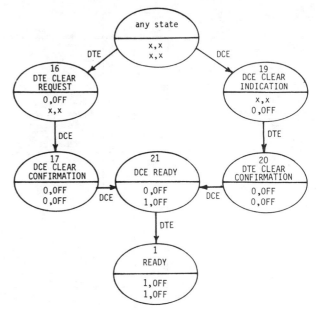

Fig. 7. Clearing phase.

DCE responds with DCE CLEAR CONFIRMATION (state 17) followed at least 24 bit times later by DCE READY (state 21). The DCE initiates clearing by sending DCE CLEAR INDICATION (state 19), and the DTE responds with DTE CLEAR CONFIRMATION (state 20). The DCE then responds with DCE READY (state 21). In a normal clearing sequence, regardless of whether the DTE or the DCE initiates clearing, the DCE must first indicate DCE READY (state 21) $r = 1$, $i = $ OFF before the DTE can signal READY $t = 1$, $c = $ OFF to enter state 1. This was necessary due to the operation of the network signaling system in CCITT Recommendation X.60. Once READY (state 1) is reached, a new call can then be processed.

4) DTE Time Limits and DCE Time Outs: In order to detect error or fault situations and provide a recovery mechanism, a family of DTE time limits and DCE time outs has been specified. Each timer is started by a transition into a particular state. For normal operation within the specified time, the timer stops when the designated next state is entered. If the timer expires before the recognized normal transition, then a recovery action can be initiated. As a result, lock up or endless loop operations are avoided so, when the problem clears, normal operation can resume.

It should be noted that these time outs and time limits are not an indication of typical response times, but are used to determine when most probably a failure in operation has occurred in either the DTE or DCE. Much faster response times under normal operation are expected for efficient network operation.

5) Optional User Facilities: There are a number of optional user facilities (special service features) defined for circuit-switched service by CCITT Recommendation X.2 [1]. These may be selected on a per-call basis by a Facility Request in the SELECTION SIGNAL SEQUENCE. A list of these facilities is given in Fig. 8.

The Closed User Group provides for communication only

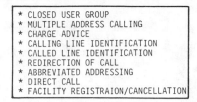

```
* CLOSED USER GROUP
* MULTIPLE ADDRESS CALLING
* CHARGE ADVICE
* CALLING LINE IDENTIFICATION
* CALLED LINE IDENTIFICATION
* REDIRECTION OF CALL
* ABBREVIATED ADDRESSING
* DIRECT CALL
* FACILITY REGISTRAION/CANCELLATION
```

Fig. 8.   Optimal user facilities.

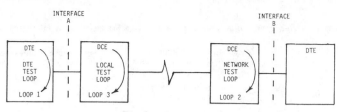

Fig. 9.   Test loops.

among a designated group of subscribers. A subscriber may belong to more than one such closed user group and, therefore, a calling DTE must then designate which group the subscriber being called belongs to. A particular closed user group can be designated by the DTE as preferential to enable a DTE to process a call to a subscriber in the preferential group without making a special facility request. Calls within nonpreferential groups would then need a facility request to specify the applicable closed user group.

Multiple Address Calling is allowed for circuit-switched service. This enables establishment of conference or broadcast types of communication.

Charge advice is a new facility established to provide a calling DTE with the charging information related to an immediate preceding call. Upon clearing of a call for which Charge Advice has been requested by a Facility Request, the network will, within 200 ms, return the charging information to the DTE by means of an INCOMING CALL (state 8). When the call is accepted by the DTE (state 9), the DCE will provide the charging information in state 10 bis. At the present time, there is no generalized error recovery defined if the DTE fails to receive the information correctly. One means that would increase the probability of successful receipt would be to repeat the information two or more times or until the DTE clears.

Called Line Identification can be requested by a DTE on a per-call basis so the network will verify the called number during state 10. Calling Line Identification can be provided on a continuing basis to called DTE's as part of state 10bis. This feature is intended to facilitate screening of incoming calls by a DTE to avoid unauthorized access.

Another facility that has been defined is redirection of an incoming call. This enables a subscriber to have incoming calls directed to an alternate number when desired, such as during nonbusiness hours.

The other facilities that are also included in X.2 for circuit-switched service are Abbreviated Addressing and Direct Call, which have been discussed in detail earlier.

These facilities can be initiated on a per-call basis using a facility request or continuously on a subscription basis. Additionally, there is a procedure defined where a DTE can dynamically change or modify a particular facility. This is the Facility Registration/Cancellation Procedure. It can be applied to reallocate or change addresses for assigned abbreviated address codes. It can also be used to add and delete subscribers from closed user groups.

6) *Test Loops*: The new CCITT Recommendation X.150 is being developed to define a family of test loops to assist in the location of faults in an interconnection. These are shown in Fig. 9.

DTE test loop 1 is implemented in the DTE and is under the full control of the DTE.

Local test loop 3 is located in the DCE and provides a loop toward the DTE. This enables the DTE to verify the operation of the DTE/DCE interface. This loop can only be activated by a switch on the DCE, although a means for automatic activation across its interfaces is being studied.

Finally, network test loop 2 is implemented in the DCE and provides a loop toward the network. This can be activated manually by a switch on the DCE. A provisional procedure has also been accepted for use in some networks to enable a remote DTE to automatically activate this loop. This, however, may cause a number of administrative as well as technical problems that still need resolution.

V. FUTURE EVOLUTION

As circuit-switched networks commence operation, practical experience will be gained as to the efficacy of this technology for data communications applications. As a result, the question can then be answered within the next few years as to whether an efficient, fast circuit-switched operation will prove more effective than the popularized packet-switched service of X.25

One significant issue that must be dealt with in future work is convergence toward common protocols to satisfy all modes of operation. It is not a practical matter on a continuing basis to have two very different protocols to satisfy identical functions, X.21 call establishment and X.25 call establishment. As the general purpose part of X.21 becomes the established universal physical layer interface for all data communications applications in the future, universal link and network layer protocols should also be established accordingly. HDLC (ADCCP) appears appropriate for the link layer [10], but considerable study remains to be done for establishment of a universal network layer standard [3].

REFERENCES

[1]   "CCITT X-Series Recommendations, Public Data Networks," in H. C. Folts and H. R. Karp, Ed., *Data Communications Standards*.   New York: McGraw-Hill, 1978, pp. 185–327.
[2]   H. V. Bertine, "Physical level protocols," this issue, pp. 433–444.
[3]   H. C. Folts, "Evolution toward a universal interface for data communications," in *Proc. Int. Conf. Comput. Commun.*, Kyoto, Japan, Sept. 1978, pp. 675–680.
[4]   H. Zimmermann, "The ISO model for open systems interconnection," this issue, pp. 425–432.
[5]   V. C. MacDonald, "The time-table and mandate of CCITT," in *Conf.*

Rec., Int. Conf. Commun., vol. I, San Francisco, CA, June 1975, pp. 1–3.

[6]   A. M. Rybczynski, "X.25 interface and end-to-end virtual circuit service characteristics." this issue, pp. 500–510.

[7]   1S0/TC97/SC6 document N 1869.

[8]   1S0/TC97/SC6 document N 1955.

[9]   J. W. Conard, "Character-oriented data link control protocols," this issue, pp. 445–454.

[10]   D. E. Carlson, "Bit-oriented data link control procedures," this issue, pp. 455–467.

[11]   H. C. Folts, "X.21. The international interface for new synchronous data networks," in *Conf. Rec., Int. Conf. Commun.*, vol. I, San Francisco, CA, June 1975, pp. 15–19.

[12]   CCITT COM VII, no. 373, "Draft recommendation X.21 draft revision 4," White Paper, Apr. 1979.

[13]   ISO Recommendation R 1538—Programming language "ALGOL," Mar. 1972.

[14]   CCITT Recommendations Provisionally Adopted, X75, X.121, Geneva, Switzerland, 1979.

Harold C. Folts received the B.S. degree in electrical engineering from Tri-State University, Angola, IN, in 1959, and the M.S. degree in systems management from the University of Southern California, Los Angeles, in 1973.

He is an active participant in federal, domestic, and international standards development activities, and is directly associated with the development of many notable data communications standards, such as RS-422, RS-423, RS-449, X.21, and X.25. He is Senior Engineer, Office of the Manager, National Communications System, a federal government activity, and serves as Chairman of the American National Standards Institute Task Group on Public Data Networks and CCITT Special Rapporteur on X.21. Additionally, he has served as Chairman of the Electronic Industries Association Subcommittee on Digital Interfaces and is the coeditor of McGraw-Hill's *Compilation of Data Communications Standards*. Throughout his career, he has served in a wide variety of telecommunication engineering activites in industry and the government from field engineer to his current position.

Implementing the X.21 interface

Vladimir Yanoschak, IBM, Research Triangle Park, N.C.

The public circuit-switching data network is gaining wider user acceptance. Designing to the recently adopted standard simplifies network access.

The new public data networks with X.21 interfaces offer several advantages over the older telephone networks with the RS-232-C (or V.24/V.28) Interface: a common interface for many data rates, connect times faster than dial-up (200 to 500 milliseconds versus 3 to 15 seconds), duplex operation, less error-prone performance, and new user functions — on either leased or switched lines. Some leased-line applications can now take advantage of switched-line benefits. Other applications will continue with leased lines, with the X.21 standard's interface.

Today, two networks using X.21 are in operation: one in Japan and one in the Nordic countries (Denmark, Finland, Norway, and Sweden). At least eight more such networks are planned. These networks require X.21 communications adapters that are functionally much different from those designed for the older EIA (Electronic Industries Association) RS-232-C/RS-366 modem/auto-dial interfaces. IBM, in building several products that can be attached to the Japanese network, has pinpointed the design criteria for an X.21 communications adapter, which network designers can apply to their networks.

Basically, the CCITT Recommendation X.21 defines a general-purpose interface between data terminal equipment (DTE) — which can range from a simple terminal to a large computer — and data circuit-terminating equipment (DCE), the network interface (Fig. 1). It describes the terminal attachment, call-control procedures, and user functions (with Recommendation X.2) for both circuit-switching and leased-line service. Leased service does not require any user software changes; switched service provides diagnostic and other features in return for the necessary new software.

The interface has four major circuits: transmit (T) and control (C), which are controlled by the DTE, and receive (R) and indication (I), controlled by the DCE. In addition, there is a signal-element timing circuit (S), an optional byte-timing circuit (B), and two ground connections. The C and I circuits denote either "on" or "off"; the signals on the T and R circuits are control characters or specific sequences of binary 1s and 0s. For example, all 1s on the R circuit may denote a connection in progress, 16 or more 0s, a clear request, meaning disconnect the call.

The S circuit generates clock pulses for the transmitting and receiving signals on the T and R circuits. The byte-timing circuit is provided by some networks to furnish 8-bit-byte timing to the DTE for the T and R circuits. Its use is optional to the DTE.

The combinations of signals on the four basic interface circuits determine the DTE/DCE states. X.21 defines 28 unique states to indicate the status of the DTE-DCE interface (see table). These can be grouped into three phases: quiescent (inactive), call control (establishment and clearing), and data transfer.

Either the DTE or DCE can cause a state change on the interface by changing a signal on one or both of the two circuits under its control. The DTE-DCE interface is transparent in the data-transfer phase, since

1. Gaining access. *The X.21 interface is used on public circuit-switching data networks between data terminal equipment (DTE)—anything from a simple terminal to a large computer—and data circuit-terminating equipment (DCE), the network interface. The interface has four basic circuits: transmit, control, receive, and indication.*

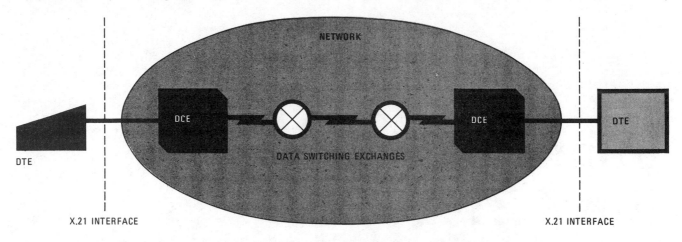

the network imposes no constraints on the bit sequences of information data that can be transmitted. On determining which state the interface is in, the DTE or DCE initiates the appropriate signal combinations needed to enter another state. The allowable sequences of states are defined in the state diagrams that are part of the X.21 standard. For example, Figure 2A illustrates the states sequence for call-control and data-transfer procedures. The quiescent states (listed in the table) are not included.

A DTE initiates a call by communicating to the network's DCE via a specified sequence of signals. First, the DTE determines if the DCE is signaling DCE Ready. If it is, the DTE then signals DTE Ready (if it is not already doing so). The coincidence of DTE Ready and DCE Ready is the Ready state (state 1, Fig. 2A). Prior to signaling Ready, the DTE was in either a DTE-Controlled-Not-Ready state (14) or a DTE-Uncontrolled-Not-Ready state (quiescent state 22 or 24).

Interstate call
From the Ready state, the DTE initiates a call by entering the Call-Request state (2), which the DCE acknowledges by entering the Proceed-to-Select state (3). The DTE next goes to the Selection-Signals state (4) by presenting to the DCE the identifying digits of the DTE being called.

At the called-DTE location, there is another X.21 DTE-DCE interface that passes through states complementary to those at the calling DTE. The DCE at the called location, on determining that the called DTE is in the Ready condition, signals the called DTE by going to the Incoming-Call state (8). The called DTE signals its willingness to accept the incoming call by entering the Call-Accepted state (9).

The DCEs at both called and calling locations now pass through several optional states, such as DCE Waiting (6) and Connection in Progress (11). Connection in Progress puts the call establishment into a temporary hold until the network finishes its "housekeeping" preparations before turning the end-to-end con-

nection over to the DTEs. The DCEs enter the Ready-for-Data state (12), and the DTEs enter the Data-Transfer state (13). The calling DTE may now begin exchanging data transparently with the remote DTE.

During call establishment, if the network determines that it cannot complete the connection or that the connection will be delayed, it signals the calling DTE with call-progress signals (state 7) over the DTE-DCE interface. If the connection is being delayed, the DCE-Waiting state is maintained until further progress toward the Ready-for-Data state can be made. If the connection cannot be completed, the DCE initiates a clearing sequence, and the call is aborted. State sequences also vary from the normal when accommodating such optional functions as line identification, direct call, and abbreviated dialing.

A clearing sequence is initiated when a DCE recognizes a DTE's Clear Request (state 16). The DCE responds with a DCE Clear Confirmation (state 17) followed by DCE Ready (state 21) and, at the same time, notifies the corresponding remote DCE of the clear request. This remote DCE enters the DCE-Clear-Indication state (19) to notify the remote DTE of the disconnection. Then, this DTE responds by entering the DTE-Clear-Confirmation state (20) and waits for its (remote) DCE to signal DCE Ready (state 21). The clearing sequence at the local and remote DTE-DCE interfaces is completed when the Ready state is attained at both interfaces.

Designing the adapter
Although RS-232-C, with auto-dial, has more than four times as many circuits as X.21, it is usually necessary to monitor and control the circuits only for the proper on-off (binary) sequence. For the X.21 interface, only two circuits (C and I) have to be controlled or monitored for their binary state. In addition, at times an appropriate number of binary 1s or 0s, or International Alphabet Number 5 (IA5—identical to USASCII) characters, must be maintained on the T circuit and detected on the R circuit by the DTE. The conditions on

Data Communications/February 1981

these circuits must be continually analyzed to ascertain that the call establishment is proceeding through the valid sequence of states within the time limits prescribed in the X.21 standard.

The data received on the R circuit during the call-control phase may have to be analyzed for the correct format and content—depending on security and data-integrity requirements—and stored for future reference. The DTE should be designed to analyze this data and make certain decisions based on its content, such as whether or not to initiate a clearing sequence and retry the call. The user's application program determines what, if anything, is done with this capability.

To provide its new functions, X.21 can have many optional states (Figs. 2A and 2B). After selection signals are sent and the DTE-Waiting state is attained, the next valid state may be the Ready-for-Data state or, depending on the circumstances, the DCE Waiting state, the DCE-Provided-Information state, or the Connection-in-Progress state. The analysis needed to handle all the possible optional sequences requires additional programming effort and hardware intelligence. The optional states also complicate test equipment and increase the number of test cases and the amount of testing time required.

In addition, various countries have different regulations that data network users must meet, which restrict the number of automatic retries or the delay time prior to a retry. The DTE, again, must be designed with the versatility to operate with all these variations.

The degree of intelligence required in a particular DTE depends on its application(s). For every application, the designer must decide which functions should be implemented in software, hardware/firmware, or combinations of both. Although hardware is less-expensive than software, the difficulty of altering hardware usually limits its use to tasks that are not susceptible to change.

Saving time with hardware

Implementation in hardware also may be preferred if certain operations must be completed within milliseconds or less, since code is executed sequentially and may not be able to control and execute an operation within the specified time. For example, X.21 requires a DTE-Clear-Confirmation response to a DCE Clear Indication within 100 milliseconds. By implementing this function in hardware, designers can avoid the continuing exchange of signals between hardware and software and ensure a timely response.

X.21 defines the valid sequence of states during call establishment, but does not define the actions to be taken by the DTE for an invalid or undefined state. An exception: certain preferred DTE actions are defined when specific time limits expire. For other unexpected conditions, the DTE designer must decide what should be considered errors and what recovery procedures, if any, are appropriate.

A DTE could consider these conditions as errors:
■ During the Proceed-to-Select or Incoming-Call states, the DTE receives characters other than the continuous IA5 + or Bel characters. (Bel characters denote an incoming call.)
■ An unexpected condition is detected on a physical interface circuit. For example, the indication circuit goes to the "on" level, while the DTE is transmitting selection signals.
■ Call-progress signals or DCE-provided information is received with some kind of format violation, such as an invalid first character or a missing delimiter.
■ The DCE does not present the DCE-Ready state within a reasonable period of time (2 to 3 seconds, but it could be as long as 60 seconds).

When detecting such conditions, the DTE designer has several options:
■ Ignore the error and depend on one of the time limits to expire, to which the DTE or DCE will react.
■ Initiate a DTE-clearing sequence and try again.
■ Initiate a DTE-clearing sequence and follow with an interface-monitoring function to determine when the DCE error condition clears up, and then try again.

The DTE designer must also decide how to catego-

Interface states

STATE NUMBER	STATE NAME
1	READY
2	CALL REQUEST
3	PROCEED TO SELECT
4	SELECTION SIGNALS
5	DTE WAITING
6A	DCE WAITING
6B	DCE WAITING
7	DCE-PROVIDED INFORMATION (CALL PROGRESS SIGNALS)
8	INCOMING CALL
9	CALL ACCEPTED
10	DCE-PROVIDED INFORMATION (CALLED DTE LINE IDENTIFICATION)
10 BIS	DCE-PROVIDED INFORMATION (CALLING DTE LINE IDENTIFICATION)
11	CONNECTION IN PROGRESS
12	READY FOR DATA
13	DATA TRANSFER
13S	SEND DATA
13R	RECEIVE DATA
14	DTE CONTROLLED NOT READY, DCE READY
15	CALL COLLISION
16	DTE CLEAR REQUEST
17	DCE CLEAR CONFIRMATION
18	DTE READY, DCE NOT READY
19	DCE CLEAR INDICATION
20	DTE CLEAR CONFIRMATION
21	DCE READY
22	DTE UNCONTROLLED NOT READY, DCE NOT READY
23	DTE CONTROLLED NOT READY, DCE NOT READY
24	DTE UNCONTROLLED NOT READY, DCE READY

(A)

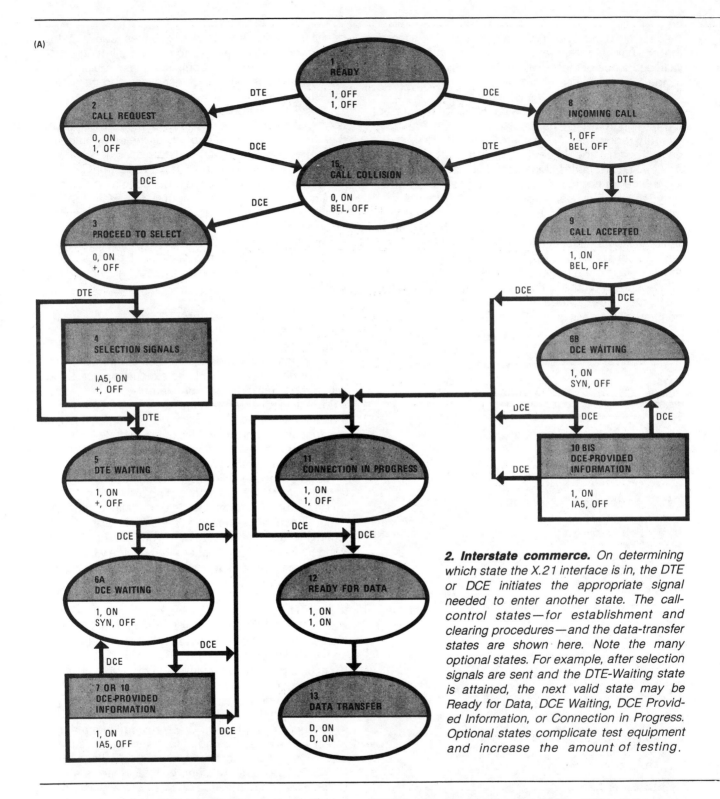

2. Interstate commerce. *On determining which state the X.21 interface is in, the DTE or DCE initiates the appropriate signal needed to enter another state. The call-control states—for establishment and clearing procedures—and the data-transfer states are shown here. Note the many optional states. For example, after selection signals are sent and the DTE-Waiting state is attained, the next valid state may be Ready for Data, DCE Waiting, DCE Provided Information, or Connection in Progress. Optional states complicate test equipment and increase the amount of testing.*

rize the various detectable errors. He may lump them all into one broad "unexpected-error" category or break them down into specific errors and even include the state in which the error is detected. When time limits expire, though, it is more meaningful to identify the specific time limit rather than to merely indicate that a timeout occurred.

The chosen method depends on the security, reliability, and error-statistics requirements of the DTE. If the DTE ignores errors, either the DTE or DCE will time out, causing a disconnection. The designer must base his decision on the application's requirements and degree of sophistication. Of course, the more sophisticated the requirements, the more resources (code, hardware, and processing time) are needed.

To the extent required by the application, the DTE can check the format of call-progress signals and other DCE-provided information and distinguish between

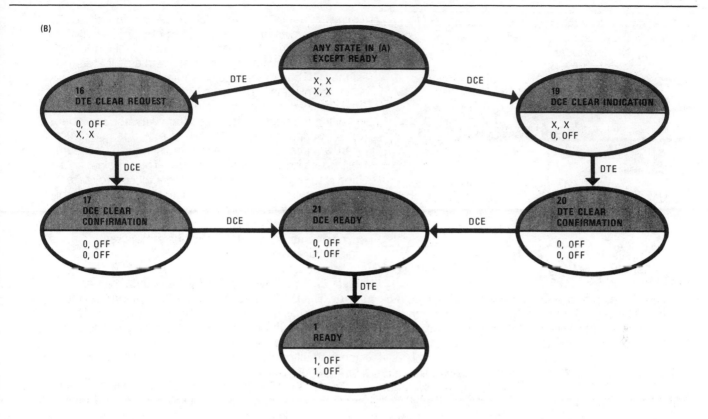

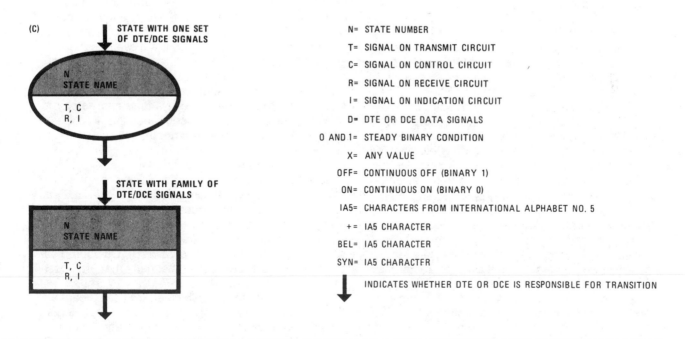

them by the first character following the leading sync characters. In this regard, an IA5 digit denotes a call-progress signal, while an asterisk or slash identifies other DCE-provided information.

Call-Progress signals always consist of one or more groups of two IA5 digits followed by the plus or comma delimiter. DCE-provided information includes a variable number of digits and a comma, plus, or slash (for charging or billing information). Other special charac-

ters may be added in future revisions to X.21.

Format checking can be affected by other factors. For example, sync characters may be randomly inserted between the characters of DCE-provided information. And, in the Japanese application, a shift-in character—originally used to indicate a specific keyboard—precedes DCE-provided information. The possible presence of the shift-in character is an exception that complicates adapter design, since the first mean-

3. Bending the boundary. *Format checking can be complicated when a state is entered on an off-character boundary. False characters may then occur.*

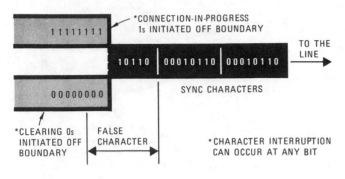

ingful character now may be either the first or the second character received by the DTE.

The designer can devise an elaborate, real-time, format-checking algorithm to check for all these conditions. However, the implementation of such an algorithm could seriously interfere with the user's required processing time, expecially at higher speeds such as 48 kbit/s. A compromise could be to check only for the presence of the delimiter and to store received data where it will be available, if required, for later analysis. Another—simpler—possibility is to abort any call when a delimiter is missing.

Off-boundary problems

Format checking also can be complicated—creating other problems—when a state is entered on an off-byte or off-character boundary, which causes receipt of a false character. This boundary condition occurs when, say, a Connection-in-Progress bit stream does not wait for the completion of a previous character, such as sync. X.21 allows two states to be entered on an off-byte boundary: Connection in Progress and DCE Clear Indication. Initiating either state off-boundary can create one or two false characters that can look like control data. Figure 3 illustrates one example of what may occur.

When an X.21 call establishment proceeds to the DCE-Waiting state (6A or 6B in Fig. 2A) and then enters Connection in Progress off-boundary from the previous sync characters, the last sync character may be altered to look like control data. This data consists of one character without a delimiter and should be ignored because the connection is subsequently made and the Data-Transfer state is attained.

However, to always discard a byte of control data not accompanied by a delimiter reduces the integrity of the error detection, since this byte could have been a legitimate error. But the legitimate error is not expected to occur frequently, so there seems to be little risk in ignoring the single character of data received prior to the successful establishment of the connection.

A similar situation occurs when a DCE initiates a "clear." Since a clear can occur at any time and can be off-boundary, and because the DTE must wait until it receives at least 16 contiguous 0s before it deter-

mines that a DCE-initiated clear is occurring, the DTE may receive as many as two characters of false control data. And it may have difficulty distinguishing this false data from legitimate control data with a delimiter error. If the DTE can determine, in some way, that a DCE-initiated clear is in progress before taking action on the received false data, the problem could be avoided.

Since the network is clearing anyway, the designer may not consider it worthwhile to provide the additional hardware or software needed to distinguish between false data and the legitimate error. The simplest solution is to program the DTE to ignore all control data received without a delimiter when it is immediately followed by a clear. Figure 3 shows how either 1s from a Connection in Progress or clearing 0s can alter the sync characters of a DCE-Waiting state, creating a false character.

Sometimes a false character created by entering a state on an off-byte boundary may contain a parity error. The DTE will need either to determine that the parity error is due to a false character or to ignore all parity errors. In view of the high reliability and low error rates expected with the new public data networks, ignoring all parity errors may not seriously hamper information reliability for the DTE.

Finally, the DTE should avoid causing a false timeout from the reception of these false characters. After selection signals are transmitted, the DTE starts a 20-second timeout. The reception of DCE-provided information aborts the 20-second timeout, and a 2-second timeout is initiated. But, if the 2-second timeout starts on receipt of a false character, it will override the 20-second timeout, which should have been allowed to continue. A false timeout can thus occur after 2 seconds. One solution—after determining that the 2-second timeout expiration is due to a false character—is to restart the 20-second timeout and allow it to expire before taking action on the timeout.

DTE-DCE clearing

If, as recommended in X.21, the DTE is designed to look for a DCE Clear Confirmation and then DCE Ready following a DTE Clear Request (request to disconnect), there is some chance of an error. Say the DTE initiates a DTE Clear Request and looks for DCE Clear Confirmation (I circuit off and 16 zeros on R). One combination of circumstances, out of the many that are possible, is shown in Figure 4.

If the DCE initiates its own clear, via DCE Clear Indication, before it has recognized the DTE Clear Request, the DCE will look for DTE Clear Confirmation. Since the conditions on the T and C circuits are identical (0, off) for both the DTE Clear Request and DTE Clear Confirmation, the DCE will detect 16 zeros from the DTE Clear Request and assume that it is DTE Clear Confirmation. The DCE may now go into the DCE-Ready state before it has transmitted the required 16 zero bits to the DTE.

In Figure 4, for example, only 12 zero bits would have been sent by the DCE. The DTE will never detect the DCE Clear Confirmation that it is looking for, and the prescribed 2-second timeout will expire. This should

4. Clear complications. *The transmit and control circuits are identical (0, off) for both the DTE Clear Request and DTE Clear Confirmation. The DCE will detect 16 zeros from the DTE Clear Request, assume that it is DTE Clear Confirmation, stop sending zero bits (at 12 here), and the DTE gets no DCE Clear Confirmation.*

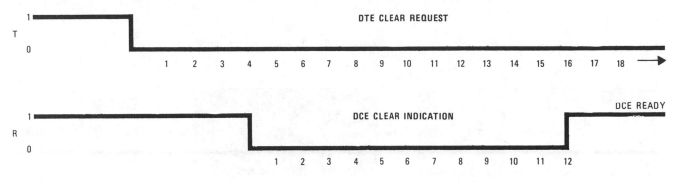

be interpreted as an error condition. To avoid this situation, the DTE may be designed to look only for DCE Ready after initiating the DTE Clear Request. Now, when the DTE detects DCE Ready, it will proceed to the Ready state to complete the clearing sequence.

However, this solution introduces the possibility of another error condition when the DTE initiates the DTE Clear Request while in the Connection-in-Progress state. The conditions on the R and I circuits for Connection in Progress (1, off) are the same as for DCE Ready. If the DCE is slow in responding to the DTE Clear Request and remains in Connection in Progress, the DTE may erroneously assume Connection in Progress to be the awaited DCE Ready response and proceed as if the clearing sequence were successfully completed. This design does not appear to be a serious problem, since either the DCE will eventually proceed with the clearing procedure or a DTE will detect an error during the next expected sequence.

Another point worth noting on the clearing sequence is that the CCITT has recently changed the definition of DCE Clearing from detecting 16 zero bits on R to an option that calls for clearing on at least 16 zeros, but for not less than 10 milliseconds of zeros. (At 48 kbit/s, this amounts to hundreds of zeros.) This may be considered necessary by some networks to filter out line disturbances, such as lightning strikes, which could result in unnecessary disconnects. Since the operational problem seems to be minimal, some networks may justifiably consider this 10-millisecond requirement optional.

DTE-DCE ready

When the DTE is preparing to initiate an outgoing call or to handle an incoming call, it must check that the DCE is ready before continuing. If the DCE is not ready this may be considered an error condition. Since the DCE may remain not ready for an indefinite period, it would be a waste of resources to reattempt the call establishment only to repeatedly detect the same error condition. Therefore, it may be advantageous to invoke a monitoring function, which would periodically (every few seconds) check for the DCE-Ready condition and, when detected, allow the call to proceed. Conversely, a function to monitor for the DCE-Not-Ready condition

could be used during idle periods as an early alert to the operator, should the DCE become not ready.

If the DTE initiates outgoing calls or is prepared to handle incoming calls only when commanded to do so by an operator or a higher-level program, it should remain in the Controlled-Not-Ready state at all other times. X.21 stipulates that the Ready state should be entered after a successful clearing sequence. During this Ready condition, it is possible for the DCE to signal an incoming call to the DTE, and, if the DTE is not prepared to respond, a DCE timeout will occur. As a result, the DCE may consider the DTE out of service. This is an inefficient use of the network. To comply with X.21 while minimizing this possibility for a timeout, the Ready state might be presented for only the minimum required 24 bit-times. After this period, the DTE may enter and maintain the Controlled-Not-Ready state until it is, once again, prepared to proceed with a call-establishment phase.

When initiating an outgoing call, the Ready state must be presented prior to the Call-Request state. During the Ready state, a window is presented to the DCE, during which it may signal an incoming call to the DTE. If a call collision results, the network should eventually resolve it in favor of the outgoing call (from the DTE). However, this is poor use of the network. The longer the DTE-Ready state is maintained, the greater the exposure to call collisions and the more likely a slowing of outgoing calls.

When the DTE starts to clear, it starts a 2-second timeout. If the timeout expires because of no response from the DCE, the preferred action, according to X.21, is for the DTE to signal DTE Ready. However, the lack of response probably means that the DCE is in a hung-up condition and is unable to participate in any further exchange. So why should the DTE go to Ready? An alternative, when this timeout occurs, is for the DTE to go directly to the Controlled-Not-Ready state.

When the DTE is ready, an incoming call is signaled as the network transmits a string of IA5 Bel characters, preceded by two or more sync characters. If the network continues to send sync characters and never sends the Bel, it is possible for the DTE to wait in this undefined state indefinitely because no DTE time limit has been defined for the situation. This can be pre-

5. Common control. *Those functions involved with communications-line maintenance and with transmission or reception of data on that line are called the common* *communications functions. The functions designers must evaluate the trade-offs between hardware and software (often microcode) implementations for each function.*

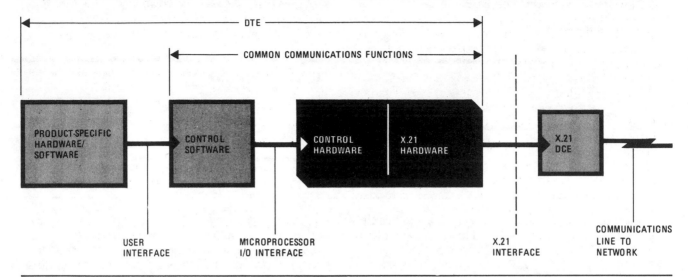

vented by introducing a time limit of several seconds, after which the DCE may be considered to be not ready, and the operator may be notified to contact network personnel.

There are several X.21 states for which the same character may be received continuously for two or more seconds. Examples are the "+" characters during the Proceed-to-Select state and Bels during the Incoming-Call state. Depending on the data-handling techniques used in the DTE, the designer may avoid the inefficiencies of handling each character and of providing storage space for them. One technique is to design the hardware to ignore all but the first few characters; another is to change the trailing characters to syncs that would be ignored by the DTE.

The DTE functions designed to execute its unique tasks may be identified as product-specific functions. Those functions involved with communications-line maintenance and with transmission or reception of data on that line may be called the common communications functions (Fig. 5).

All DTEs that attach to a communications line via the X.21 interface could be designed to use the same common communications function regardless of required product functions. Two advantages of such a division of function are (1) the efficiencies and cost reductions inherent in the production of large quantities of a component and (2) the concentration of certain specialized data communications expertise in one area.

Making comparisons
The designers of common functions must evaluate the trade-offs of implementing the various functions in hardware or in software (often microcode). Also, the design must be flexible to accommodate the variations expected in the product-specific functions. Finally, the designer needs to define a user interface between the specific and common functions, control blocks, and parameters that must be shared and understood by

both functions. A disadvantage of this approach is that it necessitates additional code and hardware in the X.21-interface design.

The product-specific function utilizes the user interface to direct the common communications function of the operation to be performed. The common function, in turn, advises the specific code of the progress made in executing the function: for example, call-progress signals are present, a retry will be attempted, or the function has been successfully completed. Software pointers (to buffer areas) and character counts relative to selection signals, call-progress signals, or other DCE-provided information may be referenced in defined areas of the control blocks.

Different approaches
Since X.21-based networks are still under development, there undoubtedly will be specification changes, new services, and national variations. Besides Japan's shift-in character variation, several changes and new functions were introduced in the 1980 X.21 revision, and the CCITT Recommendation X.22 was accepted recently. X.22 provides a multiplexed version of X.21, which greatly reduces the line-interface needed for DTEs with high traffic, such as large host computers.

There are two other interfaces related to X.21: X.21 bis, and the "mini-interface." (Bis denotes a second version.) X.21 bis, another CCITT recommendation, is an interim interface for products originally designed for attachment to current telephone networks via the RS-232-C and RS-366 (CCITT V.24, V.25, V.28, and, for higher data rates, V.35) interfaces. X.21 bis allows existing terminals to operate with the new networks without design changes and lets them migrate to the new interface. However, these existing devices will not be able to take full advantage of many new functions of the X.21 interface, such as call-progress signals, and the new capabilities, such as auto-dial. X.21 bis DCEs may show call-progress signals on indicator lights but automatic action or decision making by the DTE will not be possible, since it does not have the intelligence of the X.21 DTE version.

The mini-interface is a proposed, simplified standard based on X.21. In its current stage of development, it will use a 15-pin connector. It is now being studied by the EIA, ISO (International Standards Organization), and CCITT standards committees and may prove to be the future data communications interface. This mini-interface is expected to be usable on both voice networks and public data networks, with either full- or half-duplex service. The panel, "The mini-interface and RS-449," discusses this new interface in relation to the RS-449 and RS-232-C standards.

How quickly users and product designers change over to X.21 depends on several factors, such as the availability of the new data networks and the requirements of new applications. Today, most users transmit data over telephone networks, using modems. ∎

References

1. V. Ahuja and A. S. Barclay, "Compatibility of systems network architecture and the CCITT X.21 interface," *Proceedings of the National Telecommunications Conference,* November 1979.

2. J. R. Halsey, L. E. Hardy, and L. F. Powning, "Public data networks: Their evolution, interfaces, and status," *IBM Systems Journal,* vol. 18, no. 2, 1979.

3. F. P. Corr and D. H. Neal, "SNA and emerging international standards," *IBM Systems Journal,* vol. 18, no. 2, 1979.

4. IBM, *IBM Implementation of X.21 Interface, General Information Manual* (GA27-3287-0), August 1980.

5. Harold C. Folts, "A powerful standard replaces the old interface standby," DATA COMMUNICATIONS, May 1980, p. 61.

Progress Towards User Access Arrangements in Integrated Services Digital Networks

MAURIZIO DÈCINA, MEMBER, IEEE

Abstract—This paper deals with arrangements for local access to emerging Integrated Services Digital Networks (ISDN's). The ISDN concept is here introduced as the focal point for the ongoing international activity on multiservice digital networks. ISDN's are conceived as networks which have evolved from the basic digital telephone networks and they will provide end-to-end digital connectivity to support a wide range of services including voice, data, sound, and video applications.

After giving a general outline of the evoving ISDN network scenarios for digital communications, the paper reviews the international trends on user access arrangements in terms of 1) user equipment and interface configurations, 2) access channel structures and information transfer capabilities, 3) local distribution plant configurations (with emphasis on the copper plant), and 4) access protocols.

I. INTRODUCTION

DURING recent years, we have experienced a rapid evolution towards the use of digital techniques for telephony and data telecommunication services. Service-dedicated digital networks have been implemented employing the so-called integration of transmission, signaling, and switching techniques. The telephony Integrated Digital Network (IDN) is based on transmission and circuit switching of 64 kbit/s pulse code modulation (PCM) voice channels. The introduction of PCM local exchanges and the expected provision of digital facilities up to the user's premises represent the current evolutionary stages of the telephony IDN development.

Data communication over public networks has evolved from analog leased and switched connections, through the implementation of point-to-point digital networks, up to the establishment of data IDN's based either on circuit or packet switching techniques.

An integration of telephony and data communication services is expected to occur during the next decade in the so-called Integrated Services Digital Networks (ISDN's). More in general, ISDN's are conceived as networks which will 1) evolve from the telephony IDN, 2) provide end-to-end digital connectivity to support a wide range of services, not only voice and data, but also sound and video applications, and 3) use a variety of communication modes, including both circuit and packet switching. The key element of service integration in the ISDN is the provision of an integrated local access to the planned multiservice communication capabilities. Access protocol procedures, service features, and performance, as perceived by the user through a set of standard user network

Manuscript received May 14, 1982.
The author is with the Institute of Electrical Communications, University of Rome, 00184 Rome, Italy.

interfaces, are basic ingredients of the ISDN. This will permit an evolutionary development of the ISDN in terms of network architecture and communication technology. Equipment integration could progressively evolve from the local access facilities up to the network transport facilities.

This paper gives an overview of the emerging network scenarios for integrated digital communication and discusses current international trends on the user access arrangements to the ISDN. In particular, Section II expands on the emerging ISDN concept, while Section III gives an overview of the evolving ISDN network architectures. Section IV deals with the user access in terms of user network interface capabilities and access equipment configurations. Emphasis is given throughout the paper to voice and data integration.

II. THE ISDN CONCEPT

An overview on the emerging ISDN concept is given in the following sections. Dedicated digital networks for voice and data, ISDN's, and emerging digital communication services are briefly introduced.

A. Dedicated Digital Networks

The telephony IDN is founded on 64 kbit/s PCM coding and transmission integrated with 64 kbit/s PCM circuit switching. Both PCM transmission and switching equipment operate synchronously according to a common network reference frequency. Switching offices are controlled by software programs stored in reliable processing units. Call control (signaling) information is exchanged among offices via a common channel signaling (CCS) network. The CCS network is a computer communication network employing packet switching techniques to transfer signaling messages among office command computers (Fig. 1). CCS switching offices are called signal transfer points (STP's) and are geographically duplicated to enhance interoffice signaling reliability.

Concerning digital data services, two main network scenarios apply. The first refers to circuit-switched networks that operate on integrated digital transmission and switching facilities as for the telephony IDN. The basic user data channel rates for synchronous data networks are 2.4, 4.8, 9.6, 48, 56, and 64 kbits/s. These rates apply at the data terminal equipment/data communication equipment (DTE/DCE) interfaces. Time division multiplexing (TDM) is used to carry assemblies of lower rate channels onto a single 64 kbit/s channel. Circuit switching for digital data channels can always be performed at 64 kbits/s using appropriate padding/depadding techniques to handle lower bit rate channels.

The second scenario involves packet switching of data

Reprinted from *IEEE Transactions on Communications*, Volume COM-30, Number 9, September 1982, pages 2117-2130. Copyright © 1982 by The Institute of Electrical and Electronics Engineers, Inc.

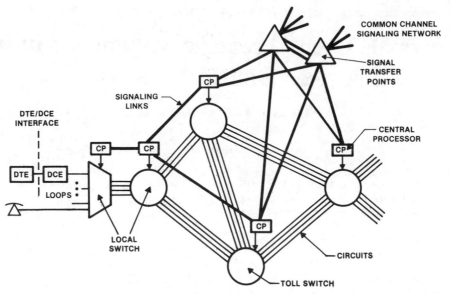

Fig. 1. Synchronous circuit-switched network.

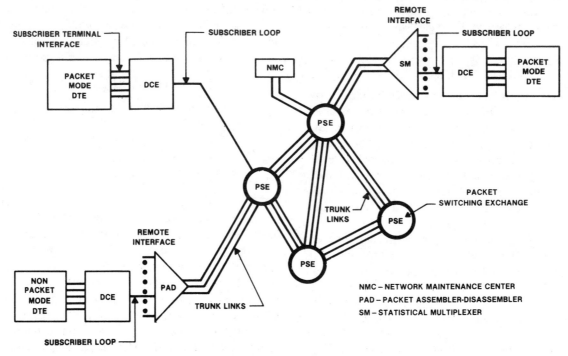

Fig. 2. Packet-switched data network.

messages (packets) that are offered by users at the same bearer channel rates as specified for circuit-switched networks. Packet-switching offices are realized by suitable interconnection of stored program processing units. Packet-switched data networks (Fig. 2) employ statistical multiplexing of data packets over digital transmission links that operate in general, at 56 or 64 kbits/s. Users can establish a bidirectional transaction involving multiple data packets: a "virtual call." Virtual calls are established by means of call setup packets that seize, throughout the network, a virtual path that will be followed by the subsequent data packets. Virtual call control information shares dynamically with data packets most communication network resources: trunks, memories, switching paths, etc. Users can also communicate by single data packets:

"datagrams." Each datagram contains sender and receiver DTE addresses in its packet header. Virtual circuit routing through the network permits less packet header overhead, since data packets are routed by using logical channel numbers instead of DTE addresses.[1] Both packet mode DTE's and nonpacket mode DTE's (e.g., start/stop terminals) can access packet-switched services. Packet assembling–disassembling (PAD) devices are used for interfacing nonpacket mode DTE's, usually via dialup connections over the analog telephone network.

[1] Virtual circuit routing also allows minimizing out-of-sequence delivery of packets belonging to the same call. Datagram routing, on the other hand, is suitable to adaptive mechanisms on a per packet basis, rather than on a per call basis.

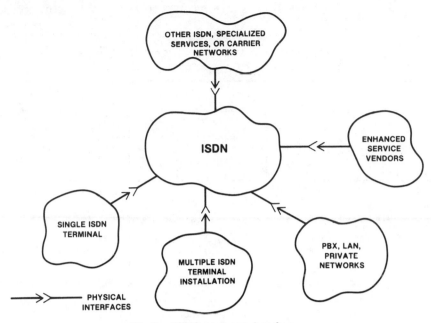

Fig. 3. ISDN user access interfaçes.

Circuit switching is a cost-effective technique to handle data applications characterized by high terminal activity during the call ("bulk" data). Facsimile and bulk data transfer among central processing units are typical examples of such applications. Packet switching is advantageous for "interactive" (with low activity during the virtual call) data applications, such as start/stop terminal-to-computer communications. As a further specific example, interactive Videotex is emerging as an internationally defined service that is well suited to packet-switched data networks.

B. The Emerging ISDN

The above scenarios for dedicated digital telephony and data networks are evolving today towards the concept of the ISDN.

Some background information on the ISDN concept is given in [1]-[4]. In particular, [3] includes six papers from various European administrations and the Bell System dealing with their respective approaches to the ISDN and with prospective field trials and early implementations of the ISDN.

A key role in establishing the ISDN concept was played by the CCITT (International Telephone and Telegraph Consultative Committee). Several CCITT study groups have undertaken activity on various aspects of the ISDN: network architecture, services, performance, user interfaces, signaling, and switching. Study Group XVIII is chartered with the coordination of these various activities and is setting up an overall network scenario to harmonize the emerging now standards [5]-[8].

The main feature of the ISDN is the support of a wide range of services (voice and nonvoice) in the same network by offering end-to-end digital connectivity. The ISDN will provide a network transport capability for a variety of services (ranging from low-speed alarms and telemetry through voice, interactive and bulk data, sound, up to broad-band video applications) using a variety of telecommunication modes (from leased and semipermanent connections to circuit- and packet-

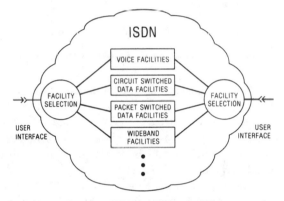

Fig. 4. ISDN transport facilities.

switched connections). We note that essential to the ISDN transport capability are the integrated operation, adminstration, and maintenance functions such as network management, billing, statistics, etc. In addition to the transport capability, depending on national regulatory arrangements, the ISDN could also incorporate information storage and processing facilities, e.g., for CCITT-defined services, such as Teletex, Videotex, Telefax, and others.

The key element of service integration for the ISDN is the provision of a limited set of standard user network interfaces (Fig. 3). Through such interfaces, users will select the requested communication facilities for single or multiple simultaneous services (Fig. 4). An ISDN is recognized by the service characteristics (procedure, performance, etc.) offered at its interfaces, rather than by its internal architecture, configuration, or technology. This concept plays a key role in permitting user applications and network technologies to evolve separately. The ISDN as shown in Fig. 4 may indeed be implemented in a variety of configurations according to specific national situations and to the progressive evolution of national networks.For example, in the early ISDN stages, the ISDN transport capability for 64 kbit/s (or 56 kbit/s)

TABLE I
EMERGING DIGITAL COMMUNICATION SERVICES

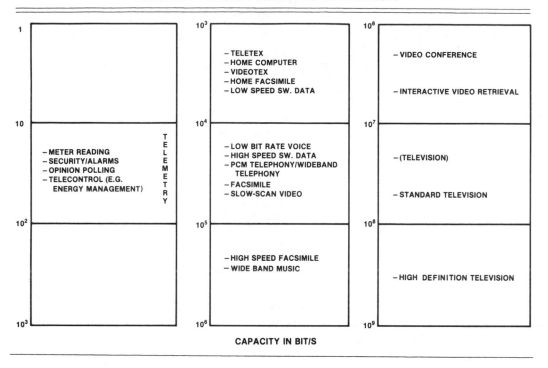

CAPACITY IN BIT/S

circuit-switched channels may be obtained by adapting the current space division local office plants to switch 64 kbit/s (or 56 kbit/s) digital signals. Likewise, on-demand broadband digital video connections (such as 1.5 or 2 Mbit/s video-conferencing channels) could be initially offered over digital satellite links and later on over terrestrial facilities.

More generally, it is expected that the ISDN should be based on and evolve from the 64 kbit/s circuit-switched telephony IDN, including digital subscriber loop facilities. The telephony IDN will provide interconnection with current service-dedicated facilities (such as data packet switching or wide-band switching) and will progressively incorporate, according to technology evolution and economic considerations, additional network functions and features, including those of any other service-dedicated facility. As the ISDN evolves, the trend will be to move towards the integration of service-dedicated facilities into common network equipment to improve cost-effectiveness. We note that the transition from the existing networks to a comprehensive ISDN may require a period of time extending over one or two decades. In the later stages, new network end equipment architectures will arise to improve efficiency of integrated voice, data, and wide-band communication.

It is expected that the ISDN transmission performance (errors, slips, jitter, etc.) and switching performance (call setup time, blocking, and delay), as perceived by the users, will be competitive with those of current dedicated networks due to the all-digital nature of the connections [8]. Special features may also be incorporated into the ISDN to offer, when required by users, a higher degree of performance (e.g., error or call setup time performance).

C. Emerging Digital Communication Services

Table I roughly assigns channel capacities for potential digital services covering a broad range of bit rates. In the first column, the group of services is labeled "telemetry" and it refers to very low rate data transmission generated by sources with low activity and burst mode of operation. These are typical of home and small business services. In the second column, the group between 1 and 10 kbits/s encompasses both home and business services for text, graphics, and data communications. A packet mode synchronous operation seems suitable for such interactive data services. Between 10 and 100 kbits/s we find, besides 64 kbit/s PCM telephony, also wide-band (4.5–7 kHz) voice at 64 kbits/s and low bit rate voice (LBRV) at bit rates $\leq$ 32 kbits/s. Reference [7] gives an overview on trends for such new standards for digital voice. High-speed switched data, digital facsimile, and slow-scan video services could also be provided in an integrated multiservice customer station operating on the basis of a single 64 kbit/s time slot. Circuit switching of voice and bulk data is suitable for such services.

All the above mentioned services are well suited to the present circuit-switched telephony IDN facilities. They can be provided by adjuncting to these facilities those for handling packet-switched data.

The remaining services in Table I comprise bulk services requiring $n \times 64$ kbits/s (such as high-speed facsimile and high-quality music), and bulk video services requiring m Mbits/s (m varying from a few to several hundred). The former services need a "multislot" circuit-switched transport capability, while the latter services require dedicated broad-band

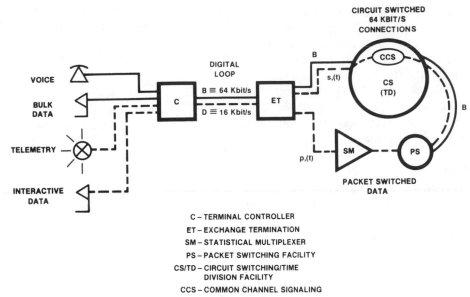

Fig. 5. Full digital approach: merging of digital voice and data networks.

digital transmission and switching facilities. We note that there is a large difference in the digital capacity required to encode business or entertainment video signals. While a videoconferencing service may adequately employ few Mbits/s (e.g., 2 or 3 [2 × 1.5 Mbits/s]), a broadcast quality television (TV) program may require about 100 Mbits/s (e.g., 2 × 45 or 3 × 34 Mbits/s). Hence, for an early deployment of entertainment video services (such as basic TV, pay TV, and video on demand) in the ISDN, consideration should still be given to provide in analog format the video signals associated with a simultaneous digital connection capability (see also Section IV-A).

III. THE EVOLVING ISDN

As explained in Section II, the ISDN may be implemented in a variety of configurations according to the particular network environment it emerges from and its progressive stages of evolution in terms of services and network architecture. Concerning the service capability, it is expected that voice and data services will be dominant in early stages, while broad-band video services such as entertainment moving picture services will be deployed at later stages. This evolution from voice and data services to broad-band entertainment video services roughly corresponds to the evolution away from the use of existing wire-pair copper loop plants to the later deployment of fiber distribution plants.

Digital access capabilities adequate for small terminal clusters up to 64 kbits/s or $n \times 64$ kbits/s (n being a small integer) are expected to be offered in the early ISDN stages to support "hybrid" switched (i.e., both circuit- and packet-switched) connections. Functionally, the transport network will be composed of overlayed facilities for voice and data, circuit switching (CS), common channel signaling (CCS), and data packet switching (PS) facilities. These overlayed facilities can share common network equipment with an

increasing degree of commonality. However, essential to the ISDN concept is the integration over the access loop. Two alternatives, the "full digital" and the "combined" (analog/digital) approaches, are described in the following Sections III-A and III-B.

Existing copper plants also can conveniently support bit rates up to 1544-2048 kbits/s. Such carrier rates can correspond to bearer media for multiple multiservice channels feeding large terminal clusters supported by PABX's or local area networks (LAN's). The primary PCM multiplexing bit rates can also correspond to a digital broad-band business video service such as televideoconferencing. Switching of 1544-2048 kbit/s channels through the early ISDN may be initially limited to on-demand satellite connections.

As the loop integration is significant in the early ISDN stages, the local exchange integration becomes the second synergetic objective of the ISDN evolution. Interconnection with current service-dedicated networks occurs at the local office and becomes a major aspect of planning for further ISDN evolution. Section III-C addresses the issue of ISDN architecture evolutions with particular emphasis to voice and data services.

A. The Full Digital Approach

Fig. 5 conceptually illustrates this approach that requires a digital loop capability for the provision, at user interfaces, of two types of digital communication channels: the "B-channel" and the "D-channel." The B-channel operates at 64 kbits/s, while the D-channel operates at 16 kbits/s. The D-channel is message oriented and carries the signaling information (s-information) that controls the circuit switching handling of B-channels through the ISDN via CCS facilities. Telemetry (t-information) and low-speed interactive data (p-information) share, by statistical multiplexing, the D-channel together with signaling messages. Information p is routed to the PS facilites and handled by virtual circuits. Information *t* could be routed to either CCS or PS facilities, where it may be handled, e.g., as a datagram or a permanent virtual circuit.[2]

Typical uses of *B*-channels include the transport of 1) PCM speech at 64 kbits/s, 2) data information corresponding to circuit- or packet-switched user classes of service at bit rates adapted to 64 kbits/s, 3) digital speech at lower rates than 64 kbits/s (LBRV) combined with data information, both directed towards the same destination, and 4) wide-band digital speech at 64 kbits/s. Alternative operation of such uses may also be provided on one *B*-channel on a call-by-call basis or by changing during an established call.

Referring to application 2) and to Fig. 5, the *B*-channel may also be used as support for packet-switched data. In this case the *B*-channel provides a 64 kbit/s circuit-switched connection to the input of a PS facility that interfaces the standard in-band packet switched protocol.

Referring to application 3), more in general, *B*-channels can be built up as a TDM assembly of subrate channels (e.g., at 8, 16, or 32 kbits/s) and each subchannel could be routed to a different destination. Handling of individual subchannels through the ISDN may be implemented in various ways. For example, 64 kbit/s circuit switching of subrate channels may be performed by employing rate adaptation at digital office terminations. Otherwise, subrate circuit-switching facilities should be deployed.

Handling subrate channels on a *B*-channel may make use of statistical multiplexing as an alternative to TDM multiplexing. The merging of packetized voice (e.g., using LBRV at 32 kbits/s) with packetized data information on a single *B*-channel (or multiple *B*-channels) is an attractive technique to be considered for the further evolution of the ISDN (see Section III-C).

Table II summarizes the ISDN services currently considered for *B*- and *D*-channel access capability in the full digital approach.

B. The Combined Analog/Digital Approach

Fig. 6(a) illustrates the combined (analog/digital) approach for the *simultaneous* provision at user interfaces of two types of channels; one (the "*A*-channel") corresponds to the conventional analog voiceband channel and the other (the "*C*-channel") corresponds largely to the *D*-channel in the full digital approach. The *C*-channel operates at 8 or 16 kbits/s and carries message interleaved signaling (*s*), telemetry (*t*), and interactive data (*p*) information. Information *t* and *p* are routed to PS facilities, while the analog voice channel is switched through space division (SD) or time division (TD) exchanges. CCS facilities and *s*-information may be used to provide enhanced voice services.

In the full digital approach the two-wire unloaded subscriber loop is equipped with digital time compression modulation (TCM) transmission systems or with digital hybrid systems with echo cancellation [9]. In the combined approach a digital-data/above/analog-voice transmission technique is ap-

---

2 A permanent virtual circuit is a virtual circuit permanently set between end-users for a period of time established on a contractual basis.

TABLE II
ISDN SERVICES CONSIDERED FOR *B*- AND *D*-CHANNELS

- **D-Channel Services (16 Kbit/s)**
  Enhanced Telephony
  Low Speed Data (PS)
  Videotex
  Teletex
  Telemetry
  EMERGENCY SERVICES
  ENERGY MANAGEMENT
- **B-Channel Services (64 Kbit/s)**
  Voice
  High Speed Data (CS & PS)
  High Quality Voice
  Voice & Data End-to-End
  Assembly of Subrate Channels
  Facsimile
  Slow-Scan Video

CS = CIRCUIT SWITCHING
PS = PACKET SWITCHING

plied on a two-wire unloaded loop. The digital data capability (the *C*-channel) is full duplex. Frequency division multiplexing (FDM) is used to separate the voiceband and the duplex data channels.

The compatibility of services provided via the *D*-channel and the *C*-channel, in the two ISDN approaches insofar described, is a key issue in the establishment of protocol standards. The current trend is in favor of developing "compatible" protocols over these channels (see Section IV-D).

Fig. 6(b) shows another type of combined approach for the *alternate* provision of two channels at user interfaces: the *A*-channel and a digital data channel currently planned to operate at 56 kbits/s and to be suitable for bulk data transfer. Signaling to support this bulk data channel is provided in-band via the *A*-channel. Analog voice and digital data are addressed to the same destination and can be switched alternately during the call. The circuit-switched 56 kbit/s connection may be implemented through space-division stored program control (SPC) local offices and time-division toll offices.

It is worth noting that, in terms of service offering, the combination of the approaches in Fig. 6(a) and (b) corresponds to the approach given in Fig. 5. The choice of one approach versus another depends on a variety of factors, ranging from the marketplace addressed (residential/business) to the actual penetration of space-division or time-division local SPC offices.

C. The Evolving Network Architecture

The previous sections have addressed the approaches for the provision of multiservice capabilities in the range of 64 or *n* × 64 kbits/s via digital copper loops. Small user terminal installations are intended to be served by such types of local access. Large terminal clusters, such as those supported by PABX's and LAN's, can be served by a TDM assembly of multiple *B*- and *D*-channels, each at 64 kbits/s. Relevant ag-

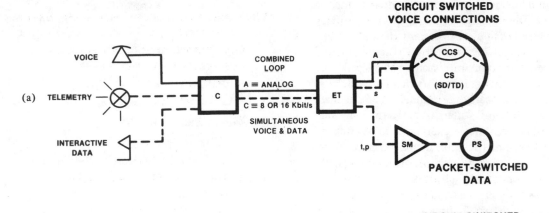

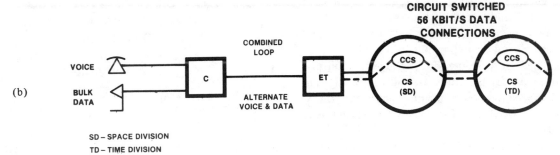

Fig. 6. Combined analog/digital approach: merging of analog/digital voice and digital data networks.

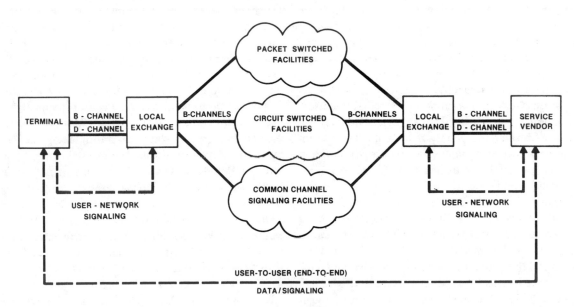

Fig. 7. The three-cloud network.

gregate bit rates at the interface are those corresponding to primary PCM multiplexing bit rates: 1544 and 2048 kbits/s. The functional network architecture described in the previous sections also applies well to this type of access.

At the primary rate, it is also conceivable to provide access for a broad-band bulk data channel W in the range of 1.5–2 Mbits/s supported by circuit-switched operations either on demand or in real time. Another possibility would be to have a broad-band statistically multiplexed channel P of about the same capacity as W. P might support a mixture of packetized voice and data information. For both alternatives, the ISDN, in its early stages, will provide leased or on-demand (via satel-

lite) connections. Wide-band circuit switching or high-capacity packet switching facilities should be deployed to provide a ubiquitous real-time circuit- and packet-switched transport capability for broad-band primary rate W and P services, respectively. The development of such "broad-band" digital facilities, where justified by technology and market demand, will occur in the later ISDN stages, likely in conjunction with the deployment of fiber distribution plants.

Fig. 7 shows the network scenario that emerges for handling the "narrow-band" digital capabilities in the ISDN. A certain degree of integration of circuit-switching and packet-switching facilities is assumed in the digital local exchange. In particular, the SM function in Fig. 5 is assumed to be incorporated in dedicated ISDN modules of the digital local office [1], [2]. Appropriate interfaces with current dedicated network facilities are required at the local office. Digital circuit-switched toll facilities and common channel signaling facilities will serve the circuit switching of *B*-channels. Packet-switched toll facilities will carry *D*-channel or *B*-channel packet switched data. Network users, i.e., terminals and vendors, may establish, in real time, packet- or circuit-switched connections or even "asymmetric multimedia" connections. These last connections involve, e.g., a simplex (unidirectional) circuit-switched connection in one direction and a simplex packet-switched connection in the other direction. In the three-cloud configuration shown in Fig. 7, the narrow-band ISDN has a hybrid switching capability realized by overlaying current carrier network facilities: bulk data and voice are treated by 64 kbit/s circuit switching and CCS, while interactive data are handled by packet switching. Even if toll exchanges using modular architectures would physically incorporate all of the three-cloud facilities, still the ISDN functionally presents a hybrid switching overlayed architecture.

But is the hybrid overlayed solution optimal for voice and data integration? Table III reviews the main switching alternatives for voice and data in integrated digital networks. These alternatives are briefly addressed below.

Circuit Switching: This technique is available today for 64 kbit/s connections. Both multislot and "subrate" switched connections can be implemented to match voice and bulk data requirements at bit rates both multiples and submultiples of 64 kbits/s, respectively. However, to handle interactive data, fast circuit switching (FCS) should be used. Connections should be set up to serve each data burst at the time it occurs. FCS is effective only if the connection setup time through the network is small (less than a few hundred milliseconds). This objective is difficult to achieve in a large carrier network using nonassociated CCS.[3]

Circuit-switched networks can also be improved ("enhanced") in their transmission link efficiency by taking advantage of voice burstiness. Voice activity is in the range of 35–40 percent so that digital speech interpolation (DSI) may be used on toll links to obtain a 2-to-3 compression factor (ratio of interpolated calls over noninterpolated calls). High compression can be obtained by operating on large enough trunk bundles and by adopting variable bit rate coding flow control to reduce the "freeze-out" effect.[4] Adaptive data multiplexing (ADM) may also be used to take advantage of data burstiness over toll links. ADM is effective only if a limited set of data protocols is allowed.

Packet Switching: This technique is available today for up to 64 kbit/s loop or trunk links and is operated by public data networks to provide virtual circuit capability. Protocols, such as CCITT Rec. X.25, have been designed to meet inter-

---

[3] In a nonassociated CCS network, such as that in Fig. 1, STP's introduce a certain delay (on the order of a few ten milliseconds) in the signaling message transfer.
[4] This annoying effect is produced by talk-spurt losses as a consequence of excessive traffic load on the DSI link.

TABLE III
VOICE AND DATA INTEGRATION ALTERNATIVES

- ● **Circuit Switching (CS)**
  - −Subrate
  - −Fast
  - −Enhanced (DSI & ADM)
- ● **Packet Switching (PS)**
  - −Virtual Circuit (Linked Packets Per Call)
  - −Data/Voice Gram (Lone Packets)
  - −High-Capacity/High-Speed
- ● **Hybrid Switching**
  - −Basic−CS for Voice & Bulk Data
    - −PS for Interactive Data
  - −Enhanced (DSI & ADM)
  - −Advanced−CS for Voice & Data
    - −PS for Voice & Data

DSI = DIGITAL SPEECH INTERPOLATION
ADM = ADAPTIVE DATA MULTIPLEXING

active data requirements, in particular, in terms of error recovery and flow control of data messages. Virtual circuit-oriented network implementations today are prevailing over datagram-oriented network implementations.

In order to adequately handle packet voice traffic, a high-capacity and high-speed packet-switched network is needed to meet the stringent delay requirements for voice (less than a few hundred milliseconds) in a large carrier network. This might require use of high-speed links (e.g., 1544, 2048 kbits/s) and of simple packetized voice/data protocols throughout the network. We note that a 1.5 or 2 Mbit/s packetized digital pipe could carry, by statistical multiplexing, besides voice and interactive data virtual calls, also a certain amount of bulk data traffic with limited peak rate (e.g., 64 kbits/s).

Hybrid Switching: This technique finds its "basic" realization in the above introduced ISDN architecture: conventional circuit switching for voice and bulk data, and conventional packet switching for interactive data. The CS portion of the basic hybrid network can be "enhanced" by using DSI and ADM over long-haul digital trunks. On the other hand, hybrid switching can also be based on more advanced implementations. In an "advanced" scenario, circuit switching of voice and data might be available in the local areas while packet switching of voice and data might be used for toll connections. Starting from the three cloud scenario of Fig. 7, possible hybrid switching evolutions can be illustrated by the two examples shown on Fig. 8(a) and (b). Fig. 8a shows the conceptual possibility of merging packet-switched data and signaling facilities in a single "cloud." In fact, data and CCS packet networks are today based on different protocol standards (X.25 and CCITT Signaling System No. 7, respectively) and different service requirements (e.g., reliability, security). Hence, this conceptual solution, although technically feasible, appears difficult to achieve due to today's commitments on packet data and CCS network development. On the other hand, Fig. 8(b) shows a conceptual scenario composed of one

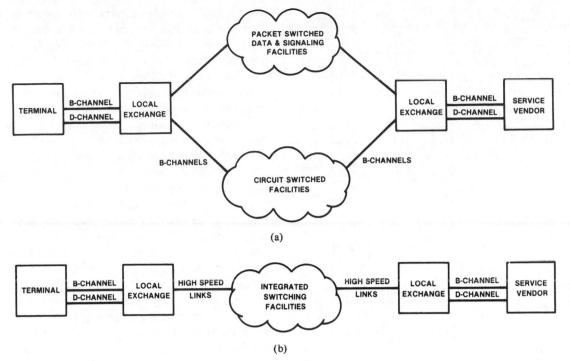

Fig. 8. (a) A two-cloud network. (b) A one-cloud network.

cloud in the toll portion. Signaling, voice, and data dynamically share the same transmission and switching facilities. This would require the emergence of a high-capacity and high-speed packet-switching technology to represent a viable solution for implementation. Substantial progress in signal processing and switching technology is required to achieve cost effectiveness for such a solution.

IV. ISDN USER ACCESS ARRANGEMENTS: INTERNATIONAL TRENDS

Much of the progress made in ISDN planning has been in the area of user access arrangements: configurations and functions of equipment on customer premises, compatibility of interfaces, capabilities to be provided to these interfaces, functions and configurations of equipment between the user's premises and the first network node, and access protocols. This section briefly describes the current international trends in each of these areas [5], [6].

A. Reference Configurations for User Access Interfaces

In defining the requirements for ISDN access, the anticipated configurations of user premises equipment and the standard equipment interfaces are critical. The first step in defining and understanding these configurations and interfaces is to group functions which may exist on the user's premises. Fig. 9 shows generic groupings of functions and corresponding "reference points" to be used in describing standardized interfaces. The functions described here need not all exist in any particular user's premises, and the list of functions is not exhaustive. Also, functions in different categories can be merged into the same physical equipment. Physical implementation examples and their relationship to these functions will be discussed below in conjunction with Fig. 10.

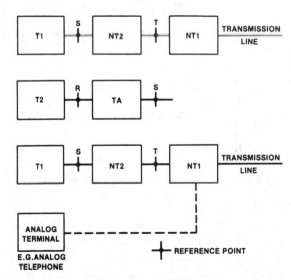

Fig. 9. Reference configurations for ISDN user access interfaces: (a) Case of ISDN terminals. (b) Case of non-ISDN terminals. (c) Combined access arrangement.

Beginning at the right of the diagram in Fig. 9(a), that is, closest to the telecommunications link into the network, is the network termination 1 (NT1) type of function. The NT1 functions include those necessary to appropriately terminate the transmission line, convert the signals, and condition them to the appropriate physical and electrical interface specifications, and provide appropriate maintenance and testing as required. The network termination 2 (NT2) functions include a wide variety of connection functions and other features. Included is protocol handling, corresponding to PABX's and terminal controllers, which serve to connect one or more terminals to each other and to the network. The terminal 1 (T1) functions correspond to individual terminals converting information to a form appropriate to be transmitted through

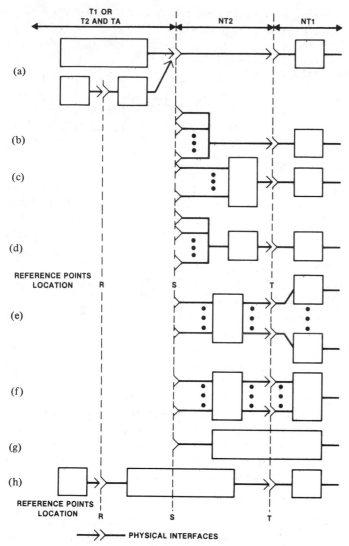

Fig. 10. Possible physical configurations for ISDN user access interfaces.

into an ISDN standard interface. Reference point *R* thus delimits the non-ISDN terminal from the terminal adapter functions. Thus, reference point *R* may correspond to a current physical interface, such as EIA RS-232 or CCITT Rec. X.21. Case (c) in Fig. 9 shows the reference configuration for the combined analog/digital access arrangement. Although an analog voice channel is considered for this arrangement today, the provision of analog video channels in a "combined" fashion may emerge in future considerations. In this case, switched analog video channels could be offered in combination with digital channels, one of which will handle the appropriate signaling information.

Having analyzed the basic interface functions, we will now consider configurations which need to be included in setting requirements for these interfaces. Fig. 10 enumerates the configurations which have been identified so far. There are several significant issues about these configurations: note that a direct connection (i.e., by wires) is a possibility between points *S* and *T* [configuration (a)]. This implies that a device intended to connect to an interface at reference point *S* could also work at an interface at reference point *T*. Another important configuration is the case where several interfaces at point *S* connect to a single connection at point *T*, using some functions of type NT2 [configuration (c)]. Multidrop connections [configuration (b)] are also being considered where several devices are directly connected to the same termination, either at reference point *S* or at reference point *T*. This is not intended to require that individual terminals can talk to each other, as in a local area network, but rather that each of the terminals can communicate with a single "host" (the exchange termination). This configuration should also not impose an undue functional or economic burden on single point-to-point connections, either on the network termination device or on devices designed to only connect to a single termination. Configurations of ring or full bus are not considered to operate across interfaces at reference point *S* or *T*. These functions are, however, included in the NT2 functional grouping. Thus, the case in Fig. 10(c) could correspond to a local area network bus, or ring inside the functional grouping NT2.

The final configurations in Fig. 10 illustrate that either *S* or *T*, but not both, need not correspond to a functional or a physical interface in a particular configuration. Thus, functions of categories T1 and NT2 could be merged or NT2 and NT1 functions could be merged. If neither reference point *S* nor *T* is identifiable then this is not considered to be an ISDN configuration.

B. Access Capabilities

Standards and the standard-setting process play a key role in ISDN, particularly for user/network interfaces. They are especially important due to the rapidly growing number of parties involved in telecommunications: end users (own terminal equipment, and use networks and services), network providers (own and operate network equipment, general purpose or specialized), enhanced service providers (own and operate information storage and processing equipment), equipment manufacturers (sell to all of the above), and standards bodies (provide a mechanism for reaching agreements).

the ISDN, and will include a wide variety of applications such as facsimile, voice, data, video, and others.

A major reason for identifying these functional groupings is to identify characteristics required by interfaces in the ISDN. In particular, reference point *T* corresponds to a point which segregates functions between NT1 and NT2 with only NT1-type functions connecting to the network. Reference point *S* defines the demarcation between terminal functions to the left and other network functions. Depending on a variety of conditions, including local regulations, some ISDN's will include functions corresponding to reference point *T* as the end of the network; others will have reference point *S* as the end of the network. Thus, reference points *S* and *T* define appropriate locations for standardized user/network interfaces and will be used in formulating associated requirements.

Case (b) in Fig. 9 depicts a case involving a terminal that is not meeting ISDN interface standards, connecting to the ISDN. In this case, terminal 2 (T2) corresponds to any type of terminal with either standard or nonstandard interface characteristics. The terminal adapter (TA) functions then correspond to those functions required to transform this other interface

TABLE IV
ISDN USER ACCESS TYPES

- **Basic Access**
  - ✳ B+B+D, Interface Net Rate: 144 Kbit/s
  - B+D ⎤ Possible Loop Net Rates:
  - D ⎦ 80Kbit/s; 16 Kbit/s
  - B ≡ 64 Kbit/s; D ≡ 16 Kbit/s

- **Combined Access**
  - ✳ A+C
  - A ≡ Analog; C ≡ 8 or 16 Kbit/s

- **Primary Rate Access**
  - ✳ nB+D, Interface Rates: 1544 or 2048 Kbit/s
  - B ≡ 64Kbit/s; D ≡ 64 Kbit/s

At the heart of the ISDN concept is the definition of a limited family of user/network interfaces. Each member of the family can support a wide range of user applications. At this stage, the primary difference among members of the family is the bit rate, going up roughly one order of magnitude between each successive member of the family. This matches the overall economies of technologies with the costs of a multiplicity of interfaces.

The interfaces are composed of one or more basic building blocks, channels, to provide "channel structures" or "access types." The channels provide compatibility across the different interfaces and are the basis for ISDN capabilities. Table IV gives the ISDN user access types insofar specified and labeled as "basic," "combined," and "primary rate."

The basic access structure $(B + B + D)$ consists of a TDM assembly of two B-channels and one D-channel. This structure applies at physical interfaces corresponding to S or T reference points. An essential feature of the basic access is that some ISDN services will not require use of one or even both B-channels so that the network (e.g., the subscriber loop) can be equipped to support a subset of $B + B + D$, i.e., $B + D$ or D only. Thus, the loop transmission systems can operate at a net rate of 144, 80, or 16 kbits/s and all utilize the basic terminal interface running at the net rate of 144 kbits/s.

The combined access structure consists of the assembly of an analog voiceband channel (A-channel) and a digital C-channel. The terminal data interface for the C-channel only, is subject of ISDN standard specifications including protocol compatibility with the D-channel.

The primary rate access is intended to interconnect integrated services digital PABX's or broad-band digital terminals. It has been specified to operate at the aggregate bit rates of 1.544 and 2.048 Mbits/s. Higher hierarchical bit rates would emerge at later stages. The primary rate access can correspond either to a TDM assembly of B-channels plus one D-channel operating at 64 kbits/s ("multiplexed access") or to a broad-band digital service, such as videoconferencing ("broad-band access"). Only the multiplexed access has been specified as shown in Table IV, n being set to 23 or 30. Cases of multiplexed access with multiple D-channels for 1544–2048 kbit/s interface or one D-channel for several 1544–2048 kbit/s interfaces are also being considered.

PABX's and wide-band service applications may also require standardization of an "intermediate access" at a bit rate between the basic and the primary rate ones. This subject is currently under international discussion. Bit rates corresponding to 4, 6, 8, and 10 × 64 kbits/s have been suggested, but no agreement is emerging today, either on the need for such an access, or on a specific bit rate.

C. Access Plant Configurations

Today most telecommunications access arrangements consist of a pair of wires from the user premises to a central office where a local exchange provides the features needed to access the toll network. In the ISDN, both in transition and in its mature state, there will be a variety of access plant arrangements. This variety is based on both technology evolution, which is continually reducing the cost of signal processing, and a wide range of user needs to be met by the ISDN.

A typical arrangement may consist of a loop from the subscriber premises to a "remote unit" (multiplexer, concentrator, remote switch). This loop may consist of copper or fiber media, or even other technologies. The bandwidth of this loop will depend on both the capabilities required by the user and the evolution of technology. The remote units serve as points of concentration in the exchange plant, reducing the bandwidth required back to the central office. This can lead to not only significant capital savings but also operations cost savings by automating monitoring and testing functions. The remote unit may include functions such as time-division multiplexing, statistical multiplexing (in particular, of C- or D-channels), switching, and an increasing variety of capabilities as technology costs continue to decline. The link from the remote unit to the exchange will operate at primary rates (1544–2048 kbits/s), or higher bit rates, and may also consist of a variety of transmission techniques, shared by many customers and different services.

At the local central office, the functionality present will depend on the network service provided, the state of technology evolution, and the state of deployment of ISDN capabilities. Thus, in many cases the local exchange will not provide all of the functionality required to access the network facilities, and in some cases may be merely a cross-connection point to provide remote access to service facilities located at higher rank offices. This remote access capability is a key feature in reducing the investment required to provide capabilities and to allow rapid introduction of new capabilities, so that every local office does not need to be converted.

D. Access Protocols

As explained in Sections III-A and III-B, both C- and D-channels are conceived to support three types of information: signaling (s), interactive data (p), and telemetry (t) messages. A first requirement to ensure compatibility of ISDN interfaces imposes that the C-channel protocol be a compatible subset of the D-channel protocol. Here we concentrate only on the D-channel characteristics at various protocol layers, to support s, p, and t information.

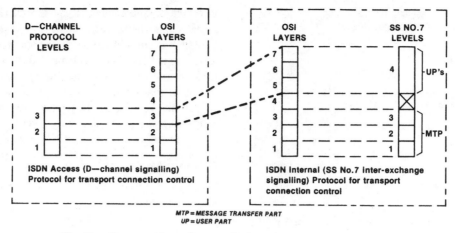

MTP = MESSAGE TRANSFER PART
UP = USER PART

Fig. 11.   Correspondence between *D*-channel signaling protocol levels,
SS No. 7 levels, and the OSI layers.

We observe that the applicability of interface standards at both *S* and *T* reference points would result in contrasting requirements for the *D*-channel protocol. On one side the *D*-protocol should be suitable for rather simple multiservice terminal stations, while on the other hand the same protocol should serve to connect complex NT2 implementations such as PABX's or LAN's. Today the tendency is towards development of a set of functional interface specifications structured in protocol levels. Only appropriate parts of such specifications will be applicable at physical interfaces either at *S* or *T* reference points.

The layering of the *D*-protocol should follow as far as possible the Open System Interconnection (OSI) Reference Model being developed by the International Standard Organization (ISO) and the CCITT [6]. While the handling of *p*- or *t*-information on the *D*-channel seems to closely adapt to the OSI layering for access protocols to public data networks, the handling of *s*-information (prime function of the *D*-channel) to support circuit switching of *B*-channels through the ISDN requires further clarification from the OSI model point of view. Fig. 11 proposes that *s*-information handling on the *D*-channel be allocated to OSI Layer 3 and illustrates the correspondence between the access signaling protocol and the internal ISDN signaling protocol implemented by SS No. 7. This interexchange protocol has been specified into a four-level structure: message transfer part (MTP) Levels 1, 2, and 3, and user parts (UP's) Level 4. The right part of Fig. 11 shows the actual correspondence between SS No. 7 levels and OSI layers. In SS No. 7, Level 3 adopts a datagram-oriented procedure, while the "transport" layer (OSI Layer 4) functions are not implemented. An adequate mapping between *s*-information and the SS No. 7 user parts to support *B*-channels circuit switching is required. Protocols to support *t*- and *p*-information on the *D*-channel will include the higher OSI layers (above Layer 3).

The following notes briefly review current trends on the characteristics of the *D*-protocol at various levels as they appear at an ISDN user access interface.

Level 1–Physical Layer: There is a strong tendency towards a four-wire transformer-coupled user/network interface for both the basic and the primary rate accesses. Two

unresolved issues are of particular relevance at Level 1: one is power feeding through the interfaces at *S* or *T* reference points, and the other is the multidrop distribution between NT1 and terminals in the basic access as shown in Fig. 10(b). The first issue faces the problem of power feeding rather complex user equipment from the local exchange and the limitations on power distribution through digital copper or fiber loops. The second issue addresses the problems of maintenance (e.g., fault isolation) and of contention resolution to access the *D*-channel in a multidrop configuration. Contention resolution mechanisms can be conceived, e.g., by exploiting the TDM frame format at Level 1 used to assemble *B*- and *D*-channels in the basic access [6]. However, such mechanisms should not impose undue burden on the terminals, taking into account that other configurations not requiring contention resolution will occur.

With reference to the functional groupings given in Fig. 9(a), NT1 should perform functions only belonging broadly to the OSI model physical layer, i.e., NT1 should convert the ISDN user interface Level 1 characteristics into those at the transmission line interface.

Level 2–Data Link Layer: The link access protocol (LAP) at Level 2 of the *D*-protocol (LAP-*D*) uses frame structures comprising frame delimiters (flags), zero insertion/deletion, and cyclic redundancy check. This provides secure alignment, transparency, and error detection. The error recovery and flow control procedures should be based on those of LAP-*B* of Rec. X.25. This solution is preferred over use of the Level 2 procedures of SS No. 7. Full LAP-*B*, or appropriate LAP-*B* subset procedures, are envisioned to cope with PABX's or simple terminal configurations, respectively.

In addition, the address byte of LAP-*D* is used to support multiple "logical links," i.e., to provide independent multiple LAP's between exchange termination and logical end points at user premises. Logical links may be used either to access different Level 3 protocols for *s*-type, *p*-type, and *t*-type information or to address different terminal end points. The support of different Level 3 procedures for *s*-type and *p*-type information is justified by taking into account that signaling does not require certain features needed by data (such as multiple virtual circuits, packet sequencing, flow control).

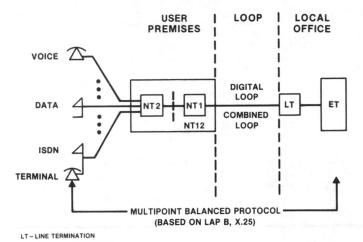

LT – LINE TERMINATION
ET – EXCHANGE TERMINATION

Fig. 12. Star distribution at user premises with simple NT2 functions.

Support of a multipoint capability is justified by referring, e.g., to the configuration given in Fig. 12. This configuration was considered in early studies on ISDN protocols [1], [10], and is characterized by the allocation of simple Level 2 functions at NT2. By using the address field to discriminate terminal endpoints, the NT2 functions can be limited to queuing for D-channel access at T and distribution towards endpoints, without handling error recovery or flow control procedures. Thus, the same Level 2 protocol appears at both S and T interfaces ("transparent" NT2). The configuration of Fig. 12 is of particular interest when the physical implementation NT12 = NT1 + NT2 is permitted. Multipoint capability is also required in the case of multidrop distribution with zero NT2 functions [Fig. 10(b)] or with simple (e.g., at Level 2) NT2 functions [Fig. 10(d)]. In the case of PABX's or complex NT2 functions, endpoint addresses may not be required, thus leaving the use of logical links just to discriminate information types.

LAP-D should also be designed to handle properly the framed message traffic composed by various information. The signaling and data delay requirements over the D-channel should dictate adoption of adequate delay control mechanisms such as limitation of the p-information frame size or adoption of a priority scheme for s-information (e.g., a preemptive priority).

Level 3–Network Layer: Multiple Level 3 procedures for s-type and p-type information are required. For logical links supporting signaling, a datagram-oriented Level 3 procedure (such as that at Level 3 of SS No. 7) seems appropriate, while procedures for p-information may take several forms. To provide compatibility with existing X.25 terminals, the procedures at Level 3 of X.25 should be supported by appropriate logical links over the D-channel. This includes the in-band call setup and clearing procedures defined in X.25. In addition, there may also be a need for other classes of p-information. This aspect is particularly critical since it involves the definition of new procedures for packet-switched data. Two possibilities should be further considered. The first refers to the handling of frame mode data. In this case, s-type information would be used to set up logical link connections on the D-

channel. Data would be transmitted over these links with no Level 3 sequencing or flow control mechanisms. This is intended to provide simple packet-switched communications. The second possibility supports data multiplexing at Level 3. In this case, data would be transferred over virtual channels in a format compatible with Level 3 of X.25. However, the procedures for virtual channel setup and clearing would be different since the s-type information would be used to set up and clear these virtual channels. Both of the above alternatives may make it possible to create calls consisting of both circuit-switched and packet-switched information, using a single, integrated signaling mechanism (multimedia calls) [11].

The s-information procedures will require capabilities to support common telephony features such as conferencing, call forwarding, call hold, and call transfer. In addition, the s-procedures should be defined so as to allow an easy mapping to both the circuit switched data (e.g., according to Rec. X.21) and telephony terminal signaling, and an easy interworking with the future ISDN user part of SS No. 7.

A functional message signaling architecture seems appropriate to cope with these requirements and is also consistent with the long-term trends favoring increasing intelligence placed at user premises equipment [11].

Telemetry information at Level 3 may follow p-type procedures (e.g., permanent virtual circuit or frame mode), or s-type information procedures.

Above Level 3–End-to-End Layers: Procedures at these levels refer primarily to p- and t-type applications end-to-end across the transport network. However, the scenario given in Fig. 7 shows that end-to-end information (e.g., between terminals and service vendors) may well be considered as signaling (s-type) and conveyed over CCS facilities, in particular when they are executed in conjunction with a circuit-switched service over B-channels. The appropriate definition of end-to-end data or signaling information over D-channels, in relation to their transport via PS or CCS facilities, represents a critical issue for the development of protocol specifications above Level 3.

V. CONCLUSIONS

This paper has addressed two main aspects of the ongoing international activity on multiservice digital networks: the evolving ISDN network scenarios and the user access arrangements to the ISDN.

The overview given on the first aspect illustrates the current efforts for the early provision of end-to-end digital connectivity in support of multiservice applications. These efforts attempt to exploit harmoniously the current service-dedicated network facilities and are focused on local access integration alternatives. Future evolution of the ISDN network architecture to take advantage of new communication technologies should not be hindered by setting up the early ISDN scenarios.

Concerning the second aspect, the current international trends on user access arrangements have been reviewed by giving emphasis to user equipment configurations, standard access structures, and protocols. Most material presented in this review has just recently emerged in the CCITT standards activity. Several controversial and unresolved issues have been briefly mentioned and left for future discussion in the international telecommunication community. The views expressed here reflect the author's opinion on these issues.

ACKNOWLEDGMENT

The content of this paper is largely influenced by the international activity of the author within CEPT (European Conference of Post and Telecommunication Administrations) and CCITT. Further understanding of the ISDN has occurred during a recent temporary assignment of the author with Bell Laboratories. W. S. Gifford, of this organization, was instrumental in developing a common worldwide understanding of the emerging ISDN in the international community.

REFERENCES

[1] M. Decina and R. Parodi, "Circuit and packet-switched data communication in integrated services digital networks," presented at the Int. Conf. Comput. Commun., Atlanta, GA, Oct. 1980.
[2] M. Dècina, R. Montemurro, and F. Villani, "Prospects for data communication handling in ISDNs," presented at the 28th Int. Sci. Cong. Electron., Rome, Italy, Mar. 1981.
[3] "The emerging ISDN," Dedicated Session, Int. Conf. Commun., Denver, CO, June 1981.
[4] W. S. Gifford, "The user perspective of the ISDN," presented at the Int. Conf. Commun., Philadelphia, PA, June 1982.
[5] CCITT Study Group XVIII, "Report of the meeting of WP XVIII/1: ISDN," COM XVIII-no. R3, Geneva, Switzerland, July 1981.
[6] ——, "Report of the Munich meeting of ISDN experts," COM XVIII-no. R9, Munich, Germany, Feb. 1982.
[7] M. Dècina, "CCITT activity on signal processing for integrated services digital networks," presented at the Int. Conf. Acoust. Speech, Signal Processing, Paris, France, May 1982.
[8] M. Dècina and U. de Julio, "Performance of integrated digital networks: International Standards," presented at the Int. Conf. Commun., Philadelphia, PA, June 1982.
[9] S. V. Ahamed, P. P. Bohn, and N. L. Gottfried, "A tutorial on 2-wire digital transmission in the loop plant," *IEEE Trans. Commun.*, vol. COM-29, Nov. 1981.
[10] R. G. Cornell and D. J. Stelte, "Progress towards digital subscriber line services and signaling," *IEEE Trans. Commun.*, vol. COM-29, Nov. 1981.
[11] J. W. Leth and S. Srinivas, "An experimental customer signaling interface for integrated voice and data services," presented at the Int. Conf. Commun., Philadelphia, PA, June 1982.

Maurizio Dècina was born in Pescasseroli (L'Aquila), Italy, on January 10, 1943. He received the Dr. Ing. degree in electronic engineering from the University of Rome, Rome, Italy, in 1966.

From 1967 to 1969, he was at the U. Bordoni Foundation, Rome, engaged on R&D of digital speech processing and transmission systems. From 1969 to 1976, he was at the SIP (Italian Telephone Operating Company) Headquarters, Rome, where he was responsible for the introduction of wire transmission systems for PCM (pulse code modulation) voice and digital data. In 1976 he joined the Institute of Electrical Communications, University of Rome, and is currently Professor for Electrical Communications. His main interest is currently focused on communication switching and protocols for digital telephony and data. In 1981, he joined Bell Laboratories, Naperville, IL, for a sabbatical year, where he was involved in exploratory activity on integrated voice/data communication switching.

Prof. Dècina has been Vice-Chairman of Study Group XVIII (Digital networks) in the CCITT (International Telephone and Telegraph Consultative Committee) since 1972, and Vice-Chairman of Working Group CD (Data Communication) of CEPT (European Conference of Post and Telecommunications Administrations) since 1973. He is a member of the Italian Electrical and Electronic Association (AEI). He also acts as a member of the Technical Program Committee of the International Zurich Seminar on Digital Communications and has been appointed as Co-Guest Editor for a Special Issue of the IEEE TRANSACTIONS ON COMMUNICATIONS.

SECTION 4 INTERNETWORKING

4.1 OVERVIEW

Packet-switched and packet broadcasting networks grew out of a need to allow the computer user to have access to resources beyond that available in a single system. In a similar fashion, the resources of a single network are often inadequate to meet users' needs. Because the networks that might be of interest exhibit so many differences, it is impractical to consider merging them into a single network. Rather, what is needed is the ability to interconnect various networks so that any two stations on any of the constituent networks can communicate.

An interconnected set of networks is referred to as a *catenet*, and the concept is illustrated in Figure 4.1. Each constituent network supports communication among a number of attached devices. In addition, networks are connected by devices that we shall refer to generically as *gateways*. Gateways provide a communication path so that data can be exchanged between networks.

4.2 REQUIREMENTS

Although a variety of approaches have been taken to provide internetwork service, the overall requirements on the internetworking facility can be stated in general. These include:

1. Provide a link between networks. At minimum, a physical and link control connection is needed.

2. Provide for the routing and delivery of data between processes on different networks.

3. Provide an accounting service that keeps track of the use of the various networks and gateways and maintains status information.

4. Provide the services listed above in such a way as not to require modifications to the networking architecture of any of the constituent networks. This means that the internetworking facility must accommodate a number of differences among networks. These include:

   a. *Different addressing schemes:* The networks may use different endpoint names and addresses and directory maintenance schemes. Some form of global network addressing plus a directory service must be provided.

   b. *Different maximum packet size:* Packets from one network may have to be broken up into smaller pieces for another. This process is referred to as fragmentation.

   c. *Different network access mechanisms:* The net-

work access mechanism between station and network may be different for stations on different networks.

   d. *Different timeouts:* Typically, a connection-oriented transport service will await an acknowledgment until a timeout expires, at which time it will retransmit its segment of data. In general, longer times are required for successful delivery across multiple networks. Internetwork timing procedures must allow successful transmission that avoids unnecessary retransmissions.

   e. *Error recovery:* Intranetwork procedures may provide anything from no error recovery up to reliable endto-end (within the network) service. The internetwork service should not depend on, nor suffer interference from, the individual network's error recovery capability.

   f. *Status reporting:* Different networks report status and performance differently. Yet it must be possible for the internetworking facility to provide such information on internetworking activity to interested and authorized processes.

   g. *Routing techniques:* Intranetwork routing may depend on fault detection and congestion control techniques peculiar to each network. The internetworking facility must be able to coordinate these to adaptively route data between stations on different networks.

   h. *User-access control:* Each network will have its own user-access-control technique (authorization for use of the network). These must be invoked by the internetwork facility as needed. Further, a separate internetwork access control technique may be required.

   i. *Connection, connectionless:* Individual networks may provide connection-oriented (e.g., virtual circuit) or connectionless (datagram) service. It may be desirable for the internetwork service not to depend on the nature of the connection service of the individual networks.

These points are worthy of further comment but are best pursued in the context of specific architectural approaches.

4.3 APPROACHES

A number of approaches have been tried for accommodating the differences among networks. At one extreme, a spe-

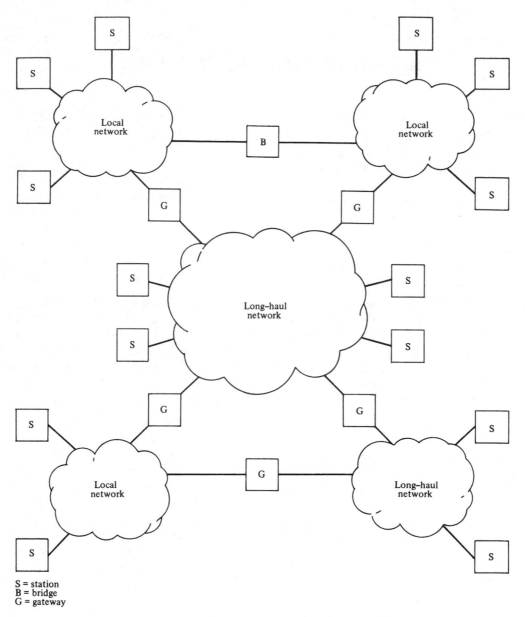

S = station
B = bridge
G = gateway

Figure 4-1: A Catanet

cial-purpose gateway, known as a protocol converter, can be built for each particular pair of networks. Typically, a protocol converter accepts a packet from one network, strips off the control field to recover the data, and then retransmits the data using the protocols of the other network. The disadvantage of this approach is, of course, that a different gateway must be built for each pair of networks. At the other extreme is the X.75 protocol. X.75 is an extension of the X.25 packet-switched network interface standard. With X.25, it is possible to set up a virtual circuit between two stations on the same network. In effect, X.75 provides a logical connection between disjoint stations by stringing together virtual circuits across several networks. The drawback of this approach is that all of the networks must use X.25, a standard

not used by many privately-owned local networks. Furthermore, public-access networks, such as Telenet and Tymnet, do not accommodate X.75 links to private networks.

A more promising approach is the internet protocol (IP), initially developed for ARPANET. IP has been standardized by DOD, and a similar approach is being pursued by ISO. The philosophy of IP is that the gateways and stations share a common protocol for internet traffic but that the stations and networks are otherwise undisturbed. In terms of the usual open system interconnection (OSI) model for communications architecture, IP fits between the network (routing) and transport (end-to-end delivery) layers.

IP makes no assumptions about the underlying network

protocol. Each host or gateway that uses IP interfaces with its network in the same fashion as it does for intranetwork communication.

4.4 ARTICLE SUMMARY

Gien and Zimmerman provide an exhaustive analysis of internetworking issues. Two specific internet protocols are described in the article by Postel: the Internet Protocol (IP) and X.75. The next two articles describe practical experience with these two protocols: IP in the article by Hinden, et al., and X.75 in the article by Unsoy. Burg, et al. examine protocol issues for interconnecting local and long-haul networks.

DESIGN PRINCIPLES FOR NETWORK INTERCONNECTION

Michel GIEN & Hubert ZIMMERMANN

I. R. I. A.
Institut de Recherche d'Informatique et d'Automatique
78150 - ROCQUENCOURT - France

With the development of individual computer networks comes the need to interconnect them. Network designers are faced with heterogeneity of networks just as they were previously faced with heterogeneity of computers within a single network.

This paper shows that similar structuring techniques, namely multiplexing, switching, cascading, wrapping and layering, can be applied, and that a set of simple principles can be derived which facilitate greatly the design of the interconnection of computer networks.

These simple principles are applied to the analysis of some typical examples of network interconnection problems, in the areas of addressing, routing, non-equivalent communication services, error control, flow control and terminal access. It is suggested that similar principles could be applied to some unresolved issues in computer network interconnection, such as congestion control or administrative functions. It is finally claimed that the final objective of network interconnection studies would be to determine the set of international standards which are required to make network interconnection straightforward in the near future.

1. Introduction

Data processing is gradually evolving from its original model, the individual human mind, to networking and distributed processing which somehow tend to resemble the human society. Computers have been linked into individual networks to satisfy the needs of individual organizations. Now, networks must be interconnected to cater to inter-organizational relationships.

Even though this requirement for interconnection of computer networks was identified early[1,2], it is only recently that the problem has been widely recognized:

- It is only in 1978 that the International Organization for Standardization (ISO) started the study of Open Systems Architecture[3].

- The question of interconnection of Public Data Networks[4] was discussed within CCITT only after an agreement had been reached on the X.25 user interface[5] (and the question of interconnection of private networks with public networks has not yet been discussed).

It is the authors' experience that a set of simple rules can tremendously help to analyse specific interconnection problems, as well as to improve potential interconnectability of a network through proper design choices.

The first question to be raised is "what is specific to network interconnection, as opposed to building a single network ?".

Basically, an interconnected set of networks can be considered from an external (i.e., from a user's) point of view and from an internal (i.e., from a designer's) point of view.

From a user's viewpoint, an interconnected set of networks is not different from a single network. It just provides an enlarged population of users with enlarged services, and this simple view must be preserved. In other words, users should not be bothered by interconnection problems.

From an internal point of view, an interconnected set of networks is not necessarily different from a single network. In particular, two identical networks (e.g., from the same computer manufacturer) can usually be integrated into a single bigger one. However, in many cases, networks to be interconnected will not be identical : they will have been designed in different environments, at different periods, with different constraints and technologies, etc... In addition, it is essential to preserve freedom in the design of future computer networks and still be able to interconnect them with existing ones. In other words, the question is "how to interconnect heterogeneous networks" rather than "how to build a world wide homogeneous network".

Before being faced with the constraint of interconnecting heterogeneous networks, network designers have been faced with the problem of interconnecting heterogeneous computers. Our claim is that the set of techniques developed for this latter purpose can be used again, with slight adaptations, for interconnecting heterogeneous networks.

In the following, we will first briefly review the set of techniques used to design heterogeneous computer networks (section 2). We will then examine (section 3) how these techniques can be applied to network interconnection and which principles can be derived. This will then be illustrated with a number of concrete examples (sections 4 to 9). We will conclude by indicating (section 10) some features which should be included in the design of any network to improve its interconnectability.

Reprinted from *The Proceedings of the Sixth Data Communications Symposium*, 1979, pages 109-119. Copyright © 1979 by The Institute of Electrical and Electronics Engineers, Inc.

2. Structuring techniques

From experience[6-12], a few simple and powerful structuring techniques[13] have emerged which now form the basis of any computer network architecture, namely: multiplexing, switching, cascading, wrapping and layering. These basic techniques are briefly reviewed in the following.

Multiplexing

In any network, many resources are concurrently shared among several users or more generally among several activities. A multiplexing mechanism will take care of distributing the resource to the various activities which need it (see figure 2-1). In simple cases the multiplexing mechanism is a local (non-distributed) activity ; i.e., its decision concern only local resources and are based on locally available information (e.g., allocation of transmission lines to packets for transmission between adjacent nodes). In addition to the economy brought by sharing, multiplexing permits activities to behave as if they were independent of each other.

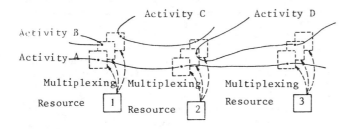

Figure 2-1 Multiplexing resources between activities

Switching

When one resource, or more generally, any logical entity, is shared among several activities(through multiplexing), it must be able to identify which activity is concerned with its successive actions, (see figure 2-2) and possibly deduce where to forward a request for the following actions.(e.g., switching a packet to the proper output line of a packet switching node or forwarding a message to the proper process in a server host). Switching implies interpretation of addresses and routing of requests.

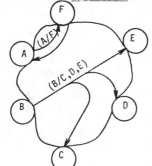

Figure 2-2 Addressing actions

Cascading

Cascading consists in forming a linear string of entities (see figure 2-3) which forward requests or propagate activities along the cascade (e.g., forwarding a packet along the path between source and destination in a packet switching network). Cascading is the only way for communication between entities which are not directly connected to each other.

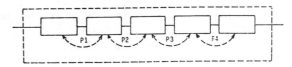

Figure 2-3 Cascading assembly

Wrapping

When functions performed by a set of cooperating entities are not exactly those required by their users, a layer of entities can be added, wrapping the initial set (see figure 2-4). Entities in this wrapping layer communicate through the initial set and perform the additional or modified functions (e.g., modems permit bits to be transmitted on a voice grade circuit, or transport stations permit reliable transmission on an unreliable packet switching network).

This technique which is generally used by providers of value-added services, offers the advantage of not modifying the initial system (this would often be overly costly if not impossible).

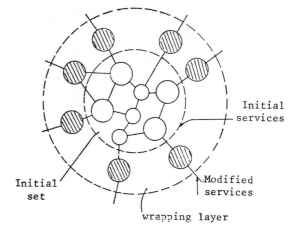

a) Topological view of wrapping

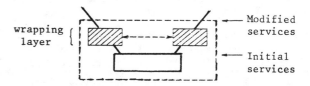

b) Simplified logical view of wrapping

Figure 2-4 Wrapping

212

Layering

Layering is the technique by which most (if not all) distributed systems are logically organized (see figure 2-5). Entities in the lowest layer are directly interconnected into a network and cooperate to provide communication services between entities in the next higher layer. These entities, in turn, communicating by means of services provided by the layer below them, cooperate to provide services to entities in the layer above them. The layering structure expands recurrently up to the highest layer, where entities cooperate for their own needs (rather than to provide services to higher entities). Layering can simply be viewed as the recurrent application of wrapping.

As an example, ISO is standardizing an Open Systems Architecture[3] composed of seven layers going from the Physical Layer at the bottom to the Application Layer on top.
Since each layer makes no assumption about the internal organization of the layers below it, which are just viewed as collectively providing a well defined set of services, layers are said to be independent.

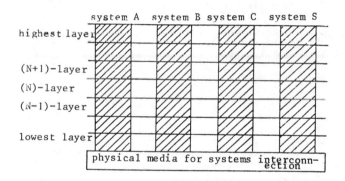

a) A physical view of layering

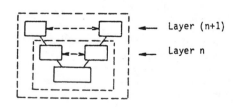

b) A simplified logical view of layering

Figure 2-5 Layering assembly

Visibility

An essential concept underlying all structuring and in particular structuring of computer networks is the concept of visibility[14] any part of a network is viewed by the rest of the network through its external relations. In other words, the internal functioning of a part of the network is not visible from outside of it ; only the external result is visible. This concept of restricted visibility permits heterogeneity (i.e., differences between systems), to be reconciled with compatibility (i.e., common conventions between systems), by restricting commonality to external relations and thus leaving room for internal freedom.

3. Architecture principles for network interconnection

3.1. Gateways

In general, networks are not compatible with each other and therefore cannot be interconnected directly. Intermediate gateways are required to perform the necessary adaptations (see figure 3-1). A gateway function may be implemented in separate equipment connected to two or more networks, but it may also be implemented in one or several pieces as additional modules in already existing equipment.[12] In the following, for the sake of clarity, we will assume that the gateway functions are physically isolated. The resulting structure is a network of networks interconnected by gateways, as illustrated in figure 3-1.

In the following, we will refer to this network of networks as the global network, as opposed to the individual networks which it encompasses.

The logical structure of the global network will take advantage of the principle of restricted visibility to permit cooperation between networks with possibly different internal structures. The question is then to identify in each individual network logical parts (possibly complemented by part of a gateway) which can be assembled to form the global structure, using the basic techniques reviewed in section 2.

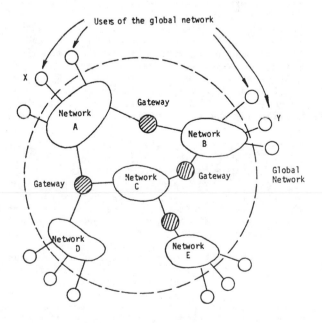

Figure 3-1 Networks interconnected by gateways

213

3.2. Cascading of services by gateways

The minimum function of a gateway is to forward information (data as well as control information) from one network to another. A gateway is thus a place where individual network functions are cascaded. In this subsection, we examine some of the implications of this cascading role of a gateway on the general structure of the global network. We will use the simple example of the gateway between two networks (e.g., networks A an B in figure 3-1). We will assume that each network (as almost any network) has a layered structure but that both structures are not identical (see figure 3-2).

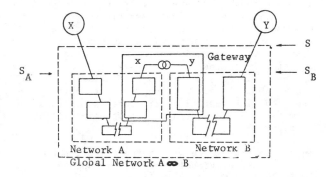

Figure 3-2 Cascading by gateway

The purpose of the gateway in figure 3-2 is to present to users X and Y the concatenation of networks A and B as a single global network A ∞ B, without intervening in the cooperation between X and Y. In other words the gateway is transparent to protocols between X and Y ; it belongs to the layers below them. In order for the gateway to be able to cascade the two networks, the logical interfaces in x and y must be mappable ; i.e., a request arriving at interface x must be translated into an equivalent request to forward at interface y and vice versa. The gateway may perform a translation of formats but not add services. In other words, services S_A and S_B cascaded by a gateway must be equivalent. They are also equivalent to the service S provided by the global network.

Another implication is that services S_A and S_B must be "cascadable" (this is not the case with most network diagnosis, which concerns internal functioning of the network and cannot be forwarded from one network to the other, since by network design they cannot be generated by a user, i.e., cannot be passed by the gateway from interface x to interface y or vice-versa).

In many cases, there do not exist equivalent and cascadable services in networks to be interconnected. In order to match these constraints, it is necessary either to select a common cascadable subset of both services (i.e., to realize only a partial interconnection) or to add a new layer to one or both networks to reach equivalent cascadable services (see figure 3-3). This new layer appears

only in the user equipment and in the gateway, thus wrapping (end-to-end) the original network without requiring any modification to intermediate nodes in the network.

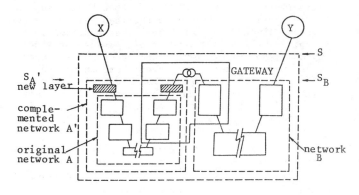

Figure 3-3 Adapting services to be equivalent

3.3. Multiplexing of gateways

As any other network resource, a gateway must be shared among a number of internetwork activities (e.g. conversations). This should normally be achieved simply by multiplexing the gateway between these activities.

Similarly, the interface between the gateway and each network must also be shared. There are cases where, by design, the network interface cannot be shared (e.g., it may for instance be restricted to one user only). In such a case, the original network will have to be wrapped (end-to-end) in an additional layer which will provide the interface multiplexing capability.

3.4. Switching by gateways

In the global network, gateways usually have to perform switching, i.e., decide to whom a given request should be forwarded.

If each individual network is able to interpret the global address space, i.e., the addresses of all users of the global network, the gateway has only to decide to which network it should forward the request.

Conversely, if an individual network is able to interpret only its own address space, the gateway must be prepared to decide for the local address of the final user (or of the next gateway), how to forward the request to it through the corresponding network. In this latter case, it is common practice to complement the individual network by wrapping it (end-to-end) into an additional layer which takes care of handling the global address space.

3.5. Level of interconnection

In the preceding subsections, the term "user" does

not necessarily apply to end-users. The only assumption we have made is that these users have common conventions, i.e., common protocols which allow them to cooperate without the help of a gateway. These users may in fact form the higher-level part of the global network conforming to a common higher-level architecture and protocols (see figure 3-4). The highest level at which the gateway intervenes is referred to as the level of interconnection of the networks (e.g., identical networks can be interconnected at line level, i.e., with a gateway degenerated into a line, while public data networks will be normally interconnected at packet level, etc...)

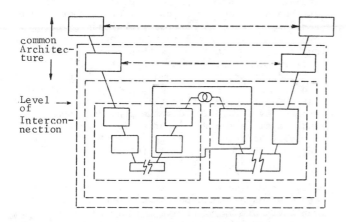

Figure 3-4 Level of interconnection

3.6. Summary of interconnection principles

As outlined above, networks to be interconnected must exhibit :

- levels of equivalent services, to be possibly merged into a global network offering these services,

- a set of properties which make interconnection viable such as cascadability of services, multiplexed interfaces and interpretation of global address space.

If these constraints are not satisfied, the network(s) must be modified, usually by wrapping it (end-to-end) in an additional layer which externally exhibits the required interconnection capability.

The principles above are illustrated by a series of examples in the following sections.

Note : Other important considerations related to economics, reliability and performance are harder to be turned into general principles. These aspects will be directly introduced through examples.

4. Addressing and Routing

The main objective of interconnecting networks is the extension of communication facilities to a larger population of users. Being able to address this large population is therefore a key aspect of network interconnection.

This section is intended to illustrate how switching can be performed in such a global network.

Packet network interconnection following the CATENET[15] approach, Public Data Network interconnection, as well as interconnection of private networks with public networks, have been chosen as examples for the purpose of this illustration.

An address is an identifier which can be interpreted within the network to ship information to a given destination.
In order to analyze addressing and routing aspects of interconnection it is important to note that an address has two aspects (see figure 4-1) :

1) a user aspect : it is used by activities (wishing to exchange requests) to name, i.e. designate, their correspondents, and

2) an internal aspect : it is processed within the network to forward requests to their destination. This processing of addresses is performed by routing functions.

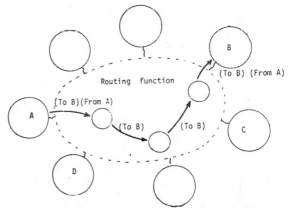

Figure 4-1   Addressing and Routing

4.1. Addressing service

The global network made of interconnected networks needs to provide a global address space allowing its end users to designate each other, (see figure 4-3). This global address space can be made by combining individual network address spaces. A simple way of doing that is to structure global addresses in a hierarchical manner ; i.e., the first part of the global address designates an individual network while the second part of the address identifies the user within that network (this second level of addressing can in turn be hierarchically structured within the context of individual networks) (see figure 4-2). Depending on the addressing capabilities provided by the individual networks, it might be necessary, as mentioned in section 3, to wrap some of these networks in an additional layer providing global network addresses.

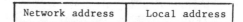

Network address	Local address

Figure 4-2 Hierarchical address

It should be noted that a limitation of a hierarchical structure of addresses is that it does not allow one user to be connected to more than one network with the same address ; i.e., "multihoming" on two networks is not possible. In practice this constraint is acceptable in most cases and anyhow unavoidable except for a happy few which might be provided with general (i.e., network independent) addresses.

Assuming a hierarchical structure of the global address space, a "numbering plan" is required to assign addresses to individual networks. If the numbering plan is such that it cannot be indefinitely extended to cover any new network joining the global network, a new level of addressing (e.g., group of networks) might be required.

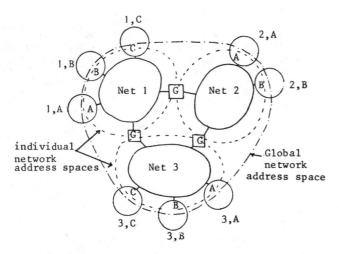

Figure 4-3 Global network addressing service

In the CATENET approach that was investigated early and proposed by IFIP[15], addresses are hierarchically structured and the proposed address format[16] includes a built-in extension mechanism which can be used to expand the numbering plan in order to cover all possible interconnected networks in the future. No additional level of addressing is therefore required.

In the case where public networks offering virtual circuit services are interconnected by means of the X.75 interface[4], addresses are also hierarchically structured and the numbering plan[17] is hopefully wide enough to cover any user connected to any public network in the world.

In the case where a private network is interconnected with a public network, by means of the X.25 interface (since, up to now, private networks are not offered the X.75 interface), the private network is provided with a single DTE address, not with a network address. Address extensions are required and these can only be performed by wrapping public networks in an additional layer of addressing covering the interconnection of public as well as private networks.

4.2. Routing functions

The global network in figure 4-3 needs to perform routing functions, i.e., switching (see section 2), associated with the processing of global addresses. As already stated in section 3.4., internetwork routing may be performed either within each individual network if they can handle global network addresses, or at an additional level wrapping them if they can only handle local addresses.

In the CATANET approach global hierarchical addresses are known by each network. Each node within each individual network is able to process both the first part of all global addresses (i.e., network addresses) and the second part of global addresses of its own users (i.e., local addresses within that network). Routing functions within each individual network aim at forwarding information closer to its final destination. The complete path is not determined by the source. It is built hop by hop at each intermediate node within the network as information progresses toward its destination. Each node gets and transmits the full destination address (which is a global address for the whole CATENET) and processes only the portion it can interpret.

This routing function can easily be cascaded, and adding a new network is no more that adding a new destination or a new node. Internetwork routing can therefore be integrated within each individual network participating in the CATENET. Gateway functions, as far as routing is concerned, could be performed at any node (see figure 4-4).

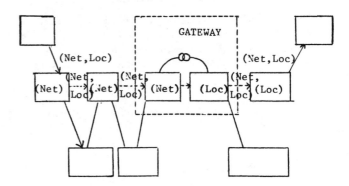

Figure 4-4 Routing in CATENET

In the interconnection of public networks by means of X.75, global network addresses are hierarchically structured. Each individual public network is able to process the network address part, i.e., the DNIC (Data Network Identification Code), and choose the proper gateway.

A network address is viewed by each individual network as a particular DTE address, coupled with a particular access point where a virtual circuit or portion of a virtual circuit begins or ends. In other words, gateways act as focal points which must be traversed by all information exchanged on a given internetwork virtual circuit. Once an internetwork path has been established through a number of gateways, it cannot be changed ; i.e., internetwork routing is fixed for the duration of the virtual circuits. No alternate paths can be used. In the example of figure 4-5 below, the alternate path through G2 and G3 cannot ' ; used once G1 and G4 have been chosen.

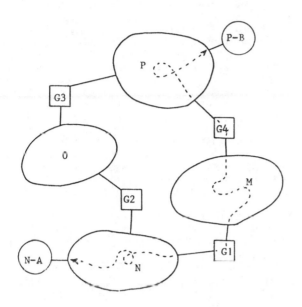

Figure 4-5   Fixed internetwork routing between public networks

When a public network is interconnected with a private network by means of X.25, the private network is viewed as a DTE on the public network. Because a DTE can be associated with only one address per access line (i.e., access lines cannot be multiplexed for several DTE addresses), the private network would need to be connected to the public network with as many access lines as there are subscribers on the private net. For obvious economical reasons, this cannot be considered as a realistic solution. An additional layer must therefore be introduced, wrapping the public network to permit multiplexing of addresses on physical lines, i.e., several global addresses onto one single DTE address. This additional layer can be considered as being made of a network of gateways, each being associated with a DTE address on each individual lower level network. The function of this additional layer is to multiplex user global addresses onto single DTE addresses. Gateways at this level (see figure 4-6) have a DTE address associated with their access line. At the source, routing decisions must be made to determine the DTE address of the gateway corresponding to the destination network. As in the case of interconnection of public networks through X.75, this routing decision may be very simple if only one gateway is permitted between the two networks (no alternate path). On the other hand, the introduction of a new layer for internetwork routing allows more sophisticated routing algorithms to be performed. For example, reliability may be improved

by allowing more than one gateway between two networks, and by making use of alternate paths. Such reliability may be provided at the cost of more elaborate routing decisions and route adaptation functions not only within the gateways but at the sources as well.

Note : Unfortunately the address extension in X.25 is of little help in practice since it is limited to two decimal digits when using the international numbering plan.

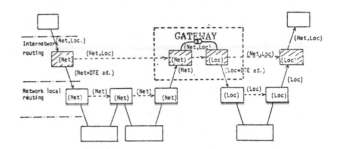

Figure 4-6   New level for internetwork routing

5. Equivalence of services

Interconnection of networks can only be performed at a level providing equivalent services on either side. In addition these services must be cascadable (see section 3).

For example, networks offering identical services such as datagram or virtual circuit services can be interconnected without great difficulty.The CATENET approach and the CCITT X.75 interface are based on this consideration.

Note : When the virtual circuit services are not completely equivalent, e.g., some features such as error and flow control may have end-to-end significance on one network only, one will generally choose not to use the additional facilities for internetwork communication.

As another example, when a private network offering a datagram service is to be interconnected with a public network providing virtual circuit services, the question of choosing the appropriate level of service where the networks can be interconnected needs to be studied.

1) One can choose to interconnect them at the level of virtual circuit services (see figure 5-1). In this case, a layer needs to be added wrapping the datagram network in order to perform virtual circuit functions on top of the datagram service. As already stated in section 3, these additional functions need to be performed in the gateway between the two networks and in the user equipment on the private network as well, at least for those which are going to communicate (at the VC level of service) with equipment directly connected to the public network.

217

These additional functions include for instance : connection set up, maintenance and clearing, maintenance of the order of information exchanges, and error and flow control detection.

In practice, because of the multiplexing constraints of X.25 already mentioned in the previous section, i.e., one access line to a public network cannot be shared by several addresses, an additional layer needs also to be provided wrapping virtual circuit functions for internetwork addressing and routing.

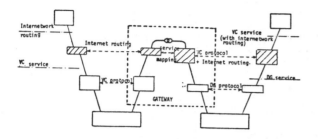

Figure 5-1 Interconnection at the VC level

2) The other alternative is to interconnect the two networks at the level of datagram services (see figure 5-2). In this case, a layer needs to be added, wrapping the virtual circuit network in order to provide datagram services on top of virtual circuits. This layer will be in charge of requesting virtual circuit establishment and release between "internetwork users" and the gateways. Datagrams can then be passed transparently over these virtual circuits.

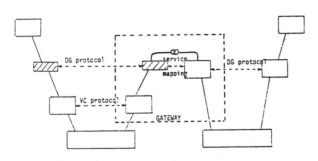

Figure 5-2 Interconnection at the DG level

6. Error control

Error control functions are generally based on transmitting, back to the source, control messages (positive or negative acknowledgements) referring to blocks of information transmitted from a source to a destination. The source keeps a copy of the block, in case a retransmission is required, until an acknowledgement has been received. Blocks are generally transmitted before previous blocks are acknowledged, i.e., anticipation on the transmission of previous blocks is performed, in order to optimize available bandwidth utilization despite a possibly long round trip delay. A queue of blocks waiting for acknowledgements (or retransmission) is therefore maintained at the source.

In most networks, error control functions are performed at various levels from the link control level up to the level of application-to-application communications over a network or a set of interconnected networks. They aim at protecting information exchange against failures in the underlying "component" used to actually transmit information. The degree of protection depends in particular on the origin of acknowledgements, e.g., application-to-application acknowledgements (end-to-end), protect against any error occuring in any intermediate component, acknowledgements exchanged between adjacent nodes protect against line failures only. In other words, error control services may provide two kinds of error protection whether they are performed end-to-end, over a complex communication system, or cascaded in a chain of error control procedures.

A cascade of error control within one network can be extended, without losing any of its properties, over another network where error control is also performed hop by hop.
For example, when interconnecting datagram networks at this level of service, error control services can be kept unchanged for the global network (see figure 6-1).

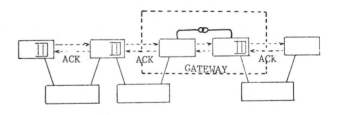

Figure 6-1   Cascade of error control

When error-control is performed end-to-end on both networks, the level of service may be preserved if the end-to-end significance of acknowledgements is also preserved. In other words, gateways must forward acknowledgements transparently (see figure 6-2) A performance problem may arise from such an interconnection, as transmission delays may increase drastically for acknowledgements coming through remote networks. Time-outs at the source may be difficult to tune due to variations in transit delays from one destination to another.

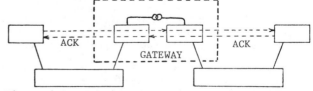

Figure 6-2   Passive gateway preserving end-to-end error control

An example of such interconnection can be found in the interconnection of CYCLADES and EIN at the transport protocol level.[18]

When error-control is end-to-end on one network and performed hop by hop on the other network, an adjustement of the levels of service is required. An example can be found in the interconnection of two public networks offering virtual circuit services with different technologies. The choice made in X.75 is to choose as a common service not to consider the end-to-end significance of acknowledgements on the network providing it, when corresponding with a user attached to the other network. The gateways between such networks will actually be considered as the end user as far as acknowledgements are concerned (see figure 6-3).

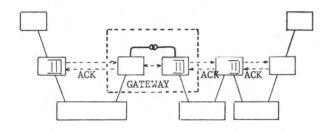

Figure 6-3 Loosing the end-to-end significance of acknowledgements

7. Flow control

As for error control functions, networks performing flow control in a cascade of flow control functions between adjacent nodes can easily be interconnected without modifying their properties. This is the case when interconnecting virtual circuit networks where flow control on virtual circuit does not have end-to-end significance. Interconnecting such networks at this level of service simply consists in adding a number of hops between internetwork users, and therefore increases the maximum number of packets that can be in transit within the global network on a given virtual circuit (see figure 7-1).

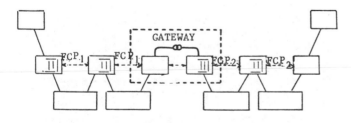

FCP$_i$ = Flow Control Protocol i

Figure 7-1 Cascade of Flow Control Protocols

As with cascading error control services with end-to-end significance, end-to-end flow control services can be cascaded if the gateway simply translates flow control information (without processing it). Performance problems may arise again because of the variations in end-to-end transit delays across the global network. The amount of anticipation for optimizing the use of the available bandwidth might be rather difficult to tune because it may vary widely depending on destinations. Optimization of anticipation with long transit delays may also lead to significantly increasing buffer requirements.

When interconnecting two public networks offering virtual circuits with different flow control characteristics, i.e., end-to-end significant or not, a choice in the common level of service for interconnection needs to be made. As for error-control services, X.75 considers that the common service is not end-to-end.

8. Terminal handling

Initially, networks will be mainly used for accessing applications in host computers from terminals. Most networks thus define the relations between applications and terminals.

These relations are often expressed in terms of a Virtual Terminal Protocol (VTP)[19] which defines the behaviour of a standard hypothetical terminal handled by applications or terminal access methods in host computers on the one side and emulated on real terminals (in a terminal concentrator) on the other side. The Virtual Terminal is usually defined as a message oriented terminal with a set of associated functions.

For public networks, CCITT has defined the relations between applications and character mode terminals connected to Packet Assembler-Disassemblers (PAD) as a set of mechanisms allowing applications or terminal access methods in host computers to know about the actual characteristics of real terminals and to drive them as character mode terminals through the network. These mechanisms are defined by recommendation CCITT X.29.[20]

Different services are thus provided by "VTP networks" and "X.29 networks" even though the physical terminals may be identical. To interconnect them at the terminal level, equivalent services need again to be found. Such an approach has been followed[14] when interconnecting CYCLADES and TRANSPAC to provide (1) character terminals connected to a PAD on TRANSPAC with access to applications on CYCLADES hosts handling Virtual Terminals, (2) access from terminals on CYCLADES concentrators, presenting a Virtual Terminal image to applications on TRANSPAC handling X.29.

In case (1) it is necessary to wrap the character oriented terminal service of TRANSPAC, to obtain a message oriented terminal service equivalent to VTP. An additional layer of functions is required in the gateway on the TRANSPAC side to express, in X.29 terms, the Virtual Terminal characteristics.

Complementary functions are performed on the terminal side by the user himself who needs to behave
as if he was using a Virtual Terminal (see figure
8-1).

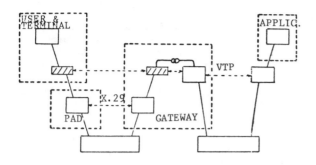

Figure 8-1 PAD to VT-application interconnection

In case (2), restrictions must be applied to the
application side handling X.29 on TRANSPAC to drive
the Virtual Terminal image presented by the Gateway,
since not all options available on a character mode
terminal can be provided by the message oriented
Virtual Terminal (see figure 8-2).

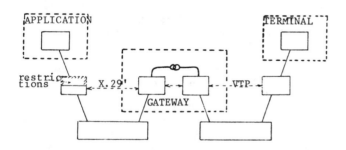

Figure 8-2 X.29 Application to VT-terminal
interconnection

This interconnection example is also a case where
the logical interfaces at the gateway level are not
symmetrical ; i.e., adaptations are different
whether a terminal or an application is concerned
on either side.

9. Other examples and issues

The principles developed in section 3 can also be
applied to other problems related to network interconnection, such as compatibilities of user interfaces[21] and control languages.
They have also been applied to adapt closed systems
to an open systems environment.
However, some areas have not yet been thoroughly
investigated and may still be considered as topics
for further research. This is in particular the

case for congestion control[22,23] and administrative
functions in general, such as network supervision
and maintenance, diagnostics, accounting and billing.
Nowadays, the most usual way to solve these problems
is to consider that the global network as such does
not benefit from those functions which are handled
independently within each network.
This is acceptable for initial usage of a small
number of networks, but would be intolerable in a
few years with the expected extensive usage of
myriads of networks.

10. Conclusion

Interconnection of computer networks is a complex
problem and largely still an open question. However,
it has been solved satisfactorily in a number of
cases, permitting partial interconnection (i.e.,
limited to a subset of network functions or services). Experience shows that a set of simple rules
can be applied to analyze network interconnection
problems.

Of course, these simple principles are not sufficient, and practical experience is still essential
(isn't this the case for most design problems ?).
It could reasonably be expected that the same type
of techniques could be applied to the remaining
network interconnection issues, but this is still
to be tried.

The final objective of all present studies and expe-
riments in network interconnection should be to
determine which common properties networks must
exhibit to make them readily interconnectable, and
to establish them as international standards. Common levels of services, expandability of network
addresses to global addresses, common layering
structure, common protocols on top of common services are such candidates for standardization.
CCITT and ISO are facing the challenge of developing
such standards.
Let us hope they will succeed for the benefit of
all !

11. References

(1) L. POUZIN, "Interconnection of packet switching
     network", IFIP WG 6.1 INWG Note 42, 19 p.,
     Oct. 1973.

(2) V. CERF, A. MC KENZIE, R. SCANTLEBURY,
     H. ZIMMERMANN, "Proposal for an international
     end-to-end protocol", ACM Sigcom Comp. Com.
     Rev., vol. 6, n° 1, pp.68-89, Janv. 1974

(3) ISO, "Reference model of Open Systems Inter-
     connection", ISO/TC97/SC16/N227, 181 p.June 79

(4) CCITT, "Recommendation X.75 - Terminal and
     transit call control procedures and data trans-
     fer system on international circuits between
     packet switched data networks", Study Group
     VII, Temp. doc. 207-E, I.T.U., Geneva,
     Switzerland, 1977.

(5) CCITT, "Recommendation X.25 : Interface between
     DTE and DCE for terminals operating in the

packet mode on public data networks", Public Data Networks, Orange Book, vol. VIII.2, I.T.U. Geneva, Switzerland, 1977.

(6) A. MC KENZIE, "Some computer network interconnection issues", Proc. NCC'74, AFIP Press, pp. 857-859, 1974.

(7) M. GIEN, J. LAWS, R. SCANTLEBURY, "Interconnection of packet switched networks : theory and practice", Proc. EUROCOMP Communications Networks, ONLINE, pp. 241-260, Sept. 1975.

(8) P. HIGGINSON, A. HINCHLEY, "The problems of linking several networks with a gateway computer", Proc. EUROCOMP Communications Networks, ONLINE, pp. 453-465, Sept. 1975.

(9) C. SUNSHINE, "Interconnection of computer networks", Computer Networks, vol.1, pp. 175-195, 1977

(10) M. GIEN, "Network interconnection and protocol conversion", Proc. COMNET'77, Budapest, Hungary, pp. 39-57, Oct. 1977.

(11) H. ZIMMERMANN, N. NAFFAH, "Protocols and network interconnection", Proc. Nato Advanced Study on Interlinking of Computer Networks, Bonas, France, Sept. 1978.

(12) V. CERF, P. KIRSTEIN, "Issues in Packet-Network Interconnection". Proc. IEEE vol. 66, N° 11, pp. 1386-1408, Nov. 1978.

(13) L. POUZIN, H. ZIMMERMANN, "A tutorial on Protocols, Proc. IEEE, vol. 66, N° 11, pp. 1436-1370, Nov. 1978.

(14) H. ZIMMERMANN, N. NAFFAH, "On Open Systems Architecture", Proc. ICCC 78, Kyoto, Japan, pp. 669-674, Sept. 1978.

(15) L. POUZIN, "Interconnection of packet switching networks", Proc. Subconference on Computer Networks HICSS-7, Honolulu, Hawaï, Janv. 1974.

(16) INWG, "Basic message format for internetwork communication", INWG Note 83, May 1975.

(17) CCITT, "Recommendation X. 121 : International numbering plan for public data networks, Study Group VII, Temp. Doc 186-E, I.T.U., Geneva, Switzerland, April 1978.

(18) M. GIEN et al, "The implementation of an End-to-End protocol by EIN centers : A survey and comparison", Proc. ICCC'76, Toronto, Canada, pp. 351-360, Aug. 1976.

(19) IFIP, "Proposal for a standard virtual terminal protocol", Doc. ISO/TC97/SC16/N23, 56 p., Feb. 1978.

(20) CCITT, "Recommendations X.3, X.25, X.28, X.29 on packet switched data transmission services", I.T.U., Geneva, Switzerland, 1977.

(21) A. NEUMANN, "A basis for standardization of User-Terminal protocols for computer network access", NBS tech. note 877, 29 p., Jul. 1975.

(22) L. POUZIN, "Flow control in data networks-Methods and tools", Proc. ICCC'76, Toronto, Canada, pp. 467-474, Aug. 1976.

(23) J.L. GRANGE, "Traffic control in a packet switching network", CYCLADES Report n° SCH 618, 19 p., May 1979.

Internetwork Protocol Approaches

JONATHAN B. POSTEL

(Invited Paper)

Abstract—The motivation for interconnecting networks is to provide one or more consistent services to the set of users of the interconnected networks. To provide these services either new end-to-end service protocols must be defined or the service protocols of the individual networks must be made to interwork. In either case the issues of addressing, routing, buffering, flow control, error control, and security must be considered. Two examples of interconnection strategy are examined: the interconnection of X.25 networks, and the interconnection of ARPA research networks. The models for interconnection of networks and the role of internetwork protocols are discussed.

INTRODUCTION

THE motivations for constructing computer communication networks—data and program exchange and sharing, remote access to resources, etc.—are also motivations for interconnecting networks. This follows from the observation that the power of a communication system is related to the number of potential participants.

This paper first discusses a few key concepts involved in computer communication networks. The view that computer networks provide an interprocess communication facility is presented. The datagram and virtual circuit services are compared. The interconnection device or gateway is discussed. The relation of the interconnection issues to the open systems architecture is described.

In this paper, two approaches to internetworking are characterized: the public data network system as implied by the CCITT X.75 Recommendation and the ARPA experimental internetwork. These two systems illustrate the virtual circuit and the datagram approaches to network interconnection, respectively. The vast majority of the work on interconnecting networks falls into one of these two approaches.

INTERPROCESS COMMUNICATION

While discussing computer communication, it is useful to recall that the communication takes place at the request and agreement of processes, i.e., computer programs in execution. Processes are the actors in the computer communication environment; processes are the senders and receivers of data. Processes operate in host computers or hosts.

The protocols used in constructing the communications capability provide an interprocess communication system. Fig. 1 shows how the combination of the network and the

host network interface (hardware and software) can be viewed as providing an interprocess communication system.

When a new host computer is to be connected to an existing network, it must implement the protocol layers necessary to match the existing protocol used in the network. The new host must join the network-wide interprocess communication system so the processes in that host can communicate with processes in other hosts in the network.

The interconnection of networks requires that the processes in the hosts of the interconnected networks have a common interprocess communication system. This may be achieved by converting the networks to a new interprocess communication system, by converting one or more levels of protocol to new protocols, or by translating between pairs of interprocess communication systems at their points of contact.

DATAGRAMS AND CIRCUITS

Two types of service are commonly discussed as appropriate for the network-provided interprocess communication service: datagrams and virtual circuits.

Datagrams are one-shot simple messages. They are inherently unreliable since they travel one-way and are not acknowledged. Datagrams may also arrive in a different order than sent (at least in some networks). Datagrams are simple to implement since they do not require the networks or gateways to record and update state information. Datagrams must carry complete address information in each message. The transmission of datagrams by a process is via send and receive actions.

Virtual circuits (or connections) are designed to be reliable and to deliver data in the order sent. Implementation of virtual circuits is complicated by the need for the networks or gateways to record and update state information. Virtual circuits are created through an exchange of messages to set up the circuit; when use terminates, an exchange of messages tears down the circuit. During the data transmission phase, a short form address or circuit identifier may be used in place of the actual address. To use a virtual circuit a process must perform actions to cause the virtual circuit to be created (call setup) and terminated, as well as the actions to send and receive data.

Datagrams provide a transaction type service while virtual circuits provide a connection type service. Each of these services is needed in a general purpose communication environment. Datagrams are most efficient for transaction type information requests such as directory assistance or weather reports. Virtual circuits are useful for terminal access to interactive computer systems for file transfer between computers.

Manuscript received June 15, 1979; revised December 18, 1979. This work was supported by the Advanced Research Projects Agency under Contract DAHC15 72 C 0308, ARPA Order 2223.

The author is with the Information Sciences Institute, University of Southern California, Marina del Rey, CA 90291.

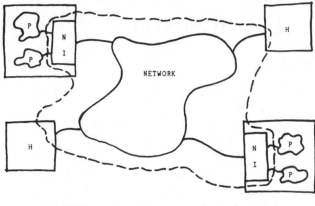

-- INTERPROCESS COMMUNICATION SYSTEM BOUNDARY

P   PROCESS

H   HOST

NI   NETWORK INTERFACE

Fig. 1.   Communications network.

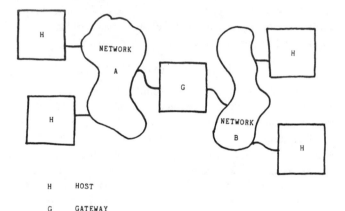

H   HOST

G   GATEWAY

Fig. 2.   Interconnected networks.

GATEWAYS

Two or more networks are connected via a device (or pair of devices) called a gateway. Such a device may appear to each network as simply a host on that network (Fig. 2).

Some gateways simply read messages from one network (unwrapping them from that network's packaging), compute a routing function, and send messages into another network (wrapping them in that network's packaging). Since the networks involved may be implemented using different media, such as leased lines or radio transmission, this type of gateway is called a media-conversion gateway.

Other gateways may translate the protocol used in one network to that used in another network by replacing messages received from one network with different messages with the same protocol semantics sent into another network. This type of gateway is called a protocol-translation gateway.

It should be clear that the distinction between media-conversion and protocol-translation is one of degree: the media-conversion gateways bridge the gap between differing link and physical level protocols, while protocol-translation gateways bridge the gap between differing network and higher level protocols.

The translation approach to network interconnection raises several issues. Success in protocol translation seems inversely correlated with the protocol level. At the lower levels, protocol translation causes no problems because the physical level and link levels are hop-by-hop in nature. It should be noted, though, that different protocols even at these low levels may have impact on the reliability, throughput, and delay characteristics of the total communication system.

At the network and transport levels, the issues of message size, addressing, and flow control become critical. Unless one requires that only messages that can be transmitted on the network with the smallest maximum message size be sent, one must provide for the fragmentation and reassembly of messages. That is, the division of a long message into parts for transmission through a small message size network, and the reconstruction of those parts into the original message at the destination. The translation of addresses is a difficult problem when one network or transport level protocol provides a larger address space than the corresponding protocol to be translated to. When end-to-end flow control mechanisms are used, as they commonly are in transport level protocols, difficulties arise when the units controlled are different. For example, when one protocol controls octets and the corresponding protocol controls letters. More difficulties arise with potential difference in the model of flow control. For example, a difference between pre- and postallocation, or between the allocation of buffer space and the allocation of transmission rate.

At higher levels, the problems are more difficult because of the increased state information kept and the lower likelihood of one-to-one translation of individual protocol messages. A further difficulty is that each level further multiplexes the communication so that each connection or stream or channel or virtual circuit must be separately translated. It should be noted that neither of the specific interconnection approaches discussed in this paper attempts higher level protocol translation.

Gateways may be thought of as having a "half" for each network they interconnect. One could model the operation of a gateway as having each gateway-half contain procedures to convert from a network specific protocol into a standard protocol and vice versa (Fig. 3).

RELATION TO OPEN SYSTEMS ARCHITECTURE

In relation to the open systems architecture, the interconnection of networks focuses on levels 3 and 4 [1].

To review, the open systems architecture defines the following levels of protocol:

Level	Function
7	Application
6	Presentation
5	Session
4	Transport
3	Network
2	Link
1	Physical

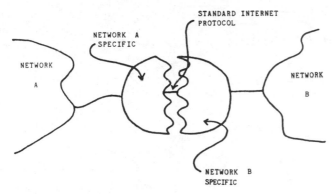

Fig. 3. Gateway halves.

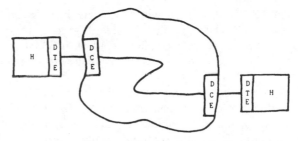

Fig. 4. PDN virtual circuit.

The lower levels, the physical and the link levels, are hop-by-hop in nature and present no interconnection issues in terms of compatibility, although there may be some performance concerns.

The higher levels, the session level, the presentation level, and the application level, have so many compatibility requirements that it seems quite unlikely that interconnection of different protocols at those levels will be workable.

Thus, it is at the network level and the transport level that the interconnection of networks finds issues of concern.

The network level corresponds to the interface to datagram service, and the transport level corresponds to the interface to virtual circuit service.

In some networks, the network level and datagram service have been hidden from the user, forcing consideration of network interconnection at the transport level.

INTERCONNECTION OF X.25 NETWORKS

Introduction

The public data networks (PDN's) that follow the CCITT X.25 Recommendation [2] are to be interconnected via an interface specified in CCITT Recommendation X.75 [3]. Recommendation X.25 specifies the interface between the customer's equipment, called the data terminal equipment (DTE); and the network equipment, called the data circuit-terminating equipment (DCE). Recommendation X.25 implies a virtual circuit operation. Thus, the PDN's offer an interface to a virtual circuit transport level protocol. Fig. 4 shows the model of a PDN virtual circuit.

The interface between two PDN's specified in Recommendation X.75 is quite similar to that in Recommendation X.25. The equipment on either side of this interface is called a signaling terminal (STE). The STE–STE interface is much like the DTE–DCE interface. The STE–STE interconnection is a split gateway with each gateway-half in a physical device controlled by the PDN connected to that gateway-half. Fig. 5 shows the interconnection of PDN's.

The interconnection of PDN's via X.75 interfaces results in a series of virtual circuits. Each section is a distinct entity with separate flow control, error recovery, etc. Fig. 6 shows a PDN transmission path with two virtual circuits (VC's) and five separate flow control (FC) steps.

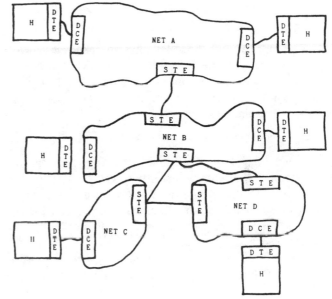

Fig. 5. Interconnection of PDN's.

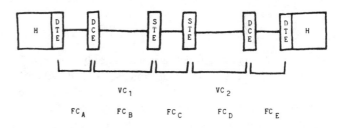

VC Virtual Circuit

FC Flow Control

Fig. 6. PDN transmission path.

Addressing

The address field is variable in length up to 15 digits, with each digit coded in a 4 bit field. The maximum address is then 60 bits (about 8 octets).

Routing

The user has no influence over routing used. To create the series of virtual circuits, a series of call setups establishes a fixed route (between pairs of STE's at least). State information must be kept for each call in the source and destination DTE's and DCE's and in each STE in the route.

Buffering and Flow Control

Each portion of the total path is a distinct virtual circuit. Each virtual circuit has an independent flow control (and

225

particular to that PDN). In addition, there is flow control across each STE–STE interface. All this flow control is on a per call basis. This stepwise flow control may introduce delay in the total path that could be avoided with an end-to-end scheme.

There are some concerns about the interaction of two types of flow control implemented in PDN's. One type allows one message in transit from source DCE to destination DCE at any one time. The other allows multiple messages to be in transit, the number being determined by the flow control window.

Acknowledgment

Each portion of the total path has an acknowledgment. The user to network interface also has an acknowledgment. This local acknowledgment means only that the first PDN has accepted the message for transmission, not that it has arrived at the destination.

Recovery

The X.25 and X.75 Recommendations do not specify how the PDN's deal with errors internally. If unrecoverable errors occur, the network will signal a Reset, which apparently means that the virtual circuit still exists, but the flow control is reset and messages may have been lost. More serious errors result in the call being cleared.

Because of the fixed route nature of the multinetwork path, an STE failure disrupts the communication.

Security

The X.25/X.75 Recommendations do not provide any security features.

Header Structure

Once the call is established, a header is only 3 octets. The call setup headers are substantially longer, typically 20 octets, but possibly as large as 166 octets. There is a tradeoff between header size and state information kept; in the PDN's, the tradeoff has been made toward small headers and large state. The details of the headers are shown in Appendix I.

Summary

The most important aspect of the interconnection of PDN's is that service provided to the using process is a virtual circuit with essentially the same properties a single PDN would have provided. This is done by concatenating a series of virtual circuits to provide the total path, resulting in a fixed route through a set of network interconnection points.

INTERCONNECTION OF ARPA RESEARCH NETWORKS

Introduction

The ARPA sponsored research on interconnections of networks has let to a two-level protocol to support the equivalent function of the PDN's X.25/X.75 service. The ARPA sponsored work on networks has developed an internet protocol (IP) [4], and a transmission control protocol (TCP) [5].

TCP is a logical connection transport protocol and is a level 4 protocol in the OSA model of protocol structure.

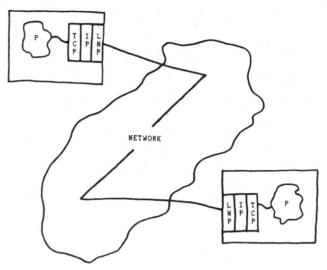

Fig. 7.   End-to-end connection.

The IP is a datagram protocol. The collection of interconnected networks is called an internet. IP is the network protocol of the internet and this is a level 3 protocol in the OSA model. The actual networks used are of various kinds (e.g., the ARPANET, radio networks, satellite networks, and ring or cable networks) and are referred to as local networks even though they may span continents or oceans. The interface to a local network is a local network protocol or LNP. Fig. 7 shows the model of an end-to-end connection.

In the ARPA model, the networks interconnect via a single device called a gateway. A gateway is a host on two or more networks. Fig. 8 shows the ARPA model of the interconnection of networks.

Each network addresses a gateway on it in the same way it addresses any other host on it. The information required to deliver a message to a destination in the internet is carried in the IP header. The IP is implemented in the gateways and in hosts. A sending host prepares a datagram (which is an IP header and the original message) and then selects a gateway in its own net to forward the datagram. The sending host then sends the datagram wrapped in a local network packet to that gateway.

A gateway receives a packet from one of the local networks to which it is attached, and unwraps the IP datagram. The gateway then examines the IP header and determines the next gateway (or destination host) address in one of the local networks it is directly connected to. The gateway then sends the datagram with its IP header in a new local net packet to that gateway (or host).

The IP has no provision for flow control or error control on the data portion of the message (the IP headers are checksummed). There are no acknowledgments of IP messages. The IP is simple and the gateway may be implemented in small machines. A key point is that a gateway has no state information to record about a message. At the IP level, there are no connections or virtual circuits.

The IP does not provide a service equivalent to the PDN's X.25/X.75. To provide that type of end-to-end reliable ordered delivery of data the ARPA internet uses TCP.

226

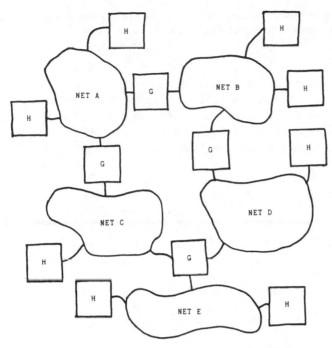

Fig. 8. ARPA model of interconnection of networks.

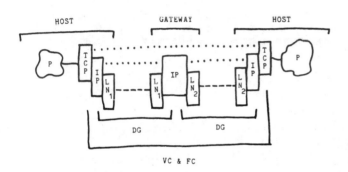

DG   DATAGRAM

VC   VIRTUAL CIRCUIT

FC   FLOW CONTROL

Fig. 9. ARPA model of transmission path.

TCP uses end-to-end mechanisms to ensure reliable ordered delivery of data over a logical connection. It uses flow control, positive acknowledgments with time out and retransmission, sequence numbers, etc., to achieve these goals. Fig. 9 shows the conceptual transmission path in this interprocess communication system, pointing out the datagram (DG) path between the IP modules and the virtual circuit path between the TCP modules at the source and destination and the flow control (FC) at that level.

ARPA has used these techniques to interconnect several very different networks including the ARPANET, packet radio nets, a satellite net, and several local networks.

Addressing

The size of the address in this experimental system is fixed. The IP provides a one octet network field and a three octet host field. Also a one octet protocol identifier in the

IP header may be considered address information. The TCP provides a two octet port field. The total of the address length is then seven octets. Provision has been made for a host to have several addresses, so the host field is sometimes called the logical host field. The total address is the concatenation of the network, host, protocol, and port fields.

Routing

Normally, the user has no influence over the route used between the gateways. There is no call setup and the route may vary from one message to the next. No state information is kept in the gateways.

A user might insert a source routing option in the IP header to cause that particular message to be routed through specific gateways.

Buffering and Flow Control

There is no flow control mechanism in the IP. The gateways do not control the flow on connections for they are unaware of connections or any relation between one message and the next message. The gateways may protect themselves against congestion by dropping messages. When a gateway drops a message because of congestion, it may report this fact to the source of the message.

The TCP uses end-to-end flow control using windows on a per logical connection basis.

Acknowledgment

The IP has no provision for acknowledgments. The TCP uses acknowledgments for both error control and flow control. The TCP acknowledgments are not directly available to the user.

Recovery

Errors in a network or gateway result in a message being dropped, and the sender may or may not be notified. This inherent unreliability in the IP level allows it to be simple and requires the end-to-end use of a reliable protocol.

TCP provides the reliable end-to-end functions to recover from any lost messages. The TCP uses a positive acknowledgment, time out, and retransmission scheme to ensure delivery of all data. Each message is covered by an end-to-end checksum.

Because of the potential of alternate routing, the end-to-end communication may be able to continue despite the failure of a gateway.

Security

The IP provides an option to carry the security, precedence, and user group information compatible with AUTODIN II. The enforcement of these parameters is up to each network, and only AUTODIN II is prepared to do so.

The TCP end-to-end checksum covers all the address information (source and destination network, host, protocol, and port), so if the checksum test is successful the address fields have not been corrupted.

Header Structure

The IP header is 20 octets (plus options, if used), but there is no call setup and no gateway state information. Thus, at the IP level, the header size versus state information tradeoff has been made toward large header and little (no) state information.

The TCP header is 20 octets (plus option, if used). There is a connection establishment procedure called the "three-way handshake," and significant state information is kept. In this case, there are both large headers and large state tables. The details of the headers are shown in Appendix II.

Summary

The ARPA networks are interconnected by using a common datagram protocol to provide addressing (and thus routing) information and an end-to-end transport protocol to provide reliable sequenced data connections.

This model has evolved from the ARPANET experience, in particular from the internetwork protocol model suggested in a paper by Cerf and Kahn [6].

CONCLUSION

Both the PDN's and the ARPA networks are interconnected by establishing standard protocols. The PDN's provide a virtual circuit service by concatenating the virtual circuit services of the individual networks. The ARPA networks use two levels of protocol to provide both datagram and virtual circuit services.

Additional discussion of the interconnection of PDN's is provided in [7], [8]. In another paper in this issue Boggs *et al.* present in detail another example of network interconnection using the datagram approach [9].

The issues of network interconnection have been discussed for at least 5 years (for example, McKenzie [10]). The recent expositions by Sunshine [11], Cerf and Kirstein [12], and Gien and Zimmermann [13], are particularly recommended.

APPENDIX I

X.75 HEADER FORMATS

The call request and the data packet formats are illustrated here. These typify the X.75 packet formats. All the X.75 packets are the same in the first two octets. The format field indicated the type of packet.

Call Request

The call request packet is variable in length from a practical minimum of 11 octets to an unlikely maximum of 160 octets.

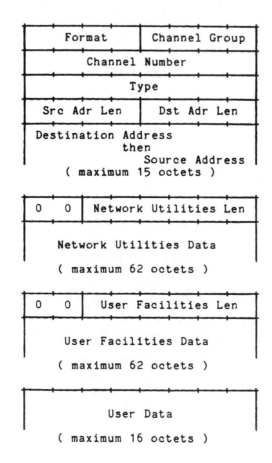

The Data packet has a three octet header.

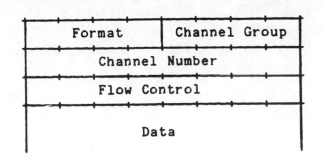

Format	Channel Group
Channel Number	
Flow Control	
Data	

APPENDIX II

ARPA PROTOCOL HEADER FORMATS

Every datagram carries the basic IP header. Every TCP segment transmitted carries the basic TCP header.

Internet Protocol

The **ARPA IP** has a basic header of 20 octets, and may carry a variable number of options up to a total length of 60 octets.

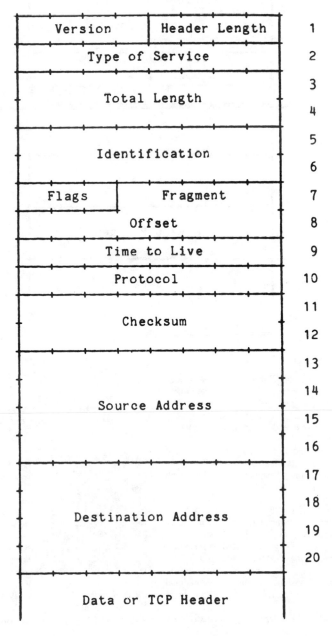

Version	Header Length	1
Type of Service		2
Total Length		3
		4
Identification		5
		6
Flags	Fragment Offset	7
		8
Time to Live		9
Protocol		10
Checksum		11
		12
Source Address		13
		14
		15
		16
Destination Address		17
		18
		19
		20
Data or TCP Header		

Transmission Control Protocol

The basic TCP header is 20 octets, and the header may be up to 60 octets long if options are used.

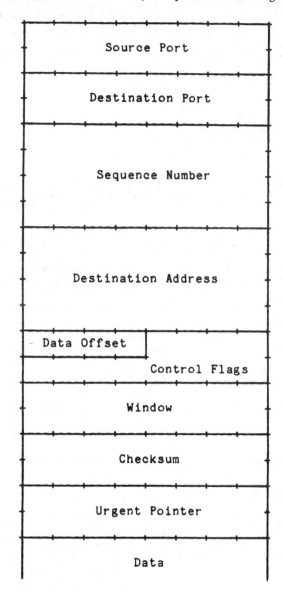

REFERENCES

[1] H. Zimmermann, "The ISO reference model," this issue, pp. 425–432.
[2] "Recommendation X.25/Interface between data terminal equipment (DTE) and data circuit-terminating equipment (DCE) for terminals operating in the packet mode on public data networks," in *CCITT Orange Book*, vol. 7, Int. Telephone and Telegraph Consultative Committee, Geneva, Switzerland.
[3] "Proposal for provisional Recommendation X.75 on international interworking between packet switched data networks," in CCITT Study Group VII Contribution no. 207, Int. Telephone and Telegraph Consultative Committee, Geneva, Switzerland, May 1978.
[4] DARPA, "DOD standard internet protocol," IEN-128, Defense Advanced Research Projects Agency, Jan. 1980.
[5] DARPA, "DOD standard transmission control protocol," IEN-129, Defense Advanced Research Projects Agency, Jan. 1980.
[6] V. Cerf and R. Kahn, "A protocol for packet network intercommunication," *IEEE Trans. Commun.*, vol. COM-22, pp. 637–648, May 1974.
[7] G. Grossman, A. Hinchley, and C. Sunshine, "Issues in international public data networking," *Comput. Networks,* vol. 3, pp. 259–266, Sept. 1979.
[8] V. DiCiccio, C. Sunshine, J. Field, and E. Manning, "Alternatives for interconnection of public packet switching data networks," in *Proc. Sixth Data Commun. Symp.*, ACM/IEEE, Nov. 1979, pp. 120–125.
[9] D. Boggs, J. Shoch, E. Taft, and R. Metcalfe, "Pup: An internetwork architecture," this issue, pp. 612–624.
[10] A. McKenzie, "Some computer network interconnection issues," in *Proc. Nat. Comput. Conf.*, AFIPS, 1974, pp. 857–859.

Jonathan B. Postel received the B.S. and M.S. degrees in engineering and the Ph.D. degree in computer science from the University of California, Los Angeles.

He has worked for the MITRE Corporation in McLean, VA, and SRI International in Menlo Park, CA. At UCLA he was involved in the development of the ARPANET Network Measurement Center and the installation of the first host on the ARPANET. Since that time, he has participated in the development of many of the higher level protocols used in the ARPANET. He is currently a Computer Scientist at the USC/Information Sciences Institute in Marina del Rey, CA, where his research focuses on the interconnection of computer networks.

Reprinted from *Computer*, September 1983, pages 38-48. Copyright © 1983 by The Institute of Electrical and Electronics Engineers, Inc.

By using gateways to form a packet-switching system on top of the underlying networks, the Internet successfully links from 400 to 500 hosts in the US and Europe.

The DARPA Internet: Interconnecting Heterogeneous Computer Networks with Gateways

Robert Hinden, Jack Haverty, and Alan Sheltzer

The BBN Computer Corporation

Armies of spiders could not weave a wider web—networks are everywhere. Networks span continents and oceans; tie office buildings in miles of wire, fiber, and other nerve media; reach into land, air, and space vehicles; and confront microcomputers as well as large mainframe computers. Some networks are incredibly fast and others are pragmatically slow; some work better than others, and some do not work well at all. However, despite the present abundance, new networks are still being developed constantly to challenge the competition.

If we had a way to interconnect various networks, many problems could be solved. For example, a user may want to communicate with a site that is not on the same public network as the host computer. Perhaps there are several hosts but no single network to which they will all connect. In some cases, the cost of connection will be a factor; connecting 100 hosts on a coaxial local net is more cost-effective than putting them all on a public net, but running 1000 miles of coaxial cable to the 101st host is absurd. In other cases, pragmatics or the basic laws of nature apply; for example, radio-based networks are about the only choice if mobility is needed. A network technology that supports a maximum of 256 hosts becomes a problem when you acquire the 257th.

Given that all hosts cannot be put on a single network, the next best option is to interconnect networks. Unfortunately, choosing how to interconnect several networks is almost as difficult as choosing the networks themselves. The box to the right outlines only some of the issues facing network and internetwork designers.

This article describes the recent experiences with a project sponsored by the Defense Advanced Research Projects Agency, called the Internet system.[1-3] The Internet system was developed as a research vehicle to interconnect the diverse types of networks sponsored by DARPA, as well as more recent types of networks such as the high-speed local area networks, some of which were developed by industry or university efforts. The gateway component of the Internet or, more precisely, the system formed by the gateways that constitute an Internet gateway system is the focus of our discussion.

Much development and operational experience has been gained over the last several years in a real communications system; the Internet now connects dozens of networks and serves users in the United States and Europe by supporting their daily activities. A set of gateways forms a packet-switching system (Figure 1) built on top of the underlying networks, just as the networks themselves are built on top of underlying circuits of varying kinds, such as telephone, satellite, or radio links. The techniques used to perform operational support activities, such as monitoring and control, are critical to the success of this system in a real-world environment.

The Internet system as it exists today offers a technology that successfully interconnects a variety of hosts homed on diverse networks. It has been easy to expand,

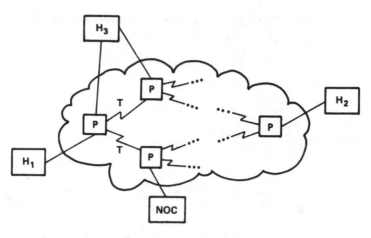

P = packet-switching node computer.

T = trunk circuits, either telephone or satellite.

H = host; a user computer attached to a network is the host on that network. A host is said to be "homed" to a network at a particular port that has a network address. A host with several attachments to a network (e.g., H_3 in the diagram) is "multiply homed."

NOC = A special-purpose host computer that performs operations and maintenance activities, such as monitoring, fault isolation, traffic flow analysis, and other activities critical to large-scale networks. In both the Arpanet and the Internet, this function is performed by a software package called NU.

Figure 1. Packet-switching network architecture.

and new network technologies can be incorporated with little difficulty. The system is designed to meet the goals and requirements of the defense community but is suitable for a wide variety of users, just as the Arpanet, developed for the Department of Defense, has proved suitable for the commercial environment. The research continues of course, since every accomplishment creates several additional goals.

Design Issues and Problems for Networks and Internetworks

Routing: Selecting a near-optimal path for a packet
  What are the criteria for optimality (delay, throughput, trunk efficiency)?
  How many different criteria can be used at the same time? (A type-of-service field could select one of several routing metrics.)

Addressing: Structuring and managing network addresses
  Do physical ports have addresses?
  Do hosts have addresses that are independent of the packet switches to which they are attached?
  Do hosts have multiple addresses?
  Do multiple hosts have the same address (e.g., for redundant services)?
  How do hosts discover other hosts' addresses?
  How are changes in this information propagated and synchronized?

Fault Isolation: Correcting problems
  How do we locate the problems?
  How do we confine the effects of the problem to minimize disruption to user traffic?
  How do we fix it?
  How do we bring the repaired component back "online"?

Flow Control: Regulating the flow of data into, out of, and within the network

How do we implement control of traffic flows to allocate resources fairly, so that each user obtains service?
How do we make system performance degrade gracefully when overloaded?
How do we assure enough resources for the internal management mechanisms of the network itself?
How do we reflect these control mechanisms back to the end users?

Congestion Control: Feedback to reduce traffic flow when internal components of the network are overloaded
  How is a congestion control mechanism integrated with the available flow control mechanisms?
  How are traffic flows allowed to increase after being throttled in response to congestion? Is there hysteresis?

Services Offered
  datagram
  virtual circuit (reliable byte-stream)
  guaranteed levels of service (e.g., delay, throughput, error rate)
  name/address translators
  higher level protocol translators
  user/process locator services
  broadcast or multicast capability

Internet architecture

The DARPA Internet architecture has evolved over the last five years. In the current Internet system (Figure 2), the basic architecture is defined by protocols adopted as DoD standards, namely the transmission control protocol[4] and Internet protocol.[5] The IP defines a datagram-based service that allows a host on one network to send datagrams through one or more gateways to a host on another network. Datagram delivery is not guaranteed. The TCP uses acknowledgment, retransmission, duplicate filtering, and other mechanisms to provide virtual-circuit services built on top of the datagram machinery.

Although the architecture of the Internet (Figure 3) does not require every datagram to be delivered, for efficient and high-throughput operation datagrams should not be discarded needlessly. The components of the Internet, such as the gateways, must be designed to successfully deliver a very high percentage of the datagrams presented. The TCP will compensate for datagrams that are lost, but at the cost of some increased overhead and delay.

The implementation of virtual-circuit service, whether end-to-end or network by network, is probably the most important discriminator between the DARPA interconnection approach and others, such as the X.25/X.75 scheme.[6,7] In either case, the communications system as a whole must implement mechanisms to build reliable virtual circuits on top of the less reliable raw communications media. In the X.25/X.75 approach, each network implements a virtual circuit service, and X.75 gateways plug circuits together, much like a telephone patch panel.

In the DARPA Internet, the reliability mechanisms are at a higher level, within the end-to-end host communications implemented by the TCP. Each underlying network has to provide reasonable datagram delivery service but need not implement virtual circuits. This approach has two major characteristics that are critical to the DoD community. First, it permits the use of datagram networks that would otherwise be difficult to employ. An example is the Packet Radio network technology, which allows hosts to be mobile in jeeps or aircraft and to maintain communications as the vehicle travels. Second, the approach increases robustness and reliability overall, since the gateways implement a dynamic routing procedure that will direct traffic around failures in the communications media without breaking the virtual circuits at the host level.

Since the Internet supplies a raw datagram service, applications can be supported that do not require true virtual circuits. A good example is real-time packetized speech, which does not require that all the data be delivered, but rather that a high percentage be delivered in a timely fashion. This application, by using raw datagrams, achieves the lowest possible delay with only some data loss.

In the DARPA Internet, the gateway, which was first implemented about five years ago, basically serves as a store-and-forward unit for datagrams. The early implementation, done as a research effort, was a basic gateway that performed the forwarding operations and interacted with other gateways using a routing protocol similar to that used in the early Arpanet. This implementation served the research community and was used to explore various ideas during the development of the TCP and IP.

The Internet has become increasingly operational, transitioning from a research environment, in which the users were the implementers, to a service environment, comprising a variety of US and European users who depend on it for their day-to-day communications. To support this kind of application, the gateway was completely rewritten last year to add facilities important for an operational communications system. This implementation is structured after a model of the Internet as a packet-switched network itself. Rather than simply interconnecting networks, we view gateways themselves as packet switches. In the Arpanet, the packet switch nodes or IMPs, are connected by telephone or satellite links; in the Internet, gateways are packet-switch nodes interconnected by various kinds of networks.

The recent gateway implementation was modeled after the Arpanet IMPs, which have been used in a variety of networks for over a decade. The most important mechanisms that have been added to acknowledge the operational character of the Internet are the monitoring and control mechanisms. These mechanisms, which include trap reporting, cumulative throughput measurement, status monitoring, and remote commands for control, debugging, and maintenance, have been critical to the success of the Arpanet, since they are tools to use in detecting, isolating, and repairing faults, and providing efficient management of the network as a communications system.

In the Internet, these tools are especially important. Since the reliability mechanisms for virtual circuits are implemented in the host TCPs, various failures can exist in the network without having visible effects at the user level. As long as some datagrams are successfully delivered, the TCP will keep user traffic flowing. The end-to-end user delay may increase, but for many applications such as electronic mail, no one is likely to notice. The network load may increase if datagrams are retransmitted several times before delivery, but again this may not be noticeable.

The management mechanisms within the Internet allow it to be operated and maintained as a communications system. The monitoring mechanisms used to operate the Internet on a daily basis are critical for a deployed system. The basic functionality is enough to create a system that operates in a small testbed configuration; the operations and maintenance mechanisms allow it to mature into an operational communications network. (Figure 4 shows a comparison between the Internet and a typical network.)

The Internet gateway

The Internet gateway provides a path between computer networks so that hosts on one network can communicate with hosts on another. The gateway is directly

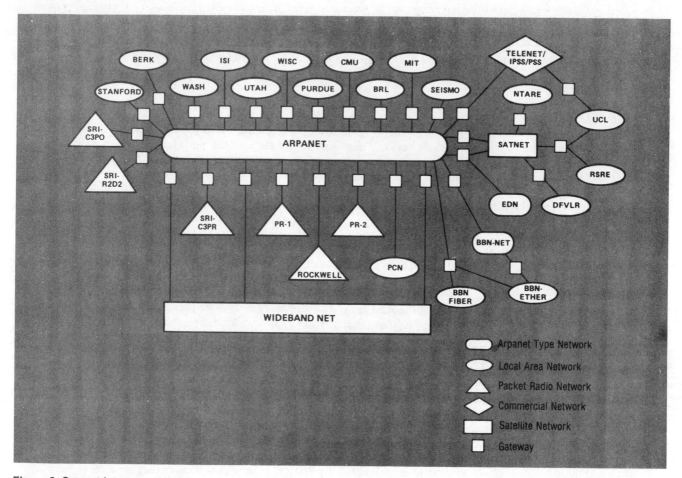

Figure 2. Current Internet system.

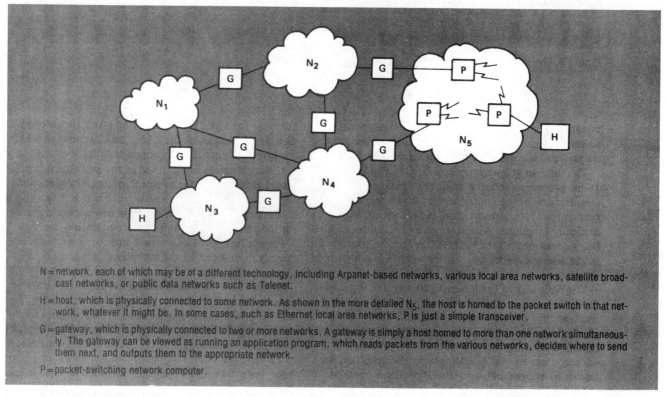

N = network, each of which may be of a different technology, including Arpanet-based networks, various local area networks, satellite broadcast networks, or public data networks such as Telenet.

H = host, which is physically connected to some network. As shown in the more detailed N_5, the host is homed to the packet switch in that network, whatever it might be. In some cases, such as Ethernet local area networks, P is just a simple transceiver.

G = gateway, which is physically connected to two or more networks. A gateway is simply a host homed to more than one network simultaneously. The gateway can be viewed as running an application program, which reads packets from the various networks, decides where to send them next, and outputs them to the appropriate network.

P = packet-switching network computer.

Figure 3. Internet architecture.

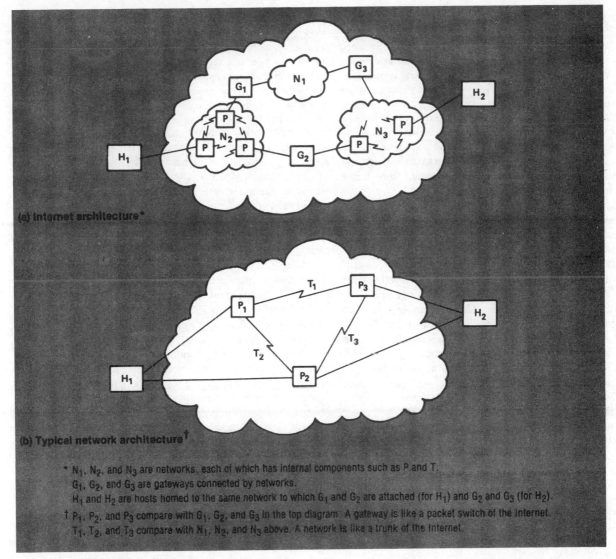

(a) Internet architecture*

(b) Typical network architecture†

* N₁, N₂, and N₃ are networks, each of which has internal components such as P and T.
    G₁, G₂, and G₃ are gateways connected by networks.
    H₁ and H₂ are hosts homed to the same network to which G₁ and G₂ are attached (for H₁) and G₂ and G₃ (for H₂).

† P₁, P₂, and P₃ compare with G₁, G₂, and G₃ in the top diagram. A gateway is like a packet switch of the Internet.
    T₁, T₂, and T₃ compare with N₁, N₂, and N₃ above. A network is like a trunk of the Internet.

Figure 4. The Internet as a network.

connected to two or more networks and supports host-to-network protocols that enable it to send and receive datagrams on each of its network interfaces.

The Internet gateway runs in a DEC PDP-11 or LSI-11 16-bit processor under a small real-time operating system. Because of the limited 16-bit address space, the current gateway implementation is written in Macro-11 assembly language. A new gateway implementation is being developed for the MC68000 processor, which has a larger address space, and will be written in a high-level language.

The basic task of the Internet gateway is to forward IP datagrams toward their destination. When a packet is received by a gateway, its local network header is checked for errors, and the gateway performs any actions required by the host-to-network protocol. If the packet contains an IP datagram, the local network header is stripped off, and the IP header is checked for validity. The destination IP address of a valid datagram is examined to determine if the datagram is for the

gateway, for a host on a network to which the gateway is directly connected, or for a host on a network to which the gateway is not directly connected.

If the datagram is addressed to the gateway, it is processed according to the protocol in the IP header. If the datagram is for a host on a network to which the gateway is connected, the gateway builds a new network header for the packet and sends it to the destination host.

Forwarding a datagram to a host on a network not directly connected to the gateway is a bit more complicated. The gateway maintains a *routing table* of all networks that can be reached through the Internet system. Each table entry contains a network number, the address of a neighbor gateway on the shortest path to the network, and the distance to the network. The distance metric is the number of "hops." A gateway is considered to be zero hops from its connected networks, one hop from networks that can be reached via one other gateway, and so on. Two gateways are neighbors if they are directly connected to a common network. The gateway will consult its routing table to choose the appropriate neighbor gateway as the next intermediate destination for the datagram. The gateway builds a new network header for the packet and maps the Internet address of the proper neighbor gateway into the local destination address of the packet. The packet is then sent toward its destination.

If the datagram is larger than the maximum packet size that the next network supports, the gateway breaks the datagram into smaller fragments, which are transported across the Internet as independent datagrams. The final destination host reassembles the fragments to re-create the original datagram.

Each host computer in the Internet system is identified by a unique 32-bit Internet address consisting of a network number assigned by the internetwork administrator and a local host address. The mapping between a host address and an Internet address is usually straightforward. For instance, the Arpanet uses 24-bit addresses that consist of a 16-bit IMP number and an eight-bit host number. The 32-bit Internet address for an Arpanet host contains the Arpanet address in the low-order, 24 bits and an eight-bit network number (which equals 10 for the Arpanet) in the high-order bits. Mapping local addresses that are greater than 32 bits, such as the 48-bit Ethernet address, is more difficult, and several address mapping schemes have been proposed—from a table lookup to dynamic address resolution protocols.

The Internet gateway system has been designed to allow new types of networks to be easily integrated. To provide gateway support for a new network type, two modules are added to the standard gateway: a device driver to support the network interface, and a module to support the network-specific host-to-network protocol. The gateway now supports the types of networks shown in Table 1.

Controlling the Internet

To provide reliable Internet service, gateways must do more then just forward datagrams. They must implement mechanisms that notify a network operations center of malformed packets, report anomalous events, and collect Internet traffic statistics. Gateways must also respond to changes in Internet topology so that new networks and gateways can be added with minimal disruption.

The Internet control message protocol[8] is used by gateways to report error and control information to Internet hosts. Hosts, in turn, interpret the information within ICMP messages to inform users about the status of the Internet. Four types of ICMP messages are used by the gateways for Internet control:

- destination unreachable,
- time exceeded,
- parameter problem, and
- redirect.

The first message type is used by a gateway to inform a source host that the destination of an IP datagram cannot be reached. The source host transmits this information to the user or program that originated the datagram so that appropriate action can be taken. For instance, if the source host is a terminal access controller, the user may receive a message such as "destination network unreachable" in response to a datagram sent to a network that either is nonexistent or cannot be reached through the Internet gateways.

Some networks, such as the Arpanet, have the ability to report host status information. ICMP provides a mechanism whereby local network status information can be transported across the Internet. A gateway can receive a status message from one of its directly connected networks indicating that a certain host is down. If the gateway then receives a datagram addressed to that host, the gateway sends a "destination host unreachable" message to the host that originated the datagram.

The second type of ICMP message takes care of packet looping, which may occasionally occur in the Internet as a result of routing transients, just as it may occur in any packet-switching network. The "time to live" field in the IP header is designed to limit the lifetime of looping packets. The source host sets the time to live field by estimating the number of gateways through which the datagram will pass. Whenever a gateway forwards a datagram, the time to live field is decremented by one. If a gateway receives a datagram that has a time to live field of zero, the datagram is dropped and a "time exceeded" message is sent to the host that originated the datagram. This procedure does not eliminate packet looping altogether, but it does ensure that looping packets are dropped after a short time.

The "parameter problem" message is used by a gateway to notify a host that it is sending datagrams with Internet headers containing incorrect parameters. Of course, if the Internet header is so broken that the source address field cannot be trusted (if the Internet checksum is incorrect, for instance), the gateway cannot return any message to the Internet source and just sends a report to the Internet network operations center.

Some networks have a large number of directly connected gateways. A host may not always choose the gateway on the shortest path to a destination network. The gateway uses the ICMP "redirect" message to advise a host to send its traffic for a given network directly to another gateway that has a shorter path to the destination, as indicated in the routing table.

**Table 1.
Internet network characteristics.**

Network Type	Message Size (bytes)	Speed*	Delay†	Guaranteed Delivery	Notes
Arpanet	1008	Medium	Medium	Yes	— —
Satnet	256	Low	High	No	Satellite Network
Pronet	2048	High	Low	Yes	Local Area Net
Ethernet	1500	High	Low	Yes	Local Area Net
Telenet	128	Low	Medium	Yes	Public Network
Packet Radio	254	Medium	Medium	No	Varying Topology
Wideband	2000	High	High	No	Satellite Network

* Low speed is less than 100K bits/sec.
Medium speed is 100K bits/sec to 1M bits/sec.
High speed is greater than 1M bits/sec.

† Low delay is less than 50 ms.
Medium delay is 50 ms to 500 ms.
High delay is greater than 500 ms.

In addition to these four types of ICMP messages, ICMP echo and echo reply, information requests and reply, and timestamp messages are used by hosts for a variety of functions, such as determining the round-trip delay across the Internet.

Gateway routing

Gateways use the gateway-to-gateway protocol[9] to determine connectivity to both networks and neighbor gateways, and to implement a dynamic, shortest path routing algorithm.

A gateway periodically sends GGP echo packets to each of its neighbor gateways to determine which neighbors are up. If a neighbor gateway fails to respond to several echo requests, it will be declared down. Connectivity to networks is determined in a similar manner. A gateway periodically sends GGP packets, called interface probes, addressed to itself to each network interface. If the network does not send back several of these probes, it is considered to be down. After several probes are successfully received, the network is considered to be up again.

Whenever a gateway detects a change in Internet topology, such as when a network interface goes down, the gateway sends a GGP "routing update" packet to each of its neighbors. The routing update contains an entry for each network indicating the address and distance of the gateway on the shortest path to the network. When a gateway receives a routing update from one of its neighbors, it recalculates its routing table to ensure that it uses the gateway on the shortest path to each network when it forwards datagrams.

Gateways dynamically learn about new neighbors and new networks. Each gateway maintains a list of neighbor gateway addresses. When a routing update is received, a gateway searches its list of addresses for the Internet source address of the routing update packet. If the Internet source address of the routing update is not contained in the list of neighbor addresses, the gateway adds this address to its neighbor address table. In this strategy of adding new neighbors, only one gateway in each pair of neighbor gateways must have the neighbor's address configured in its tables. The newest gateway is given a complete list of neighbors, so operational gateways do not have to be reconfigured when new gateways are installed. If a gateway receives a routing update that contains information about a new network, it adds this network to its routing table and forwards datagrams to the new network.

Monitoring and controlling gateways

Monitoring the operation of the gateways is an important element to ensure the operation of the Internet system. Because gateways interconnect the networks making up the Internet system, they provide information that shows when gateways, networks, hosts, or even interfaces are or are not working correctly. As a result, monitoring the gateways is, in fact, monitoring the whole Internet system.

Host monitoring protocol. The gateways are monitored using an Internet protocol called the host monitoring protocol,[10] which provides mechanisms to collect various types of performance data and status information from the gateways. The HMP is also used to monitor other types of machines in the Internet, such as Arpanet IMPs and TACs.

The HMP is built around the idea that most of the intelligence needed to monitor a gateway should reside in a monitoring center, not in the gateway. The gateway should be required only to collect data and send them to the monitoring center either spontaneously or on request. It is not responsible for ensuring that the data arrive reliably (except that it must checksum the data). Rather, the monitoring center is responsible for ensuring that data requested are received correctly.

Consequently, the HMP is used to poll gateways for messages. When the monitoring center requires a particular type of data (e.g., throughput data), it sends a poll to the gateway requesting that type of report. The gateway, upon receiving the poll, responds with its latest set of collected data. If the gateway finds that the poll is incorrect, that is if the poll was for throughput data and the gateway is not collecting throughput data, it responds with an error message. The monitoring center waits a reasonable length of time for the gateway to answer its poll. If no response is received, it sends another poll for the same data. In this way, if either a poll or the response is lost, the correct data are still collected.

The HMP is used to collect three kinds of data: spontaneous events (or traps), current status, and statistical data collected over time. Reports of spontaneous events, called traps, are sent to the monitoring center as they occur. A trap consists of a number to identify which event is being reported, the local time it occurred in the gateway, and some data pertinent to the event. The delivery of traps is not intended to be perfectly reliable, since the gateway has no mechanism to retransmit a trap. For trap reporting, simplicity and promptness have been traded for complete reliability.

An example of collected trap reports is shown in Figure 5. Each report includes the time at which the trap was received, the name and number of the gateway that sent it, the identifier of the trap, and the text. The complete text of the trap is not sent by the gateway to the monitoring center, only the raw data. The monitoring center has text associated with each trap identifier and substitutes the data received with the trap in the appropriate place in the text. For instance, in the first trap in Figure 5, which shows a gateway declaring a neighbor gateway up, the text "10.2.0.25" is the information received with the trap—in this case, the Internet address of the neighbor gateway. The monitoring center looked up the name associated with the address and output the name and the address.

The first 1010 trap, line 3 of the 10:39 trap report in Figure 5, shows a gateway reporting a redirect trap. This information indicates that a host on the Arpanet (10.0.0.27) has sent a datagram to the RCC gateway to

```
    Mon Aug 23 1982

    10:39        GWY    R2D2    13    T2004:    Neighbor LOGEX 10.2.0.25 up
                 GWY    DCEC    15    T2004:    Neighbor LOGEX 10.2.0.25 up
                 GWY    RCC      1    T1010:    RDR: 10.0.0.27→9.0.16.24 via LOGEX 10.2.0.25
                 GWY    RCC      1    T1010:    RDR: 10.0.0.27→11.3.1.42 via BBN 10.3.0.40
                 GWY    C3PO    14    T1107:    PRCHK: Bad pkt length = 0.
                 GWY    R2D2    13    T1000:    Pkt drp-rfnm blk, dest: ISIE 10.1.0.52 (2.)
    10:40        GWY    RCC      1    T1010:    RDR: 10.0.0.27→21.0.0.2 via DCEC 10.3.0.20
                 GWY    RCC      1    T1010:    RDR: 10.0.0.27→35.6.0.0 via BBN 10.3.0.40
```

Figure 5. Sample gateway trap report.

reach a host on network 9 (9.0.16.24). However, the RCC gateway does not have a direct connection to network 9, but the LOGEX gateway does. Upon receiving the datagram addressed to network 9, the RCC gateway forwarded the datagram to the LOGEX gateway and sent an ICMP redirect message to the source of the datagram advising it to use the LOGEX gateway as a better route to network 9.

The 1107 trap indicates that the C3PO gateway received a datagram with a bad length, in this case zero. The gateway discarded this packet. The next trap in the figure, 1000, indicates that the R2D2 gateway reported that it discarded two datagrams because an Arpanet flow control limit was reached for datagrams destined for the ISIE host.

The second type of data collected using the host monitoring protocol is status information. Gateway status information consists of the version number of the gateway, network interface status, buffer resources, and gateway neighbor status. Status information is useful at one point, but it does not have to be collected cumulatively over a certain time period. Only the latest status is of interest; old status provides no useful information. The monitoring center collects status information by sending a status poll to a gateway. Upon receiving the poll, the gateway responds with its latest status information, always creating a new status message. If the monitoring center does not receive a response to its poll, it sends another poll. If the monitor does not receive any responses to its polls, it will declare the gateway to be down. A typical status report is shown in Figure 6.

The third type of data the host monitoring protocol is used to collect is statistical data. These are measurements taken over time, such as the number of packets sent or received by a gateway and the count of packets dropped for a particular reason—and none of these data can be lost. When the collection time interval expires, current data are copied to another area, and the counters are cleared. The copied data are sent to the monitoring center when the gateway receives a poll requesting statistical information. If another poll is received before the collection time interval has expired, the data in the buffer are sent again. The monitoring center can detect duplicate messages by using the sequence number with the data, since each type of statistical data has its own sequence number counter.

Two types of statistical data, throughput and host traffic matrix, are collected in the gateways. Throughput reports comprise counts of datagrams sent from a gate-

way, dropped, forwarded, etc. A typical example of a weekly gateway throughput summary is shown in Figure 7. The host traffic matrix counts the number of datagrams that each host in the Internet sends to another host as the datagrams pass through the gateways. These data allow us to find out which hosts send the most traffic, where it goes, and through which gateways. The information is useful in deciding where and when to add more capacity in the Internet system.

Internet network operations center. The gateways are monitored from the Internet Network Operations Center, which is based on a monitoring system called

```
Gateway 1 BBN 10.3.0.72 (Arpanet)   Mon Jun 13 15:25:55 1983

Version 1004

Last restart: 6/5 17:28
Measurement on: THR
RUP sequence number = 016721
Memory: 7650 bytes in use, 12700 bytes idle, 318 bytes free

Interfaces:
    UP:  BBN 10.3.0.72 (Arpanet) (since 6/9 16:05)
              output q: 2, allocated: 9, data size: 1008

    UP: BBN 8.3.0.8 (BBN-net) (since 6/7 05:53)
              output q: 0, allocated: 9, data size: 1008

Buffer Pools:
    Pool 1:    20 bytes, 12 allocated,  8 idle
    Pool 2:    82 bytes, 13 allocated, 11 idle
    Pool 3: 1058 bytes, 18 allocated, 11 idle

Neighbors:
      UP:  FIBER 8.3.0.14 (BBN-net)
      UP:  DCEC 10.1.0.20 (Arpanet)
      UP:  CSS 10.2.0.25 (Arpanet)
      UP:  ISI 10.3.0.27 (Arpanet)
      UP:  PURDUE 10.2.0.37 (Arpanet)
      UP:  BRAGG 10.0.0.38 (Arpanet)
      UP:  CRONUS 10.1.0.49 (Arpanet)
    DOWN:  C3PO 10.1.0.51 (Arpanet)
      UP   R2D2 10.3.0.51 (Arpanet)
    DOWN:  C3PR 10.3.4.51 (Arpanet)
      UP:  WISC 10.0.0.94 (Arpanet)
      UP:  CIT 10.1.0.54 (Arpanet)
      UP:  VAN 10.0.0.63 (Arpanet)
    DOWN:  MINET 10.3.0.40 (Arpanet)
    DOWN:  MIT 10.0.0.77 (Arpanet)
      UP:  DCN 10.3.0.17 (Arpanet)
```

Figure 6. Sample gateway status report.

GWY NO.	GWY NAME	RCVD DGRAMS	RCVD BYTES	IP ERRORS	% IP ERRORS	DEST UNRCH	% DST UNRCH
1	BBN	6,116,586	261,409,066	1,064	0.02%	49,011	0.80%
2	CSS	1,848,089	64,402,782	1,026	0.06%	4,393	0.24%
3	UCL	649,223	32,061,290	0	0.00%	4,256	0.66%
4	NTARE	547,871	24,013,188	2	0.00%	425	0.08%
7	BRAGG	1,391,300	41,700,610	912	0.07%	4,006	0.29%
8	SAC	1,256,077	38,039,348	944	0.08%	67	0.00%
11	VAN	585,305	15,690,976	250	0.04%	1,299	0.22%
13	R2D2	1,386,622	39,693,372	1,062	0.08%	441	0.03%
14	C3PO	381,025	11,288,970	273	0.07%	25	0.00%
15	DCEC	2,662,742	98,096,188	2,076	0.08%	38,988	1.46%
22	PURDUE	1,383,770	38,538,541	983	0.07%	60	0.00%
23	CRONUS	2,525,387	90,002,975	2,459	0.10%	4,710	0.19%
25	WISC	1,746,462	51,485,898	985	0.06%	2,485	0.14%
31	C3PR	132,702	6,311,450	93	0.07%	0	0.00%
32	MINET	70,414	1,913,046	0	0.00%	2	0.00%
33	ISI	1,282,716	38,575,622	800	0.06%	1,956	0.15%
35	FIBER	2,938,534	133,874,931	718	0.02%	3,739	0.13%
TOTALS		26,904,825	987,098,253	13,647	0.05%	115,863	0.43%

GWY NO.	GWY NAME	SENT DGRAMS	SENT BYTES	DROPPED DGRAMS	% IP DROPPED DGRAMS
1	BBN	6,310,866	254,894,792	119,290	1.86%
2	CSS	2,154,639	70,559,454	6,514	0.30%
3	UCL	698,184	33,521,754	164	0.02%
4	NTARE	626,733	27,331,265	1,696	0.27%
7	BRAGG	1,564,313	43,489,127	943	0.06%
8	SAC	1,303,732	36,615,005	734	0.06%
11	VAN	626,731	16,090,557	208	0.03%
13	R2D2	1,578,736	41,256,008	8,143	0.51%
14	C3PO	389,580	11,334,163	2,929	0.75%
15	DCEC	2,947,093	105,308,427	18,067	0.61%
22	PURDUE	1,526,556	39,014,247	879	0.06%
23	CRONUS	2,624,362	87,922,290	14,849	0.56%
25	WISC	1,922,022	53,077,784	4,050	0.21%
31	C3PR	140,122	6,047,968	1,117	0.79%
32	MINET	78,251	2,051,666	0	0.00%
33	ISI	1,384,820	40,134,323	5,572	0.40%
35	FIBER	3,005,389	132,597,682	8,403	0.28%

Figure 7. Sample gateway throughput report.

NU. The NU system runs under the Unix operating system on a BBN C/70 computer.[11] In addition to the gateways, NU systems are currently being used to monitor other networks and hosts, including the Arpanet, the Atlantic satellite network (Satnet), the wideband network, and terminal access controllers.

The NU system consists of a number of processes, some of which provide general services such as receiving messages from networks, while others are specific to each type of entity being monitored. In particular, a process is responsible for sending the host monitoring protocol polls to gateways and other machines monitored by that protocol. Other specific gateway processes collect the gateway throughput data and perform detailed status processing such as keeping track of software version numbers, measurements enabled, interface status, and neighbor gateway status.

The INOC is part of the larger Network Operations Center at BBN Computer Corporation in Cambridge, Massachusetts. It is operated and staffed 24 hours a day, seven days a week. Information from the NOC is quite useful in correlating gateway operations problems, with events in those networks also being monitored by the NOC. Of particular importance is information about the Arpanet, which is in some ways the backbone of the Internet system.

An important feature of gateway monitoring and control is that gateways do not need the INOC to run and work correctly. Although the gateways send reports to the INOC, if the INOC is down for some reason, the gateways will continue to operate. The INOC diagnoses and repairs problems such as broken hardware, faulty lines, or inoperative networks. It does not, for instance, tell the gateways how to route traffic to a particular network.

Gateways of the future

The Internet architecture has been developed by a team of researchers from industry, universities, and several governments. The current system is a stable, operational communications system that supports remote host and file access and electronic mail facilities.

Experimental services are also in daily use within the Internet. Packet voice, facsimile, video graphics, and multimedia mail and teleconferencing testbeds are being developed and tested. Many of these future applications depend on the existence of the datagram-oriented service for efficiency and low delay. As file access, remote host access, and electronic mail facilities have grown from experimental services to cornerstones of network activity, so will current experimental services see increased use in the coming years.

The Internet datagram transport service is the foundation for these services. The gateway that implements the service has progressed from a relatively simple real-time communications processor to a more sophisticated system with many gateway processors interacting with each other and the INOC to implement a communications facility used daily by a growing community.

The future of the gateway, and hence the Internet datagram transport service, is likely to progress along several fronts. As the system has evolved and as users have invented new ways to use the services offered, numerous issues have been uncovered. These issues fall into two rather broad categories, growth and functionality.

In the early stages of the Internet project, projections of dozens of networks were received with some disbelief. Surely only a few long-haul networks would be needed to support the several hosts that any site might have. Now we have somewhere between 50 and 100 physically real, active networks in the system. TCP implementations exist or are in progress for mainframes as well as microprocessors, promising hundreds, or more likely thousands, of additional hosts in the next few years.

Many issues must be dealt with, such as addressing, routing protocols, resource management, and access control, to cope with this kind of growth in any packet-switching system. Some of these, such as the addressing techniques, are handled as part of the protocols, especially TCP and IP. For gateways, the major concern lies in the routing machinery, always one of the most sensitive and complicated mechanisms in a network.

In the Arpanet, the routing mechanisms underwent several stages of evolution as the network grew from a few nodes to a hundred. Arpanet technology is, in fact, supporting hundreds of nodes within a single network. The technique being investigated to support thousands of nodes is called *area routing,* since separate areas are created within the network. In this technique, routing within an area is managed separately from routing between areas, and we expect to apply similar techniques to the Internet gateways. Our approach is to create areas of the Internet, with each area containing a number of networks and hosts and areas interacting via a separate routing protocol.

In addition to addressing raw growth, this routing approach will enable separate systems of gateways to coexist, gateways that have been built and are maintained by different implementation groups. We have learned this capability from experience in operating the current Internet system, in which various gateways are not all identical, but include implementations by four or five separate organizations, all obeying a common protocol for the exchange of routing information.

This structure has several benefits: it permits innovation by allowing new ideas, and it allows support for new or experimental networks to be provided quickly, since the network developers can also implement an appropriate gateway. In the current gateway protocol architecture, however, we have identified some basic disadvantages. The primary concern arises when a gateway fails somewhere in the Internet due to either a hardware fault or an unexpected response to a condition or event in the network. Since networks are very complex, we cannot test implementations in all foreseeable situations. Therefore, we must expect some aberrant behavior.

Error-handling in Internet involves three procedures: detect, isolate, and repair. Of these, isolate is the most difficult.

Mechanisms for operating the network depend on a three-stage procedure: detect, isolate, and repair. In a system under single control, these three processes are relatively straightforward. In a system involving multiple implementers, detection is also often straightforward, but isolation is much more difficult. Networks, especially dynamic routing mechanisms, are highly complex systems, and a failure in one location might manifest itself in an apparently totally unrelated location.

In addition to handling growth, the area routing approach permits separate areas to coexist in one Internet, with the boundaries employing protocols that implement "firewalls" between the systems. Research in this area is progressing rapidly. An initial step toward such a mechanism is an exterior gateway protocol,[12] now in the final stages of design, that will permit various implementations to coexist in popular configurations. For example, a long-haul transport Internet involving several land and satellite networks may have user sites connected via the EGP. Each user site might have a complex local system using multiple local area networks and gateways that could be locally implemented and maintained.

The other major area for future activities is supplying additional capabilities. We expect to expand and improve the monitoring and control mechanisms significantly, since the operation of a system with several hundred nodes is much more demanding than that of a smaller configuration. One improvement will be to make monitoring functions better at determining why a gateway is not working (e.g., is it really down or just isolated because its associated network is not working).

Other additions will probably take the form of increased services. All datagrams are now handled identically by the gateways, although parameters such as speed or reliability may be signaled to the underlying networks. To handle a mix of real-time traffic, such as character traffic and speech streams, as well as bulk traffic such as file transfers and electronic mail, many kinds of service will be needed within the gateways. This additional service should increase the efficiency of the communications system as a whole.

Support for additional types of networks will also be provided as we see new networks or as we receive demands for gateways to networks. One significant advantage of the DARPA Internet is the relative ease with which networks can be supported. Since the basic requirements placed on any network are so minimal, most network technologies can be easily integrated into the system. The ones implemented to date have required only a month or two to put in a new driver package.

The DARPA Internet has implemented protocols and mechanisms so that a variety of networks can be used to supply communications and to provide connectivity between users, regardless of what network supports them. BBN Computer Corporation has been responsible for the development, installation, and operational support of the gateways that make up the core of the Internet system. Like the Arpanet and other networks, the gateways have progressed through several phases of research and implementation. The earlier implementations were research-oriented and were used to evaluate various approaches to Internet functionality. Over the last year, we have reimplemented the software base entirely to orient it toward the needs of an operational user community. The Internet system currently interconnects dozens of networks, providing an integrated communications service to a large and growing user community in the US and Europe. ∎

Acknowledgments

This work was sponsored by the Defense Advanced Research Projects Agency in part under ARPA order no. 3214, contract no. MDA903-80-C-0353 and ARPA order no. 4726, contract no. MDA903-83-C-0131, which were monitored by the Defense Supply Service, Washington.

References

1. V. Cerf and R. Kahn, "A Protocol for Packet Network Intercommunication," *IEEE Trans. Communications,* Vol. C-22, No. 5, May 1974, pp. 637-648.

2. V. Cerf, "The Catenet Model for Internetworking," IEN-48, Information Processing Techniques Office, Defense Advanced Research Projects Agency, July 1978.

3. A. Sheltzer and R. Hinden, "Connecting Different Types of Networks with Gateways," *Data Communications,* Vol. 11, No. 8, Aug. 1982, pp. 111-121.

4. "DoD Standard Transmission Control Protocol," ACM *Computer Communication Review,* Vol. 10, No. 4, Oct. 1980.

5. "DoD Standard Internet Protocol," *ACM Computer Communication Review,* Vol. 10, No. 4, Oct. 1980.

6. "CCITT Recommendation X.25, Interface Between Data Terminal Equipment and Data Circuit Terminating Equipment for Terminals Operating in the Packet Mode on Public Data Networks," *CCITT Yellow Book,* Vol. 8, Fascicle VIII.2.

7. "CCITT Recommendation X.75, Terminal and Transit Call Control Procedures and Data Transfer System on International Circuits Between Packet-Switched Data Networks," *CCITT Yellow Book,* Vol. 8, Fascicle VIII.3.

8. J. Postel, *Internet Control Message Protocol—DARPA Internet Program Protocol Specification,* RFC 792, USC/Information Sciences Institute, Los Angeles, Sept. 1981.

9. R. Hinden and A. Sheltzer, *The DARPA Internet Gateway,* RFC 823, Bolt Beranek and Newman Inc., Cambridge, Mass., Sept. 1982.

10. B. Littauer, A. Huang, and R. Hinden, *A Host Monitoring Protocol,* IEN-197, Bolt Beranek and Newman Inc., Cambridge, Mass., Sept. 1981.

11. P. Santos et al., "Architecture of a Network Monitoring, Control and Management System," *Proc. Fifth Int'l Conf. Computer Communication,* Oct. 1980.

12. E. Rosen, *Exterior Gateway Protocol,* IEN-209, Bolt Beranek and Newman Inc., Cambridge, Mass., Aug. 1982.

Robert Hinden has been a member of the technical staff at the BBN Computer Corporation since 1978. He is currently project manager of the Internet project, in which the current Internet gateway was developed. The project is now addressing the design of a new multiprocessor gateway. He has previously been responsible for the development of the Arpanet terminal access controller and the Pluribus terminal interface message processor. Prior to joining BBN, he held positions with the Computervision Corporation and the General Electric Company.

Hinden received a BSEE in 1972 and an MS in computer science in 1973, both from Union College in Schenectady, New York. He is a member of the IEEE Computer Society.

Jack Haverty is a program manager at the BBN Computer Corporation, where he has worked on projects in internetwork design and implementation and network security since 1977. He was also involved in the design of the DoD Internetwork protocols and did one of the first implementations for a PDP-11 Unix environment. He is now responsible for a number of ongoing projects in the design and implementation of networks, gateways, and network applications, for both government and commercial network installations.

Prior to joining BBN, Haverty was a member of the research staff at the MIT Laboratory for Computer Science for six years, and was involved in a number of different research projects in the Arpanet environment, such as computer network mail. He received a BSEE and MSEE from MIT in 1971.

Alan Sheltzer is working toward a PhD in distributed operating systems at UCLA. At the BBN Computer Corporation, he was involved in the design and implementation of the Internet gateway system and the Pluribus terminal interface message processor. He received a BA in physics from Brandeis University in 1975 and an MS in computer science from the University of Southern California in 1979.

COMPUTER

X.75 Internetworking of Datapac with Other Packet Switched Networks

Dr. Mehmet S. Unsoy

TransCanada Telephone System

ABSTRACT   In 1980, an agreement was reached by the International Telegraph and Telephone Consultative Committee (CCITT) defining the standards for the interconnection of Public Packet Switched Data Networks (PPSDNs). The CCITT Recommendation X.75 describes the standards for the internetwork signaling procedures for the interconnection of these networks. The Datapac™ network and several other PPSDNs have already implemented the X.75 procedures. This paper discusses the methodology used and the operating experience gained by the introduction of X.75 interfaces between Datapac and other PPSDNs, including GTE Telenet and Tymnet in the U.S.A., Teleglobe in Canada, PSS and IPSS in the U.K., Datex-P in the Federal Republic of Germany, KDD and NTT in Japan, and Transpac in France. First, the X.75 internetworking procedures are explained briefly. Next, those aspects of X.75 interfaces that have to be bilaterally negotiated between the network administrations are outlined; the technical agreements reached between Datapac and other networks are summarized. The last part of this paper covers the Datapac's experience in testing X.75 interconnections, both at the interface level and end-to-end, with other PPSDNs.

1. Introduction

Several public data networks based on packet switching technology have been operational around the world. Some of these are Datapac™ in Canada, GTE Telenet and Tymnet in the U.S.A., PSS and IPSS in U.K., Transpac in France, KDD and NTT in Japan, and Datex-P in West Germany. Many more such networks are currently being developed in a large number of countries [1].

By interconnecting these Public Packet Switched Data Networks (PPSDNs), international data services are offered to network users. Before any standards were reached for internetworking, interim gateways were installed to connect these public networks [2], thus achieving early introduction of international packet switched data network services.

International Telegraph and Telephone Consultative Committee (CCITT), a permanent organ of the International Telecommuni-

cations Union, (ITU) has agreed upon the Recommendation X.75, which is an internetwork signaling procedure for the interconnection of PPSDNs [3, 4].

Datapac and several other PPSDNs have implemented the CCITT X.75 procedures to interconnect with other networks [5, 6]. Datapac has established direct X.75 interconnections with the GTE Telenet and Tymnet in the U.S.A. Through the IPACS (International Packet-Switched System) transit network services of Teleglobe Canada, Datapac has also interconnected, via X.75, with IPSS and PSS of U.K., Transpac of France, Datex-P of West Germany, KDD and NTT of Japan, Ireland, Italy, Switzerland, and Austria for two-way and over 20 other countries for one-way (incoming only) traffic. This paper discusses the operating experience in introducing these X.75 interfaces between Datapac and the other PPSDNs.

This section also gives a brief description of

0276-0037/82/0103-239-13$4.55/0   © Computer Science Press, Inc.

Reprinted from the *Journal of Telecommunication Networks*, Volume 1, Number 3, Fall 1982, with the permission of the publisher Computer Science Press, Inc., 11 Taft Court, Rockville, MD 20850, USA.

Datapac and the interim interconnections with other PPSDNs prior to X.75. Section 2 provides an outline of Recommendation X.75 internetworking procedures.

CCITT Recommendation X.75 and other standards provide several options for PPSDN internetworking. There are also several internetworking issues that are left to bilateral and/or multilateral discussions and negotiations between the networks involved. Section 3 describes the characteristics of Datapac's X.75 interfaces in terms of these options and agreements reached between Datapac and other PPSDNs.

The X.75 interfaces between PPSDNs must be tested thoroughly before they are introduced into commercial service. The series of tests conducted by Datapac and other PPSDNs and the experience gained by these tests are the subject of Section 4.

1.1 Datapac Overview. Datapac is a public packet switched data communications network operated by the Computer Communications Group (CCG) of the TransCanada Telephone System (TCTS). The basic service offers the ability to set up a virtual circuit between a pair of Data Terminal Equipments (DTEs). At the end of 1982, the network topology consists of thirty-six packet switching nodes interconnected in a mesh of fifty-six Kbps digital transmission facilities and providing service to sixty-six Datapac Serving Areas across Canada (Figure 1). Each node consists of the SL-10 packet switch developed by Bell Northern Research and manufactured by Northern Telecom Ltd. The SL-10 is a multi-microprocessor which can be modularly extended to support the required number of access lines and a mix of software-based access services [7].

The Datapac network provides a number of access services. The main service is based on Recommendation X.25 of CCITT [8], and supports access from packet-mode Data Terminating Equipments (DTEs). Another Datapac service allows ASCII start-stop terminals to access the network in accordance with CCITT Recommendations X.3, X.28 and X.29 [9]. Other access services have also been designed for electronic cash registers, pollable teletypewriters, IBM 3270- compatible devices, HASP multileaving, and IBM 2780-compatible remote job entry workstations.

The Datapac network went into commercial service in June 1977, and in May 1978 Datapac started international data communications services with GTE Telenet and Tymnet in the U.S.A. The interconnections were achieved through the interim gateways implemented on

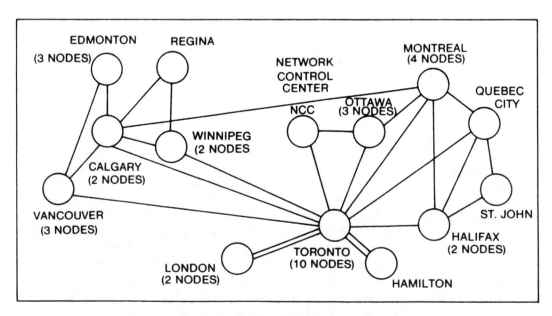

Figure 1. Datapac Network Topology.

minicomputers, connected to networks via CCITT X.25 interfaces [2]. The Datapac international overseas service was inaugurated in January, 1980 through an interim gateway, developed by Teleglobe Canada, connected to Datapac via an X.25 interface. Teleglobe Canada maintains a transit packet switched network (IPACS), administering calls between Canadian and overseas networks.

The configuration of the interim connections between Datapac and other PPSDNs, prior to the introduction of X.75 interfaces, is shown in Figure 2 [10]. These interim gateways proved to be very useful, not only to support the ever increasing international traffic between Datapac and other PPSDNs, but also to provide us with expertise in internetworking.

2. X.75 Internetworking

CCITT Study Group VII defined the Recommendation X.75 in 1978 to accomplish the interconnection of PPSDNs. The revised version of this recommendation was approved by CCITT in February 1980 [3]. CCITT has also established the International Numbering Plan for public data networks in the Recommendation X.121 [11]. This section briefly describes

the X.75 procedures and X.121 based international addressing.

2.1 X.75 Procedures. The CCITT Recommendation X.75 defines procedures at the interface between two stations called Signaling Terminal Equipments (STEs) (Figure 3). Similar to the CCITT Recommendation X.25 [8], which defines the procedures between a Data Terminating Equipment (DTE) and a Data Circuit-Terminating Equipment (DCE), the X.75 procedures are specified at three distinct levels:

1. Physical Level
2. Link Level
3. Packet Level

The Physical Level defines the electrical and functional characteristics of the interface between two STEs. The transmission link is a full duplex, point-to-point, high speed synchronous circuit.

The Link Level specifies the use of the data Link Access Procedure-Balanced (LAPB) which is compatible with the High-level Data Link Control (HDLC) specified by the Interna-

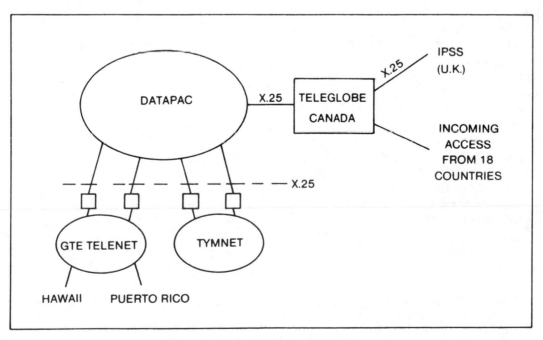

Figure 2. Datapac Interim Connections.

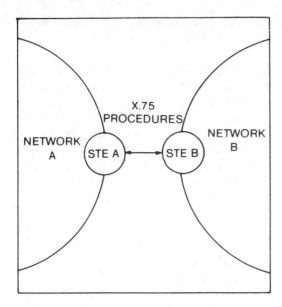

Figure 3. X.75 Interconnection.

tional Organization for Standardization (ISO) [12]. The Link Level procedures guarantee that packets provided by the Packet Level and contained in HDLC information frames are accurately exchanged between the STEs of two PPSDNs.

The Link Level procedures for X.75 are similar to Link Level procedures of X.25. However, in Recommendation X.75, the procedures for a link over a single physical circuit is called Single Link Procedure (SLP). In addition to SLP, X.75 defines the Multi-Link Procedure (MLP) which allows multiple parallel links, each using SLP independently, for a single X.75 interface.

According to Recommendation X.75, each SLP can use either modulo 8 or modulo 128 frame sequence numbering, thus allowing for the efficient use of satellite circuits between PPSDNs.

The Packet Level defines procedures by which switched Virtual Calls (VCs) are established, maintained, and cleared across the X.75 interface. The CCITT X.75 Recommendation does not allow permanent virtual circuits.

The Packet Level also specifies the manner in which control information and user data are structured into packets. The procedures and the packet formats for X.75 are very similar to those of X.25. The X.75 Call Request and

Call Connected packet formats contain an additional field, called network utilities, which are used for signaling network-oriented information between the STEs. The call establishment and clearing procedures are described in Section 2.2, data transfer in Section 2.3, and network utilities in Section 2.4.

2.2 X.75 Call Establishment and Clearing.
An STE initiates a call by transmitting a Call Request packet across the X.75 interface. The format of the X.75 Call Request packet is shown in Figure 4.

The General Format Identifier (GFI) field indicates the format of the rest of the header, including Qualifier (Q) bit and Delivery confirmation (D) bit settings and frame sequence numbering scheme. The Logical Channel Group Number (LCGN) and the Logical Channel Number (LCN) are chosen by the STE to be used to identify all packets associated with the call across the X.75 interface. The third

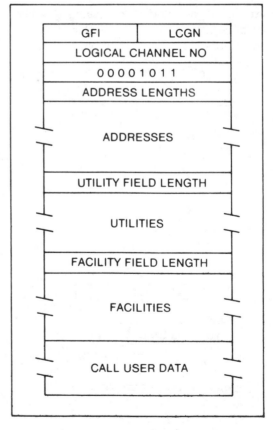

Figure 4. X.75 Call Request Packet.

octet of the header contains the bit pattern that defines the packet type.

The Call Request packet also includes the calling and called DTE addresses or international data numbers as defined in CCITT Recommendation X.121 [11]. The network utility, user facility, and call user data fields follow. The network utilities and their use are discussed in Section 2.4. The user facility field may be used to exchange user facilities requested by a DTE, as described in CCITT Recommendation X.25. The user data field may be a maximum of 16 octets in length, or 128 octets in length if the Fast Select optional user facility [8] is requested.

The calling STE will receive a Call Connected packet if the called STE can accept the call. The format of the Call Connected packet is identical to the format of the Call Request packet, except that the call user data field may be present only if Fast Select optional user facility is requested.

If the called STE cannot accept the call, then it sends to the calling STE an X.75 Clear Request packet containing the logical channel number, an appropriate clear cause (or Call Progress Signal) as specified in CCITT Recommendation X.96 [13], and a one-octet diagnostic code.

After the call is established, either STE may send an X.75 Clear Request packet to indicate the termination of the call. When an STE receives an X.75 Clear Request packet, it frees the logical channel and transmits, across the X.75 interface, an X.75 Clear Confirmation packet specifying the same logical channel number.

2.3 Data Transfer. The Data packets can be transferred across a logical channel, after the virtual call is established.

Each Data packet conveys a packet send sequence number and a packet receive sequence number. The Data packets are numbered either modulo 8 or modulo 128. The maximum number of sequentially numbered Data packets that the STE may be authorized to transmit without further authorization from the remote STE is called the window size, W. The window size for the virtual call is negotiated at the call setup time using the utility described in Section 2.4.

The packet receive sequence number, carried on the Data packet, authorizes the transmission of W Data packets on this logical channel starting with a send sequence number equal to the value of this receive sequence number. When the STE wishes to authorize the transmission of one or more Data packets, but there is no data flow on a given logical channel in the reverse direction on which to piggyback this information, it can transmit a Receive Ready (RR) packet. If the STE wishes only to confirm a Data packet but not to authorize the transmission of any more data, it can transmit a Receive Not Ready (RNR) packet. Flow control based on the conveyance of packet receive sequence numbers ensures that a sender does not transmit data at an average rate which is greater than that at which the receiver can accept that data.

The data field of a Data packet may be any length up to some maximum value. Every STE will support a maximum value of 128 octets. Other values can be signaled and negotiated via the utility field as described in Section 2.4.

2.4 X.75 Network Utilities. The CCITT Recommendation X.75 defines several network utilities in order that network-oriented information may be signaled in the Call Request and Call Connected Packets between the STEs. These utilities are:

- Transit Network Identification
- Call Identifier
- Throughput Class Indication
- Window Size Indication
- Packet Size Indication
- Fast Select Indication
- Closed User Group Indication
- Closed User Group with Outgoing Access Indication
- Reverse Charging Indication
- Traffic Class Indication
- Estimated Transit Delay
- Tariff
- Utility Marker

The **Transit Network Identification** is a network utility used to name a transit network controlling a portion of the (perhaps partially established) virtual call. A transit network is identified by the first four digits of the international data number, as described in Section 2.5.

The **Call Identifier** utility is used to uniquely identify the call by all the networks involved, for accounting, auditing, and trouble reporting purposes.

The **Throughput Class Indication** utility is used for negotiating the throughput classes applying to that call. A throughput class is an indication of maximum throughput, in bits per second, requested by a given virtual call in each direction of transmission.

The **Window Size Indication** is a network utility used by the STE for negotiating the window sizes for both directions of transmission over the X.75 interface for a given virtual call. The standard value to be supported by all PPSDNs is 2.

The **Packet Size Indication** utility is used by the STE for negotiating the maximum data field length of Data packets for a given virtual call and for each direction of transmission. The standard value to be supported by all PPSDNs is 128 octets.

The **Fast Select Indication** is a network utility used by the STE to indicate that the Fast Select user facility [8] applies to that call.

The **Closed User Group Indication** utility is used by the STE to enable the establishment of virtual calls by DTEs which are members of international closed user groups. When using the Closed User Group Indication utility in the Call Request packet, the STE indicates that the international virtual circuit is requested on the basis of valid international closed user group membership.

The treatment of the **Closed User Group with Outgoing Access Indication** utility is identical to the treatment of the Closed User Group Indication utility, except that it refers to international closed user groups with outgoing access capability. This capability enables the members of these international closed user groups to establish virtual calls with non-members.

The **Reverse Charging Indication** utility is used by the STE when the calling DTE has requested to reverse the applicable call charges to the called DTE.

The **Traffic Class Indication** utility is to indicate a service category for the virtual call

while the **Estimated Transit Delay** utility signals the expected transit delay of the virtual call. The procedures and the use of these two utilities are designated for further study by CCITT.

The **Tariff** utility is also designated for further study by CCITT; however, Datapac and some other PPSDNs have already implemented this utility as a national (non-CCITT) utility as described in Section 3.

The **Utility Marker** is used by the STE to delimit international (CCITT) utilities from national (non-CCITT) utilities that may be agreed upon bilaterally by the PPSDNs. In fact, the use of all the above international (CCITT) utilities except the Call Identifier, is subject to bilateral agreement between the PPSDNs.

2.5 International Addressing. One of the basic elements of international network connections is the international numbering plan. The CCITT Recommendation X.121 [11] defines the international numbering plan for identifying public network addressing. Each public data network is assigned a Data Network Identification Code (DNIC) which is a four-digit number. The first three digits identify the country and the fourth digit identifies a particular public data network in that country. Datapac's DNIC is 3020.

An international address (or international data number) contains a DNIC, followed by a Network Terminal Number (NTN) which specifies the address of the DTE within the public data network. The NTN is a 1 to 10 digit number and is assigned to a particular DTE by the network administration.

For outgoing international calls from a network, an international prefix digit is allowed in CCITT Recommendation X.121. The composition of this prefix digit is a national matter since the prefix digit does not form part of the international data number. The prefix digit for Datapac is 1. All international addresses supplied by DTE's on Datapac must be preceded by this digit. Thus, when a Datapac user wishes to establish an international virtual call, he specifies the destination DTE address using the following format:

1 DNIC NTN

3. Characteristics of Datapac's X.75 Interfaces

CCITT Recommendation X.75, as described in Section 2, provides several options for implementation. In addition, there are several internetworking issues that must be negotiated and agreed between the networks involved. This section describes the characteristics of Datapac's X.75 interfaces in terms of implementation options and technical agreements reached between Datapac and other PPSDNs.

Most of the internetworking issues involve the two neighboring networks with direct X.75 interfaces or gateways. An X.75 gateway consists of two STE stations in neighboring PPSDNs with an X.75 link between them. Datapac has direct X.75 gateways with GTE Telenet and Tymnet in the U.S.A., and with IPACS of Teleglobe Canada for interconnecting with overseas PPSDNs.

3.1 Link Level. Datapac and the neighboring PPSDNs agreed to use the Single Link Procedure (SLP) only. The Multi-Link Procedure (MLP) is not supported at Datapac X.75 interfaces. These administrations also agreed to use modulo 8 sequence numbering at the Link level. Since, at this time, no satellite links are expected, the modulo 128 numbering of the frames is not supported at Datapac X.75 interfaces.

The SLP in CCITT Recommendation X.75 is based upon the Link Access Procedure-Balanced (LAPB) described in Section 2 of CCITT Recommendation X.25. When the Datapac X.75 interconnections with the neighboring PPSDNs were introduced, LAPB procedures were under development in Datapac. To achieve early introduction of the X.75 interconnections, Datapac and other PPSDNs agreed to base the SLP upon the Link Access Procedures (LAP) described in the same section of Recommendation X.25 [8]. As soon as LAPB became available and tested on Datapac, the X.75 interfaces between Datapac and other PPSDNs supported LAPB.

3.2 Packet Level. Datapac and the neighboring PPSDNs have also agreed to use modulo 8 sequence numbering at the Packet level. The modulo 128 numbering of the packets is not supported at Datapac X.75 interfaces.

To reduce the occurrence of call collisions, the STEs assign logical channel numbers in a reverse order. It is agreed that the Datapac STEs assign logical channels in a descending order, starting with the highest numbered available channel, while the neighboring PPSDNs use the logical channels in an ascending order, starting with the lowest numbered available channel.

It is agreed to provide multiple X.75 gateways between Datapac and each neighboring network, thus enhancing the availability of the X.75 interconnections. The Datapac routing procedures for the outgoing international calls select the closest (in terms of hops) and the least loaded (in terms of number of VCs) gateway at the call setup time [5, 14].

To ensure the availability of the X.75 interface, the Datapac STE periodically sends an X.75 Clear Request packet, as an idle line probe, to the neighboring STE on an idle logical channel. If an X.75 Clear Confirmation packet is not received within a specified time (e.g., three minutes), a major failure must have occurred at the neighboring STE, then the Datapac STE declares the interface down, clears the existing calls, generates an appropriate Datapac alarm, and further outgoing calls are routed through other X.75 gateways [5].

The Datapac and the neighboring network STEs check and verify the DNICs of all addresses on incoming and outgoing Call Request and Call Connected packets. By specifying the authorized DNICs in the STEs, all networks can enforce any policy bilaterally agreed upon, with regards to incoming, outgoing, and transit calls.

Both the Call Request and Call Connected packets in X.75 may contain international and national utilities. What utilities are present and the values of these utilities are subject to agreements between the network administrations. To generalize the utility handling capabilities and to accommodate differing requirements of other PPSDNs, the Datapac's X.75 implementation parameterizes the way the X.75 utilities are treated. The Datapac parameters specify, for each X.75 link, the required status of utilities for Call Request and Call Connected packets, both to and from the Datapac network. A parameter for a utility field is defined to have one of four options for each packet type:

1. Mandatory—the utility must be present in the incoming packet and is verified; also it is generated for outgoing packets.
2. Optional—if the utility is present in the incoming packet, then it is verified, and generated for outgoing packet.
3. Ignored—the utility can be present, but it is not processed.
4. Clear—if the utility is present in the incoming packet, the call is cleared.

Any utility for which no parameter is defined as above at the Datapac X.75 interface, is ignored and optionally alarmed within Datapac. Currently, the X.75 utilities whose treatment can be parameterized at the Datapac X.75 interfaces are:

1. Transit Network Identification
2. Call Identifier
3. Throughput Class Indication
4. Window Size Indication
5. Packet Size Indication
6. Closed User Group Indication
7. Reverse Charging Indication
8. Tariff

Since Datapac currently does not act as a transit network, the above parameters of Datapac's X.75 utilities are optioned to block (i.e. clear) transit calls. The Datapac's X.75 interfaces do not support international closed user groups; as a result, all such calls are also blocked by optioning the appropriate parameters.

It is agreed between Datapac and two U.S.A. networks, GTE Telenet and Tymnet, that the collect calls over the X.75 gateways will be accepted, and thus the Reverse Charging Indication utility parameters of Datapac's X.75 gateways with these networks are optioned to permit them. However, it is also agreed not to support collect calls between Datapac and the overseas networks through IPACS. As a result, the X.75 gateways between Datapac and IPACS will block such calls.

The Tariff utility is a non-CCITT (national) utility which has been bilaterally agreed between Datapac and the U.S.A. PPSDNs. It has been necessitated by the need to exchange tariff related information during call establishment to allow the billing network to bill its users. For example, the tariff from Datapac to the U.S.A. networks is a function of the size and location of the Canadian city in which the customer is located and the type of network access service, as well as the type of access service in the U.S.A. The 1-octet value field of the Tariff utility that Datapac sends to the U.S.A. PPSDN signals the Datapac Band Number (which is a function of the size and location of the Canadian city) and the access service type of the Datapac DTE. A similar 1-octet value field is received, indicating the access service type of the U.S.A. network DTE.

The parameters which define the treatment of the X.75 utilities at the Datapac gateways with the U.S.A. networks are optioned to allow the exchange of Tariff utility. However, the Datapac to overseas tariff is currently flat rated and there is no need to exchange tariff related information at call establishment time. Thus, the same parameters at the Datapac gateways with IPACS are optioned to ignore and not to generate the Tariff utility.

The network access services that are allowed to establish international calls via X.75 between Datapac and other PPSDNs are currently limited to X.25 and X.28 (Interactive Terminal Interface—ITI) [9] access services on Datapac. Datapac currently supports the first twelve of the international ITI parameters, as specified in CCITT Recommendation X.3 [9]. Datapac and other PPSDNs also offer sets of national ITI parameters. For international calls, the International ITI parameters can be used transparently through the Datapac X.75 interfaces. For the use of national parameters, the users have two choices: (i) the ITI terminal user may set the local national parameters, or (ii) the X.25 host can specify and set the national ITI parameters of a foreign network if they are delimited from the International ITI parameters with a National Parameter Marker (NPM), as specified in CCITT Recommendation X.29 [9].

4. Testing of Datapac X.75 Interfaces

The X.75 interface between two PPSDNs has to be tested thoroughly before it is introduced to commercial service. This section describes the tests conducted by Datapac and other PPSDNs for the X.75 interconnections.

4.1 Test Tools. To perform thorough and accurate function and performance testing of network interfaces such as X.25, X.75, X.28 and X.29, in the limited time period available, automatic testing tools must be developed and used by the networks.

The following is a brief description of test tools that are currently used by Datapac for various purposes. Several other test tools are under development.

- ANTS (Automated Network Testing System) is a software package implemented on PDP-11, to allow automated protocol tests of X.25 and X.75 interfaces. ANTS is written in C language [15] and currently runs under RSX-11M operating system.
- BILGE (Bell Canada Interactive Load Generation Environment) is a software package, written in C language and implemented under RSX-11M operating system, to allow automated load generation and performance measurements of X.25 and X.75 interfaces and virtual circuits.
- ITI Tester is a software package implemented under RSX-11M operating system to allow automated protocol tests on ITI protocols (i.e. X.3, X.28 and X.29). It is written partly in C language and partly in Macro-11 language of PDP-11.

4.2 Testing Stages. The Recommendation X.75 specifies the signaling procedures between two STEs. However, the X.75 interface is only a portion of the international end-to-end (DTE-to-DTE) connection. Thus, the testing of the X.75 interconnection of two or more networks involves two stages:

1. X.75 interface testing
2. end-to-end testing

The purpose of the X.75 interface testing is to verify that the implementation of X.75 procedures on each network's STE conforms to the procedures specified in CCITT Recommendation X.75 and other additional interface requirements. Datapac has developed a test plan which includes over 500 individual tests to verify the functional correctness of the Datapac STE implementation. These tests cover not only the normal procedures but also abnormal conditions in cases of invalid frames or packets. The categories of the Datapac X.75 interface testing are listed in Table 1.

Other networks have developed similar test plans to verify the correctness of their STEs. Using these test plans and the test tools described in Section 4.1, both Datapac and other networks conducted the X.75 interface testing separately. During these tests, the testing system of Figure 5 is used to simulate both a foreign network's STE and a local X.25 DTE.

The purpose of the second stage of testing (i.e., end-to-end testing) is twofold. First, it is to verify that the X.75 implementations and the interface parameters of all involved networks are compatible. The second purpose is to verify and demonstrate that the international virtual calls from DTE to DTE can be established, maintained, and cleared as specified. This stage of testing requires full cooperation of the involved networks.

Table 1. Datapac X.75 Interface Test Categories.

(1) Normal Call Setup
(2) Normal Idle Line
(3) Normal Data Transfer
(4) Normal Call Clearing
(5) Normal Interrupt Procedures
(6) Normal Reset Procedures
(7) Ready State
(8) STE-X Waiting State
(9) STE-Y Waiting State
(10) Data Transfer State
(11) STE-X Clearing State
(12) STE-Y Clearing State
(13) STE-X Reset State
(14) STE-Y Reset State
(15) End-to-End Considerations
(16) Window Mechanism
(17) Restart Procedures
(18) Relationship Between Levels
(19) Busy Data Conditions
(20) Busy Interface
(21) Facility Field
(22) Utility Field
(23) Invalid Call Request Packets
(24) Invalid Call Connected Packets
(25) Invalid Data Packets
(26) Other Invalid Packets
(27) Time-outs
(28) Link Level Procedures
(29) Performance
(30) Routing

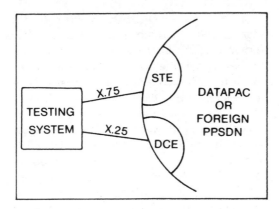

Figure 5.   X.75 Interface Testing Configuration.

Datapac has conducted this stage of testing with each of GTE Telenet, Tymnet and several overseas PPSDNs jointly, using the test configurations shown in Figure 6. An end-to-end test plan was prepared and tests were carried out according to this plan. The description and some results of these tests are given in Section 4.3.

4.3 End-to-End Testing Experience.   The current X.75 interconnections between Datapac and most other PPSDNs support virtual calls between X.25 DTEs and/or X.28 DTEs (ITI terminals). Thus, the end-to-end tests conducted can be classified into four basic categories:

1. Datapac X.25 DTE to foreign PPSDN X.25 DTE,
2. Datapac X.25 DTE to foreign PPSDN X.28 DTE,
3. Datapac X.28 DTE to foreign .PPSDN X.25 DTE,
4. Datapac X.28 DTE to foreign PPSDN X.28 DTE.

In addition to these categories, end-to-end tests were conducted with some networks' non-standard DTEs (e.g. Tymcom and Tymsat DTEs on Tymnet).

Each category included series of tests for call establishment, data transfer, call reset, and call clearing, in both foreign PPSDN to

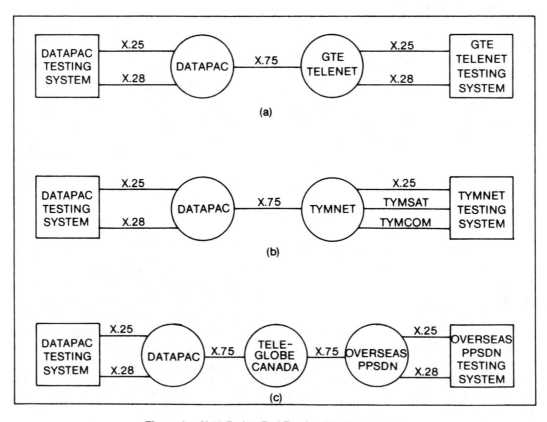

Figure 6.   X.75 End-to-End Testing Configurations.

Datapac and Datapac to foreign PPSDN directions. These series of tests were designed to check every possible end-to-end situation in every phase of a virtual call. For example, the data transfer phase was tested by sending Data packets with/without More data (M) bit, with/without Qualifier (Q) bit, with different data field lengths, and by sending Interrupt packets under various conditions (e.g., busy or non-busy channels).

During these exhaustive testings, some incompatibilities between Datapac and other PPSDNs were encountered, discussed and finally resolved. For example, immediately following the initialization of the X.75 link between Datapac and GTE Telenet, it was found that X.75 logical channel ranges did not match. Even though, for testing purposes, a range of 64 logical channels was agreed, GTE Telenet implemented 64 logical channels from 0 to 63, while Datapac implemented them from 1 to 64. This problem was corrected by increasing the Telenet's logical channel range by one [16]. In a similar way, when the X.75 link between Datapac and IPACS's Engine gateway was initialized for the first time, it was found that thirty-two of the sixty-four logical channels on Engine were incoming and the other thirty-two were outgoing only, and this created some problems. Tymshare, manufacturer of the Engine, corrected the problem by some modifications in software.

Another problem encountered during the testing was the incompatibility in the X.75 Call Connected packet format. The initial format used by Datapac STE was according to the version of CCITT X.75 provisionally approved in 1978. However, Telenet's STE was using the format specified in the 1980 version of X.75. The problem was resolved by Datapac modifying the Call Connected packet format in accordance to the 1980 version of CCITT X.75.

One problem at the call establishment phase was related to the bilaterally agreed non-CCITT Tariff utility field. This field was missing in the X.75 Call Connected packets sent by Telenet STE while it was expected by Datapac STE. The problem was resolved by modifying Telenet STE to include the Tariff utility in the X.75 Call Connected packets.

One other problem was the incorrect signaling of clear and reset causes, experienced in Datapac—GTE Telenet and Datapac—IPSS/PSS interconnections. Both GTE Telenet and IPACS undertook some software modifications to assure proper signaling of clear and reset over the X.75 interfaces and also end-to-end.

The only problem encountered in the Datapac—Datex-P interconnection via IPACS was the mismatch in the treatment of utility fields by the three networks involved. Since the treatment of the utilities at these X.75 interfaces is parameterized, the problem was resolved by fine-tuning of these parameters at Datapac—IPACS and IPACS—Datex-P X.75 interfaces.

The last problem which surfaced as a result of end-to-end testing was the incompatibility in the use of the Protocol Identifier field of Call Request packets generated by the ITI PADs. An ITI PAD (Packet Assembler/Disassembler) is that part of the packet switching node which provides X.28 (ITI) access service. According to CCITT Recommendation X.29 [9], the 4-octet field should be specified as X"01000000." Datapac ITI PADs expect the Protocol Identifier field to contain this value. However, GTE Telenet, IPSS and PSS use the second and third octets of this field to specify the type and speed of the ITI terminal. This non-standard use of the Protocol Identifier field caused call clearing by the Datapac PAD.

Telenet agreed to provide the Protocol Identifier field as X"01000000" in Datapac-destined ITI calls. In a similar way, IPSS agreed to remove the non-standard octets of this field in Call Request packets originating from PSS and IPSS and destined to Datapac.

4.4 Customer Trials. After verifying the functional correctness of the Datapac X.75 interfaces, some network users were asked to participate in customer trials where other end-to-end aspects of the X.75 internetworking were tested. Among the purposes of these trials were testing acceptability of X.75 interconnections, X.121 addressing mode, and end-to-end performance. It also provided users with an opportunity to modify and test their own software which would take advantage of X.75 interconnections between Datapac and other PPSDNs.

The customers for this trial were selected so

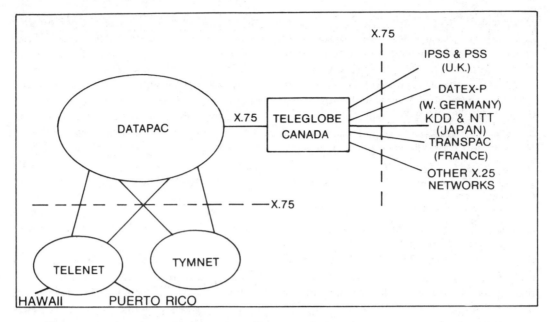

Figure 7. Datapac X.75 Connections.

that a variety of end-to-end connections and traffic profiles could be tested. They included customers with X.25 hosts on Datapac with ITI terminals on the foreign PPSDN, customers with X.25 hosts on the foreign PPSDN and ITI terminals on Datapac, and customers with X.25 hosts on both networks.

Before the trial started, these customers were informed and advised about the procedures for establishing international calls between Datapac and other networks via X.75 gateways. During the trial, full assistance was provided by Datapac to those customers experiencing some problems. The troubles and other types of feedback information from the customers, received by Datapac and other networks, were used to improve various aspects of the X.75 gateways. With the help of customer trials, much better international service between Datapac and other PPSDN is being offered.

5. Conclusions

By interconnecting public packet switched data networks, international data services are offered to network users. The interconnection of Datapac and other PPSDNs has been provided through interim gateways since May, 1978. However, after the CCITT standards

for internetworking were firmly established, the standard interconnection procedures (i.e. X.75 and X.121) have been implemented.

Before the X.75 interfaces between the networks were introduced, network administrations conducted discussions and negotiations to agree on bilateral and/or multilateral internetworking issues. These negotiations were followed by exhaustive and detailed testing of the X.75 interfaces as well as the end-to-end connections. All the incompatibilities were identified and resolved. Harmonious operation of the X.75 interfaces was demonstrated. Finally, customer trials were held to verify the acceptability of the X.75 interconnections by the network users.

As a result of these tests and trials, the X.75 interfaces between Datapac and other networks were introduced to commercial service (Figure 7), thus enhancing the quality and scope of the international virtual circuit services offered to the network users.

References

1. Kelly, P. T. F., "EURONET DIANE—A European Harmonization Project," *ICCC '80*, Atlanta, October 1980.

2. Rybczynski, A. M., Weir, D. F., and Cunningham, I. M., "Datapac Internetworking for International Services," *ICCC '78*, Kyoto, Japan, September 1978.

3. CCITT Revised Recommendation X.75, "Terminal and Transit Control Procedures and Data Transfer System on International Circuits Between Packet Switched Data Networks," COM VII—No 441 as amended and approved by Study Group VII, February 1980.

4. Rybczynski, A. M., "The X.75 Internetwork Signaling System," NTC 80, November 1980, Houston, Texas.

5. Rybczynski, A. M., Palframan, J. D., and Thomas, A., "Design of the Datapac X.75 Internetworking Capability," ICCC '80, Atlanta, October 1980.

6. Weir, D. F., Holmblad, J. B., and Rothbert, A. C., "An X.75 Based Network Architecture," ICCC '80, Atlanta, October 1980.

7. McGibbon, C. I., et al., "DATAPAC—Initial Experience with a Commercial Packet Network," ICCC '78, Kyoto, Japan, September 1978.

8. CCITT Revised Recommendation X.25, "Interface between Data Terminal Equipment (DTE) and Data Circuit-Terminating Equipment (DCE) for Terminals Operating in the Packet Mode on Public Data Networks," as amended and approved by Study Group VII, February 1980.

9. CCITT Revised Recommendations X.3, X.28, X.29, as amended and approved by Study Group VII, February 1980.

10. Unsoy, M. S., Rybczynski, A. M., and Rhynas, D., "Datapac International Packet Switching Services," ELECTRO '81, New York, April 1981.

11. CCITT Revised Recommendation X.121, "International Numbering Plan for Public Data Networks," as amended and approved by Study Group VII, February 1980.

12. HDLC, Documents IS3309, IS4335 plus approved amendments (TC97/SC6/N1300 and 1445) and DP6256-ISO, Geneva, Switzerland.

13. CCITT Revised Recommendation X.96, "Call Progress Signals in Public Data Networks," approved by Study Group VII, February 1980.

14. Sproule, D. E., and Mellor, F., "Routing, Flow and Congestion Control in the Datapac Network," IEEE Trans. on Comm. Vol. COM-29, No. 4, April 1981.

15. Kernigham, B. W., and Ritchie, D. M., The C Programming Language, Prentice-Hall Software Series, 1978.

16. Unsoy, M. S., and Shanahan, T., "X.75 Internetworking of Datapac and Telenet," Seventh Data Communications Symposium, Mexico City, Mexico, October 1981.

Acknowledgments

The successful development, implementation and testing of the Datapac X.75 interfaces was the result of team efforts. Essential roles were played by many individuals in the Computer Communications Group of the TransCanada Telephone System and in Bell Northern Research. Their considerable efforts are gratefully acknowledged. The author would also like to acknowledge the contributions of many individuals from GTE Telenet, Tymnet, Teleglobe Canada, British Telecom Inc., Deutsche Bundespost, KDD, NTT and Transpac, who participated in technical discussions and end-to-end testings with Datapac.

About the Author

Mehmet Unsoy received his BSEE from Middle East Technical University, Ankara, Turkey, in 1973, and M. Math and Ph.D. in computer science from the University of Waterloo, Waterloo, Ontario, Canada, in 1974 and 1980, respectively. His doctoral research was on congestion control in packet switched data networks. Since 1978, he has been working, as a manager, with The Computer Communications Group of the TransCanada Telephone System, on various design and planning aspects of Datapac public packet switched data network. Dr. Unsoy has been responsible for the X.75 internetworking between Datapac and other public data networks. At present, he is responsible for Datapac services planning and CCITT standards activities. He has published several papers on Datapac as well as on congestion control in packet switched networks.

Fred M. Burg and Cheng T. Chen, AT&T Information Systems, Lincroft, N. J.,
and Harold C. Folts, Omnicom Inc., Vienna, Va.

Reprinted from November 1984 *Data Communications*. Copyright © 1984.
McGraw-Hill, Inc. All rights reserved.

Of local networks, protocols, and the OSI reference model

Why are local networks viewed as 'connectionless,' and, if they are, how does X.25 fit into the picture?

Efforts to standardize local network protocols have been ongoing for over four years. Yet, only recently have completed specifications finally begun to appear. This work was originated in the United States by the Institute of Electrical and Electronics Engineers (IEEE) 802 committee, but interest in the area has since spread internationally. Similar activities are also under way within both the European Computer Manufacturers Association (ECMA) and the International Organization for Standardization (ISO).

Still, the standardization work to date has been limited in scope—oriented toward simply providing access to certain different types of local networks. Are more functions needed in a local-network environment? If so, what are these requirements, and who will develop the standards? What about internetworking between different IEEE 802 local networks and other types of networks? Moreover, how does the reference model for open systems interconnection (OSI) apply to local networks?

Starting with the last question, it can undoubtedly be concluded that OSI does apply to computer "systems" in a local-network environment—with "systems" being those devices that are intelligent and can process data. Attempting to specify a set of protocols for use in local networks, however, raises several thorny issues in relating the IEEE 802 specifications to the OSI reference model and in adapting other OSI-related protocol standardization work to local networks generally.

Studies show, for example, that communications between nodes on the same local network will predominate. Still, while designers may concentrate on these intra-local-network aspects, internetworking cannot be ignored. In establishing a single set of protocols to accommodate both of these environments, perhaps some realignment of current thinking is in order.

There is, furthermore, an often-heard contention that local networks are "inherently connectionless." But this is not necessarily the case. X.25 is capable of supporting the full range of OSI network-layer services and is likely to play an important role in any local-network protocol architecture.

The ISO is examining the application of the OSI reference model to local networks. Conceptually, the architecture of a local network does not differ from that of a wide-area network. This would seem to indicate that the OSI reference model (Data Communications, "Coming of age: A long-awaited standard for heterogeneous nets," January 1981, p. 63) is equally applicable to both types of networks. In other words, nodes or processors attached to either a local or a long-haul network need to perform the same kind of functions, such as network access or file transfer.

The reference model, which parses the total communications task into smaller, functionally separated pieces (the well-publicized seven layers), serves only as a basis for further protocol standardization. It is the use of OSI protocols, not just any set of protocols functionally compatible with the reference model, that will make a system truly compatible with OSI. With this in mind, it is interesting to examine the dichotomy of views circulating within the ISO as to how the OSI reference model should treat local networks.

Differences of opinion

One way of looking at the issue is to regard an entire local network (that is, all the nodes and devices collectively attached to it) as a single "open system." In this case, there would be little or no restriction placed on the internal protocols used by the individual local-network nodes. To communicate with other open systems outside of the local network, however, there

'Standards' acronyms

Since the language of standards consists of many acronyms, the following list includes those used in the accompanying discussion.

AEFs Address extension facilities of X.25.

CLNS Connectionless network service; describes a set of services made available to OSI layer 4.

CLP Connectionless protocol.

CONS Connection-oriented network service; describes a set of services, different from CLNS, made available to OSI layer 4.

D-bit Delivery-confirmation facility of X.25.

DCE Data circuit-terminating equipment.

DTE Data terminal equipment.

EOT End of transport-service data unit; a marker indicating the last bit of data received from the session layer.

FCS Frame check sequence; (OSI) basic error-detection mechanism.

HILI Higher-level interface; a working group (802.1) of IEEE 802.

IEEE Institute of Electrical and Electronics Engineers.

ISO International Organization for Standardization.

LAPB Link Access Procedure-B of X.25.

LLC Logical Link Control; upper layer-2 sublayer protocol of IEEE 802.

MAC Media Access Control; a series of lower layer-2 sublayer protocols of IEEE 802.

M-bit An X.25 feature used to indicate the last bit of data received from the transport layer.

MIF Minimum Internetworking Functionality; a tenet that calls for as little complexity as possible in local network stations or devices for the relatively infrequent requirement for interconnecting with resources outside the local network; relegates such chores to a gateway.

NSAP Network service access point; an abstract point at the boundary between layers 3 and 4 of the reference model through which network-layer services (CONS or CLNS) are made available to the transport layer.

PDU Protocol data unit.

PLP Packet-level protocol of X.25.

PSN Packet-switching network.

TLC Transport-layer class; Classes 0 through 4 of the transport-layer protocol.

Type A, Type B, Type C OSI network-layer service classifications.

---

nodes, or systems, would be able to communicate with each other, as well as with OSI systems outside of the local network.

Yet another view is that the nodes on the local network would consist of a mix of both OSI and non-OSI equipment. In this scenario, non-OSI gear would be able to share the local-network medium with OSI systems—assuming both still implement the same standard media-access and control protocols. However, these two different groups would still be logically segregated from one another because of incompatibilities at the higher layers.

These three considerably different points of view leave communications designers today with complete freedom in defining a communications architecture for local networks. There are, however, other factors to consider.

The real-world marketplace is already witnessing incompatible local-network approaches to performing such basic functions as file transfer and document interchange. Without a well-defined architecture that applies to all devices on a local network, incompatibilities are likely to proliferate that will hamper efficient communications. For all these reasons, not surprisingly, there is clear movement toward an environment that embraces the OSI principles—even within local networks—as witnessed in the OSI demonstration at the 1984 National Computer Conference (NCC '84) in Las Vegas.

OSI individuality

To best address today's real-world user situations, the analyses, conclusions, and proposals that follow are based on the second of the three premises listed earlier: the scenario in which each local-network node or processor is regarded as an individual open system conforming to the OSI principles and protocols. For the purposes of this discussion, the protocols corresponding to the seven layers of the OSI reference model are divided into three groups:

1. Protocols for gaining access to, and controlling operation over, the medium to which the station is attached (for local networks, these correspond to the IEEE 802 protocols and, for the most part, to the lowest two layers of the OSI reference model)

2. Protocols concerned with end-system-to-end-system connectivity (layers 3 and 4 of the OSI model)

3. Protocols that handle network functions beyond reliable data transfer (layers 5, 6, and 7 of OSI).

Discussion of the first and third protocol groups is relatively straightforward. The second group, however, is somewhat more complicated, since decisions made at these levels greatly impact both performance and internetworking. These protocols, therefore, are discussed last.

IEEE and the OSI reference model

The work of the IEEE 802 committee has been, and remains, concerned mainly with protocols for accessing and controlling the various types of local-network media. The IEEE's Higher-Level Interface group (802.1, also known as HILI) was originally pro-

---

would have to be a local-network-to-OSI gateway. Also, there would be little or no restriction on the distribution of OSI functions and protocols within the local network, such as between the gateway and the non-OSI local-network nodes.

Another school of thought regards each of the processors or nodes on the local network as individual, distinct, OSI-supporting "systems." Each, in essence, would be individually "open." In this environment, the

1. IEEE vs. OSI. *While the IEEE standards correspond to the lowest three OSI layers, no protocol standards are now contemplated for the "internetworking" layer.*

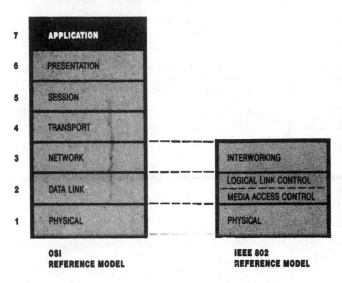

	OSI REFERENCE MODEL	IEEE 802 REFERENCE MODEL
7	APPLICATION	
6	PRESENTATION	
5	SESSION	
4	TRANSPORT	
3	NETWORK	INTERWORKING
2	DATA LINK	LOGICAL LINK CONTROL / MEDIA ACCESS CONTROL
1	PHYSICAL	PHYSICAL

hibited from developing any protocols for use in a local-network environment. Yet, while this prohibition has not changed, the HILI working group is now actively pursuing, among other things, the important issue of how local networks will interconnect with each other, and with other networks.

As Figure 1 shows, the protocol-standardization work of the IEEE 802 corresponds to the lowest two layers of the OSI reference model. Some argue that the 802 protocol specifications involve, to some degree, the functionality of the OSI's layer 3. This issue, a somewhat controversial one, will be examined later in the discussion of protocol layers 3 and 4.

The local network's physical layer specifies the means for transmitting and receiving bits across various types of local-network media. One or more physical-layer (layer 1) specifications are associated with each type of media access control (MAC) sublayer. The MAC sublayer, which is the lower sublayer in the IEEE's layer 2, performs those functions needed to control access to the physical medium.

The logical link control (LLC) sublayer, which is the upper sublayer in the IEEE's layer 2, is defined in such a way that it is independent of the particular type of MAC procedure used. Three types of LLC procedures have been defined:

1. An "unacknowledged-connectionless" protocol (LLC Type 1) in which data units are sent over "logical data links" without any correlation to previous or subsequent data units and without any acknowledgment or guarantee of delivery

2. A "connection-oriented" protocol (LLC Type 2) that provides for a data-link connection establishment procedure, transfer of multiple data units, acknowledgment, retransmission as appropriate, and the termination of the data-link connection

3. An "acknowledged-connectionless" protocol (LLC Type 3) in which a single data unit is transmitted,

and then acknowledged, before a subsequent data unit is transmitted.

The use of sublayers in layer 2 of the IEEE 802 specifications is not in itself contrary to the guidelines of the OSI reference model. Sublayering is allowed in distinct cases where a group of functions is not always needed and can, therefore, be bypassed from time to time as necessary. In a local-network environment, however, where the medium is shared by many "peer" systems, the functions of the MAC sublayer are always necessary to arbitrate access to the local-network medium. This is in contrast to cases where such functions are absent—such as when a single system uses a dedicated line to access, for example, a packet-switching network.

The IEEE 802 local-network protocols have been submitted to, and are being processed by, the ISO with the intent of making them international standards. However, these protocols are not currently viewed as OSI protocols. This is because the detailed "service definitions" for layers 1 and 2 of the OSI reference model (which define the capabilities provided by these layers to the next higher layer) have not yet been agreed to. Also, the protocols at these layers are necessarily linked very closely to the media and topologies themselves. Therefore, it is expected that a family of protocols will exist at these layers, with each optimized for a particular medium and topology.

Network independence

In the OSI reference model, the boundary between layers 4 and 5 (transport and session) is a key demarcation line. The protocols under this line are all concerned with reliable and cost-effective data transfer. If it is necessary to ensure reliability, then protocols below the boundary line must be able to correct any errors introduced between end-systems.

Above this line, protocols perform common functions that are data-transfer independent, such as the resolution of syntax differences (code conversion) or the coordination associated with a file transfer. Therefore, the OSI protocol standards for layers 5 and above (session, presentation, and application) apply just as much to an "open" system on a local network as they do to a system that uses any other networking technology.

Currently, the session-layer protocol has been standardized. Protocols for the presentation and application layers include functions such as:
- Virtual terminals
- File transfer, access, and management
- Job transfer and manipulation
- Message handling
- Document interchange.

Some of those have already been standardized. It would appear, therefore, that the choice of local-network protocols for the three upper layers is straightforward: the above-mentioned protocols will simply be included as they mature. The OSI demonstration at the NCC '84 has already showed the viability of this approach by the multiple-vendor implementation of a simple subset of the file-transfer protocol.

2. 'Network' distinction. A "subnetwork" is a collection of physical equipment and/or transmission facilities. The "network layer," on the other hand, consists of cooperating, but distributed, entities whose responsibilities include route selection between the systems containing communicating applications.

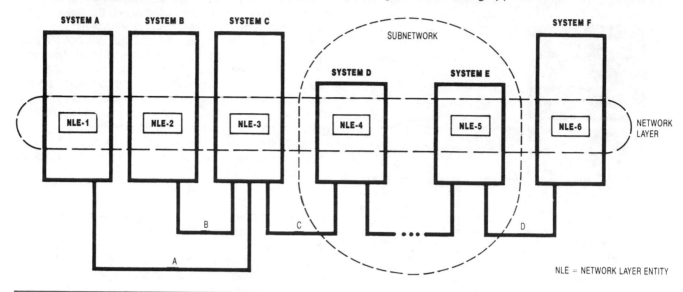

The last piece of the jigsaw puzzle needed for a comprehensive local-network protocol architecture is a set of protocols for layers 3 and 4 (network and transport). These layers are critical to allowing end-systems to communicate reliably with one another.

But before examining the protocol-standardization work at these layers, an important issue mentioned earlier must be addressed: Do the MAC/LLC protocols of IEEE 802, which are layer-2 protocols, include layer-3 functions? The problem, not surprisingly, revolves around the use of the word "network." For some time now, "network" has had at least two markedly different definitions. The more common one, which predates the OSI work, defines a network as a collection of physical equipment and/or transmission facilities (as in "distributed network").

Definitions
The work on the OSI reference model, specifically in adoption of the term "network layer," introduced the second definition: a collection of distributed entities working together, through the use of a common set of protocols, to provide a number of services, including the determination of a path or route between the systems containing communicating applications. This different definition is especially important in describing a "distributed-network" environment. Also, the routing function is added: even in simple cases where end-systems are fully connected, it is still necessary to determine which dedicated facility, for example, to use in order to reach an end-system containing a particular application.

To avoid confusion over the different meanings of "network," the term "subnetwork" has generally been adopted to denote the first usage: a collection of physical equipment and/or transmission facilities. Figure 2 illustrates the difference.

Another problem concerning the use of the term

"network" relates to addressing. It was agreed in the early stages of the IEEE 802 work that, based primarily on Ethernet, address fields in layer 2 would be used to identify the source and destination systems on a local network. This function is now included in the address fields of the IEEE's MAC sublayer. The use of a layer-2 protocol to convey a system's address, however, seems to violate the spirit of the OSI reference model, which specifies such addressing as a layer-3, or network-layer, function.

At about the same time, there was another addressing issue being debated in standards circles: the relationship of an address in X.25 packets (CCITT X.121-based) to the network service access point (NSAP) address of the OSI reference model. In OSI terminology, an NSAP address identifies a transport-layer (layer-4) entity—not necessarily the end-system containing that entity.

To illustrate the difference between an NSAP address and an end-system's address, consider the following analogy. Suppose you are told that a great treasure awaits you in a room with a golden door. Further suppose that, in all the world, there is only one such room. Your goal, of course, is to reach the room with the golden door. Your travel agent does not know the actual street address of the house containing this room but, nevertheless, sells you an airline ticket to a nearby airport. The agent assures you that all you need do is take a cab, and that all cabdrivers know where the house with the golden door is. Sure enough, upon your arrival at the airport, the cabdriver takes you to the house. You enter the house (the end-system) and find many rooms, each with a differently colored door (NSAPs). You know which specific door you are seeking, but a final "routing" decision still must be made.

This analogy illustrates several important concepts relating to network-layer addressing. First, to make any progress toward a final destination (the NSAP address, the specific room within the house), you must know something that uniquely identifies it (the golden door). Second, it is not necessary for you or your travel agent (represented by the subnetwork to which you are connected) to know every detail concerning how to get to your final destination. However, you must make your final destination known to those in a position to help (in other words, network-layer protocols must carry the NSAP address). Finally, even when you get to the house (the destination end-system), there may still be one more (routing) decision to make: picking a door.

So, sometimes it is useful, conceptually, to separate the subnetwork address of the end-system from the NSAP address (the address of the transport-layer entity with which communications is desired). The following example shows the need for this separation: a processor (system) attached to a local network acts as a "front-end" for other systems. In this case, the front-end system would have a subnetwork address distinct from the NSAP addresses of the other "back-end" systems. Of course, a house may have a golden door and yet consist of only one big room. In this case, there would only be one NSAP address per subnetwork address, and the two could even be identical.

Functional analysis

With the IEEE 802 having decided that the layer-2 MAC addresses will identify the source and destination end-systems on a local network (the MAC address is treated as a subnetwork address), the next logical question is: What other layer-3 functions are needed in a local-network environment? And this is precisely where the problem lies.

Given that the OSI protocols are to provide a reliable data-transfer mechanism, how should the required functions be distributed within a layered architecture for a local network? More specifically, how should these functions be distributed across layers 3 and 4 and, for our purposes, the logical link control (LLC) sublayer? As discussed in "To connect or not to connect," which is in part based on an addendum to the OSI reference-model document, there are two views on how to distribute the required functions throughout these layers. Before examining the approaches, only one of which "is a requirement of OSI standards," it is necessary first to determine exactly what functions are needed in a local-network environment.

One requirement that must be satisfied in a local-network protocol architecture has already been mentioned: the ability to identify NSAP as well as subnetwork addresses. Clearly, there are cases where separate NSAP and subnetwork addresses are necessary. This will again be apparent when issues of internetworking are examined.

Figure 3 depicts several cases of "off-net" communications (from the viewpoint of local network 1 in the figure) in which a system on one of the local networks could be involved. For completeness, intra-local-network communications is also shown. As illustrated, there are four types of connections to consider:
1. Between two systems (A and B) that are both connected to the same local network
2. Between two systems (A and D) on different local networks that are directly connected (two local networks linked by a leased or dial-up connection or, more simply, by a bridge)
3. Between two systems (B and C) where one (B) is on a local network and the other (C) is directly attached to a wide-area network
4. Between two systems (B and D) on different local networks that are connected by a wide-area network.

It is impractical to expect a significant degree of communications between systems on a local network with outside systems; studies suggest that most traffic flowing within a local network tends to stay within that local network. Still, figures ranging from 10 to 30 percent have been suggested for the off-net portion of the local-network traffic.

For long-haul communications, either private or public X.25 packet-switching networks (PSNs) are likely candidates for connecting two local networks. An alternative long-haul architecture might involve connection of two gateways by a leased line, or even through a PBX. Here, basically, is another "functional requirement" for a local-network architecture. It must be possible for local networks to communicate with systems on different subnetworks.

However, to reduce costs and the complexity of devices on local networks, in light of the relatively small number of such interactions expected, the functionality needed in devices on a local network for inter-networking should be minimized (this principle is referred to as "minimal internetworking functionality," or MIF). As a corollary, it is permissible to build extra complexity into a gateway for the purposes of internetworking.

Referring again to Figure 3, in cases involving connections such as C3 and C4, and even possibly C2, the separation of subnetwork addresses and NSAP addresses again comes into play. In these instances, the subnetwork address would correspond to the local-network station that serves as the gateway. For the gateway to do its job, it must be given a unique NSAP address on which to route. This minimal amount of information is consistent with the MIF principle, and anything less would not be workable.

Additional functional requirements for a local-network protocol architecture include:
■ Multiplexing. The association at the MAC sublayer between source and destination local-network devices can be viewed as providing the equivalent of a dedicated line. There is thus a need to provide multiplexing on top of this "dedicated line" for associations between multiple sets of communicating applications.
■ End-to-end flow control. It must be possible to exercise end-to-end flow control in cases where, for example, one end-system is not reading data fast enough to keep up with its transmission.
■ End-to-end acknowledgment. For a reliable data-transfer mechanism, it must be possible to know that the transmitted data has been received.
■ Error detection and recovery. It must be possible to detect and recover from errors that occur. Possible

To connect or not to connect

The evolution in the late 1960s and early 1970s from simple, dedicated-circuit networks to distributed networks bred a divergence in philosophies regarding the distribution of functionality between end-system and network. One view held that the function of the network was limited to moving bits from end-system to end-system. In addition, the network was seen as being inherently unreliable: the responsibility for recovering from errors introduced by the communications facilities remained with the end-systems. This philosophy led to the "datagram" school of thought, which believes in minimum functionality within the network and requires maximum functionality in the end-systems. Networks, the proponents say, are unreliable.

The second philosophy of networking is based on the properties of dedicated-line communications, which include the maintenance of sequentiality, as well as the provision of a low error rate (especially with conditioned lines). The application of this philosophy to distributed networks resulted in the "virtual circuit" school of thought, which endorses added functionality within the network and reduced functionality in the end-system. In dividing functionality in this way, an economic advantage is gained by minimizing functionality (and, hence, cost) wherever it may be replicated.

The two divergent philosophies have spawned two opposing views regarding protocol architectures involving layers 2, 3, and 4 of the open systems interconnection (OSI) reference model. One, which is known as the "connectionless" group, embraces the "datagram" school of thought. The second, called the "connection-oriented" group, follows the other philosophy.

In local networks, which some consider inherently connectionless, it is only the use of connectionless protocols at layers 2 and 3 in a local-network station that makes the local network connectionless. However, if the layer-2 and -3 local-network protocols are extremely simple, then the layer-4 protocols must be very robust to provide, collectively, for a reliable data-transfer mechanism.

However, recent contributions to the International Organization for Standardization (ISO) by several countries (for example, France, Japan, the U. K., and the U. S.) suggest that a connection-oriented approach for local networks is equally viable — one, that is, having a protocol architecture with the needed reli-

ability included in the first three protocol layers.

A "connection," which is an association established for the transfer of data between two or more peer entities at the same layer, is established not only between the peer entities themselves, but also between each entity and an entity at the next lower (OSI) layer. Thus, a connection proceeds through three distinct phases: connection establishment, data transfer, and connection release.

In addition to the clearly distinguishable objectives of each phase, the connection has several fundamental characteristics:
■ Allows for the negotiation between all parties involved of parameters and options, if any, that will govern the transmission of data
■ Provides for connection identification, which eliminates any overhead otherwise required for address resolution during the data-transfer phase
■ Provides a context for transmitting logically related, successive units of data between peer entities and makes it possible to maintain sequence and provide flow control for those transmissions.

Connection-oriented transmission is particularly attractive in applications that call for "relatively long-lived" interactions between entities, such as in file transfers. In these cases, the entities involved initially discuss their requirements and agree to the terms of their interaction, reserving whatever resources (such as memory space) they may need. Then after transferring a series of related data units, the entities explicitly end their interaction, thereby releasing the previously reserved resources.

Connectionless transmission is the sending of a single data unit without establishing a connection. In contrast, a connectionless transmission does not have a clearly distinguishable lifetime. In addition, connectionless transmission has the following fundamental characteristics:
■ It requires only a pre-arranged association between the peer entities involved to determine the characteristics of the data to be transmitted; no dynamic agreement is involved.
■ All the information required to deliver a unit of data (destination address, quality of service, options, and so on), as well as the data itself, is presented to the next lower layer in a single interaction; the lower layer is not required to relate this interaction to any previous or subsequent interaction.

As a result of these fundamental characteristics, it

error conditions to be considered include corrupted bits, lost data, out-of-sequence delivery, duplicated data, and erroneously delivered data.
■ Segmentation and reassembly. Because of the limits on frame size imposed by the MAC procedures, it must be possible to segment large data units at the transmitter and to reassemble the data back into its original form at the receiver.

The next task, then, is to determine how best to distribute the required communications functions between the IEEE's logical link control (LLC) sublayer and layers 3 and 4. Figure 4 presents five combinations of protocols that have been suggested by members of ISO for implementation in the LLC sublayer and in layer 3. An appropriate transport-layer protocol also must be included (at layer 4).

There are two types of OSI services shown in Figure

may also be true that each unit of data transmitted is entirely self-contained and can be routed independently.

Connection-oriented and connectionless transmission should be considered in the specific context of an application (the user of the services provided by the OSI reference model). Applications can be similarly classified:

■ Connection-oriented applications, which rely on the OSI data-transfer mechanisms to provide the reliability needed in a distributed networking environment. The error-checking capabilities of such applications may have been originally designed for "interprocess" communications, where error rates are near zero. When put into a distributed environment, however, these applications must then either be rewritten or provided with a reliable data-transfer mechanism. Usually, the latter approach is preferable.

■ Connectionless applications, which themselves perform whatever degree of error checking is required. They require no further enhancement of the OSI data-transfer mechanisms.

The figure shows a somewhat stylized version of the OSI reference model with the two types of applications discussed. In moving from the physical layer (note that physical-layer protocols, responsible for moving bits, are classified as neither connectionless nor connection-oriented) to the application layer along any permitted path, a particular configuration of protocols is employed. For example, the path that starts at the physical layer branches to the left and then proceeds straight up. It uses a protocol configuration that is entirely connection-oriented.

Note also the "crossovers" within certain layers. To provide connection-oriented services to an application over a connectionless data-link layer, a "crossover protocol" would be required. From an OSI point of view, this protocol could operate either within the network layer (even over a lower-network-sublayer protocol) or entirely within the transport layer. If done in the network layer, the protocol is then known as a "subnetwork-dependent convergence protocol," since it enhances the native access protocol operating in the network layer, if any, in a way dependent on the subnetwork. This approach allows for maximum flexibility in internetworking with other systems by avoiding duplication of similar functions in different layers. And yet, conversion from CL or CO operation in the network layer to CO or CL operation

in the transport layer, respectively, "is not a requirement of OSI standards" (hence the dotted lines in layer 4 in the figure).

Consistent with the OSI layers, alteration (or crossover) of the data-transfer capabilities of the OSI mechanisms is only permitted below the session layer. Entities at and above the session layer depend on the lowest four layers to provide the reliability mechanisms required by the application.

For many reasons, it is unreasonable to assume all applications with which another application may need to communicate are on a single subnetwork. Thus, the concatenation of different subnetworks using the same or differing technologies must also be considered. Again, philosophies on how to accomplish this vary.

When two subnetworks offer similar capabilities in terms of reliability, consistent with an application's requirements, then proceeding is somewhat straightforward. The most difficult problem arises when subnetworks provide different capabilities. Given the need to provide a highly reliable data-transfer mechanism, the connectionless philosophy would place the responsibility for network reliability with the end-systems. The connection-oriented philosophy, on the other hand, would require reliability enhancement at gateways to the "subpar" network. This would not affect the end-system on the reliable subnetwork.

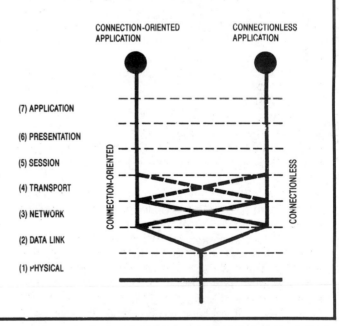

4 at the top of layer 3: the connectionless network service (CLNS) and the connection-oriented network service (CONS). Combination 1, by providing the connectionless service at the boundary of layers 3 and 4, would offer addressing and data-transfer capabilities only in layer 3. Any additional functionality needed would be deferred to layer 4. By comparison, the connection-oriented service provides more functionality at layer 3 (such as a "reset" service, invoked upon

detection of an error) while requiring less functionality at layer 4.

Combinations 2 and 3 in Figure 4 presume a totally unreliable service from the underlying subnetwork and the enhancements needed to turn this service into a connection-oriented one at the boundary of layers 3 and 4. (Combinations 2 and 3 involve the use of a network-layer protocol with the functionality and syntax of the Transport Class 4 protocol, with some minor

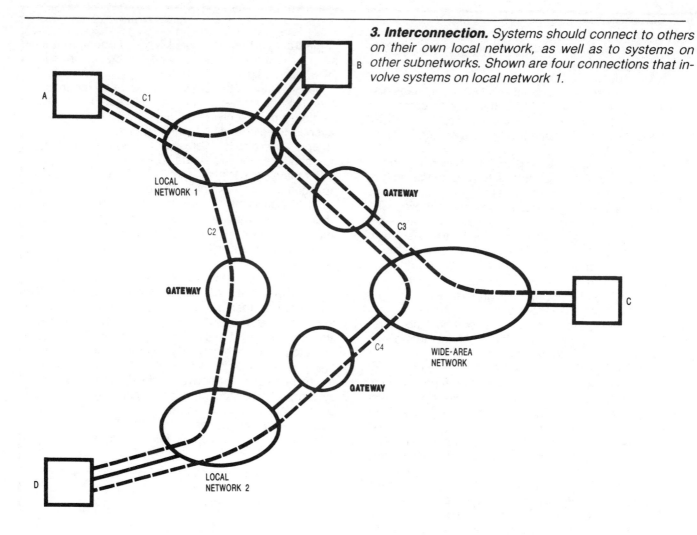

3. Interconnection. *Systems should connect to others on their own local network, as well as to systems on other subnetworks. Shown are four connections that involve systems on local network 1.*

enhancements.) While this approach appears to be viable for use with unreliable networks (which local networks are not), it is not yet clear how much support it will have in ISO.

Combinations 4 and 5 make use of the X.25 packet-level protocol (PLP). This is only the "packet" level of X.25 and not the entire set of X.25 protocols (see "The myth of X.25: Networks vs. protocols"). While LLC Type 2, which is very similar to LAPB of X.25, would seem to be the obvious choice in this case, LLC Type 1 is also a potential candidate.

The possibility of using LLC Type 1 or 2 with the X.25 PLP is a result of applying the principle of "layer independence" of the OSI reference model. In other words, as long as the services required of the lower layers are provided, it does not matter what protocol is used in providing those services. The X.25 PLP does not necessarily require the connection-oriented LAPB protocol; it only requires a "reliable" service in terms of undetected bit errors, sequence preservation, and lack of duplication. Many believe that this service can be provided in a local-network environment, even with LLC Type 1. This is because local networks are generally very reliable.

Focusing on combinations 1, 4, and 5, numerous

details and trade-offs must be considered. Ideally, the right combination of protocols will provide a reliable data-transfer mechanism to the application, across the boundary between layers 4 and 5, while minimizing excessive and duplicate functionality. By layer, the choices are:

■ LLC sublayer in IEEE 802: LLC Types 1 or 2
■ Layer 3: Connectionless Protocol (CLP, which is also known informally as the internet protocol) or the X.25 packet-level protocol (PLP)
■ Layer 4: Five classes of OSI transport-layer protocol.

It is appropriate at this time to note the classification of network-layer service types and their impact on selecting a particular transport-layer class of protocol. These classifications, taken from the OSI Transport-Layer Protocol Specification, are:

■ Type A network-layer service, which provides the transport layer with an "acceptable" residual error rate and an "acceptable" rate of signaled failures. Transport Class 0 and Class 2 have been designed for use in this case.

■ Type B network-layer service, which offers an acceptable residual error rate but an unacceptable rate of signaled failures. Transport Class 1 and Class 3 have been designed for use in this case.

4. Protocol combinations. *Shown are the various protocol combinations for the LLC sublayer and layer 3 suggested by members of ISO. For any particular combination, start at the MAC sublayer and work up to one of the circles on top of layer 3. The "protocol boxes" encountered are then part of the combination.*

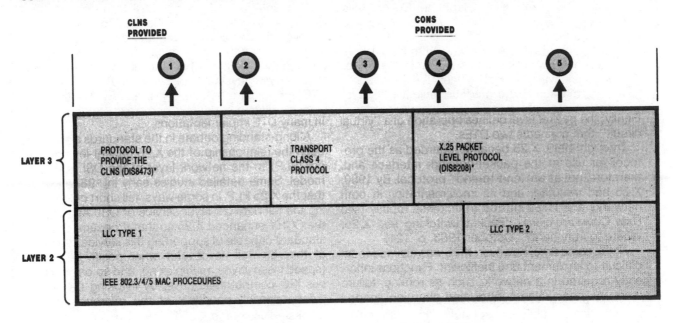

CLNS = CONNECTIONLESS NETWORK SERVICE
CONS = CONNECTION-ORIENTED NETWORK SERVICE
LLC = LOGICAL LINK CONTROL

MAC = MEDIA ACCESS CONTROL
* = DRAFT INTERNATIONAL STANDARD PLUS DOCUMENT NUMBER

■ Type C network-layer service, wherein the residual error rate is not acceptable. Transport Class 4 has been designed for use in this case.

The problem of determining an appropriate transport-layer class, or TLC, becomes one of classifying the service available across the boundary between layers 3 and 4 in a local network. As pointed out earlier, some believe local networks to be inherently connectionless. However, it is only the choice of protocols at layers 2 and 3 that results in not notifying (signaling) recognized errors to layer 4. Regardless of the choice of protocols at these layers, the residual error rate will, in all likelihood, be acceptable.

Furthermore, while the IEEE 802-specified LLC states that LLC Type 1 "may be useful when higher layers provide any essential recovery and sequencing service," local networks inherently preserve sequentiality. Yet, in the face of an error-prone medium, the use of protocols with some error detection/recovery and signaling capabilities would result in more reliable service at the boundary between layers 3 and 4 and, hence, a Type A or B service. Such protocols include LLC types 2 and 3, the X.25 packet-level protocol, and even the "Transport Class 4-based" protocol suggested in Figure 4. Use of these protocols would obviate the need for the Transport Class 4 protocol (the most powerful and complex of the lot) and result in the use of a simpler transport-layer protocol.

Given that local networks do not tend to missequence data, misdeliver it, or delay it, then it is not true that "the Class 4 protocol is well-suited to the local area networking environment and mixed communica-

tions environments, such as a local area network connected to a public data network." This was a claim made in a brochure on the OSI demonstration at this year's National Computer Conference. Indeed, Class 4, as defined for Type C networks above, is suited for the specific environment where missequencing of data and the delay of data delivery can be expected in a subnetwork. These are not, however, characteristic of either local networks or of public data networks.

Evaluating the alternatives

Each of the alternatives suggested within the ISO for the protocol architecture of a local network has certain advantages and disadvantages. Figure 5 shows the two alternatives that result from combinations 1, 4, and 5 of Figure 4, together with an appropriate choice of a transport-layer class protocol. The features of the individual protocols cited are described in more detail in "Protocol features: Which does what?" The following discussion addresses how the two alternatives meet these functional requirements:

■ NSAP identification. For communications within the local network where there is only one NSAP per end-system that corresponds identically to the subnetwork address, the NSAP address can be carried in the address fields of the MAC sublayer. In other intra-local-network cases, the address extension facilities (AEFs) of the X.25 PLP are used to carry the NSAP address under Alternative A. (While the AEFs are needed only for cases of more than one NSAP per end-system, the X.25 address fields are not needed at all.)

The inactive subset of the connectionless protocol

The myth of X.25: Networks vs. protocols

X.25, a standard adopted in 1976 by the CCITT (International Telegraph and Telephone Consultative Committee), standardizes the interface between a packet-switching network and the user's data terminal equipment, or DTE. As such, X.25 really consists of three protocols (or levels) as shown in the figure. The physical-level protocol defines the procedures for moving bits across the interface while the link level ensures reliable data transfer across this interface. Finally, the packet level defines operation of a "virtual circuit" that connects two DTEs.

Through 1980, X.25 became regarded as the protocol for use at the packet-network interface and, therefore, not as an "end-to-end" protocol. By 1980, X.25 had matured, and its implementation in both networks and DTEs started to increase rapidly (see DATA COMMUNICATIONS, "Packet switching and X.25: Where to from here?" October 1983, p. 121).

At the same time, however, X.25 was claimed to be difficult to implement and inefficient. Functions inherently required in a network, such as routing, failure recovery, congestion control, and charging, tended to complicate public packet-network implementations (as opposed to DTE implementations).

In 1980, noting that X.25 did not address a number of issues from the perspective of the user (DTE), the International Organization for Standardization (ISO) started work to specify the DTE side of the X.25 interface. This work is now in the final balloting stages as an ISO international standard.

The ISO also specified the use of X.25 in a unique manner: as a protocol between two DTEs without an intervening packet-switching network. This allows two DTEs to communicate in lieu of having an intervening packet network, or in a case where, say, a growing amount of traffic between the two justifies a dedicated line. Functionally, X.25 provides many features that would be desirable even in this environment: level 2 provides control of the entire DTE/DTE interface, while level 3, with its multiplexing capability, provides control for individual application-to-application communications.

Unlike CCITT's X.25, which was concerned only with the interface of a single DTE to a network, the ISO recognized the conceivable need for a DTE to be connected to several networks or directly to several other DTEs at the same time. This was facilitated through the definition of a "packet-level entity" that, together with levels 1 and 2, constitutes one logical DTE for each interface. This added functionality comes at little extra cost in complexity and is typical in many DTE implementations.

A long-standing debate in the standards arena had been the relationship of the X.25 packet-level protocol (PLP) to the network layer of the OSI reference model. Some detailed studies early in 1983 showed that the X.25 PLP, in some ways, fell short of supporting the full network-layer service of OSI. As a result, the CCITT enhanced X.25 so that it became the first standard capable of supporting this service. Because of this, as well as several other positive features (speed insensitivity, multiplexing, and so on), numerous ISO contributions have, by invoking the "layer independence" concepts of the reference model, suggested use of the X.25 PLP in environments other than simply in packet-switching networks.

The X.25 PLP, even without its public-packet-network-based native level-2 LAPB protocol, can be used to support the OSI network-layer service in environments other than a public data network. Before doing so, however, the following degree of service must be provided by lower-layer protocols:

- Negligible bit-error rate
- Negligible out-of-sequence rate
- Negligible packet-loss and duplication rate.

Such environments include local networks, circuit-switched data networks, and so on.

As a result of the ISO work, it is now recognized that the individual components (levels) of the X.25 protocol can be used separately. And, with the CCITT enhancements to accommodate the network-layer service, the X.25 PLP can, indeed, be used end-to-end. The X.25 protocols, it can be said, are no longer tied to X.25 networks.

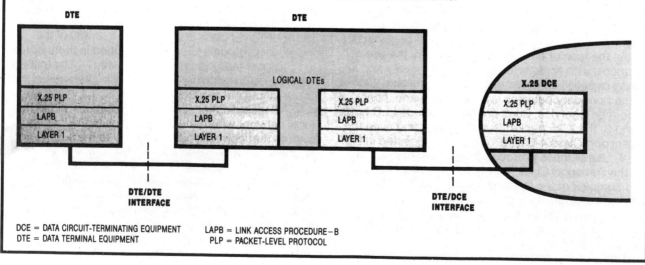

DCE = DATA CIRCUIT-TERMINATING EQUIPMENT
DTE = DATA TERMINAL EQUIPMENT
LAPB = LINK ACCESS PROCEDURE-B
PLP = PACKET-LEVEL PROTOCOL

5. Alternatives. Shown are the different alternatives considered for a local-network protocol architecture up through layer 4. With Alternative A, LLC Type 2 might be used with a noisy medium. For intra-local-network communications under Alternative B, the "inactive subset" of the connectionless protocol (CLP) is used.

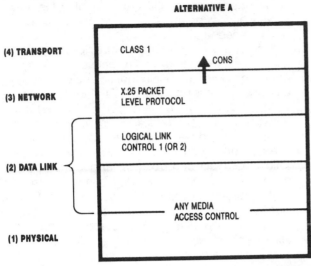
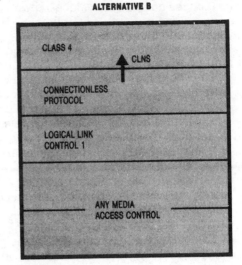

CLNS = CONNECTIONLESS NETWORK SERVICE
CONS = CONNECTION-ORIENTED NETWORK SERVICE

(CLP, in Alternative B) does not provide any means of conveying NSAP addresses. In the internetworking case, however, the CLP, as well as the X.25 PLP using AEFs, provides a mechanism for carrying the NSAP addresses to the gateway. With Alternative B, and this is crucial, the local network must know whether the destination is off-net, in which case it needs to use the full CLP. This latter requirement is not in keeping with the spirit of the MIF principle.

■ Multiplexing. Multiplexing can be provided by either alternative. In Alternative A, it is provided by the X.25 packet-level protocol; in Alternative B it is provided by the Transport Class 4 protocol.

■ End-to-end flow control. The provision of end-to-end flow control in either case is provided the same way that it is with multiplexing. With the X.25 packet-level protocol (PLP), connections are DTE-to-DTE (end-to-end), with no intervening network to decouple the X.25-PLP flow-control mechanisms at the two interfaces. When internetworking via a packet-switching network (PSN), the network provides an extra "buffering" capability. In this case, end-to-end flow control is still achieved through "back-pressure" by using the layer-3 flow control to toggle data flowing across the boundary between layers 3 and 4.

There is an added advantage to using the X.25 packet-level protocol when internetworking with a PSN: the flow-control packets used by the local network are then mapped directly to the corresponding flow-control packets on the interface between the gateway and the PSN, thereby avoiding any extra packet costs. By comparison, the layer-4 flow-control messages under Alternative B must be carried as "billable" extra data packets across the network, or else must somehow be recognizable by the gateway.

■ End-to-end acknowledgment. Both alternatives use

the same transport-layer acknowledgment procedures. Note, however, that the use of the X.25 D-bit procedure may be negotiated under Alternative A, without any loss of functionality and without added complexity. As pertains to flow control, this could result in a favorable charging advantage when internetworking with a packet-switching carrier.

■ Error detection and recovery. With either alternative, the first defense against errors is the frame check sequence (FCS) performed within the MAC sublayer. This feature guards against bit errors by discarding frames that turn up with a bad FCS. This check, in turn, leads to the need for notifying higher layers to detect missing data, and then to recover from lost data.

Contrary to popular belief, the X.25 packet-level protocol is robust enough to recover from many types of lost-packet conditions. For example, if a frame carrying a "reset request" packet is discarded due to an error, then the transmitter would eventually "time-out" waiting for a confirmation. It would then resend the reset. For a DTE-to-DTE environment within a local network, the time-outs would all be set to small values.

Likewise, when lost data packets are detected by the receiver (as determined by a gap in data-packet sequence numbers), the X.25 PLP signals a reset to the transport layer. Under Alternative A, the transport layer would then invoke the resynchronization features inherent to the Class 1 transport-layer protocol. This operation is the same for both intra-local-network and internetworking cases.

Lost data under Alternative B is detected only after a transmitter time-out in the Class 4 transport protocol. When this happens, the transport layer would retransmit any unacknowledged data. This approach has two disadvantages. First, the transmitter must wait for a timer to expire before resending data, thereby intro-

Protocol features: Which does what?

Given here, briefly, are the features of the various protocols used in the two alternative protocol architectures considered for local networks.

■ Logical link control (LLC) Type 1. This protocol, which is common to both alternatives, provides the basic capability of data transfer through the use of an unnumbered information (UI) protocol data unit (PDU). The frame check sequence (FCS), which is performed by the medium access control (MAC) sublayer, provides protection against the corruption of transmitted bits by discarding frames with an incorrect FCS. The use of the exchange identification (XID) and test PDUs, which are optional for the transmitter, are not considered here.

■ LLC Type 2. This protocol provides for added reliability by providing sequencing, retransmission upon detection of data loss, and flow control. This protocol could be used over a noisy medium.

■ X.25 packet-level protocol (PLP). As permitted by the ISO (see "The myth of X.25: Networks vs. protocols"), this protocol is used in an intra-local-network environment in a DTE-to-DTE mode. As such, it makes use of the following features: restart packets and procedures; multiplexing through the use of logical channels; call-setup and clearing packets and procedures (the DTE-to-DTE mode does not require any addresses to be used in these packets); data packets and procedures, including the M-bit but excluding the D-bit and Q-bit; flow-control packets and procedures, including sequence numbers; and the calling and called-address extension facilities (for intra-local-network communications where the MAC sublayer address is sufficient to identify the network service access point [NSAP] address, these facilities are not needed).

Not used are: permanent virtual circuits, optional user facilities other than the above, cause and diagnostic codes, or the diagnostic packet.

■ Connectionless protocol (CLP). The inactive subset of this protocol, which is considered for intra-local-network communications, only provides the basic capability of data transfer. When used for internetworking, this protocol also makes use of the following: PDU composition and decomposition; header format analysis; PDU "lifetime" control; PDU routing based on the NSAP address field; PDU forwarding; segmentation and reassembly; PDU discard; and PDU header-error detection through the use of a checksum.

Not used are: error reporting, padding, security, source routing, priority, record route, or quality-of-service maintenance features.

■ Transport-layer protocol Classes 1 and 4. These protocols provide a number of identical features for basic data transfer. The key differences are that Class 1 provides resynchronization and (connection) reassignment after the failure of a network-layer connection, whereas Class 4 provides multiplexing, flow control, checksums, resequencing, duplicate detection, and retransmission on "time-out."

---

ducing extra delay. Second, if it is the acknowledgment that had been lost, then this action would result in the wasted retransmission of data already received. While these factors would not degrade performance significantly in an intra-local-network environment, they could have a serious adverse effect on performance in internetworking scenarios. Even though data may be lost within the local network of the transmitter, recovery must be effected end-to-end. Furthermore, this requires that each receiver include the extra complexity for detecting duplicate data and resequencing data received out of order.

■ Segmentation and reassembly. Both alternatives provide a mechanism for segmenting, and then reconstructing, large transmitted data blocks. Alternative A provides it through the use of the M-bit of the X.25 packet-level protocol, while Alternative B provides an EOT-bit in the transport-layer protocol.

Internetworking and gateways
So far, this analysis has focused primarily on intra-local-network communications. The two alternatives, however, also exhibit different characteristics relating to internetworking and, especially, gateway design. While most of the following observations pertain to internetworking between a local network and an X.25-based network (a likely candidate for long-haul communications), others are more general in nature.

The use of the X.25 PLP in a local network simplifies the gateway to an X.25 network. Figure 6 shows the architecture of the gateway. The local-network side of the gateway can logically be viewed as consisting of multiple DTE-to-DTE interfaces, each one being dynamically created as the local network needs to communicate to the X.25 network. The logical channels of the various DTE-to-DTE interfaces are then mapped to a single DTE-to-DCE interface. (The DCE, or data circuit-terminating equipment, is the access node within the X.25 packet network.) To do this, the gateway must be involved in the X.25 call-setup phase to "patch" two calls together.

During call-setup, the gateway must also map the NSAP address (contained in the X.25 address extension facilities of the call-setup packet) to an X.25 subnetwork (CCITT X.121-based) address. The X.121 address could identify an end-system on the X.25 network, another gateway, or even another system on a distant local network. The gateway generally does not need to be involved with the data-transfer phase of X.25 (it need not check sequence numbers, for example), except for logical-channel-number mapping. If desired, however, the gateway could include extra functions, such as handling optional X.25 user facilities (if any are required by local networks) or handling variable X.25 packet and window sizes.

For Alternative B—using the connectionless protocol

Data Communications/November 1984

6. Gateways. *The local network-side of the gateway actually consists of one DTE-to-DTE interface per local-network station. These interfaces are then simply combined into one interface to the X.25 network. By means of this interface, the gateway actually performs multiplexing for local-network stations.*

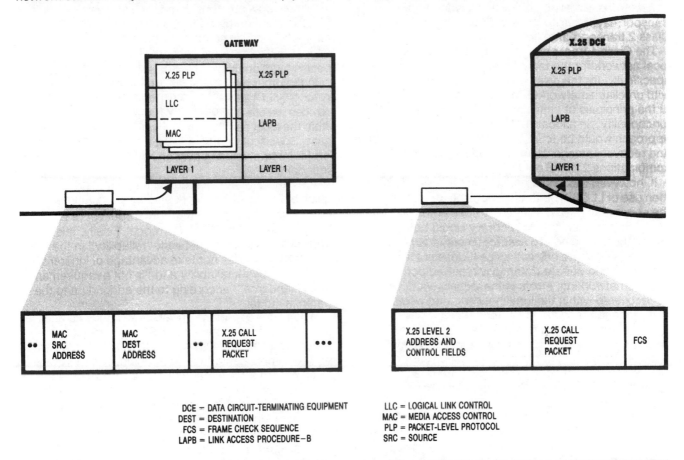

DCE = DATA CIRCUIT-TERMINATING EQUIPMENT
DEST = DESTINATION
FCS = FRAME CHECK SEQUENCE
LAPB = LINK ACCESS PROCEDURE-B

LLC = LOGICAL LINK CONTROL
MAC = MEDIA ACCESS CONTROL
PLP = PACKET-LEVEL PROTOCOL
SRC = SOURCE

and the Transport Class 4 protocol—internetworking is more complex and less efficient. First of all, the local network device must know that internetworking is necessary so that it can use the fully expanded version of the connectionless protocol, which violates the MIF principle. Mapping of NSAP addresses to X.121 addresses in the gateway is handled in much the same way for either alternative. However, the connectionless protocol of Alternative B provides no information to the gateway regarding when a call to the X.25 network should be set up or taken down. To get this information, the gateway must decode the transport-layer (Class 4) protocol to determine when a connection is being made.

Decoding of the transport-layer protocols by the gateway would seem to violate the spirit of the OSI reference model, as it is inconsistent with the principle of layer independence. Alternatively, if the gateway only looks at the network-layer connectionless protocol, then it must decide when to set up and take down X.25 calls. This, in turn, leads to the inefficient use of gateway and network resources.

There are also other problems with Alternative B regarding internetworking. For example, an in-depth functional analysis of the full connectionless protocol shows that it really does not offer any particularly

unique features to local networks with respect to internetworking. In particular:
■ Functions such as PDU (protocol data unit) composition and decomposition, header format analysis, route PDU, and discard PDU are no different from those performed by a system using any other protocol, including the X.25 packet-level protocol (PLP).
■ Functions such as data segmentation and reassembly are handled in a much simpler way in the X.25 PLP because of the inherent sequence-preserving nature of local networks.
■ Functions such as "source routing" and "record route" would have limited use in an environment consisting of two or three concatenated networks; furthermore, their use would violate the MIF principle.
■ The PDU "lifetime control" function is really needed only in an environment where data may be delayed, possibly because of looping within a subnetwork or where duplication may occur. And neither case is inherent in the environment under consideration.

The Transport Class 4 protocol is designed to guard against errors—such as missequencing—that do not normally occur in an X.25-network environment or in a local-net-to-local-net environment (or even in an intra-local-network environment). Therefore, the Class 4 transport provides excess functionality, which is a waste of resources in these cases and even leads to duplication. Measurements show that the addition of the Class 4 protocol results in a tripling of the number of central processing unit cycles needed to run a transport-layer protocol, even if only the features of a Class 2 transport are actually used.

The Class 4 transport is purportedly needed by a local network for the few cases of internetworking and, specifically, for the even fewer cases of internetworking with unreliable networks. Its use is then a clear violation of the principles of "minimum internetworking functionality" in a local network. The more prudent approach would be to include the necessary detection and recovery mechanisms in a gateway, such as with combinations 2 and 3 of Figure 4.

If, however, the local-network medium is very noisy, then use of LLC Type 2 offers several advantages over the approach used in Alternative B. First, for intra-local-network communications, recovery would be quicker since there is no need to wait for timers to expire. LLC Type 2 is also more efficient since it does not involve retransmission of data potentially received correctly. For internetworking, errors in the local network would be recovered within the local network, and would not be propagated on an end-to-end basis.

Yet another consideration is that DTEs located directly on an X.25, or other reliable, network have no need to implement either the connectionless protocol or the Class 4 transport. There are then three alternatives for a local network using this class to communicate with such a DTE:

■ Have the DTE also implement the Class 4 transport
■ Have the local network also implement the Class 1 transport, which is contrary to the MIF principle
■ Have the gateway translate the native local-network protocols (including the connectionless and the Class 4 transport protocols) into X.25 and Class 1. While this would be a clear violation of the OSI reference model (gateways "are operating below the transport layer, that is, within the network layer and below"), this alternative would also unnecessarily affect performance.

The bottom line
After having established the applicability of the OSI reference model to a local-network environment, the task then is to specify a complete protocol architecture for local networks compatible with the reference model. And, except for layers 3 and 4, the choice of protocols at each layer is straightforward. Still, these layers, together with the LLC sublayer, are critical in realizing the objective of a reliable data-transfer mechanism.

One viable alternative is to use the X.25 packet-level protocol (PLP) at layer 3. In this case, only the basic functions of the X.25 PLP are then used in providing the OSI network-layer service in a local-network environment. For communications within the local network, this alternative has several advantages, particularly in the areas of addressing and error recovery. Furthermore, this approach does not put the burden of unneeded functionality on local networks for atypical events that occur within the local network.

At the same time, this approach exhibits several pluses when typical internetworking scenarios involving local networks are considered. The analysis shows that the operation of the X.25 PLP alternative for internetworking is no different from that for communications within the local network. There is, then, no specific functionality set aside just for internetworking.

On the other hand, the use of the connectionless protocol (CLP) with the Transport Class 4 protocol provides excess functionality for communications both within the local network and in typical internetworking cases. Specifically, the use of CLP and Class 4 transport for internetworking over an X.25 network is highly redundant.

Also, this alternative requires that a station distinguish between internetwork and intra-local-network communications so it can use the proper set of procedures for the connectionless protocol. Finally, this approach, by providing network "reliability" in the transport layer, does not take advantage of inherently high local-network reliability and "is not a requirement of OSI standards," according to the addendum to the reference model.

When considering the universality of the two alternatives, it should be noted that X.25 PLP products are widely available. This is not true for connectionless-protocol implementations. In addition, commercially available products already exist that use X.25 PLP in local-network stations. One French offering, for example, uses X.25 PLP in a microcomputer-based workstation operating on a token-bus local network. This workstation, with a 16-bit microcomputer, also runs OSI transport- and session-layer protocols. The Joint Network Team (of the United Kingdom) recently issued a policy on CSMA/CD-type local networks that makes mandatory their adoption of the connection-oriented network service (CONS), via the X.25 PLP, to achieve open-systems interconnection for the support of connection-oriented applications. Clearly, for companies involved in international data communications, the X.25-PLP alternative would seem to be the most expedient and economical way to go.

The connection-oriented approach for local networks is also consistent with the capabilities and operation of the evolving Integrated Services Digital Network (ISDN). Specifically, the use of X.25 in a local-network environment would help facilitate a migration to an ISDN environment, since considerable work has already been done on specifying ISDN "terminal adapter" functions for X.25. ■

Fred Burg is manager of the Standards Planning Department at AT&T Information Systems. Cheng T. Chen is a member of the technical services staff of the Enhanced Network Services Division at ATTIS, Lincroft, N. J. He has been involved in implementing the X.25- and transport-layer protocols. Harold C. Folts is executive director of Omnicom Inc., Vienna, Va. He holds a BSEE degree from Tri-State University, Angola, Ind., and an M. S. in systems management from the University of Southern California.

SECTION 5 TRANSPORT AND SESSION PROTOCOLS

5.1 TRANSPORT PROTOCOLS

The transport protocol is the keystone of the whole concept of a computer-communications architecture. Lower-layer protocols are needed, to be sure, but they are less important pedagogically and to designers for a number of reasons. For one thing, lower-level protocols are better understood and, on the whole, less complex than transport protocols. Also, standards have settled out quite well for most kinds of layer 1 to 3 transmission facilities, and there is a large body of experience in their use.

Viewed from the other side, upper level protocols are also of lesser importance. The transport protocol provides the basic end-to-end service of transferring data between users. Any process or application can be programmed to directly access the transport services without going through session and presentation layers. Indeed, this is the normal mode of operation for DOD's transport protocols.

The purpose of a transport protocol is to provide a reliable mechanism for the exchange of data between processes in different systems. The transport protocol ensures that data units are delivered error-free, in sequence, with no losses or duplications. The transport layer may also be concerned with optimizing the use of network services and providing a requested quality of service to session entities. For example, the session entity might specify acceptable error rates, maximum delay, priority, and security. In effect, the transport layer serves as the user's liaison with the communications facility.

The size and complexity of a transport protocol depends on the type of service it can get from layer 3. For a reliable layer 3 with a virtual circuit capability, a minimal layer 4 is required. If layer 3 is unreliable and/or only supports datagrams, the layer 4 protocol should include extensive error detection and recovery. Accordingly, NBS has defined two versions of its Transport Protocol (TP): a relatively simple version for reliable networks and a more complex one for unreliable networks. The former is a subset of the latter. The more complex version is comparable in capability to another transport protocol standard, DOD's Transmission Control Protocol (TCP). ISO has gone even further and defined five classes of transport protocol, each oriented toward a different underlying protocol.

5.2 SESSION PROTOCOLS

The essential purpose of a session protocol is to provide a user-oriented connection service. The transport protocol is responsible for creating and maintaining a connection between endpoints. A session protocol would provide a "user interface" by "adding value" to the basic connection service. Let us consider some of the value-added features. We can group them into the following categories:

- Session establishment and maintenance.
- Dialogue management.
- Recovery.

Session Establishment and Maintenance

The minimum service that a session protocol entity provides its users is the establishment, maintenance, and termination of sessions. When two users wish to establish a connection, their respective entities will create a session that is mapped onto a transport connection and will negotiate the parameters of the session (e.g., data unit size; see below for further examples).

Let us refer to the unit of data exchanged between a session user and a session protocol entity as a record. Then the entity accepts records from the user and transmits the data over a transport connection in a sequence of letters. The data are received on the other side and delivered to the user in the proper order. The sending entity may, at its discretion, fragment records into multiple letters if the record size is too large. Alternatively, multiple records may be blocked into a single letter for efficiency of transmission. In any case, the receiving entity recovers the original records and passes these on to the receiving user.

The simplest relationship between sessions and transport connections is one to one. It might be desirable to multiplex multiple sessions onto a single transport connection. This reduces the processing burden and amount of state information required of the transport entity. However, caution must be observed. For example, a session supporting inquiry/response should not be multiplexed with a session supporting a file transfer, since the sending of the inquiry text may be significantly delayed when entering a long transport queue of text from the other session. Furthermore, if the receiving session entity is forced, for any reason, to stop receiving the file transfer text, the receiving queue may soon fill up. This will cause the source queue to fill up as well, and any text from the session multiplexed with the halted session may remain trapped in it.

A session might also be split between two transport connections. This could facilitate the transfer of expedited or interrupt data.

Dialogue Management

The session entity may impose a structure on the interac-

EHO226-1/85/0000/0271$01.00 © 1985 IEEE

tion or dialogue between users. There are three possible modes of dialogue: two-way simultaneous, two-way alternate, and one-way.

The two-way simultaneous mode is a full-duplex type of operation. Both sides can simultaneously send data. Once this mode is agreed upon in the session negotiation phase, there is no specific dialogue management task required. This would probably be the most common mode of dialogue.

Similarly, the one-way mode requires no specific dialogue management mechanism once it is established. All user data flows in one direction only. An example of this is if data are to be sent to a temporarily inactive user, and are accepted by a "receiver server," whose only task is to accept data on behalf of other local users and store them. Note that the characteristic of being one-way is not absolute. There is a two-way dialogue required to establish the session. During data transfer, the receiving session entity may transmit acknowledgments and other control information. Furthermore, the receiving session user may need to send back some interrupt data. For example, the receiver may need to halt reception temporarily because of a local system problem.

The most complex of the three modes is two-way alternate. In this case, the two sides take turns sending data. An example of the use of this mode is for inquiry/response applications. The session entity enforces the alternating interaction by informing each user when it is its turn. This is actually a three-step process:

- The user who has the turn informs its session entity when it has completed its turn.

- The sending session entity sends any outstanding data to the receiving entity, and then informs the receiving entity that the turn is being passed.

- The receiving entity passes up any outstanding data to its user, and then informs the user that it is its turn.

An economical means of accomplishing this process is to mark the data with a delimiter. Specifically, the sending user includes a delimiter in the last record of its turn. Let us call the sequence of records sent during one user's turn a *session interaction unit*. Then, on the last record of its turn, the user would include an end-of-interaction unit (I) delimiter. This delimiter is, in effect, a token that is passed to the other user.

With two-way alternate, the user is prevented from sending normal data unless it is its turn. However, a user may send interrupt data to, for example, demand the turn. As an example of the use of the demand-turn mechanism, consider a user who has requested data and is viewing them as they scroll onto a screen. The user may wish to abort the transmission once the first few lines have been viewed.

Recovery

Another potential feature of a session protocol is a recovery support service similar to the checkpoint/restart mechanisms used in file management.

This feature could be provided by defining a *session recovery unit*, which corresponds to the interval between checkpoints. Each user specifies the point at which a recovery unit ends, and the recovery units are numbered sequentially. To recover lost data (e.g., following a disk fault or a paper break on a printer), a user can issue a command to recover, using the recovery unit number to identify the point to which the session should be backed up.

Once a session has been backed up, some form of recovery will generally be attempted. This is a complex function, which would doubtless extend beyond the bounds of the session layer.

One fundamental point does need to be mentioned, namely, the degree of responsibility of the session protocol entities. When the session is backed up to the beginning of a session recovery unit, the session protocol entities may be requested to retransmit all records from that point forward. If so, the session entity must maintain a copy of each record. To avoid unbounded storage requirements, the user should periodically issue a release command, so that some prior session recovery units can be discarded. Alternatively, the session entity might only be required to remember the records of the current recovery unit.

On the other hand, the session entity may only be required to discard outstanding records and back up its recovery-unit counter to the point indicated, with the primary recovery responsibilities being handled at higher levels. In this case, there does not seem much point in having any recovery feature in the session layer. Indeed, NBS takes the position that recovery is inherently an application function and, based on the principle of functional separation of layers, should not be visible in the session layer (see accompanying reprint).

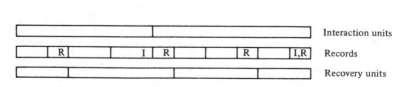

Figure 5-1: Session Delimited Data Units

Figure 5.1 indicates that a session recovery unit is made up of one or more records. However, there is no need for a defined relationship between session recovery units and session interaction units.

5.3 ARTICLE SUMMARY

The report from NBS discusses the features and services that should be provided by the transport and session layers. Sunshine provides a functional look at transport protocols. Stallings provides a detailed discussion of transport protocol mechanisms, plus a summary of current standards. Emmons and Chandler look at session layer standards.

Report No. 4361   Bolt Beranek and Newman Inc.

FEATURES OF THE TRANSPORT AND SESSION PROTOCOLS

John Burruss

FOREWORD BY THE NATIONAL BUREAU OF STANDARDS

The National Bureau of Standards, Institute for Computer Sciences
and Technology (ICST), has initiated a program to develop
computer network protocol standards as Federal Information
Processing Standards (FIPS). The objectives of this program are
(1) to make possible distributed computer networks, and (2) to
enable the interconnection of different components selected based
on cost, performance, availability, and competitive procurements.

This draft report is one of a series of draft reports being
prepared under the network protocol standards program for
distribution to government agencies, voluntary standards
organizations, computer and communications equipment
manufacturers, and other interested parties. We urge readers to
provide comments and to further interact with us on this draft
report. Written comments should address both the advantages and
disadvantages (from the reader's viewpoint) of individual
features described in this draft. Responses should be directed
to the address below, and **NOT** to the NBS Contractor that prepared
the draft report.

Reply to:

> National Bureau of Standards (Code HLNP-80-1)
> Institute for Computer Sciences and Technology
> Systems and Network Architecture Division
> Technology Building Room B218
> Washington, D.C. 20234

March 1980

Prepared for:
Institute for Computer Sciences and Technology
National Bureau of Standards

Table of Contents

1 Introduction

This report holds a place in the development of communications protocols for the transport and session layers (these protocols are also known as host-to-host protocols). A description of the development sequence and of the encompassing program may be found in <u>Federal Computer Network Protocol Standards Program</u>: <u>An Overview</u>, published by the National Bureau of Standards, Institute for Computer Sciences and Technology, 1980.

It must be noted that the protocols which formed the basis for this features analysis are all in a state of evolutionary development; the descriptions found in this report may be put out of date at any time.

1.1 Feature Analysis

A feature analysis is a means of determining the kernel set of essential features of a protocol, along with the clusters of value-added features which will support various application categories. Among the criteria for selecting the kernel and ranking the value-added features are relative cost-effectiveness, level of demand, implementation expense, elegance, and sufficiency. At the end of the exercise, we will be left with the kernel set of features which must be integrated into a basic

protocol, and several levels of value-added functionality which
may be integrated with the protocol to form a protocol family
answering the needs of disparate applications.   The reasoning
used to define the kernel and added functions will form the basis
for the justification of choices made in the following step in
protocol design, the protocol specification itself.

1.2 Layers

The first questions to be answered in a feature analysis of
transport and session protocols must be: What are transport and
session protocols?   Why group them together in one report?
Transport and Session form layers four and five of the seven
layers defined in the ISO Reference Model for Open Systems
Interconnection [ISO79a]. Simply put (more complete definitions
will follow in the appropriate sections), the transport layer
actually moves data, while the session layer co-operates with the
high-level protocols to manage and structure data movement.   The
two layers are conveniently considered together since together
they correspond to what is commonly called the host-to-host
protocol.   The host-to-host protocol, considered as a unity,
performs two dispara e functions: that of the supplier of
network service, and that of the interface for high-level
protocols to obtain network service.   By considering transport
and   session   protocols separately, these functions can be

distinguished, and feature definition and analysis can proceed along straightforward lines.

1.3 Distinction Between Service and Protocol Features

Before embarking on discussion or cataloging of features, we should try to clarify just what a feature is. Just what sort of things a host level protocol must do is well known; differenc protocols do those things in different ways. For example, most host level protocols provide a connection-oriented means for moving data. But how is this connection to be established? Should all connections be full-duplex? Half-duplex? Some flow-control scheme must regulate data transfer between transport services--but methods for this vary from protocol to protocol.

The point of mentioning this diversity (of method) within unity (of function) is to point out that there are two sorts of features in a host level protocol: let us call them _service_ features and _protocol_ features. Service features are the features of the protocol visible to the immediate user of the protocol; i.e., the service features of the host/host protocol are the services it provides to the higher-level protocol-entity using it. Protocol features, however, are for the most part invisible to the immediate user: duplicate detection is an example of a protocol feature. Carl Sunshine makes a similar distinction between specifying protocol services and specifying the operation of the protocol itself [SUNC79]. Obviously, the distinction between service and protocol features subdivides our previous separation of transport features from session features. We must consider transport protocol features and transport service features, as well as the corresponding classes of session features.

2 Transport Service

2.1 Purpose of the Transport Service

A transport service exists to provide interprocess data transfer in a network environment. Data submitted to the transport service must be delivered to a specified destination. Furthermore, it is desirable that the transport service provide communication services between processes not necessarily resident on the same network.

2.2 The Network Environment

The nature of the communications subnetwork to which the transport layer interfaces will have a considerable impact on the operation of the layer and therefore on its protocol features. This is especially true with respect to the reliability of the subnetwork. If the subnetwork provides reliable, sequenced delivery, then the transport layer need not include error-checking, sequencing, and duplicate-detection features: the burden of reliability will be carried by the subnetwork. This is true, for example, in the ARPANET IMP subnetwork [MCQJ75]. However, if the subnetwork does not provide reliable communication, the transport layer must itself assume the burden of making transport service reliable, and perform error-checking, duplicate-detection, and sequencing operations accordingly. Examples of transport protocols which perform these operations themselves are TCP [POSJ79b] and the CYCLADES transport protocol [ZIMH75].

In this report, we will note which protocol features are affected by the nature of the subnetwork.

2.3 Transport Features

Let us examine the consequences of this statement of purpose. First, the transport service provides communication: its primary function must then be __data__ __transfer__. As noted in the section above, if the subnetwork does not provide reliable service, the transport layer must perform __error__ __checking__ to ensure intact delivery and __duplicate-detection__ and __sequencing__ to ensure in-order delivery, and must provide an __acknowledgement__ mechanism to exchange information about the integrity of peer transport communication. A __flow-control__ mechanism is needed to keep that communication synchronized. A transport service must provide a method for transport-users to __address__ their

correspondents.   It is expected that corresponding transport-
users will be bound together in some sort of <u>connection</u> for the
lifetime of their communication. Further desirable features are:
provision of <u>transaction</u> and <u>broadcast</u> services as well as
connection-oriented stream service; selection of a <u>grade of</u>
<u>service</u> to be provided during communication; some means of
<u>expediting delivery</u> of some data which may supersede previously
sent information; and finally, <u>internetwork compatibility</u>.

It is not expected that all transport protocols surveyed in
this report will have all these features. Certain features, for
example data transfer, are so basic as to be universal.   Others,
although desirable, are rare or even nonexistent among the
protocols examined in this report.

We must divide these features according to our distinction
between service and protocol features; the distinguishing test in
this case is whether a feature is derived from user requirements
(and is therefore perceptible from above the transport/user
interface) or whether it is derived from the nature of the
communication environment (and therefore lies below the user
interface). Some features will seem to have both service and
protocol characteristics: these we will simply assign to the
class that seems most natural. In this preliminary discussion of
transport features, the language of the ISO Reference Model will
be adopted for its generality.

2.3.1 Transport Service Features

2.3.1.1 Type of Service

The ISO Reference Model suggests three different types of service: connection-oriented (stream) service, transaction-oriented service, and broadcast service; transaction and broadcast services are left undefined.

Stream data transfer takes place between two transport-users on a transport-connection. The connection passes through three phases distinct to the user: an establishment phase, a transfer phase, and a termination phase. Communication on a connection may be full-duplex, half-duplex, or simplex (with two connections necessary to model duplex behavior).

Transaction or datagram service entails sending a data message from one transport-user to another with a single transport service request. No connection need be established, and error-checking, sequencing, and acknowledgement may be unnecessary.

Broadcast service is the sending of a single data message to all hosts (perhaps to all listening processes on all hosts or to a single process on all hosts). Again, no connection need be established.

A type of service not mentioned in the ISO Reference Model is multi-cast service. In this case, a message could be sent to all of a specified list of correspondents, and the sending transport-user would need to make only one request for service, rather than make a request for each correspondent.

Because transaction and broadcast services are not as widely understood as connection-oriented service (on account of its historical priority, if for no other reason), descriptions of network services have traditionally been couched in terms of connections and connection service. In fact, one of the shortcomings of the ISO Reference Model itself is just that orientation in its language and definitions of transport services. As we have chosen to use the language of the ISO Reference Model, the following definitions necessarily share its connection orientation.

2.3.1.2 Grade of Service

Transport users may request a grade of service during transport-connection establishment. This would define acceptable error and loss levels, desired delay, priority levels, security, and other considerations. It may be, of course, that only one level of quality is available: for example, correct in-order delivery with some average network delay. Different grades of

service are significant in the case of a user of an unreliable
subnetwork who will accept the unreliability of the subnetwork in
return for bypassing the extra processing performed by the
transport layer.

2.3.1.3 Data Transfer

The basic function of a transport service is the delivery of
data. The quality of this delivery agrees with the requested
grade of service.

2.3.1.4 User Interface

The details of the user/transport interface are heavily
dependent on the host environment, but a few characteristics of
the interface must be specified. How is the user to be prevented
from swamping the transport service with data? How is the user
to be notified of the success of a send or a receive? One could
imagine a very primitive interface which blocked the user until
his request completed, which easily leads to deadlocks unless a
timeout returns control to the user. Another choice is that a
request should return an immediate synchronous reply accepting or
refusing the request and should later notify the user that the
request has completed.

2.3.1.5 Connection Management

The transport service establishes and terminates connections between transport-users. Termination should not interfere with the usual orderly transfer of data on the connection.

2.3.1.6 Connection Abort

The transport service may also provide a peremptory abort facility in case of unrecoverable errors perceived at any protocol level.

2.3.1.7 Expedited Delivery

Some data submitted to the transport service may supersede data previously submitted. A mechanism for expedited delivery would allow transport-users to exchange such high-priority information. The ISO Reference Model leaves undefined the effect of expedited data transfer on normal data transfer.

2.3.2 Transport Protocol Features

2.3.2.1 Error Checking

A transport service transmitting on an unreliable subnetwork must insure that data accepted for delivery is delivered correctly in accordance with the requested grade of service. For a reliable grade of service, the transport service must guarantee the integrity of each data unit delivered.

In the case of a reliable subnetwork, error checking need not be performed in the transport layer.

2.3.2.2   Duplicate Detection and Sequencing

Also in accordance with the requested grade of service, the transport service must identify and destroy any duplicate data which might have been generated by the communications subnetwork or by the sending transport service during retransmission. Arriving data may not be delivered to the receiving process until it has been sorted into the order in which the sender submitted it to the transport service.

A transport service employing a reliable, sequencing subnetwork may not need to include duplicate-detection and sequencing facilities.

2.3.2.3   Retransmission

A transport service employing an unreliable subnetwork may require retransmission by the transport layer of lost or discarded data. The sender usually decides that data has been

lost after spending a certain time awaiting acknowledgement. The
receiver may also request retransmission of damaged data.
Retransmission will not ordinarily be required in services using
reliable subnetworks.

2.3.2.4 Acknowledgement

We have noted that the transport service must be prepared to
retransmit data units which are lost or damaged by an unreliable
subnetwork. The transport service identifies lost or damaged
units by the absence of an end-to-end acknowledgement.
Acknowledgement schemes are of two sorts: positive (signaling
the receipt of an intact unit) and negative (requesting the
retransmission of a lost or damaged unit). Other information
passed end-to-end (synchronization information, pacing windows)
might be piggybacked with acknowledgements, even though the other
information is functionally distinct from the acknowledgement.
Similarly, the acknowledgement might itself be piggybacked on
other messages, especially on data messages (this is obviously
possible only when both correspondents have data to send, that
is, in dialogues, not in monologues).

Transport-to-transport acknowledgement may not be required
in services transmitting over reliable subnetworks.

2.3.2.5 Flow Control

Two kinds of flow control regulate the movement of data in and out of the transport service: interface flow control and peer flow control. The communicating transport services regulate the flow of data between them via peer flow control. Peer flow control is usually accomplished by some window or allocation scheme, and keeps one transport service from sending more data than the other service can accept.

Flow control exists at both interfaces to the transport service. However, flow control at the transport/network interface is part of the network layer specification and beyond the scope of this report. Flow control at the user/transport interface has been discussed as a service feature.

2.3.2.6 Buffering

The ISO Reference Model does not include any discussion of buffering in the transport layer. Buffering will, however, be a concern in many implementations. Any transport layer which buffers incoming data will need to be notified when its buffers must be flushed and accumulated data passed to the user. Going in the other direction, the user must be able to tell the transport service to submit accumulated data to the network without waiting for any more data.

2.3.2.7 Transport Addressing

A transport address is the means by which the transport service identifies transport-users. A process desiring to establish a connection must be able to identify its correspondent in a way intelligible to the transport service. Typical choices for an addressing scheme are hierarchical addressing, in which local names are concatenated with global identifiers to form a unique identifier; allocated addressing, in which each system in a network is allocated certain global identifiers (these identifiers may be assigned only once or may be assigned and reassigned dynamically); and mapped addressing, in which a defined set of global identifiers is distributed among all processes and files to which network access is required.(the local system maps these global names onto its local names). Hybrid schemes are also possible.

2.3.2.8 Internetworking

It is desirable for the transport service to allow communication not only between processes on different hosts belonging to the same network, but between processes on different, interconnected networks. To accomplish this, the transport service should make as few assumptions about the nature of the underlying communication medium as possible.

Communication on one network should not be constrained by any limitations of connected networks, e.g., the obtainable reliability of the transmission medium or the maximum packet size.

2.3.2.9 Accounting

If billing for network services is done on the basis of transport services (number of transport-service-data-units transmitted, for example), the transport layer would be the logical place to put accounting services.

2.3.2.10 Security

The basic security feature expected of a transport service is that it not allow unauthorized processes to manipulate connections. This might mean defining a concept of connection "ownership"; alternative meanings of "authorized" may be appropriate. Furthermore, the transport service might provide encryption service on demand. Other security precautions could be provided if they are supported by underlying layers: routing through secure nodes or on secure links, for example.

3 Transport Features Analysis

3.1 Considerations for Feature Analysis

It is natural that we should examine protocols from three conceptual viewpoints: as the absolute minimum protocol which provides the primitive functionality of a layer; as a robust and flexible protocol which provides the commonly demanded functions of a layer; and as a protocol or protocols to some degree enhanced with special, less frequently demanded or more expensive functions. If we consider the features we have described above as the components of a protocol, then the minimal protocol will be made up of the set of features defined in their minimal sense. Each feature will have an aspect corresponding to the minimal, common, and enhanced protocols just mentioned. Thus, for each protocol feature described above we will describe a _foundation definition_ of the feature, a _kernel definition_ of the feature, and one or more _value-added features_ or enhancements. The foundation definition is a minimal definition of the feature which will still allow a protocol layer to perform its primitive function. The kernel definition is one commonly agreed upon by the protocols examined for this report. Value-added features are extensions or additions which are found in some examined protocols, but which were judged too expensive or not of frequent enough demand to justify inclusion in the kernel. These value-added features do not necessarily group themselves into layers;

the clusters of additions and extensions are not hierarchically dependent on one another, as one expects layers to be, but will form at some layer a protocol family able to satisfy the requirements of particular application categories. Any or all of foundation, kernel, or value-added features may have alternate definitions depending on the network environment in which the protocol will operate.

A foundation protocol constructed from the foundation definitions of the component features might be implementable, but would surely be uselessly primitive. Our foundation is intended to have a mental existence only; it is the basis from which protocol definition proceeds.

3.2 Transport Features Analysis

It must be admitted that the analysis of transport features leaned strongly in the direction of connection-oriented stream transfer service, perhaps at the expense of transaction and broadcast services. The near universality of stream service in the protocols studied accounts for such a bias.

3.2.1 Type of Service

FOUNDATION: The protocol shall provide any single type of data transport service.

KERNEL: The protocol shall provide a connection-oriented stream data transport service.

VALUE-ADDED FEATURES: (1) The protocol may provide a transaction transfer service.   (2) The protocol may provide broadcast service.   (3) The protocol may provide multi-cast service.

Connection service, as has been noted above, was nearly universal among the protocols studied for this analysis.   In fact, nearly all provided no other type of service.

Several protocols provided a datagram transaction service (e.g., User Datagram [POSJ79a].   In these cases, a transaction datagram was sent in a single transport message, with no error-checking, flow control, or acknowledgement expected. This sort of transaction would put the burden for such actions on the upper-level protocol, where we feel it does not belong.

One protocol provided only a reliable transaction service: the Livermore Laboratories Delta-t protocol [WATR79b].   The protocol performs error-checking, duplicate detection, and acknowledgement.   The protocol maintains the state information associated with a transaction for certain periods of time after transmission or reception to allow duplicate detection and recognition of associated messages or replies. However, for stream-type communication to take place in a Delta-t environment, some rather obscure information must be passed in packet headers to permit multi-transaction messages to flow in a simulated "connection." The main advantage of the Delta-t protocol is that a transaction may be sent reliably with only two packets (the message and its reply) although with a certain amount of increased overhead based on the timer mechanism and the requirement that state information be retained for a fixed time on both sides.

There is a sequence of three TCP-4 segments which will model transaction service. This is done by beginning the three-way handshakes for connection establishment **and** termination in the same segment, which will also contain the transaction data. The TCP user interface could easily be extended to allow such an exchange from a single transport service request. The three-segment TCP exchange compares favorably with the two segments used in the Delta-t protocol, with one palpable advantage: TCP's retransmission facility would allow an implementation which included the transaction interface to exchange transactions with an implementation which did not include it.

There were no instances of broadcast service among the examined protocols. Indicative of the cause of its omission is a statement by McQuillan and Cerf [MCQJ78]: "Broadcasting reliably is not yet well-understood, since the usual acknowledgement schemes become unpalatable when a single broadcast would cause hundreds or thousands of acknowledgements."

Our experience with TCP and the TCP three-segment transaction leads us to believe that transaction service could be quite inexpensively integrated into a connection-oriented protocol; the example of the Delta-t protocol, however, demonstrates that addition of connection service to a transaction protocol is likely to be complex and inelegant if not costly. For this reason connection service has been included in the kernel, with the recognition that transactions are the most desirable of the additional features, and need not be costly to add.

3.2.2 Grade of Service

FOUNDATION: The protocol shall provide a reliable, sequenced service in which messages are transmitted at a single priority level.

KERNEL: The protocol shall provide a reliable, sequenced service in which messages are transmitted at a single priority level.

VALUE-ADDED FEATURES: (1) The protocol may provide multiple levels of priority for users. (2) The protocol may provide unsequenced or unreliable services at time/cost savings to the transport-user.   (3) The protocol may provide low-delay/low-throughput service or high-delay/high-throughput service.

Protocols which provide connection-oriented service almost always perform error-checking and sequencing on the data transferred if necessary. An unreliable service is limited to datagram-type service in those protocols which provide it, such as the User Datagram Protocol. Provision of different grades of service is usually dependent on the communication subnetwork: a protocol on a reliable, sequencing subnetwork will not ordinarily be able to bypass the error-checking and sequencing functions in the subnetwork. The CYCLADES transport protocol allows the user to choose whether the protocol should perform error-checking and flow-control on his connection.   However, the provision of reliable service in so many of the protocols examined must indicate that demand is largest for that grade of service.

3.2.3 Data Transfer

FOUNDATION: The protocol shall allow data transfer on full-duplex connections; control information must be passed on a separate logical connection. Transmitted data will be carried in octets.

KERNEL: The protocol shall allow data transfer on full-duplex connections; data and control information may flow over the same

logical connection. Transmitted data will be carried in octets.
VALUE-ADDED FEATURES: (1) The protocol may impose no byte size
format on transmitted data. (2) The protocol may allow both
simplex and half-duplex connections in addition to full-duplex
connections.

Most of the examined protocols impose an octet format on the
transmitted data; NCP [MCKA78] was the notable exception (byte
size is limited to the range 1 through 255 bits, and must be
constant for the life of a connection). It is true that control
and data can be separated on two logical connections, and that
two simplex connections can be used to provide two-way
communication. However, the tendency in protocol design seems to
be towards the integration of control and data on one connection
(as in TCP, CYCLADES, and NCR [NCR79]) and the provision of
full-duplex communication (as in TCP and CYCLADES). The issue of
a separate control channel for an out-of-band signal mechanism
will be addressed later.

3.2.4 User Interface

FOUNDATION: The user interface shall be synchronous, with the
provision that any request will terminate after a system-defined
timeout.
KERNEL: The user interface shall be asynchronous, with immediate

notification of a request's acceptance or rejection by the transport layer, and some later notification of request completion.   Notification of completion is dependent on the host operating system capabilities.

VALUE-ADDED FEATURE: The timeout in a synchronous interface may be user-defined rather than system-defined.

Although the user interface is very dependent on the particular host operating system, a few things about it can be specified. First, a synchronous interface is indeed minimal, but highly liable to deadlock; a timeout on all requests should eliminate permanent deadlock. In the asynchronous interface, the transport layer would be free to accept or reject user requests, thereby providing user/transport flow control.   Notification of request completion might occur through an event queue, interrupts, or some other signaling or scheduling facility provided by the operating system.

3.2.5 Connection Management

FOUNDATION: Either correspondent shall be able to initiate connection establishment and termination.

KERNEL: Connection establishment and termination procedures shall be symmetrical. Connection termination shall not interfere with the delivery of all data sent on the connection.

Some remarks have been made above about connections: they have been defined to be full-duplex. If the protocol is enhanced to allow simplex connections, even though the establishment procedures must be different for sender and receiver, it is not safe to say that establishment is always initiated by the sender. In the case of one host collecting data from other hosts, the receiver might want to initiate connection establishment. The NCR end-to-end protocol has just such a facility. It is equally clear that either correspondent must be able to initiate termination of a connection.

In the case of duplex connections, the establishment and termination sequences can be symmetrical, since there is then no distinction between sender and receiver, unless both correspondents make a conventional agreement to assume those roles. A symmetrical procedure eliminates the errors arising from colliding requests, and is on the whole simpler and more elegant.

3.2.6 Connection Abort

FOUNDATION: The protocol shall provide a means for a correspondent to request a peremptory abort of a connection. A connection will be aborted if an expected reply is not received within a system-defined timeout.

KERNEL: The protocol shall provide a means for a correspondent to request a peremptory abort of a connection. A connection will be aborted if an expected reply is not received within a system-defined timeout.

VALUE-ADDED FEATURE: The timeout for connection abort may be user-specified.

Since connection termination has been defined so as not to interfere with data transfer, some means is clearly required to end a connection without processing all the data queued on that connection. The timeout is required to detect host failure or loss of communication line.

3.2.7 Expedited Delivery

FOUNDATION: The protocol shall provide no expedited data transfer service.

KERNEL: The protocol shall provide a method for notifying transport-users of the presence of urgent data.

VALUE-ADDED FEATURE: The protocol may arrange for the delivery of urgent data to the transport-user before the delivery of pending data on the connection.

The expedited delivery service provides, among other things, a means to interrupt the remote transport-user. The exact method in which the notification of urgent data is done depends on the host operating system (e.g., one method would be via an interrupt sent by the transport service). The user is then at liberty to treat the urgent notification as he sees fit, for example, by discarding the pending messages until he reaches the urgent information. This method is used by TCP. NCP sends the interrupt through the control connection, thereby insuring that it will not be blocked by pending data. The DECnet protocol [DEC78] actually delivers some data to the transport-user at the time of the interrupt.

Garlick [GARL76] points out that a true out-of-band interrupt need not be synchronized with data and other control transmissions, and must, in fact, be independent of data flow control. His solution to this problem is to transmit the interrupt signal over a second logical channel. This prevents the transmission of the interrupt from interfering with data transmissions, as it does in TCP, where pending data must be flushed in order to keep data flow control from blocking the delivery of the interrupt.

The designers of the Delta-t protocol contend that no expedited transfer or out-of-band interrupt is necessary when transport associations are easily set up and terminated. This is apparently true of all transaction systems.

3.2.8 Reliability Issues

FOUNDATION: The   protocol   shall   perform   error-checking,
sequencing, and duplicate detection.   The receiving transport
layer shall acknowledge the correct receipt of all transmissions.
If acknowledgement of a transmission has not been received after
a   system-specified   timeout,   the   information   shall   be
retransmitted. These functions need not be performed if they are
redundant with the operation of the communications subnetwork on
an end-to-end basis.

KERNEL: The protocol shall perform error-checking, sequencing,
and duplicate detection.   The receiving transport layer shall
acknowledge the correct receipt of all transmissions.   If
acknowledgement of a transmission has not been received after a
system-specified timeout, the information shall be retransmitted.
These functions need not be performed if they are redundant with
the operation of the communications subnetwork on   an   end-to-end
basis.

VALUE-ADDED FEATURES: (1) Error-checking,   sequencing,   and
duplicate-detection mechanisms may be bypassed if the transport-
user so requests in his grade-of-service specification. (2) The
retransmission timeout may be user-specified. (3) Data may be
repackaged for retransmission.

These features are obviously dependent on the nature of the
underlying subnetwork.

Negative acknowledgement alone is not sufficient to guarantee the integrity of a connection; positive acknowledgements will guarantee it. To allow the receiver to request retransmission of damaged data or data it thinks is lost, as in the NCR protocol, is to place the burden of reliability on the receiver. This increases traffic over the network (as the receiver must acknowledge correctly received data as well as request retransmission of damaged data).

If value-added feature (3) is included in the protocol specification, it is clear that each data byte must be identifiable, since, if only messages bear identification numbers, two messages cannot be concatenated for retransmission. Such repackaging has the advantage of reducing message leader overhead. This can be very significant, for example, in the case of TCP (which allows re-packaging for retransmission), where each message carries a leader of 288 bits.

3.2.9 Flow Control

FOUNDATION: The protocol shall provide for peer flow control.
KERNEL: The protocol shall provide for peer flow control.
VALUE-ADDED FEATURES: (1) The transport-user may bypass the protocol's peer flow control if he has so specified in his request for a certain grade of service. (2) The transport

buffers allocated to a connection may be varied to provide the transport user with the requested grade of service.

All examined protocols included some method of flow control, with the exception of the User Datagram Protocol. The CYCLADES transport protocol allows the user to bypass the transport layer's flow control mechanism; however, in both the CYCLADES and the User Datagram Protocols, the user is expected to provide his own flow control. The TCP and ECMA [ECMA79a] protocols use a window mechanism to advise the sender of the receiver's capability to receive data. In both cases the window limits are included in the acknowledgement messages. A window is a range of data sequence numbers acceptable to the receiver. Generally, anything to the left of the window (i.e., out of range on the low side) is redundant, and anything to the right of the window (out of range on the high side) exceeds the receiver's resource allocation. The NCP, IBM-SNA [AHUV79], and CYCLADES protocols are based on a credit-allocation scheme; the effect is similar to the window mechanism. In the credit-allocation system, the receiver tells the sender how much data he has allocated resources for. The sender may transmit that much but no more: in essence, the "credit limit" must not be exceeded.

Because of transmission delay the window or the credit information will always be at least slightly out of date. Thus, it is reasonable to transmit the flow control information with

every message transmitted in an attempt to keep that information
as current as possible. Therefore, all data messages, control
segments, and acknowledgements might bear the pacing parameters.

In all the protocols examined, if the allocated credit falls
to zero, serious delays will be introduced. With zero credit or
with a closed window, neither process would normally be
transmitting, so even when the window opened or the credit
raised, there would be no way of informing the correspondent.
Therefore, the sender must periodically send a message giving the
current pacing parameters to provoke some reply from the
receiver.

The NCR end-to-end protocol contains a second means of flow
control used for emergency stop: the Receiver-Not-Ready
indication, which is a primitive mechanism like XON/XOFF. While
this is the least expensive flow control scheme (one bit/packet),
it has serious flaws which are obvious if one translates the
Receiver-Not-Ready bit into a window report. The R-N-R bit off
means the receive window is open; R-N-R bit on means the window
is completely shut. We have mentioned above the serious effects
a closed window will have on performance; the consequences of
XON/XOFF flow control will similarly restrict performance.

3.2.10 Buffering

FOUNDATION: The transport layer will flush its internal buffers
and deliver accumulated data to the user, or to the network, on
demand.

KERNEL: The transport layer will flush its internal buffers and
deliver accumulated data to the user, or to the network, on
demand.

An implementation of a transport layer is not required to
buffer either incoming or outgoing data. Yet it is clear from
experience that buffering will commonly be required for reasons
of efficiency. For example, to interrupt the transport-user upon
the arrival of every incoming packet (even though other packets
might be in transit and the received packet itself contain no
information which could be acted upon without information from
packets yet undelivered) imposes significant system overhead on
the transport layer without enabling any useful processing to
take place.   The usual solution is to hold data until a
significant amount has arrived before notifying the transport-
user. A mechanism to force data delivery costs little or nothing
to provide—and if it is not provided no implementation of the
protocol can buffer data. Hence it seems worthwhile to define
such a facility for those who require it.

TCP and the CYCLADES protocol force delivery by marking a segment of data "end-of-letter," and NCR calls its marker "end-of-message." The British Post Office Protocol [BPO79] clears buffers by transmitting the special "PUSH" packet. Comparing these two schemes, one notes that the "end of letter" marker requires but one bit in every packet whereas the PUSH packet requires transmission of (at least) the minimum-sized packet every time buffers are to be cleared.

3.2.11 Transport Addressing

FOUNDATION: There shall be a set of fixed global names with a fixed mapping onto transport-users.

KERNEL: Transport-addresses shall be the concatenation of a network-wide host address with local allocated names which are dynamically associated with transport-users.

VALUE-ADDED FEATURE: A global network name may be prefixed to the transport address to allow internetwork addressing.

The kernel definition of transport addressing, while simple enough, is not at all flexible. Consider the case of a new transport-user joining the community: all hosts must update their addressing tables and make the new information available to the users. The hierarchical concatenation of host address with a dynamically assigned local transport-address is far more flexible, but depends on the community to agree on the meanings of at least a few local names so that common resources can be accessed--this is the idea of the well-known socket familiar to NCP, TCP and DECnet.

Since a transport-user may participate in several connections, his address alone is not sufficient to identify a single connection. TCP identifies the connection by the concatenation of both transport-addresses. NCP requires a complicated Initial Connection Protocol to allocate a unique identifier for a connection. The TCP identification scheme is evidently simpler and more elegant, and it allows for agreement between transport-users even in cases where the connection establishment requests collide.

Internetwork addressability may be purchased at the cost of a few bits in the transport-address. Among the protocols examined, TCP and the User Datagram Protocol provide internetwork addressing.

3.2.12 Accounting

FOUNDATION: No accounting takes place in the transport layer.
KERNEL: No accounting takes place in the transport layer.
VALUE-ADDED FEATURE: The transport layer may keep accounts of network use.

As none of the protocols examined specified any accounting procedures and the ISO Reference Model does not locate accounting procedures within the Open Systems Environment, we felt it best to postpone a kernel definition pending further discussion of the issue. It is nevertheless clear that the transport layer is the only host-level layer which can do "per-packet" accounting.

3.2.13 Security

FOUNDATION: The protocol shall enforce no security measures.
KERNEL: The protocol shall enforce no security measures.
VALUE-ADDED FEATURES: (1) The protocol shall not allow unauthorized use of a connection. (2) The transport service may provide encryption and decryption of transmitted data on demand. (3) The protocol may support routing through secure links or nodes if such a service is available from the subnetwork. (4) The protocol may support remote verification of the receiver.

Again, as the locus of security in the Open Systems Environment is unfixed, we intend to let a kernel definition wait on further discussion. All protocols presumably contain some mechanism to prevent unauthorized use of connections, although the meaning of "unauthorized" is more or less dependent on the host operating system facilities for security, identification, and authorization. No protocol examined provided encryption or decryption services, secure routing, or remote validation.

4 Session Service

4.1 Purpose of Session Services

The purpose of the session layer is to manage data traffic between cooperating high-level protocol entities. The cooperative relationship between these entities is known as a session. The session layer forwards requests for data transfer to the transport layer.

4.2 Session Features

The first service performed by a session layer must be the administration of sessions. Sessions must be established and released. Furthermore, one may expect an emergency abort facility. The two cooperating session layers must be able to address each other through session-service-access-points. The session layer controls the delivery of data to the high-level user (quarantining), controls the interactions between high-level users (dialogue management), and imposes a structure on the data it transfers (data delimiting). Some security functions relevant to the operation of distributed systems may also fall within the domain of session control.

4.2.1 The Session

A session, or session-connection, is a cooperative relationship between high-level protocol entities. The session passes through three phases: <u>establishment</u>, <u>data transfer</u>, and <u>termination</u>. It will be noted that these phases are closely related to the phases of the transport connection (or connections) which supports the session. In the simplest case, in which the mapping between transport connections and sessions is one-to-one, the phases of the session would be equivalent to the phases of the transport connection. However, more complex relationships are possible: a session might employ more than one transport connection (to provide an expedited or interrupt data path, for example), or several sessions employ the same transport connection consecutively or possibly simultaneously. In such cases, the phases of the session would be distinct from the phases of the transport connection.

4.2.1.1 Session Establishment

Establishment of a session will include the establishment of at least one transport-connection with an appropriate type and grade of transport service and appropriate security authentication.

Certain characteristics of a session will be demanded by the initiating session-user and negotiated between corresponding session-entities. Such characteristics would include the configuration of transport connections into a session (e.g., to provide interrupt service), the type and grade of transport service to be used, the maximum size of quarantine-units, and so on.

4.2.1.2 Session Termination

Termination of a session will dissolve the cooperative relationship between session-users in an orderly way, so that no data is lost and resources of the distributed system are released appropriately.

4.2.1.3 Session Abort

The session may be aborted with possible loss of data, for example, if a higher-level protocol-entity should perceive unrecoverable errors.

4.2.2 Addressing

A session-address obviously must have at least the scope of a transport-address. We have conceived of session addressing in terms of workstation names. A workstation name is a logical name (unique within the open system), independent of the network's physical topology, which addresses a workstation. A workstation is a process or collection of processes which carries out a particular application. It is then the function of the session layer to translate a workstation name into a transport address at the appropriate host in order to establish the proper session-connection.

4.2.3 Data Transfer

The session layer calls on the transport service to transfer data.

4.2.4 Quarantining

It may happen that one session-user desires to withhold some data from his correspondent for some length of time--for example, because none of the data being generated will be significant until a certain quantity has been produced, or until some validation procedure has been completed. The data thus held back by the session layer is said to be _quarantined_ and is known as a _quarantine-unit_. The end of a quarantine-unit is interpreted to mean that the quarantined data will be made available to the receiving session-user; thus, the quarantining facility may be used to force data delivery (that is, to flush the session buffers) as well as to hold data back from delivery. The receiving session layer will not deliver any fragment of the quarantine-unit to the session-user until all the data in that unit is available for delivery; this does not mean that the unit be delivered all at once, but only that no part will be delivered until all has arrived in the receiving session layer.

A session-user may destroy a quarantine-unit he has created if he has not yet terminated it, and it has therefore not yet been delivered to his correspondent.

4.2.5 Dialogue Management

The session layer imposes a structure on the interaction' between correspondents: this structure is a <u>dialogue</u>. There are three possible varieties of dialogue: two-way-simultaneous, two-way-alternate, and one-way (these names should indicate the dialogue structure). The two-way-alternate case requires further consideration. One correspondent at a time will have the "turn," or permission to send. At the end of an interaction, the sender will release the turn, thus allowing the other correspondent to send. Thus there must be a method for assigning the first turn, a means for exchanging the turn, and a facility for interrupting the correspondent with the turn.

The information sent during a single turn is called an
interaction unit. When a session-user terminates an interaction
unit, he at the same time relinquishes the turn.

4.2.6 Interrupt

The basic interrupt service of a two-way-alternate dialogue
is the ability to demand the turn. However, this is not of much
use to session-users in a two-way-simultaneous dialogue or
monologue. A more generalized interrupt facility is required for
these cases. According to the negotiated configuration of the
session, the interrupt facility would use either the transport
layer's expedited delivery service or a **separate** transport
connection intended for interrupts.

4.2.7 Data Delimiting

The session layer imposes a minimal level of structure on
the flow of data in a session. Thus Presentation Entities may
assemble meaningful units of data and have these units
transported by the session layer. Of course, any imposition of
structure upon a raw stream of data could be deferred by each
layer to the layer above until ultimately the two highest level
correspondents inherit the responsibility. In a sense, this is
contrary to the principles of functional layering: the point is

to find useful common functions and offer them as services at the lowest possible layer. The imposition of structure on the data stream, by segmenting it into Session-Service-Data-Units (SSDUs), is just such a service.

The SSDU can be seen as a way for session-users to segment the data stream into chunks, the boundaries between which will be maintained across the network. It is the responsibility of the local user to identify the beginning and end of an SSDU (or just the end, perhaps) for the session layer. This information would be passed across the interface as parameters in session service calls. The session layer would assume the responsibility of passing this information to its peer correspondent. The remote session layer would in turn delimit the beginning and end of the SSDU for its session-user by similarly passing parameters across the interface.

The end result of this activity is that the local session-user has a certain amount of control over how data will be transferred across the remote session user interface. The foreign user may need to post some number of receives to acquire data from its serving session layer (the amount of data it gets in each receive is what the ISO Reference Model calls a Session-Interface-Data-Unit). When the remote session-user does the receive which includes the last octet of data in the SSDU, notification is made of the End-of-SSDU. This last receive contains only data belonging to the currently "open" SSDU. More data may actually be available (belonging to the next SSDU), but it will not be passed until the next receive.

4.2.8 Security

The session layer enforces certain high-level security procedures. It may validate the security domains of its correspondents, or regulate information flow between correspondents in different security domains.

4.3 Protocol Layering and the Definition of Session Features

The ISO Reference Model has been designed based on the concept of architectural layering. Section 4 of the Model describes the principles considered during layer definition. These include:

        3) create separate layers to handle functions
which are manifestly different in the process performed
or the technology involved,

        4) collect similar functions into the same layer,

        9) enable changes of functions or protocols within
a layer without affecting the other layers.

These three principles may be generalized into a principle of Layer Independence or Transparency:

The performance of a layer should not depend on

information which does not affect its functions.

Attention to this principle of transparency during layer definition will result in truly independent layers, any of which may be modified or replaced without affecting any other layer. For instance, one example of proper application of the principle is found in the description of the network layer, section 5.5.2.1:

> The basic service of the network layer is to provide the transparent transfer of all data submitted by the transport layer. This service allows the structure and detailed content of submitted data to be determined exclusively by layers above the network layer.

If we apply the principle of transparency to peer interactions between correspondent protocol-entities, we will find that it forbids the division of a single function between two layers. That is, one must not require one layer to delimit data on behalf of another layer for which the resulting units have significance. Rather, the same layer for which a data unit has significance should delimit that unit. This points up two layering flaws in the definition of the session layer: the commitment and recovery unit delimiting, and quarantining. In both cases, the session layer could end up marking data for the use of the presentation layer.

Let us address the quarantining function first. The ISO Reference Model allows either the session layer or the presentation layer to perform quarantining. If the presentation layer performs quarantining, the session layer is still required to mark the quarantine-units and pass these delimiters on to the presentation layer. Clearly, this is an unacceptable division of a single function between two layers. The layers can be made independent by concentrating the quarantining function in a single layer; it is our opinion that quarantining is a function appropriate to session control, different in kind from the functions associated with the presentation layer. For that reason we will define quarantining as a session feature (we will return presently to the question of quarantine-unit delimiting).

The recovery- and commitment-units have meaning only to presentation-entities or application-entities (although the ISO Reference Model says these units are "defined and managed by presentation-entities [5.3.2.7.4]," commitment and recovery control are listed as application management functions within the application layer [5.1.3.4]). If the session layer is to transparently transmit the data it receives, it should not introduce any delimiters which must be passed to higher layers. Recovery- and commitment-units should be delimited in the same layer at which the peer-to-peer integrity protocol functions. We will define the session layer without recovery- or commitment-unit delimiting, leaving that function to the higher layer which carries out the integrity protocol.

4.4 Further Notes on Data Delimiting

Even after having made the session layer independent by concentrating quarantining in the session layer and the integrity protocol in a higher layer, the locus of quarantining is still not entirely clear: buffering of the quarantined data may take place in the local session layer, in the remote session layer, or in both. Wherever quarantining takes place, the idea of a quarantine-unit is not really useful: a quarantine-unit has no significance as a unit, and quarantining is more usefully thought of as a temporal concept. An end-of-quarantine-unit delimiter may be more naturally thought of as a token of permission to deliver the quarantined data instead of a data delimiter. In any case, the session layer must not notify the presentation layer of the end-of-quarantine-unit; to do so would violate the principle of transparency by forcing on the presentation layer information which should have no effect on its functions.

The other data unit delimited by the session layer is the interaction-unit. In this case, an end-to-end interaction-unit-delimiter is required; but the concept of an interaction is, like quarantining, temporal, and rather than considering delimited interaction-units, it may be more natural to think of the unit delimiter as an end-to-end turn-exchange token. That is, we will not speak of interaction-units, but model the exchange of turns by the exchange of the token: only the correspondent holding the token will be allowed to send. Such an idea makes it easier to consider interactions in a round-robin multiple-correspondent situation, where the unit concept is unnatural and confusing.

4.5 Session Control and Transport Transaction Service

The concept of Session Control, as presented in the current version of the ISO Reference Model, is strongly based on the use of the transport layer's connection-oriented service (which is itself the only type of transport service discussed). The definition of a session makes explicit this dependence (section 5.3.1.2.2):

> For the transfer of data between two presentation-entities, the session is mapped onto and uses a transport-connection.

In fact, the authors of the current draft seem uneasy about a session's strong identification with a transport-connection. One of several "urgent issues" is (5.4.5.1):

> What is the precise difference between 'sessions' and 'transport-connections'?

The whole notion of a session which binds two presentation-entities into a relationship of some temporal duration is an upwards extension of the idea of connections at the transport layer or virtual circuits at the network layer.

It is hard to see how two corresponding session layers could establish, manipulate, and release a session during a single transport transaction (that is, a "single-access" data transfer request to the transport service). If the session layer must make more than one transport transaction during the life of a transaction/session, it might as well open a transport-connection and go through normal session-establishment procedures rather than trying to use the other type of service. It is equally hard to see why one would establish a session for a series of transport transactions, or even how such a session would be established. How then is the session layer to use the transport transaction service?

The point of transport transaction service is to provide a means of sending a certain amount of data with a single transport access (no assumption is made about the number of network layer accesses corresponding to a single transaction). We will assume that there is an analogous single-access "transaction" primitive in the session layer, which will cause the usual address transformation, security check (if necessary), et cetera, to take place, but which performs data transfer of a single Session Service Data Unit in a single transport access. The receiving session layer would recognize the SSDU as a transaction requiring little or no session action and pass the SSDU on to the appropriate session-user. This idea perhaps sidesteps the issue of how the session layer uses transaction service, by essentially promulgating transaction service transparently through the session layer. It does seem, however, to follow in near perfect analogy: the session transaction stands in the same relationship to the transport transaction as the session-connection to the transport-connection.

5 Session Feature Analysis

We must again note that the session layer protocols discussed in this part of the report are in a state of evolutionary change. This is furthermore true of the definition of the session layer itself and services it requires and provides. Descriptions found in this part of the report describe protocols as they existed during the study it describes; these protocols may change at any time.

5.1 Considerations for the Feature Analysis

In our feature analysis of the transport layer, we had a good deal of material from which to extract features and to use as fixed points for comparison: this material included transport protocols from commercial vendors, from government networks, and contributions from national and international standardization groups. As a result we felt that our analysis had not wandered far from the thinking of the networking community. When we turned to the session features analysis, however, we found a far smaller pool of material with which to start. This scarcity is understandable since session control has until recently been a relatively undefined area in the ISO Architecture.

Of the commercial network architectures available to this study, only NCR [NCR79] has a distributed layer which includes any session functions (although this layer 5-C is more of an interface to the transport layer than a real session layer). IBM's SNA defines the concept of session and half-session, but these turn out to have more to do with layer 4 functions than with layer 5; SNA does not seem to support a distributed session layer (in the sense of the ISO Reference Model) [CORF79] and [MCFJ76]. The only fully-defined session layer (available to this study) which exploits all the functionality of the ISO Reference Model definition is a specification by the German Hahn-Meitner-Institut (HMI) [VOGF79]. The European Computer Manufacturers Association has distributed two working papers giving provisional sketches of the services offered by a session layer, [DEBC79] and [ECMA79b]. Beyond these few attempts at real specification of a session layer, we have had to rely on the ISO Reference Model itself, and explications of the Model by Bachman and Canepa [BACC79] and desJardins and White [DESR78].

Thus it is easy to see that features analysis cannot proceed along the comparative lines of the transport layer analysis. Rather than begin by grouping already defined features into clusters based on our judgement of relative cost and usefulness, we ourselves shall have to define groups of features and try to discuss them in terms of costs and benefits. Benefits will include such considerations as the power of a given feature and proposed uses for it. Costs will include complexity of protocol machinery required to provide a feature and the degree of effective use of transport services. We shall follow a format for discussion the reverse of that which we used in the transport analysis: through our discussion we shall arrive at definitions for the minimum foundation and standard features, which follow at the end of each section.

5.2 A Minimal Foundation for the Session Layer

The minimal foundation for any protocol layer will be the minimal functionality which must be included in the layer for a host to participate in distributed processing. This is important with regard to the session layer, since many network architectures developed before the ISO Reference Model define no session layer. Regarding such architectures, we must ask if session control functions are being carried out somewhere else in the architecture? If so, where? How can such functions be concentrated in an identifiable layer? These questions are of particular interest with respect to the government networking community, especially ARPANET and TCP-4 developers. It has been the practice of such systems to concentrate transport functions in a host-to-host protocol and to place presentation functions in the end-user application processes. To what extent can we say a session layer exists in such an architecture?

The minimum functionality for a session layer is merely the transparent promulgation of transport services. That is, there would be no difference between a session and a transport-connection; a session establish request and a transport-connection open would be the same, for example. A clever implementation of such a session layer might take advantage of this one-to-one relationship between layer services and implement only the transport service requests. Thus the session layer would be empty or null, since the implementation contains no code and transport and session services are apparently identical. From an architectural viewpoint, then, one can speak of a session layer existing in such a case, but to do so is not particularly meaningful.

In short, we need not address the question of a minimum foundation for the session layer. Experience with network architectures which do not define a session layer shows that the minimum session requirement for participation in distributed processing is an empty layer.

5.3 Session Establishment

Several characteristics of a session may not be determined until session establishment. Many of these characteristics will be services requested by the session-user, such as a particular grade of transport service, the first turn in a dialogue, or similar requests. However, it is not sufficient for one correspondent to demand a session of a certain type; that type must be acceptable to both session-users, and agreed upon by both session layers. In order to allow the session layers to establish an acceptable session, the possible options must be encoded and a negotiation procedure must be defined in our protocol. This procedure must meet several requirements: neither correspondent should be forced to accept a session which does not meet its requirements, the negotiation should not result in a non-terminating series of requests and responses, and the negotiation procedure should not introduce a master/servant distinction between the session layers.

Neither the NCR Layer 5-C nor the HMI session protocol defines a negotiation procedure or service options. The ARPANET protocols TELNET [DAVJ77] and THP [POSJ76], which perform some session-like functions, do allow for negotiation of service options.

We can imagine two different styles of negotiation: a request/response negotiation dialogue (as used in TELNET and THP) or a rule-directed scheme in which the attributes of the session are determined by applying a fixed set of rules to the session requirements of both session layers.

The request/response procedure has the advantage of being well-known and widely used in TELNET's and THP's WILL/WONT, DO/DONT scheme; however, it may require the introduction of a priority distinction between correspondents or result in a non-terminating sequence of exchanges. Such situations might arise, for example, if both session layers simultaneously demanded the first turn in a dialogue. Furthermore, the negotiation of any single option cannot happen faster than the round-trip time of the request and response (this for an uncontested option requiring only a single exchange). The flurry of exchanges one would expect when setting up a session could add appreciably to establishment delay and the transmission overhead of establishment.

The rule-directed procedure would require only two exchanges: one of attribute codes, another accepting or rejecting the session. However, since both session layers must apply the same rules independently to the same input, there is some redundant computation. It is clear that some care must be devoted to designing the rules.

We do not propose here to make a choice between the two possibilities. That will be left to the service specification.

KERNEL: The establishment of a session will allow negotiation of various service options between session layers.

5.4   Session Termination

Release of a session is seen as a cooperative enterprise which preserves the integrity of any data still in the connection. This means that both sides must agree when to close the session. In a two-way-alternate dialogue, only the side with the turn may initiate release procedures. In a two-way-simultaneous dialogue or a monologue, either side should be able to initiate release.

Both NCR Layer 5-C and the HMI protocol behave in this manner.

KERNEL: Either one of a pair of cooperating session-users must be able to initiate release of the session, with the exception of the correspondent without the turn in a two-way-alternate dialogue. Session release will not cause loss of session data.

5.5   Session Abort

A session-user should also be able to unilaterally abort a session--but such a termination may cause loss of data still in transit. One use of this facility would be to end a session if the higher-level protocol entities discover unrecoverable errors.

Neither NCR nor the HMI protocol have a user abort service.

KERNEL: Either session-user may unilaterally abort a
session; this termination will not respect pending data in the
connection.

5.6 Addressing

It is common, on ARPANET systems, in DECnet, and in systems
using TCP-4 as a transport layer, for certain widely used network
services (or workstations, in the language of Open Systems
Interconnection) to await connections at the same address in
different hosts. For example, an FTP server might be contacted
through port 10 at Host A, port 10 at Host B, and port 10 at Host
C as well. Any customer seeking FTP service is familiar with
this well-known address, called a well-known socket. A simple
type of session addressing would be to translate a string
workstation name into a logical transport address using tables of
well-known sockets. For example, a user desiring to use FTP from
or to a host called BBN-UNIX * might specify "FTP@BBN-UNIX."   If
networks have been interconnected, it might be necessary to
specify "ARPANET:FTP@BBN-UNIX." The many conceivable variations
in format of the string are not significant.

---

* UNIX is a trademark of Bell Laboratories.

Session address translation is a local service provided to a session-user and has no peer-to-peer significance.

KERNEL: The session layer will translate symbolic names into the proper transport-address.

5.7 Data Transfer

When a user requests the session layer to transfer data, he may have to include other information not related to the actual transfer of the data--information concerning data delimiting or dialogue turn exchange, for example. Such extra information, while an essential part of session service, is distinct from data transfer _per se_. The session layer will transparently forward the data to the transport layer, which will actually transfer it. Of course, if necessary, the session layer may indicate control conditions in the data stream as it is submitted to the transport service.

KERNEL: The session layer will transparently forward to the transport layer data to be transferred.

5.8 Quarantining

Some peer-to-peer mechanism is necessary for proper quarantining. We have defined a quarantine-unit as a portion of data none of which will be delivered until all of it is available. It does not seem reasonable to require that all data lie in a quarantine-unit; one should be able to turn quarantining on and off as needed. If quarantine-units are not contiguous, the data will have to be marked at the beginning of a quarantine-unit and at the end of the unit.

The ISO Reference Model leaves open the question of where quarantining takes place; that is, which session layer holds the data until the sending session-user closes the unit. Even if the sending session layer accumulates a whole quarantine-unit before beginning transmission to the receiver, the receiving session layer must have a buffer big enough to hold the whole unit, since the session layer must have the last byte of the unit in hand before it can deliver the first byte. The sender must have equally large buffers for holding the accumulating unit. Nevertheless there are some benefits to having the sender perform quarantining on outgoing data. First, it evenly distributes buffer use between two session layers: each will quarantine its own outgoing data. Second, no protocol machinery is required for cancelling a quarantine-unit--this becomes a local procedure. Finally, holding an open unit locally evades the problem of the relationship of interrupts to open quarantine-units. To prevent deadlock, the sender must not transmit a quarantine-unit larger than the receiver is prepared to accept. Therefore each session layer must negotiate the maximum size of quarantine-units it will transmit.

Neither the HMI protocol nor NCR layer 5-C define quarantining procedures. The ECMA working paper on session control defines the existence of quarantine-units without mentioning any quarantining procedures or localizing the action in either of the communicating hosts.

KERNEL: Quarantine-units may appear intermittently in the data stream. The beginning and end of a quarantine-unit must be marked. None of a quarantine-unit may be delivered to the receiving session-user until the receiving session layer is prepared to deliver the last octet of the quarantined data. None of a quarantine-unit may be transmitted by the sending session layer until that layer is prepared to transmit the last octet of the quarantined data. Cancellation of the currently open quarantine-unit is performed locally. The size of receive quarantine-unit buffers will be negotiated during session establishment, and no quarantine-unit larger than a receiver's buffer shall be sent.

5.9 Dialogue Management

We have already suggested that the type of dialogue to be used in a session and the initial turn (if the dialogue is two-

way-alternate) should be negotiated during session establishment.
No management is necessary in two-way-simultaneous dialogues, and
during a monologue, the local session layer need only refuse send
or receive requests appropriately as the local user is the sender
or receiver of the monologue.

In two-way-alternate dialogues, however, some management
procedures are required. A session layer will indicate when its
session-user relinquishes the turn by a control indication (end-
of-turn). Presumably, a session layer will notify its user that
he is now permitted to send when it receives the end-of-turn
indication. Each session layer will refuse send or receive
requests appropriately as the user does or does not have the
turn.

During a two-way-alternate dialogue we have assumed the
possibility of one user interrupting the other. This is done by
transmitting a "demand turn" message—either on the interrupt
channel or by transport expedited service. Some rule must be
established for what action must be taken on receipt of the
demand, lest the structure of the dialogue break down.

Neither NCR layer 5-C nor the HMI protocol defines dialogue
management procedures.

KERNEL: The session layer shall enforce constraints on its
session-users appropriate to the nature of the dialogue in

progress and the possession of the turn.   The turn shall be exchanged by means of an end-of-turn indication.   The demand-turn request shall not be ignored, but the session layer with the turn must   immediately   relinquish   it.   The   end   of   a   turn   will automatically   close   the   open   session-service-data-unit   or quarantine unit.

5.10   Interrupts

We have noted the use of interrupts with respect to the demand-turn facility. This, however, is only of use during two-way-alternate dialogues, and then restricted to a narrow meaning. A general interrupt facility would be of use in all types of dialogue. We could imagine provision of a signal which would deliver no data but provide only an interrupt indication. However, both transport expedited service and a separate interrupt channel allow sending more than a simple signal--an interrupt could carry with it some amount of data. The interrupt facility could use whatever type of expedited service had been arranged when the session was established.

The HMI protocol allows session-users direct access to transport expedited service, which gives it approximately the power of the interrupt with data described above. However, that protocol also proposes a purge facility, noting that purge may make expedited transfer superfluous. We felt that the interrupt is more general and, in many applications, more useful than a purge service. The action to be taken on receipt of an interrupt (which perhaps might be to effectively purge the connection) would be left up to the correspondents and the content of the data sent with the interrupt, if any.

KERNEL: The session layer shall, on request, transmit an interrupt message which may contain a certain amount of data, using the expedited transfer service or interrupt channel agreed upon during session establishment.

5.11 Data Delimiting

The only data delimiting facility of the HMI protocol is inherent in its data transfer request: the session-user sends or receives a single Session-Service-Data-Unit in what it calls a NSSDU request. This means that the SSDU and the Session-Interface-Data-Unit are identical. This identity is not essential to the operation of the layer, however, if one considers the SSDU to be a low-level data structuring facility. There is no reason a SSDU should not cross the session/user interface in several pieces. We require only that each SSDU be distinguishable to the session-user.

Our session protocol will mark the end of each SSDU. Since, in agreement with the ISO Reference Model, SSDUs will be continuous through the data stream, there will be no need to mark the beginning of an SSDU.

Finally, the hierarchy of data delimiting functions must be defined. Clearly, relinquishing the turn requires delivery of any backed-up or quarantined data, so end-of-turn entails end-of-quarantine-unit (if there is an open quarantine-unit). As it is supposed that quarantining affects only an integral number of SSDUs, end-of-quarantine-unit entails end-of-SSDU as well.

KERNEL: The session layer shall divide the data stream into a sequence of SSDUs according to the directions of the sending session-user. Incoming SSDUs shall be distinguishable to the receiving session-user. No interpretation shall be placed on the SSDU by the session layer.

5.12 Security

None of the session protocols available to this study defines any session-level security procedures. We shall leave this area undefined until further study clarifies the locus and requirements of security in the Open System environment.

KERNEL: No security procedures are defined in the session
layer.

5.13 Session Transaction Service

As we noted earlier, no session protocol available to this
study has addressed the question of how a session layer uses
transport transaction service. Most aspects of session control-
-quarantining, dialogue management, and so forth--make sense in
the context of a data stream; it makes little sense to apply such
control functions to single-access transactions. We have argued
that the session-user should essentially be given direct access
to the transport layer's transaction requests.

When a session-user requests that a transaction be sent, the
session layer might mark data to indicate that session
establishment procedures are unnecessary.   The data in the
transaction will merely be handed to the receiving session-user:
no long-term association is created.

We consider the transaction to be a single Session-Service-
Data-Unit because, although data delimiting is primarily a
stream-oriented function, it is convenient to imagine all data
divided into SSDUs.   Although any option which might apply to
normal data transmission might be legal in a transaction, not all
of them would be meaningful in that context (for example, an

end-of-turn indication).

Transactions might be delivered to session-users which have declared a desire to receive them. It seems that applications would normally deal exclusively in either stream or transaction service, but not mix them.

KERNEL: The session layer will deliver single-access transactions on behalf of its users by means of the transport layer's transaction service.

References

[AHUV79]   Ahuja, V. "Routing and Flow Control in Systems Network Architecture." IBM Systems Journal, 18 (1979), 298.

[BACC79]   Bachman, Charles, and Mike Canepa. "The Session Control Layer of an Open System Interconnection." OSIC/TG 6/79-10.

[BPO79]   (British) Post Office Packet Switching Study Group 3. A Transport Service. BIG/CP(79)7, 4 April 1979.

[CBEMA79] Computer and Business Equipment Manufacturers Association, Task Group X3S33 on Data Communications Formats. Third Draft Proposed American National Standard for Heading Format Structure for Code Independent Communication Headings. 281F/3, OSIC/80-10, November 29, 1979.

[CORF79]   Corr, F.P., and D.H. Neal. "SNA and Emerging International Standards." IBM Systems Journal, 18 (1979), 244.

[CRAR79]   Crawford, Robert. "Comparison of Transport Services." SPARC/OSIC/TG6/79-18, December 20, 1979.

[DAVJ77]   Davidson, J., W. Hathaway, J. Postel, N. Mimno, R. Thomas, and D. Walden. "The ARPANET TELNET Protocol: Its Purpose, Principles, Implementation, and Impact on Host Operating System Design." Fifth Data Communications Symposium, 1977. Reprinted in [MCQJ78].

[DEBC79]   de Bourbon, [Charles]. "Session Control Overview."
            European   Computer   Manufacturers   Association,
            ECMA/TC23/79/57, August 1979.

[DEC78]   DECnet/Digital Network Architecture: Network Services
            Protocol (NSP). Functional Specification, Version 3.1.
            Digital Equipment Corp., March 1978.

[DESR78]   desJardins, Richard, and George White. "ANSI Reference
            Model for Distributed Systems." IEEE Compcon 78, 5-8
            September 1978.

[ECMA79a]   European Computer Manufacturers Association. Standard
            ECMA Transport Protocol, First Draft. ECMA/TC24/79/70,
            ECMA/TC23/79/46, July 1979.

[ECMA79b]   European Computer Manufacturers Association, TC 23 (ad
            hoc group on Common Services). "Working Paper on
            Session Control." ECMA/TC23/79/70, OSIC/TG 6/79-7,
            September 1979.

[FLEJ78]   Fletcher, John G., and Richard W. Watson. "Mechanisms
            for a Reliable Timer-Based Protocol." Computer
            Networks, 2 (1978), 271-290.

[GARL76]   Garlick, Lawrence L. "Out of Band Control Signals in a
            Host-to-Host Protocol." Network Information Center,
            September 1976. Request for Comments 721. Network
            Information Center 36636.

[GARL77]   Garlick, Lawrence L., Raphael Rom, and Jonathan B.
            Postel. "Reliable Host-to-Host Protocols: Problems and
            Techniques." Proc. Fifth Data Communications Symposium,
            September 1977.

[ISO79a]   International Standards Organization. Reference Model
            of Open Systems Interconnection. ISO/TC97/SC16 N227,
            August 1979.

[ISO79b]   International Standards Organization. Transport
            Service Functions and Services. ISO/TC97/SC6 N1861,
            September 1979.

[MCFJ76]   McFadyen, J.H. "Systems Network Architecture: An
            Overview." IBM Systems Journal, 15 (1976), 4.

[MCKA78]   McKenzie, Alex. "Host-to-Host Protocol for the
            ARPANET," ARPANET Protocol Handbook. Ed. Elizabeth
            Feinler and Jonathan Postel. Defense Communications
            Agency, January 1978. Network Information Center 7104.

[MCQJ75]   McQuillan, John M.   "The   Evolution   of   Message
           Processing Techniques in the ARPA Network." 1975.
           Reprinted in [MCQJ78].

[MCQJ78]   McQuillan, John M., and Vinton G. Cerf. Tutorial: A
           Practical View of Computer Communications Protocols.
           IEEE Computer Society, 1978. IEEE Catalog No. EHO 137-
           0.

[NCR79]   NCR Corporation. Personal Communication, 1979.

[POSJ76]   Postel, Jonathan B., Larry L. Garlick, and Raphael Rom.
           Terminal-to-Host Protocol Specification. Augmentation
           Research Center, Stanford Research Institute, July
           15,1976.

[POSJ79a] Postel,   Jonathan   B.   User   Datagram   Protocol.
           University of Southern California, Information Sciences
           Institute, 2 May 1979. Internet Experimental Note 88.

[POSJ79b] Postel, Jonathan B. Transmission Control Protocol.
           University of Southern California, Information Sciences
           Institute, August 1979.   Internet Experimental Note
           112.

[POSJ79c] Postel, Jonathan B. Internet Protocol. University of
           Southern California, Information Sciences Institute,
           August 1979. Internet Experimental Note 111.

[SLOL79]   Sloan, Lansing J. "Limiting the Lifetime of Packets in
           Computer   Networks." Lawrence Livermore Laboratory,
           Preprint UCRL-82825 Rev. 1, November 27, 1979.

[SUNC79]   Sunshine, Carl A. Formal Methods for Communication
           Protocol Specification and Verification.   The Rand
           Corporation, September 1979.   No.   WD-335-ARPA/NBS.
           (Working Draft)

[VOGF79]   Vogt, F., E. Dregger, H. Eckert, and B. Lausch.
           Specification of a Transport and Session Layer Protocol
           Based on the Message Link Protocol, Version 1.0.
           Hahn-Meitner-Institut   fuer   Kernforschung G.m.b.H.,
           Bereich Datenverarbeitung und Elektronik.   Berlin
           September, 1979.

[WATR79a] Watson, Richard W., and John G. Fletcher.   "An
           Architecture for Support of Network Operating System
           Services."   The   Fourth   Berkeley   Conference   on
           Distributed Data Management and Computer Networks,
           August 28-30, 1979. Lawrence Livermore Laboratory,
           Preprint UCRL-82568 Rev. 1, August 8, 1979.

[WATR79b] Watson, Richard W. _Delta-t Protocol Preliminary Specification_. Lawrence Livermore Laboratory, November 1979.

[WATR80]   Watson, Richard W. "Rough Comparison of TCP and Delta-t Connection Management." Private Communication, January 4, 1980.

[ZIMH75]   Zimmerman, Hubert. "The CYCLADES End to End Protocol." IEEE Fourth Data Communications Symposium, October 1975.

2

TRANSPORT PROTOCOLS
FOR COMPUTER NETWORKS

CARL A. SUNSHINE

University of Southern California
Information Sciences Institute

2.1 INTRODUCTION

As computer networks have proliferated, the set of procedures used to control communication has grown commensurately. These *protocols* or rules governing the timing and format of data exchange have become an important and complex feature of computer networks. As described in Chapter 1, protocols are needed at each level of a network system, such as physical link, host-to-host, and application levels, with each protocol level depending on the features provided by the next-lower-level protocol.

A major watershed in this protocol hierarchy typically coincides with the division of equipment between communication subsystem and user or host computer. We shall be primarily interested in the cases where communication services are provided by an explicit network of switching nodes and transmission lines (see Fig. 2.1a), such as a public packet-switching network or the ARPANET. In this case, the host-to-network interface becomes the dividing line between network protocols on one side and user or end-to-end protocols on the other side.

In other cases where some or all network functions are integrated into host equipment (see Fig. 2.1b), there is still a protocol layer which deals with communication between end users as opposed to the individual physical hops along the path between users. This chapter focuses on protocols to provide general-purpose reliable end-to-end communication between users of a computer

Reprinted from *Protocols and Techniques for Data Communications Networks*, F. Kuo (Editor), 1981, pages 35-77. Copyright © 1981 by Prentice-Hall, Inc.

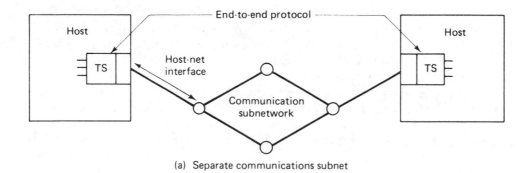

(a) Separate communications subnet

(b) Network functions integrated into hosts

FIGURE 2-1 *End-to-end transport protocol; TS = Transport station.*

network (or networks). These protocols have been called *host-to-host protocols* in the ARPANET community and *transport protocols* in Europe. They provide a type of service frequently described as a "virtual circuit" between their users. Higher-level protocols that provide more specialized functions, such as file transfer, terminal handling, and message distribution, are discussed in other chapters.

The primary functions of a transport protocol are to provide reliable transmission service for each conversation or *connection* under way, and to multiplex many connections over a single physical access path to the network. Some networks provide a simple datagram service that delivers limited length messages or datagrams to their destinations independently (see Chapter 1). In such networks, occasional damage, loss, duplication, or reordering of data in transit may occur, so the transport protocol must employ mechanisms such as retransmission and acknowledgment to achieve reliable operation for its users. Other networks provide more reliable virtual-circuit service, but a transport protocol may still be desirable to provide greater reliability; additional functions, such as flow control, buffering, packetizing; and providing for priority or end-to-end operation across multiple networks (see Sec. 2.4.4).

To show the need for these and other transport protocol functions, we take a problem-oriented approach in Sec. 2.2. Each major problem to be overcome or service to be provided by a transport protocol is presented in a separate section, followed by alternative techniques and protocol mechanisms used to solve the problem. Basic functions such as error recovery and multiplexing are discussed first, followed by more advanced or optional functions such as priority and multidestination communication. Examples are drawn from a variety of existing protocols to illustrate the options in each problem area.

In addition to describing how transport protocols work, we will try to shed some light on the process of protocol design. Although this process remains more in the realm of art than engineering, certain key steps can be identified. Techniques for protocol specification, analysis, and verification have begun to receive attention in their own right and will be discussed in Sec. 2.3.

As the number of computer communication systems and accompanying protocol implementations grows, standardization becomes an increasingly important issue. Ideally, protocols performing similar functions in different systems should be the same. In reality, differences in system configuration or requirements and different approaches to protocol design result in a wide variety of functionally similar protocols. Protocol standardization promises significant economies by fostering the use of existing products rather than repeating the development cycle. When previously independent systems are interconnected, standards become even more necessary to allow uniform service throughout the interconnected systems. Unfortunately, there are also potentially severe diseconomies that can result from premature or ill-advised standardization. Section 2.4 reviews the history of transport protocol development and future prospects for standardization.

2.2 TRANSPORT PROTOCOL PROBLEMS AND SOLUTIONS

The purpose of transport protocols is to provide reliable general-purpose communication between processes in host computers (or intelligent terminals) attached to a computer communication network. Transport protocols find their main application in packet-switching networks, although the principles elaborated in this section are applicable in any situation where the transmission medium is not fully reliable or must otherwise have its capabilities augmented.

The implementation of a transport protocol in a particular software environment has been called a network control program, transmission control program, and similar names, but we will adopt the widely used term *transport station* (TS) (see Fig. 2.1). A transport station normally supports many connections between processes simultaneously, but most of its functions concern each connection independently. When it is necessary to distinguish the overall transport station from the portion serving a single connection, we will call the latter a *connection machine*.

We approach the subject of transport protocols by identifying a number of major problem areas. For each area the problem to be overcome or the service to be provided is described, followed by protocol mechanisms typically used to achieve this purpose. We start with the problem of providing reliable communication between a single pair of users, temporarily ignoring the requirements for multiplexing. We then discuss a number of additional service features, such as flow control, priority, and resource allocation. Finally, several advanced topics, such as internetwork operation and multidestination or broadcast protocols, are addressed.

2.2.1 Transmission Error Recovery

Perhaps the most fundamental protocol problem is the possibility that a packet may be damaged or lost by the communications system somewhere along the path between sender and receiver. The first step toward error recovery must be error detection. This is typically accomplished by the sender attaching an error-detecting code or checksum to the data in each packet. This code is then recomputed by the receiver for each arriving packet. Any difference between the computed code and the transmitted code indicates a transmission error. In practical situations, codes of modest length (e.g., 16 bits) achieve highly effective error detection (one erroneous packet in 10^6 will remain undetected) [13]. Throughout the remainder of this chapter, we shall assume that this error-detection rate is adequate and that for all practical purposes error detection is perfect.

If a packet is received correctly, a *positive acknowledgment* (ACK) is returned to the sender. If the ACK arrives undamaged at the sender (the ACK must also carry a checksum), it provides positive confirmation that the data packet was transmitted successfully. The receiving protocol may return the ACK after simply receiving a packet or after having delivered it to the user, depending on the design goals of the protocol. It is important to note that an ACK from the transport level means at best that the packet was made available to the receiving user, not that it has been processed or that its contents are acceptable to the user.

If a data packet is received in error, the protocol may optionally return a *negative acknowledgment* (NAK). Unlike a link protocol, the sender cannot rely on receiving a NAK if an error has occurred because the communications subsystem may completely lose a packet or acknowledgment as well as simply damaging it. This may occur, for example, if a node of a packet-switching network fails or becomes congested and discards excess packets. Therefore, the sending protocol employs a *timeout*. Each data packet transmitted starts a timer, and if an ACK is not received before the timeout occurs, the data packet is retransmitted. If NAKs are used, they also serve to stimulate retransmission. If a positive acknowledgment is not received after some number of retransmissions, the protocol may take some special action, such as closing the connection and notifying its users.

The time interval used for the retransmission timeout is a critical parameter determining protocol performance. If the interval is too short, extra retransmissions will waste channel capacity. If the interval is too long, the mean transmission delay increases if there is a significant error rate. Ideally, the retransmission interval should be just long enough to receive an acknowledgment under normal circumstances. Unfortunately, this round-trip delay may vary widely in packet-switching networks. This topic is treated further in Sec. 2.3.1 on protocol efficiency.

2.2.2 Duplicate Detection and Sequencing

Retransmission until positive acknowledgment guarantees that every packet transmitted will be delivered to the receiver. Whenever an acknowledgment is lost, the retransmission will be a duplicate to the receiver. Some packet switching networks themselves may generate and deliver duplicate packets under certain circumstances (see Chapter 1). The receiving protocol must have a means of differentiating both sorts of duplicates from new packets.

This mechanism consists of a unique identifier attached to each packet by the sender. The receiving protocol must keep track of identifiers of packets it has successfully received and delivered to its user. The identifier in each arriving packet is checked against this information. If it is new, it is added to the information and the packet is delivered to the user. Otherwise, an acknowledgment is sent and the packet is discarded as a duplicate.

Theoretically, packet identifiers should be unique for all time; in practice, however, this is not always possible or desirable. Identifiers may be reused as long as there is no possibility that previous packets with the same identifiers may arrive at the receiver. In a "benign" environment, this means that identifiers may be reused after the maximum packet "lifetime" (i.e., the maximum length of time a packet may exist in the transmission medium). This is typically a few seconds to minutes in a packet-switching network. In a more hostile environment, where malicious intruders may record packets for playback at indefinite future times, duplicate detection is a more severe problem. Additional mechanisms, such as encryption, for use in these cases are discussed in Chapter 9. For the remainder of this chapter, we shall consider an environment without malicious intruders.

Even in a benign environment, hundreds or thousands of packets may be transmitted within a maximum packet lifetime. If identifiers of succeeding packets were assigned arbitrarily, the receiver would require large storage resources to maintain a list of all identifiers received and large processing resources to check arriving packets against the list. Therefore, identifiers are normally assigned sequentially by the transmitter and play the role of both a unique identifier and a sequence number.

Using sequence numbers for identifiers allows the receiver to remember a single number which indicates that that packet and all its predecessors have been received. If packets are to be delivered out of order, a small number of individual sequence numbers for nonconsecutively received packets may also need to be remembered.

This sequence number maintained by the receiver for duplicate detection may be considered as the left edge of a "window" of acceptable sequence numbers. The size of the window is the number of packets the sender may transmit without hearing acknowledgments and must be less than half the size of the sequence number space, as shown by the following argument. Suppose that the sequence space is $2n + 1$ and the sender transmits packets 1 through n. These are all received successfully at the receiver, but all the acknowledgments are lost. At this point the receiver's window of acceptable packets stretches from $n + 1$ through $2n$. The sender may transmit any packet 1 through n and it will be detected as a duplicate. If the window size were increased by 1, to $n + 1$, the receiver's window would be $n + 2$ through 1 (all sequence number arithmetic is modulo the sequence number space size) and the retransmission of packet number 1 would be accepted as a new packet.

This demonstrates that using sequential numbers for packet identifiers with a finite sequence number space places a constraint on the number of packets that may be transmitted but not yet acknowledged at the sender. A similar constraint is derived more formally in [33].

The other fundamental constraint mentioned above is to prevent the premature reuse of sequence numbers. Hence, sequence numbers must not "cycle" in less than a maximum packet lifetime. The size of the sequence number must be adequate to accommodate the desired transmission rate of the sender and the packet lifetime characteristics in the network(s) in question.

If packets need not be delivered sequentially, the receiving protocol must remember the individual sequence numbers of all packets delivered after a missing packet. When the missing packet arrives, the left window edge may be advanced over all consecutively received packets and the appropriate individual sequence numbers "forgotten." If packets must be delivered in order, packets arriving out of order may simply be discarded (they will be retransmitted) or they may be queued for later delivery. Therefore, a sequencing protocol typically imposes greater delay and requires more retransmissions or more buffer storage than a protocol that does not attempt to deliver packets in order. These performance differences are discussed further in Sec. 2.3.1.

The units used for sequencing packets may be small (bits) or large (packets or messages). Small units allow error recovery, flow control, fragmentation, and other protocol functions discussed below to work on smaller units of information, but require longer sequence number fields to provide a desired transfer rate without violating the cycle-time constraints.

2.2.3 Multiplexing and Addressing

Another basic requirement of a transport protocol is to allow for communication between any pair of users. This requires a common name space for the users of the transport protocol and a means for specifying the intended recipient of information in transit. Each packet transmitted must carry an address field identifying its source and destination. The address field may carry a full address or an abbreviated address that serves to identify previously established complete information.

Addresses are composed of at least two components: a transport station address and a *port* or subaddress within the transport station. In the case that TS addresses are equivalent to network customer addresses, the TS address may be used directly by the network to route packets to the proper host computer. Otherwise, logical TS addresses must be mapped into the corresponding network customer addresses. For an internetwork protocol, the TS address may itself have two components, identifying the network and the address within the network. The TS address is thus used primarily by the transmission medium, although the receiving TS may check the addresses of arriving packets to make sure that they have been delivered correctly.

The port address component is used by the transport station to differentiate traffic on different virtual circuits. Each virtual circuit may be said to be managed by a logically separate *connection machine* which handles all per-connection functions. Packets produced by each connection machine have the appropriate port address attached to their headers by the overall TS so that they may be multiplexed onto the access path to the network. Arriving packets are demultiplexed by the TS and delivered to their individual connection machine.

In large systems, full addresses may be lengthy (48 bits each for source and destination were used in TCP [7]. This may impose a significant overhead or delay, particularly in situations where network access lines are of low or moderate speed. Rather than transmitting full addresses with every packet, a short *connection ID* may be assigned to stand for a particular address pair when a virtual circuit is established. This requires connection tables in both host and network, which map ID numbers to the corresponding true addresses. Thus, short addressing trades shorter header length and lower transmission delay for the cost of increased storage and processing for the connection tables.

Ports merely provide a set of logical addresses within a transport station. Some additional mechanism is needed to associate ports with particular processes or services desired. One such mechanism is the use of *well-known ports*. Certain ports in each transport station are reserved for use by particular processes. Directories are published giving port numbers and the services associated with them so that any user desiring a particular service may address the corresponding well-known port. This approach has been used in the ARPANET TCP and NCP to provide access to time sharing (TELNET), file transfer, and remote job entry services. With TCP, well-known ports accept these service requests directly, whereas with NCP the well-known port (socket) can participate in only one connection at a time, so that requests must be passed off to another unused port. After this passoff (called the *initial connection protocol*), the requested service is provided through the new port, while the well-known port is free to wait for new requests.

Another approach used in DECNET and SNA allows specification of the desired service by name when the connection is being established (see Sec. 2.4.3). This name is passed to a directory service which locates the requested service, if it exists, and looks up or assigns a particular port to that service. If the service is not already available, the request may be rejected or queued, or the service may be spawned. The directory may be a centralized facility, as in SNA, or distributed among the network nodes, as in DECNET.

With either approach, a table giving the correspondence between ports and processes using them must be maintained by the TS. For active ports, this table shows the processes currently using each port. If short addressing is used, this information may be combined with the connection table. For inactive ports, access control information must be maintained, indicating which processes are allowed to use the ports in the case of well-known ports, or that the ports are free for use by anyone.

2.2.4 Fragmentation

All packet transmission media impose a limit on the size of packets they will transmit. Transmission errors in circuit-type media also lead to a limit on the size of data blocks that can be effectively transmitted. Thus data provided by the user must be formed into blocks or packets of suitable length by the transport protocol before transmission.

The transport protocol may provide either a stream-oriented or a record-oriented service interface to its users. A *stream-oriented* interface accepts data from the user as if it were a continuous stream of bits and reproduces the continuous stream at the destination without conveying any information about the breakpoints in the stream submitted by the sender. With a *record-oriented* interface, the user has a means of signaling logical breakpoints in the source of data, and the transport protocol must convey this information when it delivers the data. The units of information provided by the user may be called *letters*, in analogy to the post office and to distinguish them from packets or segments, which are transmission units produced by the transport protocol.

In the case of stream interface protocols, the protocol must collect enough bits to form an efficient packet. With record interfaces, the problem is usually the reverse of breaking a large letter into smaller packets. This requires a mechanism for marking the end of letters in addition to sequencing packets.

The error-control and sequencing mechanism described above require as a minimum that packets be numbered sequentially. If multiple letters are carried in a single packet, letter termination information must also be carried. Otherwise, a single end-of-letter bit, indicating that the packet is the last in a letter, is sufficient. Segments produced by the source transport protocol may need to be broken into even smaller packets at some later point in the transmission system. Normally, this would occur at the entry to another network with a smaller packet-size limit. This intermediate fragmentation may use a separate mechanism and separate protocol header field, or it may share the mechanism used by transport stations [6]. In the latter case, smaller units than segments (e.g., octets) must be used as sequence numbers by the source transport station to allow intermediate points to do further fragmentation, as illustrated in Fig. 2.2. If a common mechanism is used, the receiving transport station can reassemble fragments produced by any intermediate points and by the source transport station in a common fashion.

The optimal length for packets depends on many factors, including error rates, transmission delays, and desired performance. Short packets generally provide lower delay at higher cost and overhead, while longer packets provide maximum throughput at lower cost with greater delay, as discussed in Sec. 2.3.

2.2.5 Flow Control and Buffering

Mechanisms that limit the amount or rate of information transfer come under the category of *flow control* (see Chapter 4). At the transport level, it is most often the receiver who wishes to limit the activity of the sender. In simple systems, where the receiver is guaranteed to be able to "dispose" of information at a fixed rate (e.g., output-only terminals), no explicit flow control may be necessary beyond limiting the sender to a fixed rate of transmission provided by the transmission medium. A simple form of dynamic flow control may be provided by a start–stop or X-on or X-off mechanism. The receiver issues start and stop commands that place the sender in the transmission-allowed or transmission-

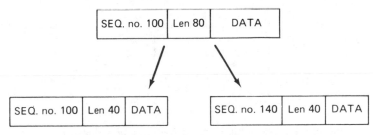

FIGURE 2-2 *Packet fragmentation.*

blocked states. Unfortunately, this mechanism works poorly in a system with variable transmission delay, since the receiver is uncertain at what point in time his or her flow-control command will take effect. The stop command may be followed by more data arriving, and start commands are followed by a significant delay before new data arrive.

A better flow-control mechanism for transport-level protocols is based on granting "credit" for transmission. The receiver grants credits for a certain amount of data to the sender so that both know exactly how much data will be exchanged. The unit of credit may be bits for stream-oriented communication or letters for record-oriented communication. In the latter case, users generally agree on a maximum letter size.

Credits may be passed from receiver to sender in special control packets dedicated to that purpose or as part of the control information in normal data packets flowing in the reverse direction. If credits are absolute, as in the ARPANET NCP, they must be transmitted with complete reliability. Otherwise, a lost credit message may result in deadlock, with the receiver waiting for a new transmission while the sender is blocked, thinking he or she has no credit. Credits may be transferred with greater tolerance for error if they are expressed relative to the sequence number of packets flowing in the reverse direction [6, 28]. In this case, both the sequence number and the number of credits beyond that sequence number are transmitted. If such a flow-control message is lost, subsequent credit messages will restore proper information to the sender.

The number of credits provided by the receiver is frequently called the "window size" when credits are expressed relative to packet sequence numbers. The receiver indicates the *window* of acceptable packets by specifying the low sequence number and the number of bits or segments beyond that sequence number which the sender is allowed to transmit.

A window-based flow-control mechanism may be implemented efficiently by using the acknowledgment sequence number both for error-control and flow-control purposes (see Fig. 2.3). This number then provides an acknowledgment for all lower-numbered packets and the base for the window-size information, since there is no point in specifying a transmission window for already acknowledged packets.

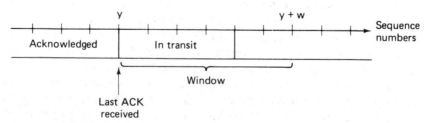

FIGURE 2-3 *Typical flow control window after receiving a segment with acknowledgment = y and window size = w.*

However, it is important to note that acknowledgment for error-control purposes is *not* identical to granting new flow-control credits. In protocols such as X.25 (see Sec. 2.4.4), where the window size must remain fixed, acknowledgments and new credits are synonymous. In more flexible protocols, such as TCP (see Sec. 2.4.1), acknowledgments and credits are independent. A packet may be acknowledged without granting new credit by advancing the acknowledgment sequence number and reducing the window size by a corresponding amount, thus leaving the upper edge of the window in a fixed position. New credits may be granted without acknowledging any received packet by increasing the window size but leaving the acknowledgment sequence number unchanged.

The time at which to grant new credits and the number of credits to allow are important factors in protocol performance. If too many credits are granted, arriving packets may have to be discarded for lack of buffer space, causing excessive retransmissions. Hence, the granting of credits is often tied to the availability of buffer space. A "conservative" flow-control strategy delays advancing the window until buffers for the promised space are available [11, 36].

But conservatism has its own costs. By limiting the window size, it may constrain the sender to a lower transmission rate than the receiver could support [4]. Under ideal conditions, when packets arrive at regular intervals and in order, minimal buffering is needed to handle an arbitrarily large window size and throughput. Under these circumstances, an "optimistic" flow-control strategy returning a larger window size than the buffer space available may improve performance. These questions are discussed further in Sec. 2.3.1.

Flow control, which is an end-to-end function between sending and receiving portions of a transport protocol, should not be confused with *congestion control*, which is the mechanism by which the communication network protects itself from excessive traffic (see Chapter 4). Congestion control is needed in addition to flow control because a combination of connections, each within its own flow-control constraints, may together exceed the capacity of the network. Although flow-control constraints are normally imposed by the receiver, the sending transport station may also limit the flow over one connection for fairness considerations (i.e., to provide a fair share of service to other connections).

Although the cost of memory continues to drop, limited buffer space remains a fact of life in protocol design. Transport protocols require significant buffer space for two main purposes: storing out-of-order arrivals and matching uneven sending and receiving rates. When packets arrive out of order, it is desirable to store them until their predecessors arrive rather than discarding them and requiring retransmission from the source. Mismatched scheduling of sender and receiver, variable transmission delays, and differing production and consumption rates all lead to uneven arrival and receiver acceptance times which require buffering to prevent unnecessary blocking. Since flow control is closely tied to buffer availability, the amount of buffer space needed for efficient operation under different circumstances is an important factor in protocol performance. This is discussed further in Sec. 2.3.1.3.

2.2.6 Synchronization

Since delay is highly variable in a packet-switching network, packets may arrive with much different timing than that in which they were submitted, or even out of order. Sequence numbers allow the receiver to reestablish the proper order of packets but not their exact relative timing. Some applications with real-time constraints, such as packetized speech, graphics, or some forms of teleconferencing, may require data to be delivered with correct timing. This requires an addition of a *time stamp* to the packet header information, giving the time at which the packet was produced or emitted. The time stamp is then used by the receiving transport protocol to deliver packets at the proper real time. The clocks at the receiver and the sender must be running at the same rates, although not necessarily showing the same time, in order for the correct time spacing of packets to be reproduced. The delay in delivering the first packet determines the delay for all succeeding packets and the amount by which the delivery time of the data stream lags the production time [10].

Because transmission delay varies widely, it is possible that a packet will not have arrived at its destination at the moment it should be delivered. To minimize this difficulty, the receiver normally delays a moderate amount after receiving the first packet of a real-time data stream in order to provide "time buffering." Packet-switching networks may have to adopt some form of path setup or resource allocation mechanisms to support such traffic within acceptable delay bounds.

In some cases, the proper timing of data may be more important than its completeness (i.e., in packet speech). In these cases time stamps may completely control the acceptance and delivery of information, while sequence numbers are omitted and long-delayed packets are simply dropped. The normal acknowledgment and retransmission mechanisms may be dropped if the application can tolerate occasional lost packets [10].

Another requirement for timing information comes when multiple data streams must be synchronized with each other. This might occur, for example, in multimedia teleconferencing when speech and text display or graphics must be transmitted over parallel data streams and replayed in proper synchronization. This requirement again calls for the introduction of time stamps or some other synchronization markers into the control information of each data stream.

2.2.7 Priority

The ability to send a small amount of data or an attention signal that sidesteps the normal data stream is a useful communication facility found in many interprocess communication schemes. To provide this facility over a network, the transport protocol must provide an "out-of-band" channel which is not constrained by the flow-control mechanisms applied to normal data. This may be achieved by a special "interrupt" type of control packet, which carries a small amount of data (e.g., 8 bits in X.25) or an attention signal. The interrupt information may also be sent along with a normal data packet if one is pending. The sending protocol requests priority transmission from the transmission medium for such packets if available, and the receiving transport protocol processes them as soon as they arrive. The interrupt or out-of-band signal is then passed to the receiving process to handle appropriately.

In addition to carrying a small amount of interrupt information, the out-of-band signal may also indicate where in the normal data stream the signal was generated. This is useful when the action prompted by the signal involves the data stream as in a "flush input" request. The out-of-band signal may itself carry a reference to the data stream, or a special "mark" code corresponding to a signal with no reference may be sent in the data stream [19]. In other cases, the signal has a meaning independent of the data stream as in an "are you there?" request, and no reference is needed.

A typical use of such out-of-band signals is for a sender to gain the attention of a receiver who has been slow in accepting or processing previously sent data. Since the interrupt signal goes ahead of any data that may be waiting, it hopefully gains the prompt attention of the receiver. In this case, the receiver may wish to purge or discard data up to the point at which the interrupt was generated or may enter some special fast scanning mode for rapidly examining waiting data (see Chapter 3). Since the desired processing of interrupts may vary from application to application, transport protocols themselves do not normally include such additional processing of interrupts. However, owing to the frequent utility of the "purge" operation in association with interrupts, this facility may be optionally requested along with an interrupt in some protocols.

2.2.8 Security

Although sequence numbers and checksums provide protection against normal transmission-medium behavior, they do not protect against "malicious intruders" who can examine data in transit, replay old data at arbitrary times, or fabricate spurious data. Protection against these and related difficulties is normally provided by encrypting data to be transmitted. This requires establishment of a common encryption key at both sender and receiver before data transfer begins. Authorization for communication and distribution of the keys must themselves be done in a secure fashion. Once the keys are distributed, all data may be encrypted while only necessary control information, such as addresses and sequence numbers, appears in the clear. When damaged or spurious information is decrypted by the receiver, its checksum or sequence number will be incorrect, allowing it to be discarded. Further discussion of this topic may be found in Chapter 9.

2.2.9 Initialization and Crash Recovery

Several of the mechanisms described above, such as flow-control windows, encryption keys, and particularly sequence numbers, require proper initialization between the two transport stations supporting a conversation. It is vital that the receiving module of one transport protocol and the sending module of the other transport protocol coordinate properly the sequence numbers to be used in transmitting and accepting packets. Since a TS needs a significant amount of state information and processing to support each conversation, it is desirable to maintain this information only while partners are actively communicating, and to release TS resources when the conversation is finished.

This leads to the idea of establishing a connection in order to initialize control information necessary for reliable communication between two transport stations. The connection must be established (control information initialized) before data communication can begin and must be terminated (TS resources released) when communication is finished. Special control packets for establishing and terminating connections are part of most transport protocols. Other functions, such as the name lookup described in Sec. 2.2.3, may also be performed during connection establishment.

Although transport protocols are able to recover from the full range of transmission-medium errors, they must also handle a failure by one or both transport stations. When the computer supporting a TS crashes and is restarted, some or all memory of connections in progress may have been lost. Under some circumstances, it may not be possible to avoid either loss or duplication of data that were in transit at the time of failure. However, the newly restarted TS must cooperate with the TSs on the other side of previously active connections to signal the failure and then restart reliable communications. Mechanisms for connection establishment, termination, and crash recovery are discussed further in Sec. 2.3.

2.2.10 Internetworking

As networks proliferate it becomes increasingly desirable for users on different nets to be able to interact. Although the general problems of network interconnection are beyond the scope of this chapter, we will consider the basic alternatives for providing virtual-circuit service between users on different networks.

If networks already have or are willing to adopt a common transport protocol, a fully end-to-end service may be provided with minimum requirements on the interface or "gateway" between networks. Only basic datagram facilities are needed across nets, since the common transport stations on either side provide the additional functions, just as in a single net. This "endpoint" approach provides full flexibility of alternate routing and error tolerance at all points between the end users, including the gateways. It has been successfully employed in ARPANET and the European Informatics Network [14].

If it is not possible to adopt a common protocol, each net maintains its own local protocol and the gateway is required to join the two virtual circuits to each other. This "stepwise" approach leads to a more complex and costly gateway, and may not be fully successful if incompatible features (e.g., for priority or flow control) occur in the two nets. The resulting service is not fully end to end, but rather the concatenation of independent virtual-circuit segments. Nevertheless, it does allow two dissimilar nets to interconnect with some degree of success, and may have some advantages for accounting and congestion control that appeal to public networks. A more complete treatment of these issues may be found in [18, 37, 40].

2.2.11 Multidestination Communication

Most of the protocol mechanisms discussed above are suitable for point-to-point communication between two parties. With the advent of broadcast communication technology using satellites, radio, and cables, it becomes possible for many or all computers on the network to hear a transmission. Broadcast or *multidestination* communication is useful in such applications as electronic mail (the same message may go to many people) or distributed systems where bids for service or action commands may be broadcast to many servers. Without knowing the exact number or even the identities of all destinations, the normal sequencing and acknowledgment mechanisms used in point-to-point transport protocols are not applicable. Effective use of broadcast technology and the feasibility of reliable multidestination communication remain important research questions.

2.3 PROTOCOL MODELING AND ANALYSIS

Section 2.2 described the problems that a transport protocol must solve and the mechanisms used in dealing with those problems. This section discusses the performance of transport protocols in greater detail and introduces techniques for predicting or optimizing protocol performance. The two main aspects of protocol performance are efficiency and reliability. *Efficiency* concerns throughput, delay, buffering requirements, overhead, and other quantitative measures. *Reliability* concerns the correct operation of the protocol in managing connections and transferring data.

In both areas, transmission-medium characteristics play an important role in determining protocol performance. To avoid overly complex models and successfully analyze transport protocol performance, transmission-medium behavior must be abstracted into a small set of relevant characteristics. For example, rather than modeling the detailed store-and-forward delay of the packet as it travels through successive switching nodes of the network, end-to-end delay may be modeled as a random variable coming from a particular probability distribution. This process of abstraction transforms a detailed transmission medium into a "black box" with specified characteristics which connects two transport stations. The relevant characteristics include delay distribution (including maximum packet lifetime), bandwidth, packet-size limits, and probability of loss, damage, or duplication of packets.

A basic task in protocol design or analysis is specification. As a minimum, protocols must be clearly described for purposes of human understanding and implementation. If protocol performance is to be analyzed beyond debugging errors after they occur, suitable specifications of both the protocol and the services it is intended to provide must be developed to facilitate simulation, correctness proofs, exhaustive case studies, and other forms of analysis [20, 35, 38]. Since the questions to be answered and techniques used to answer them are quite different for reliability and efficiency, these two areas are considered separately in Secs. 2.3.1 and 2.3.2.

2.3.1 Efficiency

The main efficiency performance measures of interest are traditionally throughput and delay. For transport protocols, *throughput* is the transmission rate of useful data between processes, excluding any control information or retransmissions that the protocol requires. *Delay* is the time from starting to transmit a packet at the sender to successful arrival of the entire packet at the receiver, or arrival of an acknowledgment at the sender in the case of round-trip delay. Other measures of interest include number of retransmissions, line efficiency (the ratio of useful traffic to total traffic), and buffer requirements. Although much has been written concerning these problems within communication networks, very little research has been reported on the efficiency of transport protocols.

Transport protocol performance is limited on one side by transmission-medium characteristics and on the other side by user process behavior. Within these constraints, the main protocol parameters that determine performance are retransmission interval, flow-control strategy, buffering, acknowledgment scheme, and packet size. Understanding how these parameters affect performance and determining optimal values for them is the purpose of this section.

We will focus on performance determining factors for a single end-to-end connection rather than the competition for resources among many connections. Although the management of demand from many sources is a major problem within transmission networks, a transport station must also try to share its resources fairly among all connections [11, 23]. Controls to achieve this are applied in addition to the perconnection controls we shall discuss.

Two basic features of transport protocol operation largely govern protocol efficiency: overhead and retransmission. Overhead results from the control information, including checksum, address, sequence number, length, window, acknowledgment, and so on, which must be carried in packet headers or separate control packets to achieve reliable communication. These header fields provide useful services and reliability but lead to increased delay and reduced throughput. Retransmission leads to a different kind of overhead, in that the data group itself must be transmitted more than once, thereby using up channel capacity. Flow control causes a third type of degradation, in that the channel is forced to remain idle when it could be carrying useful data because of the flow-control constraints. Each of these basic factors is discussed in a following section.

2.3.1.1 Packet Size

In transmitting large amounts of information between processes, a transport protocol may package the data in a varying number of packets. Transmission delay in a store-and-forward network will be lower for smaller packets because the transmission time on each hop between switching nodes is proportional to the packet length [11] (although some networks either fragment or combine submitted packets before internal transmission). Unfortunately, overhead for short packets increases, since each packet carries a fixed-length header, and more acknowledgment and general processing for the same amount of data will be necessary. Hence, maximum throughput attainable decreases while line efficiency (and total cost in bits transmitted) increases for shorter packets. Longer packets reduce overhead and allow higher throughput at the cost of increased delay [24, 36].

To illustrate some of these trade-offs, Fig. 2.4 shows the total time to transmit a large block of information using different packet sizes, assuming typical network characteristics and a delay proportional to packet length. Using the smallest packets, throughput is so low that total delay is high. For very large packets the increasing delay per packet also leads to high total delay. The optimal value for this application is an intermediate packet size.

Other applications may have other priorities for cost, throughput, and delay performance. Real-time or interactive applications may select short packets to achieve low delay at somewhat higher cost. Applications desiring minimum cost or maximum throughput and willing to tolerate larger delays may use long packets [11]. Hence, to provide optimal service the transport protocol must be given an indication of the type of performance the user desires.

2.3.1.2 Retransmission

As described in Sec. 2.2, transport protocols overcome loss or damage of packets in the transmission medium by retransmitting the packets if no positive acknowledgment is received. The interval R at which packets are retransmitted has a major impact on protocol efficiency. In general, a large R allows higher

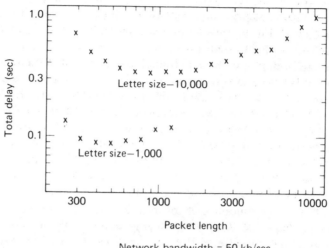

Network bandwidth = 50 kb/sec
Number of hops = 5
Header length = 200 bits
Packet less probability = 0

FIGURE 2-4 *Total delay vs packet length for two block (letter) sizes.*

throughput, since no bandwidth is "wasted" on unnecessary retransmission, while a small R reduces mean delay because lost or damaged packets are retransmitted sooner.

To quantify these general observations, packet transmission delay through the network may be modeled as a probability density function $f(t)$, which typically has a high peak around the nominal delay and a long tail representing the possibility of occasional long delays. The probability LS of lost or damaged packets can be included in $f(t)$ as an impulse at $t = $ infinity with value LS (the probability that a packet never arrives).

The function $f(t)$ and its associated cumulative distribution $F(t)$ model the delay for a single transmission of the packet, while we wish to find the probability distribution for the first *successful* delivery of possibly many retransmissions, called $G(t)$. Assuming that packets are retransmitted at intervals R and that $f(t)$ is identical for each retransmission of a packet, $G(t)$ is given by the following expression:

$$G(t) = \text{Prob}\{\text{at least one successful delivery by time } t\}$$

$$= 1 - \text{Prob}\{\text{no success by time } t\}$$

$$= 1 - \prod_{i=0}^{n-1} [1 - F(t - i \cdot R)] \qquad n = \lceil t/R \rceil$$

$G(t)$ provides the basis for computing the mean delay until first successful delivery and the mean number of retransmissions required. This also gives a measure of the mean throughput attainable, which is proportional to the inverse of the number of retransmissions [36].

Figure 2.5 shows a plot of delay versus throughput for varying retransmission interval R and a typical $f(t)$ with mean of 1. Small R yield points toward the left of the curves and large R yield points toward the right. High packet-loss probabilities LS are used for a more graphic illustration. The definite "knee" in the curves for nonzero LS indicates an optimum value of R. For larger R, delay is increased with little savings in throughput. For smaller R, throughput is reduced (because of excessive retransmission) with little improvement in delay. This optimal value of R occurs for $R = t$ such that the $f(t)$ curve indicates that most single transmissions would have arrived by this time if they were going to arrive.

If the transport protocol is sequencing packets as well as doing error correction, the assumption of independent identically distributed transmission delays for successive packets must be modified. This is because loss of a packet or its acknowledgment causes acknowledgment of all subsequent packets to be delayed until the earlier error is corrected, even though other packets are successfully received. In this case, negative acknowledgments may improve performance by forcing prompt retransmission of the damaged packet. Even with negative acknowledgment, the general effect of sequencing is to increase apparent delay so that a larger R should be used for optimal performance. The amount of this increase depends on the variance in $f(t)$ and hence the amount that packets are likely to arrive out of sequence [36].

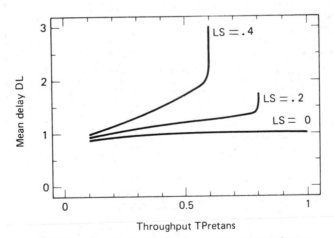

FIGURE 2-5 *Mean delay DL vs throughput factor TPretrans for Erlangian network transmission delay with mean = 1 and k = 16.*

Transmission of new packets from a sender is limited by the number of credits granted by the receiver. Since round-trip delay is typically an order of magnitude greater than host-to-packet-switch transmission time in a packet-switching network, several packets must be in transit simultaneously to achieve high throughput. On the other hand, the receiver may wish to limit the sender's transmission rate by granting few credits. In either case, the number of credits or window size to be used to achieve the desired throughput must be determined.

A simple closed queueing model with the transmitter as one server and the network and receiver as the other server provides a first-order answer to this question. Service time 1 at the transmitter (T_{local}) is the host-to-network transmission time for a packet, while service time 2 (T_{net}) includes propagation of a packet through the network, receiver processing, and return of an acknowledgment, or approximately the round-trip delay. The second server is an infinite server, since packets can proceed in parallel through the network (see Fig. 2.6). The window size N_{win} defines the number of customers (packets) in the system. Let N be the ratio of service time 2 to service time 1.

The utilization of server 1 is the fraction of time that the transmitter is active with a given window size and hence provides a good indication of throughput attainable. Standard results from queuing theory show that throughput rises linearly with window size to a maximum value at a window size of N when round-trip delays are fairly constant [2, 36]. A somewhat larger window size will

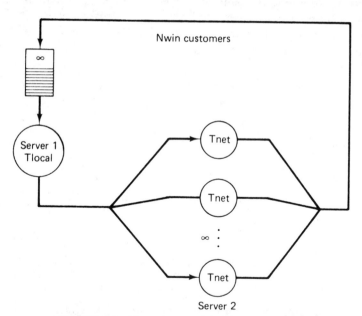

FIGURE 2-6 *Queueing model of flow control.*

be required to obtain maximum throughput if the round-trip delay is highly variable. To limit the throughput to a fraction F of the nominal bandwidth available, a window size of $F \cdot N$ should be used.

As long as packet loss and damage probabilities remain low, the foregoing analysis shows that throughput will be flow-control-limited by a small window size. In networks where transmission errors are more likely, throughput may become retransmission-limited because retransmissions of pending packets have priority over new transmissions. In general, achievable throughput will be the minimum due to either flow control or retransmission constraints. Further transmission restrictions may be imposed by the source transport station in order to share its communication resources fairly among all connections.

As noted in Sec. 2.2.5, flow-control policy is often tied to buffer availability. The amount of destination buffer space required for efficient operation depends on the relative rates and timing of packet arrival and consumption. Let M be the ratio of arrival rate to consumption rate. If $M \gg 1$, simple queueing models show that no matter how many buffers are available, nearly all will be filled in the steady state, and most arriving packets will have to be discarded. Throughput is limited by the receiver's acceptance rate, and a conservative strategy with small window size and few buffers will avoid wasting resources. If $M \ll 1$, very few packets will be discarded and little buffer space is needed. Throughput is limited by the sender's production rate.

When $M = 1$, the smoothness or relative timing of packet arrival and consumption becomes the dominating factor. The transmission system may be the main contributor to variation in delays, or the sender and receiver may themselves produce or consume packets at uneven rates (e.g., because of periodic scheduling in multiprogramming systems). Smooth arrival and consumption behavior requires minimal buffering. More uneven behavior requires more buffering for arriving packets, and a conservative policy with window size tied to buffer availability is more effective.

2.3.2 Reliability

The object of reliability analysis is to demonstrate that a protocol meets specified performance goals concerning correct operation. This requires a clear formulation of performance goals which cover the features of operation to be verified, such as proper delivery of data and avoidance of deadlocks. Assumptions about transmission-medium characteristics and protocol mechanisms must also be specified. From this starting point, a proof or convincing demonstration that the protocol meets the desired performance goals must be constructed.

Since the data-transfer and connection management elements of transport protocols address different problems, they are frequently treated separately. Once a connection is established, the protocol operates cyclically, transmitting one data packet after another, and the main performance goals concern correct data transfer. In connection establishment, on the other hand, the objective is to move from an unsynchronized initial state to a properly synchronized final state (e.g., sequence numbers properly initialized). Other connection management functions, such as terminating connections and recovering from failures, also involve transition from an initial state to a desired final state. Hence data transfer and connection management are treated in separate sections below.

2.3.2.1 Data Transfer

The basic model of data transfer through a transport protocol is a stream of data, provided by a source process, which are packaged into packets by the source transport protocol, sent through a transmission medium, and reconstituted into a stream of data for the destination process (see Fig. 2.7). Since the main cause of difficulties is transmission-medium behavior, we shall assume that the packetizing and reassembly functions work properly and focus on any differences in the delivered packet stream from the submitted packet stream.

We shall call the protocol elements on the sending side a "sending discipline" and those on the receiving side a "receiving discipline." Of course, a full duplex connection has sending and receiving disciplines on each side, and for greater efficiency, acknowledgment information may be carried along with data in the reverse direction. However, for purposes of analysis, the two directions of information flow may be considered logically separate.

Detailed performance goals may be formulated in terms of the submitted and delivered stream of packets [34]. These concern the possibility for damage, loss, duplication, or out-of-order delivery of packets by the transmission medium. Each submitted packet must not be lost (not delivered), delivered in a damaged condition, delivered more than once, or delivered in a different order than submitted.

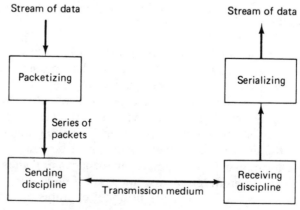

FIGURE 2-7 Data transmission model.

The sending and receiving disciplines may be specified as follows:

SENDING DISCIPLINE

The sending discipline maintains a variable called *next sequence number* (NSN). Each packet submitted has NSN attached and then NSN is advanced to its successor.[1] The packet with NSN and a checksum is transmitted, a timer is started, and a copy retained in a "pending" queue.

Arriving acknowledgement packets (ACKs) are checked for errors and damaged ones are discarded. ACKs for discarded packets are ignored.

When an ACK referencing the sequence number of a pending packet is received, the pending packet is discarded (and the sender notified of success). If no ACK is received for a pending packet within the retransmission interval R, the pending packet is retransmitted and the timer is restarted.

RECEIVING DISCIPLINE

The receiving discipline maintains a variable called the *expected sequence number* (ESN). Each packet received is checked for errors and discarded if damaged. If not damaged, the packet sequence number (PSN) is compared with ESN and action is taken as follows:

If less, transmit an ACK referencing PSN and discard the packet as a duplicate.

If equal, transmit an ACK, deliver the packet to the process, and advance ESN to its successor.

If greater, discard the packet as out of order.[2]

The foregoing protocol definitions assume that all damage to packets or acknowledgments will be detected. In fact, it is not possible to detect all transmission errors, resulting in occasional acceptance of a faulty packet or

---

[1] The simplest and most widely used successor function is to increment by one, although others may be used based on the length (in bytes or other units) of each packet.

[2] For greater efficiency, the receiving discipline may choose to keep some number of out-of-order packets for a time.

ACK. However, the probability of an undetected error can be made extremely small by the use of modest-length checksums [13], so we will ignore this source of error.

We also assume that the protocol is properly initialized (i.e., the connection is established). This means that NSN in the sending discipline is equal to ESN in the receiving discipline on the other side of the connection and that no data packets have been sent. Connection establishment is itself a difficult problem discussed later in this section.

The definitions also assume an infinite sequence number space and that the protocol will go on trying to retransmit an unacknowledged packet forever. Relaxation of these assumptions is discussed below. Flow-control constraints and the possible use of negative acknowledgments are also ignored, since they will affect the efficiency but not the correct operation of the protocol.

With these assumptions in mind, we construct an informal proof that the performance goals are met by considering each possible type of error.

- *Duplication*. No duplicate packet generated by the sending discipline or the transmission medium will ever be delivered to the receiving process because the receiving discipline advances its ESN after delivering the first copy. Hence, all other copies will be detected as old duplicates and discarded by the receiving discipline.

- *Damage*. Any packet damaged by the transmission medium will be detected and discarded by the protocol (this is an assumption).

- *Loss*. Any data packet lost by the transmission medium will not be acknowledged and hence will be retransmitted by the sending discipline. A lost acknowledgment will result in retransmission of the data packet by the sending discpline and a later acknowledgment from the receiving discipline.

- *Sequencing*. If a packet arrives at the receiving discipline before one of its predecessors, the ESN check will cause it to be discarded. Only the next packet in order can be accepted by the receiving discipline for delivery.

In reality, sequence numbers must be finite in length and hence eventually wrap around to previously used values. If packets could persist an arbitrarily long time in the transmission medium, old packets could arrive at the receiving discipline and be accepted instead of new packets with the same sequence numbers. Acknowledgments may also be delayed, causing the sending discipline to think a packet has been transmitted successfully when in fact it has not been. This leads to the constraint expressed in Sec. 2.2—that sequence numbers must not wrap around within a maximum packet lifetime. More specifically, a data packet must not be transmitted with a given sequence number until any previous data packet or acknowledgments carrying that sequence number are certain to be absent from the transmission medium. This is normally ensured by providing a large enough sequence number size for the highest anticipated transmission rate and packet lifetime. A more formal derivation of this constraint may be found in [26].

Failure Consequences: The foregoing analysis assumes that sending and receiving disciplines continue to operate correctly without loss of memory throughout the lifetime of a connection. It is also important to consider the consequences when one side of a connection fails with loss of memory, as would occur in a host crash. Under these circumstances, packets that have been transmitted but not yet acknowledged will lead to either loss or duplication of information.

The details of this situation are as follows. Suppose that a sending discipline A has accepted a packet and transmitted it but has not yet received an acknowledgment or reported successful delivery to its user. If the receiving discipline B has accepted the packet and then fails and restarts with an incorrect ESN, it may accept the packet a second time. Alternatively, B may reject all packets after restarting and signal its predicament to A. If A resends the packet after recovery is complete, it will again be delivered twice. If A chooses not to resend the packet, it may never have been delivered if B did not receive it before failing. Failure of the sending dicipline results in a similar set of cases, leading either to duplicate delivery or failure to deliver a packet. Deadlock is another possible failure consequence, since no packets will be accepted by the receiving discipline if NSN and ESN are not properly synchronized.

This analysis shows a fundamental limitation of transport protocols. As long as they continue to function normally, they successfully mask all errors by the transmission medium. But when part of the protocol itself is violated, owing to failure of sending or receiving disciplines, they can no longer guarantee reliable transmission, and either loss or duplication of information may result [3, 34]. The safest course of action is to signal the uncertain state of data in transit at the time of failure to the users of the protocol, who must recover from the error with higher-level mechanisms outside the transport protocol. Another approach is to reduce the rate of protocol failures to an acceptable level by use of backup storage, redundant machines, or other means.

2.3.2.2 Connection Management

Connection management provides for the initialization and subsequent release of the resources needed for reliable data transfer. This includes connection establishment, termination, and failure recovery as described in Sec. 2.2.9. Connections follow a life cycle starting in a nonactive state, passing through intermediate opening states to an established state where data transfer takes place, and finally returning to the nonactive state through some intermediate closing states. Each of these phases is discussed in the following sections. The greatest difficulties surround connection establishment, since it must be accomplished over an unreliable transmission medium with no prior synchronization of sender and receiver.

Connection Establishment: The main function of connection establishment is to initialize the next sequence number (NSN) used by the sending discipline and the expected sequence number (ESN) used by the receiving discipline for subsequent data transfer. The simplest approach to this problem might be to use a fixed value (e.g., 0) for these variables every time a connection is started. Unfortunately, this simple scheme can easily lead to violation of the constraints on sequence number reuse described above with the consequent duplicate delivery of data. Figure 2.8 shows two successive connections between the same pair of processes *A* and *B*. If a duplicate packet from the first connection is delayed in the network until the second connection has started, it may look like a valid new data packet and be accepted.

One solution to this problem is to wait at least a maximum packet lifetime before starting a new connection between the same pair of processes (with the same ports), guaranteeing that all old packets are gone. This may not be acceptable in large systems with long packet lifetimes. In some networks a user may explicitly request destruction of any remaining packets on a connection (a "reset"), but this is only possible if the network has knowledge of transport connections (i.e., can locate and distinguish packets of a particular connection from all others).

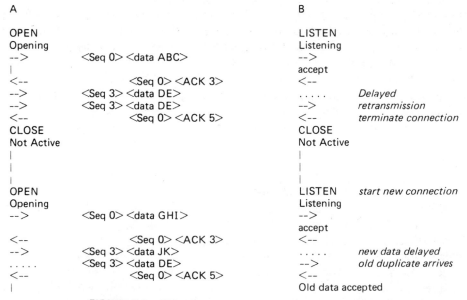

FIGURE 2-8 *Old data delivered instead of current data.*

Other solutions require a more careful selection of the initial sequence number (ISN) used for a new connection. This may involve adding additional control information to distinguish packets from different connections, such as an *incarnation number,* which is incremented for each new connection [17], or generating unique addresses for each connection [39].

If the sequence number alone is used to distinguish packets from different connections, it must be carefully selected based on memory of previous connection sequence numbers or based on a clock. In the memory approach, the ISN is set to the last sequence number used in the previous connection plus one. This requires maintaining state information for inactive connections at least for a maximum packet lifetime. In the clock approach, the ISN is set from a single clock for all connections at a host [41]. This minimizes the state information to be maintained for inactive connections or through host crashes, but requires resetting the sequence number on an active connection if the clock is about to catch up with the sequence numbers in use [39].

Once ISN is selected, it must be transmitted to the receiving discipline in a special synchronization control packet (SYN). The receiver uses the sequence number in the SYN packet to set ESN in his receiving discipline and replies with an SYN packet, giving his or her own ISN. Each SYN packet must be acknowledged. When a transport station has received an acknowledgment for its own SYN and received its partner's SYN packet, the connection is established.

Unfortunately, errors may still occur if SYN packets from old connections are delayed and delivered just as a new connection is being opened. The careful selection of ISN prevents data from an old connection from being accepted on a new connection but does not protect against SYN packets themselves being duplicated. As shown in Fig. 2.9, an old SYN may arrive at B just at the moment when B is ready to establish a new connection; B will accept the SYN as a new connection request, reply with its own SYN, and consider the connection

```
A                                                  B

Listening                                          Listening
.....              <Seq z> <SYN>                   -->           Old connection request
|                                                  Set ESN = z + 1
<--                       <ACK z + 1>              <--
Discard                                            |
|                                                  Pick ISN = y
<--                       <Seq y> <SYN>            <--
Set ESN = y + 1                                    |
-->                <ACK y + 1>                     -->
|                                                  Established
Pick ISN = x                                       |
-->                <Seq x> <SYN>                   -->
|                                                  Discard
<--                       <Seq y + 1> <ACK z + 1>  <--
Discard                                            |
```

FIGURE 2-9 *Deadlock with simple connection establishment.*

established. As a result, *A* will receive the replying SYN and interpret it as a new connection request. *A*'s attempt to reply will be discarded by *B*, who thinks the connection is already established, causing a deadlock that prevents data transfer.

To avoid this problem, a more reliable means of transmitting a new connection request to the remote transport station must be used. The transport station receiving the request asks for verification of the request at the same time it sends its own ISN. The initiating transport station then acknowledges the verification request, as shown in Fig. 2.10. This "three-way handshake" mechanism was suggested in [41] and has been successfully used in TCP [8].

Connection Termination: A simple mechanism for terminating connections is for each user to tell his or her transport station to close the connection. The transport station then immediately halts all operation on behalf of that connection and frees all resources. This requires agreement between the users at a level above the transport protocol on a safe time to terminate the connection.

Alternatively, the transport protocol itself may provide a mechanism by which one of the processes can inform the other that communication over this connection is to cease. A special control packet indicating that the conversation is finished (FIN) may be used to accomplish this. The FIN packet carries a sequence number just like a normal data packet. Several procedures for exchanging FIN packets are possible. In the simplest, the FIN is acted upon as soon as it is received and another FIN packet is returned. If a FIN arrives before some preceeding data packets (e.g., out of order), those data will not be delivered before the connection is terminated.

To "gracefully" close a connection, a FIN must be processed only after all preceding data. This allows any data in transit to be delivered first. When the user asks the transport station to close a connection, he or she may not transmit any further data but must be willing to receive any arriving data until his or her partner complies with the close request.

```
A                                              B

OPEN                                           LISTEN
Opening                                        Listening
Pick ISN = x                                   |
-->         <Seq 0> <SYN>                       -->
|                                              Remember x
|                                              Pick ISN = y
<--                 <Seq y><SYN><ACK x + 1>     <--
Set ESN = y + 1                                 |
Established                                     |              Wait for verification
|                                              |
-->         <Seq x + 1> <ACK y + 1>             -->
|                                              Set ESN = x + 1
|                                              Established
```

FIGURE 2-10 *"Three-way handshake" connection establishment.*

Failure Recovery: When a transport station or the host computer supporting it fails and then subsequently restarts, knowledge of connections in progress may have been lost. In this case, connections that were established become "half open," with the failed side thinking they are not active and the other transport station believing the connection is still established.

Since the established side is consuming resources, it is desirable to reset half-open connections promptly. One way to close half-open connections is to have a watchdog timer in each transport station that goes off if an established connection has not actively received any correct packets for some time or if a retransmission counter exceeds some specified value. The occurrence of such events will cause the transport protocol to unilaterally close its side of the connection.

To recover more promptly, another type of control packet, indicating that the connection should be reset (RST), may be used. If the failed side of the connection restarts and receives data packets, it returns an RST packet, referencing the sequence number of the data packet. When the RST reaches the established side, it is checked for validity and the connection may be immediately terminated. An old duplicate RST packet would not pass the validity check and hence would have no effect. Attempts to establish a new connection from the failed side to an already established side are cleared in a similar fashion.

2.3.3 Formal Verification

An informal narrative type of analysis such as that performed above is very valuable in providing motivation for and intuitive understanding of transport protocol mechanisms. However, the number and complexity of control procedures used in transport protocols require more rigorous analysis if their correct operation is to be demonstrated with a high degree of certainty.

This requires a precise model of the protocol whose detailed operation can be analyzed. This model typically consists of a pair of protocol machines connected by a transmission medium. The machines receive commands from their respective users, and messages from each other via the transmission medium. The transmission medium is itself a simple kind of machine that may introduce errors, delays, and other perturbations between its input and its output.

Attempts at rigorous verification have followed two main approaches: program proofs and state models [38]. In the former each machine is described algorithmically, and assertions that reflect the desired reliability goals must be formulated and proved. This approach has been effectively applied to verifying the data-transfer features of transport protocols where large or infinite numbers of interaction sequences are possible due to large sequence number spaces and retransmissions.

The state modeling approach has used such formalisms as Petri nets, state diagrams, state transmission matrices, flowcharts, and programs to define the protocol machines. Some form of reachability analysis is then performed to generate all possible interactions of the machines, followed by a check for undesirable states. This approach has been successful in verifying data-transfer features where simplifying assumptions are made to keep the number of states tractable, but is most applicable to connection management where the number of states is inherently small.

Some of the most fruitful work has involved a mixture of both techniques, where a relatively small state model of the basic features of the protocol is combined with additional context information or variables which reflect such information as sequence numbers [35, 38]. Rather than attempting a cursory survey of this complex area, we present a moderately detailed example which illustrates the flavor of the approach. The example shows the technique used in [34] to formally verify portions of an early version of the TCP connection management procedures.

Each transport station is modeled as a classic state machine with an input set, an output set, a set of internal states, and functions giving the next state and output for each combination of input and current state. Inputs consist of user commands, messages from the other protocol machine (or the network), and internally generated events such as timeouts. The two machines operate independently, with synchronization achieved by one machine waiting for a particular type of packet from the other machine.

We define the composite state of the system as the state of the protocol machine on each side of the connection, plus any relevant packets in the transmission medium between them. Transitions from one composite state to another are derived from the state transitions of the individual protocol machines by including all possible transitions of either protocol machine, given the state of the transmission medium.

The number of composite states is then the number of protocol machine states squared times the number of different states of the transmission medium. In a "pure" state machine approach, this would quickly lead to an unworkable number of states. This potential state explosion may be limited in two ways: by reducing the number of protocol machine states, and by treating as equivalent different sets of packets in transit.

For TCP, only four states are used to model the basic steps of connection establishment: *Not Active*, *Established*, and two intermediate steps representing the initiation or reception of a new connection request (*SYN-Sent* and *SYN-Received*). Additional information used in determining the processing of packets (such as used or expected sequence numbers) is kept as separate "context" variables. To limit the number of transmission-medium states, worst-case assumptions are made about delayed duplicate arrivals. All types of "old" packets are allowed to arrive in any state, so that no acknowledged packets need to be explicitly represented in the composite state [39].

By taking advantage of these reductions, a relatively compact model of connection establishment in TCP may be developed (Fig. 2.11). Each composite state is represented by a pair of process states and a list of packets in the transmission medium. Some context is represented along with the basic state of each process. This consists of the sequence number for outgoing packets in the SYN-Sent, SYN-Received, and Established states, and also a received sequence number for incoming packets in the Established state. This allows us to determine whether the protocol has correctly initialized sequence numbers when the Established state is reached.

Packets are represented by their packet types, with a subscript giving their own sequence number if relevant, followed by the sequence number of another packet they may refer to (in parentheses). An arrow above the packet shows its direction of travel. Symmetric states (identical except for switching process identities and packet directions) have been eliminated to simplify the figure. Transitions to the same state, such as retransmissions, are not shown. Composite transitions resulting from simultaneous transitions of both protocol machines are perfectly legal but are shown as sequential individual transitions to reduce the number of arrows.

This composite state model demonstrates several aspects of protocol correctness for the normal case where both protocol machines start in the *Not Active* state and function according to their definition (no failures). This includes safety considerations (absence of deadlocks, correctness of outcome), and viability considerations (progress and eventual termination), as follows.

The only terminal state shows both machines in the Established state, with sequence numbers for both directions properly initialized. Hence, there is no deadlock in the procedure for connection establishment. All paths leading back to the Not Active state for either machine are caused by collisions (simultaneous open requests), which will cause a later retry to establish the connection. (The need for retries was avoided in a later version of the TCP.) Assuming that perpetual collisions are avoided by the random retry timeout, and that the transmission medium provides a nonzero probability of delivering any packet, the protocol will eventually succeed in establishing a connection.

A great deal of other work on formal verification has begun to appear in the literature (see [38] for a partial survey), and there is every indication that this will remain an active research area until more automated techniques, which can handle more complex protocols, are developed.

2.4 HISTORY AND STANDARDS

Up to this point we have described transport protocol design and analysis from a general point of view, largely avoiding the details of particular protocols. Such a presentation brings together the lessons learned in many separate research and development efforts. In this section we briefly present some of the history of transport protocol development, various protocols that have resulted from these efforts, and the status of standardization efforts. For each protocol, the approach

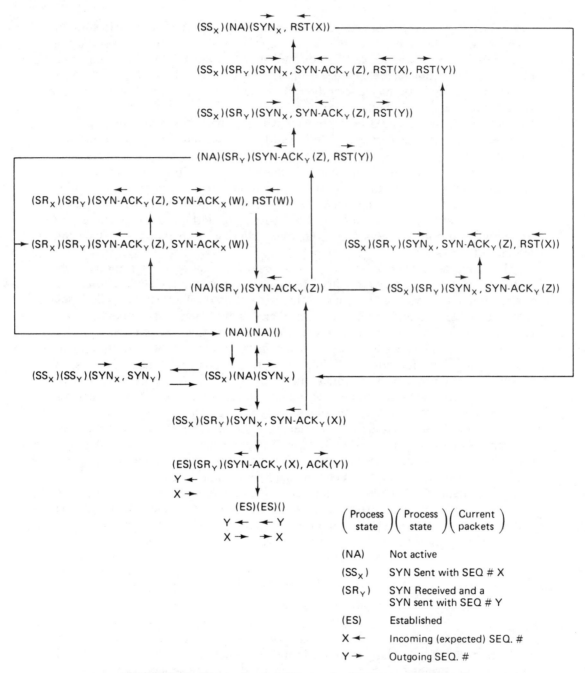

FIGURE 2-11 *Composite state diagram for "three-way handshake".*

taken in providing major transport functions (see Sec. 2.2) is described, allowing a comparison of different protocols.

The first transport protocols were developed as part of scientific research projects. These were the host–host protocol in the ARPANET [5] (with its implementation in the network control program or NCP), and the transport protocol of the French Cyclades network [42]. Further adaptations of these pioneering efforts are being used in other research environments, and more recently have been applied to particular commercial applications such as banking or utilities networks. Computer manufacturers and public data communication networks have also found a need to provide virtual-circuit-type services. As networks proliferate, the need to provide these services across multiple networks becomes ever more complex but necessary. Developments in each of these areas will be outlined in the following sections.

2.4.1 ARPANET

The ARPANET provided the environment for the earliest transport protocol. Since the communications subnet of switching computers provided a datagram or individual message-oriented communication service, the need for additional connection-oriented services was felt at an early date (see Chapter 1). Since the network provided highly reliable and sequenced message delivery, the host–host protocol focused on flow control, interrupt, multiplexing, and convenient addressing. In combination with the initial connection protocol (ICP), it provided a set of well-known addresses and procedures by which many connections to various services could be supported.

The ARPANET host–host protocol established an important principle of protocol specification. While the format and procedures for message exchange between protocol machines was exactly and completely specified, the interface between the user and the protocol was only functionally specified. The basic functions included open, close, send, receive, and interrupt operations. This allowed implementations of the protocol (the NCPs) and particularly the user interfaces to them to be successfully tailored to different machines, while NCPs for different machines were all guaranteed to be able to talk to each other.

The user interface to the NCP was stream-oriented, with flow control in both bits and messages provided by incremental "allocate" control messages between NCPs. Interrupt signals were not synchronized with the data stream. Control messages for all connections between a pair of NCPs were sent over a single control connection, while data messages were sent on their individual connections.

2.4.2 Research Nets

The French Cyclades network, designed somewhat later than the ARPANET, employed a simpler communication subnet with less responsibility for reliable transmission of packets. Hence the transport station (TS) developed for the

Cyclades net included procedures for error detection and recovery as described in Sec. 2.2. The user interface was record-oriented with the TS handling letters. Error control was on letters, with a complete letter being retransmitted in case of any error. Sequencing and flow control were also on a letter basis with agreement on maximum letter size forming part of connection establishment.

In parallel with the Cyclades TS, a second-generation ARPANET protocol was developed. This internet protocol [6], soon came to be called TCP, after its implementation in a *transmission control program* [7]. As the name implied, its goal was to provide fully reliable virtual-circuit service across many networks. Unlike the NCP, full error-detection and recovery procedures were included in TCP with the anticipation that some networks in a multinetwork system might not provide full reliability. Postel [27] provides a more detailed comparison of NCP and TCP.

To allow fine-grained flow control and more efficient error recovery, TCP sequence numbers were in units of bytes. This also allowed repeated fragmentation of data into arbitrary-length packets if necessary between networks with varying packet sizes. The user interface to TCP was record-oriented, as in the Cyclades TS, but error and flow control were performed on a byte basis.

While the original TCP had long sequence numbers and highly reliable procedures for data transfer once a connection was established, the procedures for first establishing a connection were rather simple. Several weaknesses in these simple connection management procedures were identified in the course of TCP development, leading to invention and adoption of the more sophisticated techniques described in Sec. 2.3.2. In particular, techniques for initial sequence number selection, the three-way handshake for connection establishment, and resynchronization for clock-based sequence numbering were proposed and implemented.

More recently [8], some TCP functions, including fragmentation/reassembly and TS addressing, have been moved into a separate "internet" protocol, which is essentially a multinet datagram protocol. For a priority mechanism, the original short interrupt packet has been dropped in favor of an "urgent pointer" that indicates a place in the normal data stream requiring urgent attention (see Chapter 3). An optional block-oriented flow control has also been adopted.

From an early date, the Internetwork Working Group (INWG, Technical Committee 6.1) of IFIP (the International Federation for Information Processing) has played an active role in transport protocol development. From the combined experience of ARPANET, Cyclades, and other networks represented by researchers in the group, several proposed transport protocol standards, most notably INWG 96 (known by its report number) [21], have been prepared and are periodically revised and updated. The latest revision specifically provides for adaptation of the transport protocol to the characteristics of the underlying transmission medium. In particular, greater efficiency may be achieved with networks providing a high level of service by negotiating the omission of procedures at the transport protocol level that are already provided by the network, such as flow control. This may be particularly useful for public networks with X.25 interfaces as described below.

Numerous adaptations have grown out of the early ARPANET, Cyclades, and INWG protocols. The European Informatics Network (EIN) provides a test bed for INWG protocols in a multinetwork multinational environment [14]. The MIT Laboratory for Computer Science has developed a TCP-like protocol called DSP, optimized for use in a local network environment. DSP uses unique addresses, which may never be reused, to help distinguish packets from different connections. Xerox Palo Alto Research Center has developed transport protocols and a wide range of other protocols based upon them for use in a local network office automation system. At Lawrence Livermore Laboratory, a very high bandwidth local network with small maximum packet lifetimes has led to a TCP-like protocol with connection establishment based on timers and memory of sequence numbers [16].

Some commercial applications of these protocols have also appeared. The U.S. Defense Communications Agency has adopted a TCP-like protocol that includes additional procedures to support military security and priority for its AUTODIN II common user data network. A large French gas and electric utility network has adopted a modified TS protocol [9]. A large Belgian bank has added encryption to a TS-like protocol for use in its banking network [15]. The strong similarity of these systems and their lack of interoperability due to small differences argues strongly for the early standardization of a common transport protocol from this family. Such a standard is being developed in INWG for presentation to ISO (TC97 SC16) and other relevant standards bodies.

2.4.3 Computer Manufacturers

With few exceptions, computer manufacturers' "networks" have been oriented toward connecting terminals to a large central computer. A variety of such network products have been announced in recent years. Despite the inherent asymmetry of the terminal-to-computer relationship, a protocol layer providing the functions of a transport protocol may usually be identified in these systems. We briefly describe Digital Equipment Corporation's DECNET and IBM's SNA as representative examples.

2.4.3.1 DECNET

DECNET followed the ARPANET approach of strong protocol layering with a data link control level, a logical connection or virtual-circuit level, and a user or application-level protocol. The network services protocol (NSP) is the DEC-NET equivalent of a transport protocol. Unlike the ARPANET, there is no strict distinction between host computers and switching nodes in DECNET, and both functions may be implemented in the same machine. One portion of NSP is concerned with routing packets and maintaining current routing information. The remainder of NSP forms a transport protocol concerned with opening and closing connections and sending and receiving data packets or interrupts. As with the INWG 96 protocol, various elements of procedure, such as flow control, sequencing, and acknowledgments, may be selected by the user. This allows the full range of transport protocol mechanisms to be used when needed, or lesser services to be used when they are adequate (e.g., across single physical link) with a minimum of transport protocol overhead.

Addressing in DECNET may be to specific numeric ports which are known to the routing algorithms, or generic names which must be looked up at either source or destination when the connection is established. Connection establishment also involves an exchange of version numbers between the protocol modules to ensure protocol compatability. Error control and flow control are on a message basis, with source and destination having to agree implicitly on message size limits. Flow control, when enabled, is "conservative," with the sender granted credits only for the number of buffers the receiver has made available. Connection termination procedures are "ungraceful," any pending data messages being discarded. All connections start with the fixed sequence number 0. Messages may be broken into up to 16 segments by the source, but no further fragmentation at intermediate nodes is allowed. Addressing may be single level for small networks or hierarchical for larger systems.

2.4.3.2 IBM Systems Network Architecture (SNA)

Like most computer manufacturers' networks, IBM's SNA is oriented toward secondary terminal nodes accessing a single or small number of primary main computer nodes, rather than arbitrary nodes conversing with each other on a more equal footing. This asymmetry permeates many of the SNA protocols.

Transport protocol functions are provided primarily by the *transmission control* (TC) layer of SNA (see Chapter 8 for further details on SNA). Connections (called *sessions*) are established between TCs (actually between "service managers," which correspond to what we have called connection machines in each "network addressable unit") with the help of a third party, the *system services control point* (SSCP). The SSCP converts names to addresses, checks access permission, optionally queues requests, and returns initialization information to the TCs on each side of the session. The primary TC then actually initiates a connection to the secondary TC, avoiding any possibility for race conditions. Connection termination is also mediated by the SSCP, and may be either immediate or graceful. An SNA system may have more than one SSCP.

Blocks of information are formed into a series (called a chain) of *request units* (RU) and sequencing is performed by the level above TC. Flow control is performed by TC on request units, but acknowledgments and error recovery are on entire chains at a higher protocol level. As in the ARPANET NCP, error control relies primarily on the hop-by-hop link error-detection mechanisms below the transport level. Two logical full duplex connections are provided in each session: normal and expedited. The expedited channel provides for out-of-band signaling between processes, and also carries all control messages. Flow control (called *pacing*) is only provided on the normal channel and uses an essentially fixed window size determined at session establishment.

2.4.4 Public Networks

As packet switching proved itself in the research environment, interest in providing public data communications service using packet switching has grown. Networks providing public service are already in operation in the United States, Canada, and the United Kingdom, and are in advanced stages of development in Japan, France, and several other countries. These networks are operated either by government postal, telephone, and telegraph authorities, or by regulated private companies.

In an effort to provide standardized and compatible services throughout the world, these organizations cooperate through the International Telephone and Telegraph Consultative Committee (CCITT) to formulate "recommendations" for providing various types and levels of service. Several recommendations for packet-switching network operation have been adopted in recent years, most notably the X.25 recommendation specifying the interface or protocol to be followed by subscribers accessing public networks.

An important feature of X.25 is that it specifies only the interface between the customer's computer (*data terminal equipment or DTE*) and his local attachment point to the network (a switching node or *DCE*). X.25 includes a protocol for managing the physical link between customer and network which is a version of the ISO HDLC protocol, and a higher-level virtual circuit protocol which provides for many simultaneous virtual circuits over the physical link. This latter packet-level or level 3 protocol has many features of a transport protocol but operates only between the subscriber computer on one side and the local network switching node on the other side (but see below).

To achieve end-to-end service between two subscribers, the network must establish connections and transmit data between source and destination DCEs using an internal protocol not specified in X.25. The destination node provides a third portion of a virtual-circuit path by using X.25 with the destination subscriber (see Fig. 2.12). In some networks, the internal protocol uses a single virtual circuit between source and destination nodes, while in others an independent virtual circuit between each intermediate node is used. Hence, end-to-end service is provided by a concatenation or series of at least three independent virtual circuits. The outer two links are governed by the X.25 protocol while the inner link or links are implemented as desired by each local network.

The X.25 level 3 protocol performs sequencing and flow control on a packet basis. Two logically separate full duplex data streams are provided in each connection, a normal stream and a "qualified" stream, but both are sequenced and flow-controlled together. Flow control uses a window mechanism with a size

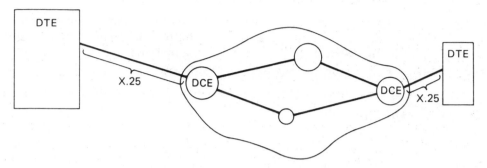

FIGURE 2-12 X.25 interface.

of one to eight packets. The window size is fixed at the time the connection is established, based on the class of service requested. No checksums or acknowledgments are used at level 3 (the ''acknowledgment'' actually serves to advance the flow-control window), but the link-level protocol provides common error detection and correction for all virtual circuits. An out-of-band signal or interrupt of 8 bits is provided which must be acknowledged by the destination subscriber before a second interrupt can be transmitted.

Connections are established by a special *call request* packet, specifying the destination address and optional service features required. The request is forwarded through the network to the destination subscriber, who returns an accept or reject packet. Simultaneous requests by a pair of subscribers to call each other may result in 0, 1, or 2 calls being set up, depending on local network procedures. Connections may be terminated (''cleared'') at any time, with any data in transit discarded. The user or network may also ''reset'' a virtual circuit under unusual circumstances, causing discard of any data in transit and reset of sequence numbers and flow control, but not closing the connection.

Although, strictly, X.25 specifies only the *interface* between customer and network, it provides a basis for inferring the subscriber-to-subscriber service that will be offered by public networks. Some of the level 3 protocol features, such as interrupt and call establishment, are defined to have end-to-end significance. Other features, such as sequencing and flow control, are only required to have local significance (as in TRANSPAC), but may also be implemented to have end-to-end significance (as in DATAPAC). Thus, when a receiving subscriber advances the flow-control window, the effect on the sending subscriber's flow-control window is uncertain and depends on local network implementation. Call clearing and resets may also be handled either way. Hence, the end-to-end service characteristics of public networks require further definition beyond X.25 and will vary from network to network.

Because there is no end-to-end error control in X.25 and because resets may occasionally occur, users with high-reliability requirements may need to implement their own error-control procedures in an end-to-end protocol on top of X.25. The uncertainty of X.25 flow control may also require end-to-end flow-control procedures. Some public network subscribers thus find themselves in need of end-to-end transport protocols on top of X.25 [9, 15]. To reduce the inefficiency of similar mechanisms being used at both levels, two approaches are possible. The transport protocols may be streamlined and adapted to take advantage of the high grade of service offered by X.25 [15, 19, 21], but some duplication is inevitable.

Alternatively, public network interfaces may be expanded to include a simpler datagram-type service without connection establishment, sequencing, or error control [22, 31]. These functions could then be provided by an end-to-end transport protocol. Such a datagram service should be cheaper to provide and would also be useful to point-of-sale and other transaction-oriented users who do not need virtual-circuit service. During the original development of public packet networks, it was strongly argued that datagram and not virtual-circuit service should be the basic service provided, with transport functions left to the users, and an initial version of DATAPAC did operate in this way.

When public packet-switching networks are interconnected, the uncertainties concerning end-to-end service characteristics are multiplied. A CCITT recommendation for the interface between networks (numbered X.75) has been formulated. X.75 closely resembles X.25 and specifies a virtual-circuit-type protocol for the link between networks with a separate virtual circuit for each internet call. Although like X.25, X.75 addresses itself only to the link between networks and not to end-to-end architecture, it seems clear that the overall architecture will be a series of concatenated virtual circuits through each local network and across each internetwork link, as shown in Fig 2.13 [18, 40]. This increases the number of elements that must operate reliably and increases the number of intermediaries participating in virtual-circuit functions, raising doubts about the optimality of this approach [18]. Quality of service resulting from this architecture will have to be assessed when multinetwork operations using X.75 become a reality.

2.4.5 International Standards Organization (ISO)

The most recent major development in protocols has been the formation of the ISO TC97 SC16 to study "open systems interconnection." The goal of this group

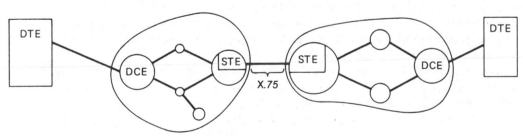

FIGURE 2-13 X.75 interface.

is to define an overall architecture for all levels of protocol in "open" systems of interconnected computers, and a preliminary architecture with seven levels has already been proposed [1]. Level 4, called the transport level, appears to contain most of the functions of traditional transport protocols. However, some functions, particularly concerning addressing of multiple processes within a system, have been placed in level 5, called "session control."

Initially, ISO is focusing on defining the services provided at each level rather than designing specific protocols at any level. However, this work will undoubtedly have a strong impact on the future development of transport protocols.

REFERENCES

[1] BACHMANN, C. W. and others, "Session 8: Standard Interfaces and Protocols for Distributed Systems" (3 papers), *Proceedings of the 7th IEEE Computer Society International Conference (COMPCON),* Washington, D.C., pp. 139–156, November 1978.

[2] BELSNES, D., "Flow Control in Packet Switching Networks," *Proceedings of the European Computing Conference on Computer Networks*, (Online Conferences, Uxbridge, England.) pp. 349–361, 1975. Also *INWG Note* 63.

[3] BELSNES, D., "Single Message Communication," *IEEE Transactions on Communications,* COM-24(2), pp. 190–194, February 1976.

[4] BENNET, C. J., and A. J. HINCHLEY, "Measurements of the Transmission Control Program," *Proceedings of the Symposium on Computer Network Protocols,* Liège, Belgium, February 1978, pp. G1:1–11, February 1978. Also in *Computer Networks Journal,* 2(4/5) 1978.

[5] CARR, S., S. CROCKER, and V. CERF, "Host/Host Protocol in the ARPA Network." *Proceedings of the AFIPS Spring Joint Computer Conference,* 36 pp. 589–597, 1970.

[6] CERF, V. G., and R. E. KAHN, "A Protocol for Packet Network Intercommunication," *IEEE Transactions on Communications*, COM-22, pp. 637–648, May 1974.

[7] CERF, V. G., Y. DALAL, and C. SUNSHINE, "Specification of Internet Transmission Control Program," *INWG Note* 72, December 1974.

[8] CERF, V. G., and J. B. POSTEL, "Specification of Internetwork Transmission Control Program Version 3," unpublished report, January 1978.

[9] CHESNEAU, C., and others, "Normalisation des Fonctions de Communication à Travers un Réseau de Transmission de Données à Commutation de Pacquets à Electricité de France et Gaz de France" (in French), *Proceedings of the Symposium on Computer Network Protocols,* Liège, Belgium, pp. B2:1–15, February 1978.

[10] COHEN, D., "A Protocol for Packet Switching Voice Communication," *Proceedings of the Symposium on Computer Network Protocols*, Liège, Belgium, February 1978, pp. D8:1–9. [Also in *Computer Networks Journal,* 2(4/5), 1978.]

[11] CROWTHER, W., and others, "Issues in Packet Switching Network Design," *Proceedings of the AFIPS National Computer Conference*, pp. 161–175, 1975.

[12] DANTHINE, A., and F. MAGNEE, "End-to-End Protocol Performance," *Proceedings of the Conference on Computer Performance Evaluation*, (Online Conferences, Northwood Hills, England), pp. 569–587, 1976.

[13] DAVIES, D. W., and D. L. A. BARBER, *Communication Networks for Computers*, John Wiley & Sons, Inc., New York, 1974.

[14] DEPARIS, M., and others, "The Implementation of an End-to-End Protocol by EIN Centers: A Survey and Comparison," *Proceedings of the 3rd International Conference on Computer Communications*, Toronto, Canada, pp. 351–360, August 1976.

[15] EOCHENAUER, E., and V. OBOZINSKI, "The Network Communication Manager: A Transport Station for the SGB Network," *Proceedings of the Symposium on Computer Network Protocols*, Liège, Belgium, pp. C2:1–21, February 1978. [Also in *Computer Networks Journal*, 2(4/5), 1978.]

[16] FLETCHER, J. G., and R. W. WATSON, "Mechanisms for a Reliable Timer-based Protocol," *Proceedings of the Symposium on Computer Network Protocols*, Liège, Belgium, pp. C5:1–17, February 1978. [Also in *Computer Networks Journal*, 2(4/5), 1978.]

[17] GARLICK, L. L., and R. ROM, "Reliable Host–Host Protocols: Problems and Techniques," *Proceedings of the 5th Data Communications Symposium*, Snowbird, Utah, pp. 4:58–65, September 1977.

[18] GROSSMAN, G. R., A. HINCHLEY, and C. A. SUNSHINE, "Issues in International Public Data Networking," *Computer Networks Journal*, 3(4), pp. 259–266, September 1979.

[19] HERTWECK, F., E. RAUBOLD, and F. VOGT, "X25 Based Process–Process Communication," *Proceedings of the Symposium on Computer Network Protocols*, Liège, Belgium, pp. C3:1–22, February 1978. [Also in *Computer Networks Journal*, 2(4/5), 1978.]

[20] "Systems Network Architecture Format and Protocol Reference Manual: Architectural Logic," *IBM Corp. Document SC30-3112-1*, June 1978.

[21] "A Proposal for an Internetwork End to End Protocol," *INWG Note* 96, July 1975. (Revised version in *Proceedings of the Symposium on Computer Network Protocols*, Liège, Belgium, pp. H:5–25, February 1978.)

[22] JACQUEMART, Y. A., "Network Interprocess Communication in an X25 Environment," *Proceedings of the Symposium on Computer Network Protocols*, Liège, Belgium, pp. C1:1–6, February 1978. [Also in *Computer Networks Journal*, 2 (4/5), 1978.]

[23] KLEINROCK, L., and H. OPDERBECK, "Throughput in the ARPANET—Protocols and Measurement," *Proceedings of the 4th Data Communications Symposium*, Quebec City, Canada, pp. 6:1–11, October 1975.

[24] KLEINROCK, L., W. E. NAYLOR, and H. OPDERBECK, "A Study of Line Overhead in the ARPANET," *Communications of the ACM*, 19(1), pp. 3–13, January 1976.

[25] LE LANN, G., and H. LE GOFF, "Verification and Evaluation of Communication Protocols," *Computer Networks Journal*, 2(1), pp. 50–69, February 1978.

[26] MERLIN, P. M., and D. J. FARBER, "Recoverability of Communication Protocols — Implications of a Theoretical Study," *IEEE Transactions on Communications*, COM-24(9), pp. 1036–1043, September 1976.

[27] POSTEL, J., "An Informal Comparison of Three Protocols," *Computer Networks Journal*, 3(1), pp. 67–76, 1979.

[28] POUZIN, L., "Basic Elements of a Network Data Link Control Procedure," *INWG Note* 54, January 1974. [Also in ACM SIGCOMM *Computer Communication Review*, January 1975.]

[29] POUZIN, L., "Virtual Call Issues in Network Architectures," *Proceedings of the European Computing Conference on Communication Networks* (Online Conferences, Northwood Hills, England), pp. 603–618, September 1975.

[30] POUZIN, L., "Network Protocols," in *Computer Communication Networks* (R. L. Grimsdale and F. F. Kuo, eds.), Nato Advanced Study Institute Series, P. Noordhoff N.V., Leyden, Netherlands, pp. 231–255, 1975.

[31] POUZIN, L., "Virtual Circuits vs. Datagrams — Technical and Political Problems," *Proceedings of the AFIPS National Computer Conference*, New York City, pp. 483–494, June 1976.

[32] POUZIN, L., "Flow Control in Data Networks — Methods and Tools," *Proceedings of the 3rd International Conference on Computer Communications*, Toronto, Canada, pp. 467–474, August 1976.

[33] STENNING, N. V., "A Data Transfer Protocol," *Computer Networks Journal*, 1(2), pp. 99–110, September 1976.

[34] SUNSHINE, C., "Interprocess Communication Protocols for Computer Networks," *Digital Systems Lab, Technical Report* 105 (Ph.D. thesis, Stanford University), December 1975.

[35] SUNSHINE, C., "Formal Techniques for Protocol Specification and Verification," *Computer* 12(9), pp. 20–27, September 1979.

[36] SUNSHINE, C., "Efficiency of Interprocess Communication Protocols for Computer Networks," *IEEE Transactions on Communications*, COM-25(2), pp. 287–293, February 1977.

[37] SUNSHINE, C., "Interconnection of Computer Networks," *Computer Networks Journal*, 1(3), pp. 175–195, February 1977.

[38] SUNSHINE, C., "Survey of Protocol Definition and Verification Techniques," *Proceedings of the Symposium on Computer Network Protocols*, Liège, Belgium, pp. F1:1–4, February 1978. [Also in *Computer Networks Journal*, 2(4/5) 1978.]

[39] SUNSHINE, C., and Y. DALAL, "Connection Management in Transport Protocols," *Computer Networks Journal* 2(6), pp. 454–473, December 1978.

[40] SUNSHINE, C., "Current Trends in Computer Network Interconnection," *Advances in Data Communications Management*, Heyden & Sons, Philadelphia, Penna., 1980.

[41] TOMLINSON, R. S., "Selecting Sequence Numbers," *INWG Protocol Note* 2, August 1974. Also in ACM SIGCOMM *Operating Systems Review*, **9**(3), July 1975.

[42] ZIMMERMAN, H., "The CYCLADES End to End Protocol," *Proceedings of the 4th Data Communications Symposium*, Quebec City, Canada, pp. 7:21–26, October 1975.

William Stallings, Honeywell Information Systems, McLean, Va.

A primer: Understanding transport protocols

Mechanisms for managing data encapsulated at the transport protocol layer form the basis of communications architecture.

The transport protocol is the keystone of the whole concept of a computer communications architecture. Within the structure of a communications architecture, it is the transport protocol that provides a reliable mechanism for the exchange of data between processes in different computers. The protocol typically ensures that data is delivered error-free, in sequence, with no loss or duplication. The transport service relieves higher-level software of the burden of managing the intervening communications facility. Because the transport protocol provides for high-quality service, and because it may need to deal with a range of communications services, it can be the most complex of all communications protocols.

The transport layer shields applications from the details of the underlying communications service. This is depicted in Figure 1. Stations 1 and 2 each have one or more applications that wish to communicate. For each such application (for example, electronic mail) an application-oriented protocol is needed that coordinates the activities of the corresponding application modules and assures common syntax and semantics. The transport protocol in turn makes use of a network's services module, which provides access to the intervening communications network (for example, using X.25).

The basic service provided by a transport protocol is the transfer of data between two transport users, such as a session protocol or an application. Data is passed from a transport user to a transport protocol entity. This entity encapsulates that data into a transport protocol data unit (TPDU), which contains the user data plus control information, such as the destination address. Beyond this basic service, there are a number of other services offered to the transport user:

■ *Connection type.* This provides for the logical connection between transport users. Connectionless service transmits each unit of data independently and generally does not guarantee delivery.

■ *Grade of service.* Transport users can specify the grade of transmission service, such as acceptable error and loss levels, desired average and maximum delays and throughput, and priority.

■ *Connection management.* With this connection-oriented service, transport entities are responsible for establishing, maintaining, and terminating logical connections between endpoints.

■ *Expedited delivery.* This is an interrupt mechanism used to transfer occasional urgent data, such as a break character or alarm condition. The sending transport entity endeavors to have the transmission facility transfer the data as rapidly as possible; the receiving transport entity interrupts the user to signify receipt of urgent data.

■ *Status reporting.* This service allows the transport user to receive information on the condition or attributes of a transport entity or connection.

■ *Security.* The transport entity may be able to request security services from the transmission facility.

The complexity of a transport protocol depends upon the type of service it provides and the type of service it receives from the communications facility below it. Typically, a transport protocol provides a connection-oriented service. That is, a logical connection is established between two transport users. The transport protocol may guarantee the delivery of data over such a connection in the order in which it is sent with no losses or duplication.

The most difficult case for a transport protocol is that of an unreliable network service. There are two problems: TPDUs are occasionally lost; and TPDUs may arrive out of sequence due to variable transit delays. As we shall see, elaborate mechanisms are required to cope with these two interrelated network deficiencies. We shall also see that a discouraging pattern emerges. The combination of unreliability and nonsequencing creates problems with every mechanism. Generally, the solution to each problem raises new problems. While there are problems to be overcome for protocols at all levels, it seems that there are more difficulties with a reliable connection-oriented transport protocol than with any other sort of protocol.

The four key transport protocol mechanisms are:
- Ordered delivery
- Connection establishment
- Error control
- Flow control

Ordered delivery
If two entities are not directly connected, there is the possibility that TPDUs will not arrive in the order in which they were sent, because they may traverse different paths. In connection-oriented data transfer, it is generally required that the TPDU order be maintained. For example, if a file is transferred between two points, we would like to be assured that the data in the received file is in the same order as in the transmitted file, and not shuffled. If each TPDU is given a number, and numbers are assigned sequentially, then it is a logically simple task for the receiving entity to re-order received TPDUs on the basis of sequence number.

Thus, the header in the TPDU contains a sequence number field. The only hitch in this scheme is that sequence numbers repeat; when the maximum number is reached, the numbering sequence starts over again at zero. It is evident that the maximum sequence number must be greater than the maximum number of TPDUs that could be outstanding at any time.

Connection establishment
To provide connection-oriented service, any transfer of data between transport entities must begin with a connection-establishment procedure.

Connection establishment serves three main purposes:
- It allows each end to assure that the other exists.
- It allows negotiation of optional parameters (for example, TPDU size and grade of service).
- It triggers allocation of transport entity resources (for example, buffer space and entry in connection table).

Connection establishment is by mutual agreement and can be accomplished by a control TPDU (a TPDU that contains no user data, just control information). The side wishing to initiate a connection sends RFC X, which is a request for connection, and indicates that the requesting entity will begin issuing data TPDUs with sequence number X. The other transport entity accepts the connection by issuing an RFC Y, indicating that it

---

1. Shielded from details. *The transport protocol layer shields applications from the details of the underlying communications service. The two stations depicted here have applications that wish to communicate. Therefore, an applications protocol is needed that coordinates activities and assures common syntax and semantics.*

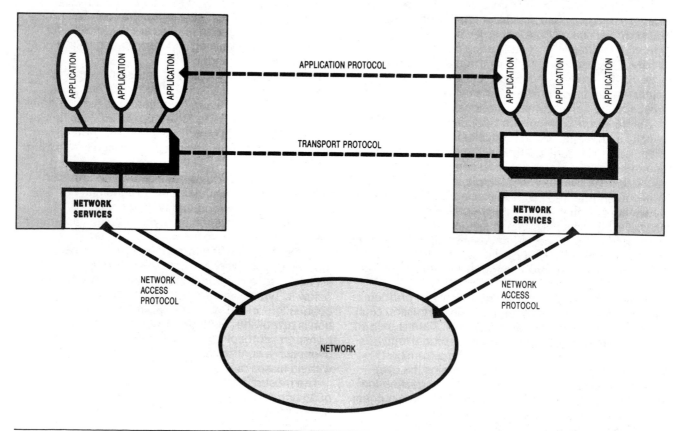

will send data TPDUs beginning with sequence number Y. Note that either side can initiate a connection, and if both sides initiate a connection at about the same time, it is established without confusion.

As with other protocol mechanisms, connection establishment must take into account the unreliability of the network service. Suppose that A issues an RFC to B. It expects to get an RFC back, confirming the connection. Two things can go wrong: A's RFC can be lost or B's answering RFC can be lost. Both cases can be handled by using a retransmit-RFC timer. After A issues an RFC, it will reissue the RFC when the timer expires.

This gives rise, potentially, to duplicate RFCs. However, if A's initial RFC is lost, there are no duplicates. If B's response is lost, then B may receive two RFCs from A. Further, if B's response is not lost, but simply delayed, A may get two responding RFCs. All of this means that A and B must simply ignore duplicate RFCs once a connection is established.

Now, consider that a duplicate RFC may survive past the termination of the connection. RFC X arrives at B after the connection is terminated. B assumes that this is a fresh request and responds with an RFC Y. Meanwhile, A has decided to open a new connection with B and sends RFC Z. B discards this as a duplicate. Subsequently, A initiates data transfer with a TPDU numbered Z. B rejects the TPDU as being out of sequence.

The way out of this problem is for each side to explicitly acknowledge the other's RFC and sequence number. The procedure is known as a three-way handshake. With this strategy, the transport entity hesitates during the connection opening to assure that any RFC that was sent has also been acknowledged before the connection is declared open. Plus, there is an additional control TPDU to reset (RST) the other side when a duplicate RFC is detected.

Figure 2 illustrates typical three-way handshake operations. An RFC is sent that includes the send sequence number. The responding RFC acknowledges that number and includes the sequence number for the other side. The initiating transport entity acknowledges the RFC acknowledgment in its first data TPDU. Next shown is a situation in which an old RFC X arrives at B after the close of the relevant connection. B assumes that this is a fresh request and responds with RFC Y, ACK X. When A receives this message, it realizes that it has not requested a connection and therefore sends a RST, ACK Y. Note that the ACK Y portion of the RST message is essential so that an old, duplicate RST does not abort a legitimate connection establishment. The final example shows a case in which an old RFC ACK arrives in the middle of a new connection establishment. Because of the use of sequence numbers in the acknowledgments, this event causes no mischief.

Error control
If the underlying communications facility is unreliable, the transport facility must cope with lost or damaged data TPDUs. For this purpose, a positive acknowledgment (ACK) scheme is used: the receiver must ac-

knowledge each successfully received TPDU. For efficiency, we do not require one ACK per TPDU. Rather, a cumulative acknowledgment can be used. Thus, the receiver may receive TPDUs numbered 1, 2, and 3, but only send ACK 3 back. The sender interprets ACK 3 to mean that number 3 and all previous TPDUs have been successfully received.

Now, if a TPDU is lost in transit, no ACK will be sent. To cope with this situation, there must be a timer associated with each TPDU as it is sent. If the timer expires before the TPDU is acknowledged, the sender must retransmit.

So, the addition of a timer solves that problem. Next problem: At what value should the timer be set? If the value is too small, there will be many unnecessary retransmissions, wasting network capacity. If the value is too large, the protocol will be sluggish in responding to a lost TPDU. The timer should be set at a value slightly longer than the round-trip delay (send TPDU, receive ACK). Of course, this delay is variable even under constant network load. Worse, the statistics of the delay will vary with changing network conditions.

2. Three-way handshake. *Here are three examples showing connections initiated, accepted, acknowledged, or rejected before transmission begins.*

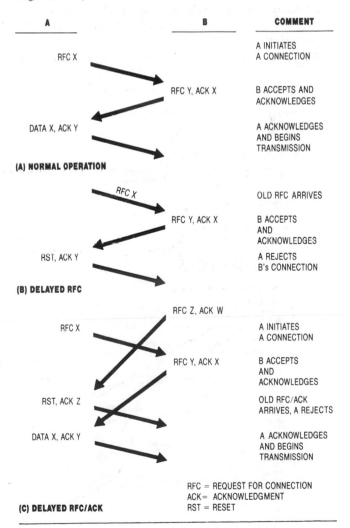

A	B	COMMENT
RFC X		A INITIATES A CONNECTION
	RFC Y, ACK X	B ACCEPTS AND ACKNOWLEDGES
DATA X, ACK Y		A ACKNOWLEDGES AND BEGINS TRANSMISSION

(A) NORMAL OPERATION

A	B	COMMENT
RFC X		OLD RFC ARRIVES
	RFC Y, ACK X	B ACCEPTS AND ACKNOWLEDGES
RST, ACK Y		A REJECTS B's CONNECTION

(B) DELAYED RFC

A	B	COMMENT
	RFC Z, ACK W	
RFC X		A INITIATES A CONNECTION
	RFC Y, ACK X	B ACCEPTS AND ACKNOWLEDGES
RST, ACK Z		OLD RFC/ACK ARRIVES, A REJECTS
DATA X, ACK Y		A ACKNOWLEDGES AND BEGINS TRANSMISSION

(C) DELAYED RFC/ACK

RFC = REQUEST FOR CONNECTION
ACK = ACKNOWLEDGMENT
RST = RESET

Two strategies suggest themselves. A fixed timer value could be used, based on an understanding of the network's typical behavior. This solution suffers from an inability to respond to changing network conditions. If the value is set too high, the service will always be sluggish. If it is set too low, a positive feedback condition can develop, in which network congestion leads to more retransmissions, which increase congestion.

An adaptive scheme has its own problems. Suppose the transport entity keeps track of the time taken to acknowledge data TPDUs and sets its retransmission timer based on an average of the observed delays. This value cannot be trusted, for three reasons:
■ The peer entity may not acknowledge a TPDU immediately. Recall that it has the privilege of cumulation acknowledgments.
■ If a TPDU has been retransmitted, the sender cannot know whether the received ACK is a response to the initial transmission or a retransmission.
■ Network conditions may change suddenly.

Each of these problems is cause for some further tweaking of the transport algorithm; but the problem admits no complete solution. There will always be some uncertainty concerning the best value for the retransmission timer.

If a TPDU is lost and then retransmitted, no confu-

3. Exhausted. *When the sequence space is exhausted, A cycles back to the original TPDU 0, which is accepted by B before the duplicate TPDU 0 arrives.*

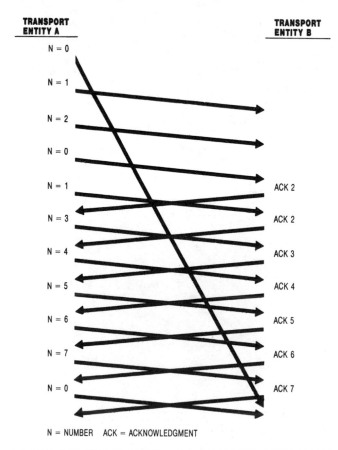

TRANSPORT ENTITY A   **TRANSPORT ENTITY B**

N = 0
N = 1
N = 2
N = 0
N = 1   ACK 2
N = 3   ACK 2
N = 4   ACK 3
N = 5   ACK 4
N = 6   ACK 5
N = 7   ACK 6
N = 0   ACK 7

N = NUMBER   ACK = ACKNOWLEDGMENT

sion will result. If, however, an ACK is lost, one or more TPDUs will be retransmitted and, if they arrive successfully, they may be duplicates of previously received TPDUs. Thus, the sender must be able to recognize duplicates. The fact that each TPDU carries a sequence number helps, but, nevertheless, duplicate detection and handling are not easy. There are two cases:
■ A duplicate is received prior to the close of the connection.
■ A duplicate is received after the close of the connection.

Notice that we say "a" duplicate rather than "the" duplicate. From the sender's point of view, the retransmitted TPDU is the duplicate. However, the retransmitted TPDU may arrive before the original TPDU, in which case the receiver views the original TPDU as the duplicate. In any case, two tactics are needed to cope with a duplicate received prior to the close of a connection:
■ The receiver must assume that its acknowledgment was lost and therefore must acknowledge the duplicate. Consequently, the sender must not get confused if it receives multiple ACKs to the same TPDU.
■ The sequence number space must be long enough so as not to "cycle" in less than the maximum possible TPDU lifetime.

Figure 3 illustrates the reason for this latter requirement. In this example, the sequence space is of length 8. A transmits TPDUs 0, 1, and 2 and awaits acknowledgment. For some reason, TPDU 0 is excessively delayed. B has received 1 and 2, but 0 is delayed in transit. Thus, B does not send any ACKs. A times out and retransmits TPDU 0. When the duplicate TPDU 0 arrives, B acknowledges 0, 1, and 2. Meanwhile, A has timed out again and retransmits 1, which B acknowledges with another ACK 2. Things now seem to have sorted themselves out, and data transfer continues. When the sequence space is exhausted, A cycles back to sequence number 0 and continues. Alas, the old TPDU 0 makes a belated appearance and is accepted by B before the new TPDU 0 arrives.

It should be clear that the untimely emergence of the old TPDU would have caused no difficulty if the sequence numbers had not yet returned to 0 The problem is, how big must the sequence space be? This depends on, among other things, whether the network enforces a maximum packet lifetime and on the rate at which TPDUs are being transmitted. As we shall see, the standard transport protocols allow stupendous sequence spaces.

A more subtle problem is posed by TPDUs that continue to rattle around after a transport connection is closed. If a subsequent connection is opened between the same two transport entities, a TPDU from the old connection could arrive and be accepted on the new connection. Similarly, a delayed ACK can enter a new connection and cause problems.

There are a number of approaches to this particular problem. We mention two of the more promising. First, the sequence numbering scheme can be extended across connection lifetimes. This requires that a transport entity remember the last sequence number that it used on transmission for each terminated connection. Then, when a new connection to a transport entity is attempted, the RFC contains the sequence number to be used to begin data transfer. Of course, this procedure is symmetric, with each side responsible for declaring the sequence number with which it will commence transmission.

The above procedures work fine unless a crash occurs. In that case, the transport entity will not remember what sequence number was used last. An alternative is simply to wait a sufficient amount of time between connections to assure that all old TPDUs are gone. Then, even if one side has experienced a crash, the other side can refuse a connection until the reconnection timer expires. This, of course, may cause undesirable delays.

Flow control

Flow control is the process of controlling the flow of data between two points. This seemingly simple concept leads to a rather complex mechanism at the transport layer, primarily for two reasons:
■ Flow control at the transport layer involves the interaction of transport users, transport entities, and the network service.
■ The transmission delay between transport entities is generally long compared with actual transmission time and, what is worse, is variable.

When a transport user wishes to transmit data, it sends that data to its transport entity. This triggers two events: the transport entity generates one or more TPDUs and passes these on to the network service. It also acknowledges to the user that it has accepted the data for transmission. At this point, the transport entity can exercise flow control across the user-transport interface by simply withholding its acknowledgment. The protocol entity is most likely to do this if the entity itself is being held up by a flow control exercised by either the network service or the target transport entity.

In any case, once the transport entity has accepted the data, it sends out a TPDU. Some time later, it receives an acknowledgment that the data has been received at the remote end. It then sends a confirmation to the sender.

At the receiving end a TPDU arrives at the transport entity. It unwraps the data and sends it on to the destination user. When the user accepts the data, it issues an acknowledgment. The user can exercise flow control over the transport entity by withholding its response.

Now, the target transport entity has two choices regarding acknowledgment back to the source transport entity. Either it can issue an acknowledgment as soon as it has correctly received the TPDU, or it can wait until it knows that its user has correctly received the data before acknowledging. The latter course is the safer. In this latter case, the acknowledgment is in fact a confirmation that the destination user received the data. In the former case, it merely confirms that the data made it through to the remote transport entity.

With the above discussion in mind, we can cite two reasons why one transport entity would want to restrain the rate of TPDU transmission over a connection from another transport entity:
■ The user of the receiving transport entity cannot keep up with the flow of data.
■ The receiving transport entity itself cannot keep up with the flow of TPDUs.

How do such problems manifest themselves? Presumably, a transport entity has a certain amount of buffer space. Incoming TPDUs are added to the buffer. Each buffered TPDU is processed by examining the transport header and the data sent to the user. Either of the two problems mentioned above will cause the buffer to fill up. Thus, the transport entity needs to take steps to stop or slow the flow of TPDUs to prevent buffer overflow. Due to the annoying time gap between sender and receiver, it is not always easy for the

4. Credit allocation. *In this example of a credit allocation protocol, data flows in one direction. Sending machine A is granted a credit allocation of 7.*

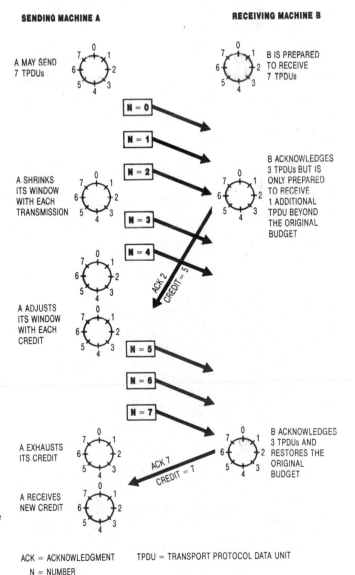

ACK = ACKNOWLEDGMENT   TPDU = TRANSPORT PROTOCOL DATA UNIT
N = NUMBER

ISO and DOD TPDU fields

ACKNOWLEDGMENT NUMBER (32 BITS)
A piggybacked acknowledgment.

ACKNOWLEDGE TIME
An estimate of the time taken by the entity to ac-knowledge a DT TPDU. This helps the other entity select a value for its retransmission timer.

ALTERNATIVE PROTOCOL CLASS
Specifies whether only the requested protocol class (2 or 4) is acceptable, or if both classes are acceptable.

CAUSE (8 BITS)
Reason for rejection of a TPDU.

CHECKSUM
For the ISO standard, the result of checksum algo-rithm for the entire TPDU. The checksum is used only for Class 4 and, within that class, it is mandatory for all CR TPDUs and for all other TPDUs when the checksum option is chosen.

CHECKSUM OPTION
For the ISO standard, it indicates whether checksum should be used.

CLASS (4 BITS)
Protocol Class 2 or 4.

CREDIT (CDT) (4 BITS)
Flow control credit allocation. Initial credit is granted in CR and CC, subsequent credit is granted in ACK. As an option, a 16-bit credit field is used with ACK and is appended after the TPDU-NR field.

DATA OFFSET (4 BITS)
Number of 32-bit words in the header.

DESTINATION PORT (16 BITS)
Identifies destination service access point.

EOT (1 BIT)
Used when a user letter has been fragmented into multiple TPDUs. It is set to 1 on the last TPDU.

FLAGS (6 BITS)
URG: Urgent pointer field significant
ACK: Acknowledgment field significant
PSH: Push function
RST: Reset the connection
SYN: Synchronize the sequence numbers
FIN: No more data from sender

FLOW CONTROL CONFIRMATION
Echoes parameter values in the last ACK TPDU re-ceived. It contains the values of the TPDU-NR, CDT, and sub-sequence number fields.

LENGTH INDICATOR (LI) (8 BITS)
Length of the header (fixed plus variable), excluding the LI field, in octets.

OPTION (4 BITS)
For the ISO standard, specifies normal (7-bit se-quence number, 4-bit credit) or extended (31-bit se-quence number, 16-bit credit) flow control fields.

OPTIONS (VARIABLE)
At present for the DOD standard, only one option is defined, one that specifies the maximum TPDU size that will be accepted.

PRIORITY
Priority of this connection.

REASON (8 BITS)
Reason for requesting a disconnect or rejecting a connection request.

RECEIVER TRANSPORT SUFFIX
Service access point that identifies the calling trans-port user.

REJECTED TPDU
The bit pattern of the rejected TPDU up to and includ-ing the octet that caused the rejections.

RESIDUAL ERROR RATE
Expresses the target and minimum rate of unreported user data loss.

SEQUENCE NUMBER (31 BITS)
Sequence number of the first data octet in this TPDU, except when SYN is present. If SYN is present, it is the initial sequence number (ISN), and the first data octet is ISN + 1.

SOURCE PORT (16 BITS)
Identifies source service access point.

SOURCE REFERENCE (16 BITS)
Reference used by the transport entity to give a unique identifier to the transport connection in its own networks.

SUB-SEQUENCE NUMBER
Number of the ACK that assures the sequentially cor-rect processing of ACKs with the same TPDU-NR.

THROUGHPUT
Specifies the user's throughput requirements in oc-tets per second. Four values are specified: the target and minimum acceptable throughput in both the call-ing-called direction and the called-calling direction.

TPDU CODE (4 BITS)
Type of TPDU:
- Connection request (CR)
- Connection confirm (CC)
- Disconnect request (DR)
- Disconnect confirm (DC)
- TPDU error (ER)
- Data (DT)
- Expedited data (ED)
- Acknowledgment (ACK)
- Expedited acknowledgment (EA)
- Reject (RJ)

TPDU SIZE
Maximum TPDU size in octets. The range of options is from 128 to 8,192 in powers of 2.

TRANSIT DELAY
Specifies the user's delay requirements in millisec-onds. Four values are specified: the target and maxi-mum-acceptable transit delay in both directions.

URGENT POINTER (16 BITS)
Points to the octet following the urgent data. This allows the receiver to know how much urgent data is coming.

VERSION NUMBER
Version of protocol to be followed. The current ver-sion is number 1.

WINDOW (16 BITS)
Flow control credit allocation, in octets.

transport entity to meet this requirement.

The most commonly used transport flow control technique is credit allocation, and it makes use of the fact that the TPDUs are numbered. At any time, the sender is allowed to transmit only a "window" of sequence numbers. Each time a TPDU is sent, the window is narrowed by 1. From time to time, the receiver will issue a credit, allowing the sender to widen the window by the granted amount. Credit allocation and acknowledgment are independent of each other. Thus a TPDU may be acknowledged without granting new credit and vice versa.

Credit allocation

Typically, the credit allocation scheme is tied to acknowledgments in the following way: to both acknowledge TPDUs and grant credit, a transport entity sends a control TPDU of the form (ACK N, CDT M), where ACK N acknowledges all data TPDUs through number N, and CDT M allows TPDUs numbers N + 1 through N + M to be transmitted. Figure 4 illustrates the protocol. For simplicity, we show a data flow in one direction only. In this example, TPDUs are numbered sequentially modulo 8. Initially, through the connection establishment process, the sending and receiving sequence numbers are synchronized, and A is granted a credit allocation of 7. A advances the trailing edge of its window each time that it transmits, and advances the leading edge only when it is granted credit.

This mechanism is quite powerful. Consider that the last control TPDU issued by B was (ACK N, CDT M). Then:
■ To increase or decrease credit to X when no additional TPDUs have arrived, B can issue one credit (ACK N, CDT X).
■ To acknowledge a new TPDU without increasing credit, B can issue (ACK N + 1, CDT M - 1).

In the credit allocation scheme, the receiver needs to adopt some policy concerning the amount of data it permits the sender to transmit. The conservation approach is to only allow new TPDUs up to the limit of available buffer space. If this policy were in effect in Figure 4, then the first credit message implies that B has five free buffer slots, and the second message implies that B has seven free slots.

A conservative flow control scheme may limit the throughput of the transport connection in long-delay situations. The receiver could potentially increase throughput by optimistically granting credit for space it does not have. For example, if a receiver's buffer is full but it anticipates that it can release space for two TPDUs within a round-trip propagation time, it could immediately send a credit of 2. If the receiver can keep up with the sender, then this scheme may increase throughput and do no harm. If the sender is faster than the receiver, however, some TPDUs may be discarded, necessitating a retransmission.

The credit allocation flow control mechanism is quite robust in the face of an unreliable network service. If an ACK/CDT TPDU is lost, little harm is done. Future acknowledgments will resynchronize the protocol. Further, if no new acknowledgments are forthcoming, the sender times out and retransmits a data TPDU, which triggers a new acknowledgment. However, it is still possible for deadlock to occur. Consider a situation in which B sends (ACK N, CDT M), temporarily closing the window. Subsequently, B sends (ACK N, CDT M), but this TPDU is lost. A is awaiting the opportunity to send data and B thinks that it has granted that opportunity. To overcome this problem, a window timer can be used. This timer is reset with each outgoing ACK/CDT TPDU. If the timer ever expires, the protocol entity is required to send an ACK/CDT TPDU, even if it duplicates a previous one. This breaks the deadlock and also assures the other end that the protocol entity is still alive.

An alternative is to provide acknowledgments to the ACK/CDT TPDU. With this mechanism in place, the window timer can have a quite large value without causing much difficulty.

ISO transport protocol standard

The International Organization for Standardization (ISO) has developed a family of transport protocol standards tailored to various levels of service and communications facilities. (For further reference on the ISO transport protocols, as well as on the similar Department of Defense transmission control protocol discussed below, see "ISO and DOD TPDU fields.") The ISO has defined three network types:
■ Type A: Network connection with acceptable residual error rate and acceptable rate of signaled failures.
■ Type B: Network connection with acceptable residual error rate but unacceptable rate of signaled failures.
■ Type C: Network connection with residual error rate not acceptable to the transport service user.

In this context, an error is defined as a lost or duplicated network protocol data unit. If the error is caught and corrected by the network service in a fashion that is transparent to the transport entity, then no damage is done. If the network service detects an error, cannot recover, and signals the transport entities, this is known as a signaled failure. An example would be the notification by X.25 that a reset has occurred. Finally, there are residual errors, that is, those which are not corrected and of which the transport entity is not notified.

In order to handle a variety of user service requirements and available network services, ISO has defined five classes of transport protocol:
■ Class 0: Simple
■ Class 1: Basic error recovery
■ Class 2: Multiplexing
■ Class 3: Error recovery and multiplexing
■ Class 4: Error detection and recovery

These classes are related to the three types of network service defined earlier, as follows: Classes 0 and 2 are used with Type A networks; Classes 1 and 3 are used with Type B networks; and Class 4 is used with Type C networks.

Class 0 was developed by CCITT (International Telephone and Telegraph Consultative Committee) and is oriented to Teletex, a text-transmission upgrade to Telex. It provides the simplest kind of transport con-

5. Fixed. *Shown below are the fixed-header formats for the International Organization for Standardization transport protocol. Fixed headers are required in a TPDU.* *The fixed header contains the frequently occurring parameters. CC and CR use parameters from a variable header field in the connection establishment process.*

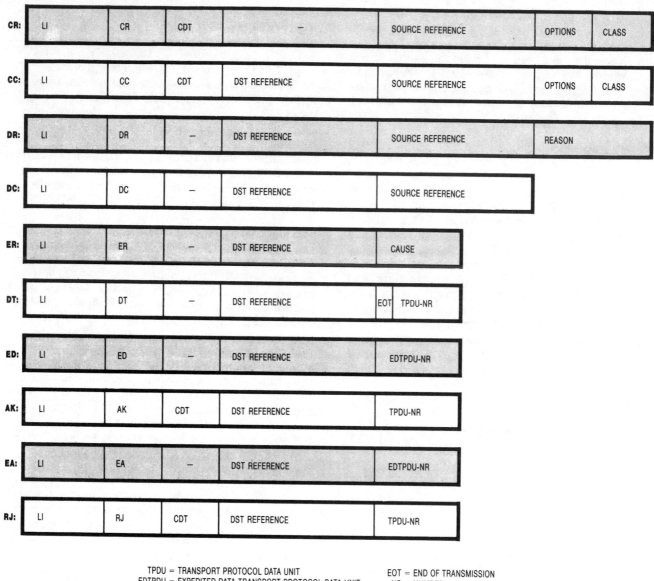

nection. It is assumed that a Type A, connection-oriented network service is available. Transport connections are mapped one-to-one onto network connections (for example, an X.25 virtual circuit). No explicit ordering, or error control, is provided.

Class 1 was also developed by CCITT and is designed to run on an X.25 network and provide minimal error recovery. Its key difference from Class 0 is that TPDUs are numbered. This allows the protocol to resynchronize after an X.25 reset. When the network resets its virtual circuit, some TPDUs may be lost. Each

transport entity informs the other of the number of the TPDU that it received last. In this way, the lost TPDUs may be retransmitted. Expedited data transfer is also provided.

Class 2 is an enhancement of Class 0 that still assumes a highly reliable network service. The key enhancement is the ability to multiplex multiple transport connections onto a single network connection. A corollary enhancement is the provision of explicit flow control, since a single network connection flow control mechanism does not allow individual flow control of

6. TCP header. *The transmission control protocol, whose header format is shown here, functions similarly to the International Organization for Standardization* *(ISO) Class 4 protocol. TCP uses only a single type of TPDU. One header performs all protocol mechanisms, and the TCP header is longer than ISO's.*

BIT POSITION

| | | | | | | | | | | 1 | 1 | 1 | 1 | 1 | 1 | 1 | 1 | 1 | 1 | 2 | 2 | 2 | 2 | 2 | 2 | 2 | 2 | 2 | 2 | 3 | 3 |
| 0 | 1 | 2 | 3 | 4 | 5 | 6 | 7 | 8 | 9 | 0 | 1 | 2 | 3 | 4 | 5 | 6 | 7 | 8 | 9 | 0 | 1 | 2 | 3 | 4 | 5 | 6 | 7 | 8 | 9 | 0 | 1 |

SOURCE PORT	DESTINATION PORT
SEQUENCE NUMBER	
ACKNOWLEDGMENT NUMBER	

DATA OFFSET	RESERVED	URG	ACK	PSH	RST	SYN	FIN	WINDOW
CHECKSUM								URGENT POINTER
OPTIONS								PADDING

URG = URGENT POINTER
ACK = ACKNOWLEDGMENT
PSH = PUSH FUNCTION

RST = RESET THE CONNECTION
SYN = SYNCHRONIZE THE SEQUENCE NUMBERS
FIN = NO MORE DATA FROM SENDER

transport connections. A credit allocation scheme can be used.

Class 3 is basically the union of the Class 1 and 2 capabilities. It provides the multiplexing and flow control capabilities of Class 2. It also contains the resynchronization and reassignment capabilities needed to cope with failure-prone networks.

Class 4 assumes that the underlying network service is unreliable. Thus, most, if not all, of the mechanisms described in this article must be included.

The protocol makes use of 10 types of TPDUs:
■ Connection request (CR)
■ Connection confirm (CC)
■ Disconnect request (DR)
■ Disconnect confirm (DC)
■ TPDU error (ER)
■ Data (DT)
■ Expedited data (ED)
■ Acknowledgment (ACK)
■ Expedited acknowledgment (EA)
■ Reject (RJ)

Each TPDU consists of three parts: a fixed header, a variable header, and a data field. The latter two need not be present in a TPDU. The fixed header contains the frequently occurring parameters, as shown in Figure 5, and the variable header contains optional or infrequently occurring parameters. Each parameter field in the variable header consists of three subfields: a parameter code (8 bits), a parameter length (8 bits), and the parameter value (one or more octets). Most of the parameters are used by CC and CR in the connection establishment process.

The ISO transport protocols have only recently been approved as international standards. There are, conse-

quently, comparatively few vendor-supported implementations. In contrast, the transport standard (MIL-STD-1778) from the Department of Defense (DOD), known as TCP, is well-established and implemented on a variety of machines.

TCP functions comparably to the ISO Class 4 protocol. It has, however, considerably more overhead bits. TCP uses only a single type of TPDU. The header is shown in Figure 6. Because one header must serve to perform all protocol mechanisms, it is rather large. Whereas the ISO fixed header is from five to seven octets long, the TCP header is a minimum of 20 octets.

Summary

ISO has been working away at its own protocol standard, which is now an international standard. It appears that the ISO standard will get early and widespread acceptance by computer vendors. As evidence of this, a number of vendors participated in a multivendor demonstration of the Class 4 protocol at this year's National Computer Conference. In addition, DOD has committed to eventually abandoning TCP in favor of the ISO Class 4.

The long-awaited arrival of standard transport protocols is welcome news for the customer and user. Customers can now begin the migration from proprietary protocols to the ISO standard. The widespread use of that standard is the key to open systems interconnection. ■

William Stallings is a senior communications consultant at Honeywell Information Systems. This article is based on material in his book "Data and Computer Communications," published by Macmillan Inc.

Reprinted from *Proceedings of the IEEE*, Voluime 71, Number 12, December 1983, pages 1397-1400. Copyright © 1984 by The Institute of Electrical and Electronics Engineers, Inc.

OSI Session Layer: Services and Protocols

WILLARD F. EMMONS AND A. S. CHANDLER

Invited Paper

Abstract—This paper describes the principles of the Session Layer of Open Systems Interconnection and the current standardization status. The Session Layer provides the means necessary for cooperating Presentation-entities to organize and synchronize their dialogue, and to manage their data exchange. To do this, the Session Layer provides services to establish a session connection between two Presentation-entities, and to support orderly data exchange interactions.

INTRODUCTION

THE Open Systems Interconnection (OSI) standards effort is producing two basic standards for each layer of the model:

1) *Layer Service Definition*, which defines, in an abstract way, the externally visible service provided by the OSI layer. The description is in terms of Session Service Data Units (SSDU's) that are passed between the layer itself and the layer user. In the case of the Session Layer (SL) this would be between the Presentation-entities (the Session Service User, SS user) and the Session-entity (the Session Service Provider, SS provider).

2) *Layer Protocol Specification*, which defines the interactions between peer Session-entities in order to provide the requested layer service. In the case of the SL, the protocol consists of sending and receiving Session Protocol Data Units, SPDU's, which carry the SS user data and/or control information in the SSDU's.

Because of previous SL work done by the several standard organizations and national bodies, there were several candidates proposed for the OSI Session standard. This required close cooperation and interaction between the ISO, CCITT, and ECMA standards organizations on the subject of SL standards. At the SC16 meeting (June 1982, Tokyo, Japan), ISO decided to synthesize the SL capabilities of the CCITT Recommendation S.62 (TELETEX) and the ECMA-75 Session Protocol standard into a single OSI Session Layer (SL) standard. This synthesis effort by ISO, with the assistance of CCITT and ECMA, culminated 9 months later at the SC16/WG6 meeting in March 1983 (Vienna, Austria) with the submission of two SL Draft Proposals (DP) for ballot:

1) DP8326, OSI Session Service Definition, [2].
2) DP8327, OSI Session Protocol Specification, [3].

Upon completion of the ballot period these SL DP's will be edited (August 1983) and the decision will be made at the SC16 plenary (October 1983, Ottawa, Canada) to further process the DP's as ISO standards if the ballot is favorable, or to resubmit them for a second ballot if the first ballot results in significant changes to the SL DP's.

Manuscript received August 1, 1983; revised August 12, 1983.
W. F. Emmons is with the IBM Corporation, Research Triangle Park, NC 27709.
A. S. Chandler is with ICL, Letchworth, Hert., England.

SESSION CONCEPTS

The SL provides functions for the SS user to manage and control the dialogue between the two SS users. Essentially the functions are as follows.

1) *Normal Data Exchange* function which allows the SS users associated with the session connection to exchange SSDU's with usual dialogue and/or flow control.

2) *Expedited Data Exchange* function which allows SS users to exchange data where the exchange is not constrained by the dialogue control or flow control of normal data; in some instances expedited data may bypass previously transmitted normal data. This service requires Transport Expedited Service.

3) *Token Management* function which allows the SS users to request and transfer tokens which control the exclusive right to exercise certain functions.

4) *Dialogue Control* function which permits the SS users to agree to operate in either a two-way alternate style, where only one of the two users (the owner of the data token) has the right to send data at any particular point in time, or a two-way simultaneous style, where both of the users are permitted to send data at any time. These two styles are called half-duplex and duplex, respectively.

5) *Synchronization* function which allows the SS users to place synchronization marks in the data flow to mark and acknowledge identifiable points and, should an error be detected, to reset the session connection to a defined state and agree on a resynchronization point (mark). Each mark has an associated serial number which is unique within a given session connection. The right of the SS user to place such marks is controlled by the assignment of major/activity token. Synchronization marks are of two types:

Major marks which allow the SS user to clearly delineate the dialogue before and after the mark. The major mark, after it is confirmed by the receiver, prevents any backward penetration of the dialogue and, as such, is closely related to resynchronization.

Minor marks which allow the SS users to place marks in the data flow and optionally acknowledge them, without the same clear delineation in the data flow as major marks.

6) *Resynchronization* function which allows the SS users to "move back" in the dialogue flow; i.e., designate a resynchronization point, discard part of the data transfer, and then restart data transfer as though the data after the resynchronization point had not been previously sent. The resynchronization point in the dialogue is identified by a serial number associated with a (preceding) mark. The SS user is not permitted to synchronize to a point earlier than the last confirmed major synchronization point. An alternative style of resynchronization allows the SS user to request that the present dialogue be "abandoned" and that a new serial number (i.e., one greater than any preceding serial number)

TABLE I
SESSION SERVICE PRIMITIVES

SESSION SERVICE	SESSION PRIMITIVE	TYPE
Session Connection Establishment	S-CONNECT	confirmed
Orderly Release	S-RELEASE	confirmed
U-Abort	S-U-ABORT	non-confirmed
P-Abort	S-P-ABORT	provider initiated
Normal Data Exchange	S-DATA	non-confirmed
Expedited Data	S-EXPEDITED-DATA	non-confirmed
Exception Reporting	S-P-EXCEPTION-REPORT S-U-EXCEPTION-REPORT	provider initiated non-confirmed
Typed Data	S-TYPED-DATA	non-confirmed
Token Management	S-TOKEN-GIVE S-TOKEN-PLEASE	non-confirmed non-confirmed
Session Synchronization	S-SYNC-MAJOR S-SYNC-MINOR S-RESYNCHRONIZE	confirmed optionally confirmed confirmed
Activity Management	S-ACTIVITY-BEGIN S-ACTIVITY-END S-ACTIVITY-INTERRUPT S-ACTIVITY-DISCARD	non-confirmed confirmed confirmed confirmed
Capability Data Exchange	S-CAPABILITY-DATA	confirmed

TABLE II
SPDU'S, FUNCTIONAL UNITS AND SUBSETS

Functional Unit	SPDU Code	SPDU Name	BCS	BSS	BAS
Kernel	CN	CONNECT	M	M	M
	AC	ACCEPT	M	M	M
	RF	REFUSE	M	M	M
	FN	FINISH	M	M	M
	DN	DISCONNECT	M	M	M
	AB	ABORT	M	M	M
	AA	ABORT ACCEPT	R	R	R
	DT	DATA TRANSFER	M	M	M
Use of Half-duplex	PT	PLEASE TOKENS (2)	O	M	M
	GT	GIVE TOKENS (2)	O	M	M
	GTA	GIVE TOKENS ACK (1) (2)	-	-	M
Exceptions	ER	EXCEPTION REPORT	O	-	M
	ED	EXCEPTION DATA	O	-	M
Typed Data	TD	TYPED DATA	O	M	O
Negotiated Release	NF	NOT FINISHED	O	M	-
	PT	PLEASE TOKENS (3)	O	M	-
	GT	GIVE TOKENS (3)	O	M	-
Minor Synchronize	MKB	MINOR SYNCHRONIZATION POINT	-	M	M
	MCB	MINOR MARK CONFIRMATION	-	M	M
	PT	PLEASE TOKENS (4)	-	M	M
	GT	GIVE TOKENS (4)	-	M	M
	GTA	GIVE TOKENS ACK (1) (4)	-	-	M
Major Synchronize	MKD	MAJOR SYNCHRONIZATION POINT (6)	-	M	-
	MCD	MAJOR MARK CONFIRMATION	-	M	-
	PR	PREPARE (7)	-	M	-
	PT	PLEASE TOKENS (5)	-	M	-
	GT	GIVE TOKENS (5)	-	M	-
Resynchronize	RS	RESYNCHRONIZE	-	M	O
	RA	RESYNCHRONIZE ACK	-	M	O
	PR	PREPARE (7)	-	M	-
Expedited	EX	EXPEDITED DATA	O	-	-
Functional Unit	SPDU Code	SPDU Name	BCS	BSS	BAS
Activity Management	AS	ACTIVITY START	-	-	M
	AR	ACTIVITY RESUME	-	-	M
	AI	ACTIVITY INTERRUPT	-	-	M
	AIA	ACTIVITY INTERRUPT ACK	-	-	M
	AD	ACTIVITY DISCARD	-	-	M
	ADA	ACTIVITY DISCARD ACK	-	-	M
	MKD	ACTIVITY END (8)	-	-	M
	MCD	ACTIVITY END ACK	-	-	M
	PT	PLEASE TOKENS (5)	-	-	M
	GT	GIVE TOKENS (5)	-	-	M
	GTA	GIVE TOKENS ACK (1)(5)	-	-	M
Capability Data Exchange	CD	CAPABILITY DATA	-	-	M
	CDA	CAPABILITY DATA ACK	-	-	M
Use of Transport Expedited			O	M	O
Use of Duplex			O	O	O

Legend:
M = mandatory
R = reception mandatory; transmission optional
O = optional; may be used if implemented and negotiated
- = not required in this functional unit

BCS = Basic Combined Subset
BSS = Basic Synchronized Subset
BAS = Basic Activity Subset

SPDU Codes are acronyms for the SPDU Name.

Notes:
1. Only required on Session connections where the activity management functional unit has been selected; used to acknowledge receipt of all tokens.
2. Required to manage the data token.
3. Required to manage the release token.
4. Required to manage the synchronize minor token.
5. Required to manage the major/activity token.
6. MAJOR SYNCHRONIZATION POINT SPDU with a parameter, which indicates a major synchronization point rather than end of activity.
7. PREPARE SPDU is only used when transport expedited flow is available to this session connection.
8. MAJOR SYNCHRONIZATION POINT SPDU without a parameter, which indicates the end of an activity rather than a major synchronization point.

be used for the next synchronization point. Note that any semantics attached to serial numbers and the effect of resynchronization is left entirely to the SS user.

7) *Activity Management* function is an extension of the major synchronization concept. It provides the SS user with the means to break the dialogue into discrete activities. Each activity can be regarded as a "separate" data transfer, however, the activity management function also has mechanisms which allow the SS user to identify a particular activity (with a user-provided identifier), transfer data, interrupt the activity, and then resume the activity at a later time on the same or even a different session connection. It should be noted that activity identification is left to the SS user. As with synchronization points, any associated semantics are left entirely to the SS user. The right to issue an activity function is restricted to the owner of the major/activity token.

8) *Exception Reporting* function permits SS users to notify or be notified of unanticipated situations not covered by other services; e.g., protocol errors. Also see section on Error Handling.

9) *Typed Data* function permits SS users to transfer transparent user data independent of the token availability and position.

10) *Capability Data* function permits SS users transfer of a limited amount of transparent data outside of an activity for special control purposes.

Table I specifies the session service primitives which are currently defined. Note that some services are confirmed, others not confirmed, and that for minor synchronization any confirmation is left to the discretion of the receiving SS user.

PROTOCOL OVERVIEW

The protocol is specified in terms of an abstract Session Protocol Machine (SPM). This abstract machine is involved in all of the service events associated with the Session Layer and performs the required service or protocol operations. The SPM defines all functional units and is, therefore, applicable to all SL subsets. Typically, if an incoming SPDU is delivered by the Transport Service Provider, an appropriate service indication or confirmation is generated to the SS user; if a service event is received from the SS user, an appropriate outgoing SPDU or Transport Service Request is generated.

An SPDU generated by the SPM may contain parameters and associated values derived from the service requested by the SS user, although this is not a prerequisite. Additionally, parameter values may also be derived from information held by the SPM; e.g., parameter values mutually agreed to when the session connection was established.

In the case where an SPDU is generated as a result of an SS user service request, SS user data may be included in some types of SPDU's. Such SS user data may be restricted to one or two octets, or may be of unlimited size, depending on the particular service request and the resulting SPDU.

Table II contains a list of presently defined SPDU's.

PHASES OF A SESSION CONNECTION

The SPM can be considered as being created afresh for each new session connection; i.e., there is a new agreement on session connection parameters for each session. As far as the session SS provider is concerned there is no relationship between session connections.

A session connection has three distinct phases:

1) *Session Connection Establishment Phase*, during which a session connection is set up between the two SS users and parameters related to the desired functions are decided or negotiated through a series of one or more exchanges of SSDU's (e.g., proposed by the initiator of the session connection and either accepted or altered by the acceptor of the session connection). The session connection request is either assigned to an existing, unused transport connection, or to a new transport connection which has been established for the purpose.

2) *Data Transfer Phase*, during which SSDU's are transferred between the two SS users via the previously established session connection. The SS user passes data to/from the SS provider in the form of S-DATA SSDU's and the SS provider, in turn, sends it in DATA TRANSFER (DT) SPDU's to the remote SS provider; see examples. A DT SPDU may contain all the data in an S-DATA SSDU or only a portion of the S-DATA SSDU (called segmenting). Additionally, the DT SPDU and an associated control SPDU('s) may be placed in a single Transport Service Data Unit (called concatenation); e.g., to place synchronizing marks in the data stream, or start/stop an activity. Use of segmenting and concatenation must be negotiated during the Session Establishment Phase. During the Data Transfer phase the SS user is allowed to:

a) transfer data
b) control the dialogue (if half-duplex style has been selected)
c) insert either/both types of synchronization marks into the data flow
d) resynchronize the session connection to a previous synchronization mark
e) perform activity management to: start or confirm an identified activity (also starts synchronization); end an identified activity (also ends synchronization); and interrupt or discard an activity in progress.

3) *Connection Release Phase*, during which the session connection is disconnected. This disconnection can be: orderly, where both SS users have completed their data transfer and there is no loss of data; or disorderly, where the session connection is aborted with possible loss of data. Additionally, if the negotiated release functional unit was selected, the SS user which receives

the disconnect request may refuse the release and the session connection is continued.

EXAMPLES OF PROTOCOL EXCHANGES

1) Session connection establishment:

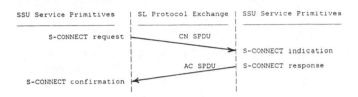

2) Data transfer when the data token is not available (duplex):

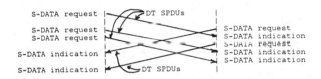

3) Data transfer when the data token is available (half-duplex):

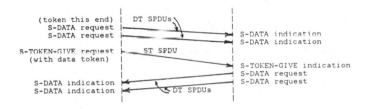

4) Major synchronization and data transfer when the data token is available (half-duplex). Note that the major/activity token will also be available.

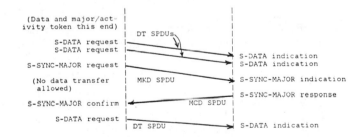

5) Orderly but nonnegotiated release of the session connection:

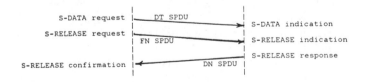

Abbreviations for Examples

CN	CONNECT SPDU	MCD	MAJOR MARK CONFIRMATION SPDU
AC	ACCEPT SPDU		
DT	DATA SPDU		
GT	GIVE TOKEN SPDU	FN	FINISH SPDU
MKD	MAJOR MARK SPDU	DN	DISCONNECT SPDU

ERROR HANDLING

Errors may be detected either by the SS user or by the SS provider. Errors detected by the SS user will be handled in the following way:

S-U-EXCEPTION-DATA will be used to pass an error indication to the peer SS user, and put the two SPM's into an error state from which recovery is possible. Only certain service requests will cause exit from this error state;

S-U-ABORT will be used to pass an error indication to the peer SS user and abort the session connection with possible loss of data.

Errors detected by the SS provider will be handled in the following way:

S-P-EXCEPTION-DATA will be used to pass an error indication to the two SS users and put the peer SPM into an error state from which recovery is possible. Only certain service requests will cause exit form this error state.

S-P-ABORT will be used to pass an error indication to the two SS users and abort the session connection with possible loss of data.

FUNCTIONAL UNITS AND SUBSETS

SPDU's have been logically grouped into functional units which provide certain functional capabilities as shown in Table II, for the purposes of:

negotiation during the session connection establishment phase; specifying conformance requirements.

Note that the SPDU's related to token management appear in every functional unit which has a related token, in order to manage that token.

During the session connection establishment phase, the initiating SS user will propose use of some functional units. The accepting SS user can indicate an alternative list. The intersection of the two capability lists will be used during the session connection. A choice must be made between the half-duplex and the duplex capability. Either one or both can be indicated in the CONNECT SPDU from the initiator. If only one has been proposed, the acceptor must agree to (or reject) the session connection establishment attempt. If both have been indicated, the acceptor must indicate in the ACCEPT SPDU which is to be used.

Functional units have been further grouped into subsets that provide specific SL capabilities. These subsets identify recommended groups of functional units for use by applications. However, the functional units in a particular subset may be altered by the addition of optional functional units when application requirements are fully specified.

The currently defined subsets (see Table II) along with their expected applications are as follows:

BCS, Basic Combined Subset. This subset provides the fundamental SL capability, called the Kernel, with either the duplex functional unit or the half-duplex functional unit. The BCS is intended for applications which do not require synchronization.

BSS, Basic Synchronized Subset. This subset provides the BCS capability plus major/minor synchronization, resynchronization, negotiated release, and typed data. It is intended for complex applications which require synchronization.

BAS, Basic Activity Subset. This subset provides the BCS capability plus exception reporting, minor synchronization, and activity management. It is intended for the extended telematic applications of CCITT.

S.62, Teletex. The SPM using the BAS and driven in a particular way with a particular set of parameters provides the capability of the S.62 Teletex application.

CONFORMANCE

The Session Protocol Specification includes a conformance statement in order to express the requirements on a system which implements the protocol. A conforming implementation will have implemented the Kernel functional unit and at least one of the half-duplex or the duplex functional units, or both. Additionally, an implementation may contain any other functional units. Use of functional units is agreed when the session connection is established.

If a functional unit is implemented, the complete unit must be implemented; i.e., all of the SPDU's in that functional unit must be implemented. There is no conformance to the session service since it is conceptual in nature.

FUTURE SL WORK

The OSI SL DP standards provide the presently identified basic session services. These services may be enhanced or altered in the future as requirements are better identified. There is also ongoing work on formal description techniques to provide a common description method for all-layer protocol state machines; when finalized it will be used to describe the SPM.

SUMMARY

The OSI Session Layer provides the logical associations necessary to perform orderly data exchange interactions. The SL Service Definition and Protocol Specifications standards have advanced to the stability of ISO Draft Proposal status. It is anticipated that these standards will be advanced to Draft International Standard (DIS) status in early 1984.

ACKNOWLEDGMENT

The authors wish to thank the many people who have worked so very hard over the last 5 years in the Session Layer Groups of ISO/TC97/SC16/WG6, CCITT SGVII/WP5, ECMA TC23, and the national standards bodies. Their cooperative efforts are responsible for the success of the OSI SL standardization effort.

REFERENCES

[1] IS7498, "Open Systems Interconnection—Basic reference model."
[2] DP8326, "Open Systems Interconnection—Basic connection oriented session service definition," Doc. ISO/TC97/SC1 N1442, Mar. 1983.
[3] DP8327, "Open Systems Interconnection, basic connection oriented session protocol specification," Doc. ISO/TC97/SC16 N1443, Mar. 1983.
[4] DIS8072, "Open Systems Interconnection—Transport service definition," Doc. ISO/TC97/SC16 N1435, Mar. 1983.
[5] DIS8073, "Open Systems Interconnection—Connection oriented transport protocol specification," Doc. ISO/TC97/SC16 N1576, Sept. 1983.
[6] CCITT Recommendation S.62 (Revision version 4; Aug. 1983).
[7] Standard ECMA-75, "Session protocol," Jan. 1982.

SECTION 6   PRESENTATION AND APPLICATION PROTOCOLS

6.1 PRESENTATION PROTOCOLS

The *presentation layer* is concerned with the syntax of the data exchanged between application entities. Its purpose is to resolve differences in format and data representation. The presentation layer defines the syntax used between application entities and provides for the selection and subsequent modification of the representation to be used.

Examples of presentation protocols are teletext and videotex, encryption, and virtual terminal protocol. A virtual terminal protocol converts between specific terminal characteristics and a generic or virtual model used by application programs.

6.2 APPLICATION PROTOCOLS

The *application layer* provides a means for application processes to access the OSI environment. This layer contains management functions and generally useful mechanisms to support distributed applications. Examples of protocols at this level are virtual file protocol and job transfer and manipulation protocol.

6.3 ARTICLE SUMMARY

Sproull and Cohen discuss principles and implementation strategies for higher-layer protocols. Bartoli looks at the standards at the two highest layers. The forthcoming presentation level standard for videotex is analyzed by Wetherington. Magnee et al. survey virtual terminal protocols. Lewan and Long look at the evolving application level standard for file transfer. Horak examines the layered set of protocols defined by CCITT for document interchange.

PROCEEDINGS OF THE IEEE, VOL. 66, NO. 11, NOVEMBER 1978

Reprinted from *Proceedings of the IEEE*, Volume 66, Number 11, November 1978, pages 1371-1386. Copyright © 1978 by The Institute of Electrical and Electronics Engineers, Inc.

High-Level Protocols

ROBERT F. SPROULL AND DAN COHEN

Invited Paper

Abstract—High-level protocols (HLP's) are the high-level languages of distributed systems. In a resource-sharing network, HLP's link processes working on a common application. The design of an HLP is decomposed into three components: language, coding, and transport. The language expresses the commands and data passed between processes. It is designed to provide standardization and device independence, in order to use a small number of HLP's to address a range of applications implemented on a variety of computer systems. Coding converts the language into digital messages. Finally, a transport system is used to transmit the messages from one process to another—experience with HLP's has shown that different HLP's require different transport behaviors. This paper describes some examples of HLP's (ARPA network voice and graphics protocols), and argues that modern techniques for expressing structure and control in programming languages should be applied to analogous problems in communication among application processes in a network.

I. INTRODUCTION

HIGH-LEVEL PROTOCOLS (HLP's) are the high-level languages (HLL's) of a distributed computing environment. They are the means by which a communications network and processing resources in the network are harnessed in an orderly way to accomplish some task. Using different resources in an application on a single computer is by now natural, aided by operating systems, high-level languages memory management, and other well-established tools. But a resource-sharing computer network offers to an application the resources available throughout the network [18], [29]—to harness these distributed resources requires the collaboration of several computers and many computational processes, and, therefore, a set of conventions for harmonious communication that extends throughout the distributed environment. HLP's are these conventions.

The term "high-level protocol" attempts to distinguish protocols designed to control the computing processes involved in an application from "low-level protocols" designed primarily to control communication processes. Two computer processes require communications in order to transmit collections of bits from one to the other. But it is the HLP that assigns an interpretation to the bits, and thus allows each process to control the other. An analogy may be helpful. To call a department store on the telephone is simply to establish communication. But when the caller says, "Please send me two pillowcases, catalog number X802, and bill my account," he is using an HLP that controls ordering goods. Thus the HLP is implemented "on top of" the low-level communication protocols.

Manuscript received February 25, 1978; revised June 9, 1978. This work was supported by the Advanced Research Projects Agency of the Department of Defense under Contract DAHC-15-72-C-0308, ARPA Order 2223, and under Contract F44620-73-C-0074, monitored by the Air Force Office of Scientific Research.

R. F. Sproull is with the Computer Science Department, Carnegie-Mellon University, Pittsburgh, PA 15213.

D. Cohen is with USC/Information Sciences Institute, Marina del Rey, CA 90291.

Of course, HLP's that control computer processes need precise definitions of commands and responses, and cannot rely on human intelligence to provide an interpretation. (The paper by Pouzin and Zimmermann [26] in this issue introduces the notion of "protocol" and the concept of "layering" by which an HLP is implemented in terms of lower level communications protocols. Their term "application control" is equivalent to our "high-level protocol.")

The services available in a resource-sharing network are sufficiently diverse that several different HLP's need to be designed. For example, HLP's have been developed to control job entry, interactive terminals, file systems, graphics displays, resource allocation, and voice transmission in distributed environments. But why are HLP's required to control these services? Is not the communication provided by a network sufficient? The need can be demonstrated by an example. At first, using a file storage service seems to be a simple matter of sending a file to the service as a serial stream of bits, and subsequently retrieving the same stream. But additional attributes of the file must also be saved and retrieved: a file name, some information about how the file is to be protected from unauthorized access, accounting information to permit charging for the storage of the file, and so forth. Moreover, a file service must provide more operations than storage and retrieval: enumerating names of files stored, deleting or renaming files, moving files from one storage medium to another, etc. The HLP must select among these operations, provide the information needed by them, and report errors encountered as the operations progress, in addition to simply transmitting file data.

A resource-sharing network becomes increasingly valuable as more HLP's that offer services are designed and implemented. Thus an overall objective of protocol development is to seek methods and tools that simplify HLP design and implementation. Already, experience with HLP's has uncovered common design techniques, some of which are reviewed in this paper. But techniques for specifying HLP's and for implementing them remain primitive. We argue that methodology and tools for designing and implementing HLP's can be improved by applying notions developed for HLL's—in effect extending the HLL into a distributed environment. Just as the HLL frees the programmer from many tiresome details of programming a particular computer, the extension frees the programmer from the tiresome details of dealing with network communications.

To construct such an argument, a better understanding of actual HLP's is required. The remainder of this introductory section illustrates the range of HLP's used in a resource-sharing network. Section II builds a detailed understanding of the ingredients and requirements of HLP's by defining a model and characterizing some very different protocols in terms of the model. Section III reviews the issues faced in the design of HLP's, and common techniques used in the designs. Finally,

EHO228-1/85/0000/0405$01.00 © 1978 IEEE

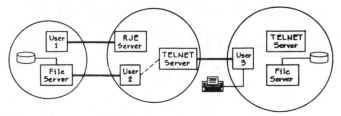

Fig. 1. A resource-sharing network. "User processes" obtain services from "server processes," under the control of HLP's. Heavy lines linking processes in the illustration denote the logical connections that carry HLP. These connections are unrelated to the physical organization of the network.

Section IV shows how many of the needs of HLP's can be addressed by HLL facilities.

A. The Role of HLP's

HLP's are used in two slightly different ways in networks. In the first use, the basis of resource-sharing networks, HLP's control the *services* offered by resources in the network. Various sites in the network implement *server processes* that offer a specific service to any *user process* that communicates requests to it (Fig. 1). In these settings, activities are instigated by the user process; the server is a willing slave. Examples of important services are as follows.

a) Remote job entry service: A user process submits to the server a file of text that controls running batch jobs (job control language). Later, the user process may retrieve from the job entry server the "listing" text produced as a result of the job.

b) Remote terminal service: A user process can "log in" to a timesharing system service, and subsequently send and receive characters as if it were a terminal on the system. We shall use the term "TELNET" for this service, adopting the name of the protocol used in the ARPA network [7].

c) File service: A user process can send data files to the service for storage and subsequent retrieval. The file service may be provided with conventional disk equipment, or may have special file-storage resources such as a mass memory.

d) Mail service: A service accepts text messages addressed to individual people. Later the individuals can interrogate the service through a user process to receive any mail that has been left for them.

e) Resource-sharing service: This service accepts requests from user processes to allocate resources of the computer system on which the service executes (jobs, processes, files, I/O devices), and makes these resources available to other processes in the network [36].

Each of these services has a corresponding HLP for accessing and controlling the server process. These services are analogous to the services that are offered on a single computer by an operating system. A mechanism for storing files, for example, is a vital service provided by an operating system. Extending this service into a resource-sharing network allows greater sharing of the file data, as well as economical storage of files with specialized hardware. Thus HLP's are not entirely new phenomena—similar concepts have existed within operating systems—but are now being revealed as they are extended into networks.

A second use for HLP's links in a symmetric fashion two processes that are part of a single application. Such a link may be the result of the division of a software system into separate modules. Or it may be that the communicating parties them-

selves are symmetric, as is the case in the network voice protocol described in Section II-D. In these cases, the user–server distinction is not relevant. Thus applications may use HLP's both to access services and to communicate among parts of an application.

HLP's offer many new opportunities to distribute applications. An application can be divided into processes, each of which can be executed on the computer best suited to its needs: signal processing tasks are accomplished on fast parallel machines; symbolic computation on computers with large address spaces suited to list processing. Processes that communicate directly with a human by voice, graphical, or textual information can travel with the user, communicating with collaborating processes in the network by packet radio links [19]. Distributed applications can evolve as requirements change, by modifying HLP's, adding new services, distributing the computing activity among a wider set of resources, etc. The ease with which HLP's can be designed and implemented will control the extent to which these opportunities can be fulfilled.

B. Standardization

Achieving the standardization required to offer services on a variety of computers is a major goal of HLP's. Before the appearance of large computer communication networks, HLP's were largely a private matter. A programmer who wanted to design an application consisting of several processes and wanted to provide a method for communicating among them, had only to establish some personal conventions for the interprocess communication. Networks spoiled this simple approach. Communication protocols became a matter of public decision in the hope that a single standard design could serve a wide community of computers and users; interconnecting a variety of computers unleashed a barrage of problems due to different representation conventions in different machines (word lengths, character sets, and the like) and in different operating systems (files, naming, and protection mechanisms); networks forced slower communication among processes than did tightly coupled systems and seemed to magnify problems of synchronizing processes.

The importance of standardization is demonstrated by the "n^2 problem." Imagine a network of n computers, each of which offers a *mail server* that uses a distinct HLP. Each computer will require a separate user program to send and receive mail for each protocol—a total of n programs on each computer or n^2 in all. By contrast, if the mail servers all implement a *standard* HLP for sending and receiving mail, only n user programs, one on each computer, are required to obtain access to all mail services in the network. The high cost of writing and maintaining software makes protocol standardization essential. The techniques and conventions that permit standardization over a range of computing equipment are a major ingredient in the design of HLP's.

II. THREE HIGH-LEVEL PROTOCOLS

This section describes three HLP's as a prelude to a more general discussion of issues involved in designing and implementing HLP's. These examples are couched in terms of a model of three components of an HLP: language, coding, and transport. The first example, a *plotter protocol*, illustrates the model. The two remaining examples, a *graphics protocol* and a *voice protocol*, are actual HLP's that demonstrate a range of HLP design techniques.

A. The Components of an HLP

Designing HLP's seems at first to require a large number of decisions, ranging from communication formats to application requirements. The design problem can be decomposed into three aspects of HLP's: the *language*, the *coding*, and the *transport* mechanism.

Language: The language describes the functional intent of the communications exchanges between processes: What does one process "say" to the other? What responses does the other process generate? How does one process cause the other to alter its *state*? The language may include *commands* or other *control* information, and will usually include *data* as well. The designer of a language to offer a service must anticipate how other processes will use this service, and provide within the language the means for those processes to request and receive the service they need.

Coding: Any communication between two processes must be coded into a collection of bits that the processes know how to generate and interpret. For example, if the language requires transmission of a character string, it may be coded into a sequence of 8-bit bytes according to the ASCII standard, an integer value into a 32-bit two's complement binary representation, and so forth. Just as data structure declarations in an HLL impose structure on an otherwise homogeneous memory, coding imposes structure on a previously homogeneous communications path.

Transport: The communication path is provided by the transport mechanism, the means to collect bits from one process and deliver them to another. If both processes reside in the same computer, this mechanism is provided by the operating system or by the language environment in which the processes execute (e.g., "pipes" in Unix [28]). If the processes execute on separate machines, the transport may be provided by a network. We prefer to avoid stating which processes execute in which computer and consequently which transport is provided by networks and which by other means. We may be concerned with performance properties of the transport mechanism (e.g., speed, delay, buffering, errors), but not with the communications methods themselves. As a consequence of this view, we must assume that HLP's cannot depend on the processes sharing other resources, such as memory or files: the protocol must provide *all* of the interprocess communication. We shall use the term *message* to refer to the individual packages of bits that are transmitted from process to process. A network will typically use additional messages to help the transport mechanism operate smoothly: these lower level protocols are concerned with flow control, error recovery, and the like (for more discussion of lower level or "host–host" protocols, see [1], [2], [26]).

When designing and describing HLP's, it is important to separate these three aspects of interprocess communication (IPC). The language can be likened to HLL constructs involving control and data: procedure calls, coroutine calls, etc. Coding is analogous to choosing a computer representation based on collections of bits: integers, text characters, or computer instructions. The design of the transport mechanism is concerned with issues such as bandwidth, delay, and error recovery, and with the low-level protocols that provide the transport. If these three aspects are not kept separate, and we think of HLP's as configurations of bits flowing along communications lines, we will become hopelessly confused. Imagine trying to describe how a PDP-11 works by describing only bit patterns and signal transitions on the Unibus!

Fig. 2. Two processes using the plotter protocol. The application sends messages to the plotter process that completely describe the figures to be plotted. The two processes may execute on separate computers linked by a network, or on a single computer that provides message communication between the two processes.

The three components are not independent, but interact in ways that must be addressed by the HLP designer. Transport bandwidths or errors may affect the choice of coding techniques. Language choices often affect coding, and can also impact the design of transport methods. In the sections that follow, some of these interactions are demonstrated by the three example HLP's.

B. A Plotter Protocol

We shall illustrate in this section a simple HLP for controlling a pen plotter. Such a protocol could be used to offer "plotting services" in a distributed system: one or more "plotter server" processes are provided, each controlling plotter hardware in response to commands and data provided by the plotter protocol. In order to make plots, an application process such as a curve-fitting package establishes communication with a plotter process that will provide the plotting services. Fig. 2 shows the logical arrangement of these processes.

Language: The language for the plotter HLP is designed to allow the application program to produce drawings by issuing commands to the plotter process. The application program needs to be able to start a fresh plot, to raise and lower the plotter pen, and to draw straight lines. These commands in the language might be provided by procedures that are called by the application program:

BeginPlot	Procedure to place a new sheet of paper in the plotting area.
EndPlot	Procedure to signal that a plot is complete.
Up	Procedure to raise the plotter pen so that it no longer touches the paper.
Down	Procedure to lower the plotter pen so that it will mark on the paper.
LineTo(x,y)	Procedure to cause the plotter pen to move from its present location in a straight line to the point (x,y). The Cartesian coordinates specify a location on the paper, in units of centimeters from the lower left corner.

Notice that these procedures show no effect of the presence of a network—the same procedures could be used to control a plotter connected directly to the application program.

Coding: In order to transmit to the plotter process the commands invoked by the application process, each command must be encoded as a sequence of bits. For our example, we shall use 8-bit ASCII characters as the basis for the coding. A command is designated by a single character corresponding to the procedure name (B, E, U, D, L). The (x,y) arguments to the "L" command can be represented as two four-digit numbers in units of 1/100 cm. Thus the protocol sequence

B U L 0100 0100 D L 0200 0100 L 0200 0350 L 0100 0100 E

will plot a triangle with vertices (1,1), (2,1), and (2,3.5) cm. Of course, another encoding could be devised that requires fewer bits to code the same language. In any case, very little computation is required to encode and decode the plotter language.

Transport: The transport system must deliver the individual 8-bit bytes to the plotter process. If a packet-switched network is used for transport, it is sensible for the application process to pack several dozen bytes into a message before the message is transmitted. However, the EndPlot procedure must force the transmission of the last message, even if it is only partially full, to insure that the final "E" code is delivered to the plotter process.

For the plotter protocol, a general-purpose interprocess transport mechanism such as TCP [2] is ideal. The transport reliability obtained from such a mechanism is essential for the plotter protocol: errors in the data, or disorder in the sequence of messages decoded by the plotter process will have disastrous effects. However, the protocol requires neither extremely high transmission rates nor extremely short transmission delays, because most plotters are quite slow.

Discussion: The plotter protocol illustrates two important aspects of HLP's: *standardization* and *device independence*. A resource-sharing network may offer several plotter server processes, all of which use a standard plotter protocol. Standardization is required for all components of the HLP: language, coding, and transport. The method of packing bytes into messages and the low-level protocols used to achieve reliable transport of messages must be standardized. Coding is standardized by the ASCII character standard and the definition of character sequences used by the plotter protocol. Finally, the concepts of the language are standardized: Up, Down, and LineTo are but one way to control a plotter, but they are chosen as the standard. The language standard imposes a method for controlling the plotter that may have far-reaching ramifications in the structure of the application program.

Standardization begets generalization: if a single standard is to be designed, it should be able to cope with as many similar uses as possible. This property is often called "device independence," although a physical device is not always involved. The idea is to make the protocol independent of particular hardware details by abstracting the elements common to the control of a range of devices. The plotter protocol described above is somewhat device independent: plotters with various resolutions (e.g., 100 steps per centimeter, 173 steps per centimeter) can clearly be used—the plotter process converts the standard units of 1/100 cm into the coordinate system used by the hardware it controls. Electrostatic plotters or storage-tube displays, even though they have no pen to be raised and lowered, can also be correctly controlled by the protocol because the only effect of protocol commands is to describe visible lines. However, colored pens on a plotter cannot be handled properly by our protocol—it is not general enough to handle more than one color.

The protocol illustrates a style of HLP design that derives the language from a standard subroutine interface. Each procedure call causes a record of the procedure name and arguments to be encoded and sent through the network. The receiver decodes the messages and usually calls corresponding procedures that actually drive the plotter. The network thus provides a *binding* mechanism by which calls to the five procedures in the application program are converted into calls to procedures in the plotter process. Ideally, the network is "transparent" to the application program—its presence cannot be detected!

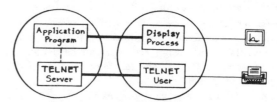

Fig. 3. An application using two HLP's. A person uses the TELNET service to control a curve-fitting application running on a time-sharing system. This program, in turn, uses a high-level graphics protocol to control a display that shows the curve-fitting results.

The plotter protocol is extremely simple compared to most real HLP's, which attempt greater device independence and which require bidirectional communication between processes. The following two sections describe two actual HLP's developed by the ARPA network community: a network graphics protocol (NGP) and a network voice protocol (NVP). Because these two descriptions are rather long, the reader may prefer to skip to Section III, which contains a summary of techniques used in designing HLP's.

C. A Network Graphics Protocol (NGP)

The objective of an NGP is to provide a standard way for an application program to control an interactive graphics display. It is a natural extension of the idea of the TELNET protocol which allows an alphanumeric terminal connected to one computer to act as a terminal to another. A user with a graphics display and computer capable of obeying the NGP would have access to a potentially large number of network resources that use graphical interaction (Fig. 3). Because users with different display devices will want to use these services, the NGP design must be independent of the particular device being used.

The plotter protocol developed in the previous section could be used as an NGP: it can control the generation of line-drawing images on a display. If a storage-tube display is used, the commands to the hardware are almost identical to those provided by the protocol. But an NGP needs greater generality, including the ability to handle a wide variety of display hardware, to provide fast interaction, and to cope with different kinds of graphical input devices.

The methodology we find appropriate for developing an NGP is to first design a device-independent graphics package (or copy an existing design) and then adapt it to network use. The device-independent design wrestles with the functional capabilities of the system and the model that the application program uses to invoke them. The network adaptation then need address only coding and transport.

The particular NGP described in this section was developed for use by the ARPA network [33], [14]. It is based on a "general-purpose graphics package" [31], [40], which attempts to cover a range of applications requiring interactive line-drawing displays.[1] We cannot, in this paper, take up the many issues that surround the design of such a package (see [24], [25]). However, we will discuss how network communications interact with the design. A summary of the protocol is given in Table I.

Language: The functions of a graphics package can be divided into three categories: those for defining an image to be

---

[1] Other protocols have been proposed for graphical needs that lie outside the NGP's objectives: carefully formatted text [32] and sampled images such as might be captured with a TV camera [22].

TABLE I
SUMMARY OF ARPA NETWORK GRAPHICS PROTOCOL. EACH HAS THE
SAME FORMAT, A COMMAND FOLLOWED BY ARGUMENTS. THE ARGUMENTS
ARE LISTED INSIDE BRACKETS (⟨ ⟩). DETAILS OF THE PROTOCOL ARE
FOUND IN [33]

```
Segment control:
  seg.open <seg.name>
  seg.close
  seg.post <seg.name>
  seg.unpost <seg.name>
  seg.kill <seg.name>
  seg.append <seg.name>
  end.batch.of.updates

  seg.dot <x.coordinate> <y.coordinate>
  seg.move <x.coordinate> <y.coordinate>
  seg.draw <x.coordinate> <y.coordinate>
  seg.text <text.string>

  set.intensity <count>
  set.type <count>
  set.character.orientation.discrete <count>
  set.character.orientation.continuous <fraction>
  set.character.size.discrete <count>
  set.character.size.continuous <fraction>

  change.attribute <seg.name> <attribute>
  ...possible <attribute> arguments:
    <set highlight attribute> <on/off>
    <set.hit.sensitivity.attribute> <on/off>
    <set.intensity.attribute> <count>
    <set.screen.select.attribute> <mask>
    <set.position.attribute> <x.coordinate> <y.coordinate>

  seg.readback.seglist
  seg.readback.seg <seg.name>

Positioned text:
  ptext.open <ptext.name> <count> <x.coordinate> <y.coordinate>
          <x.coordinate> <y.coordinate> <count>
  ptext.kill <ptext.name>
  ptext.set <ptext.name> <mask>
  ptext.scroll.up <ptext.name> <string.number> <string.number>
  ptext.scroll.down <ptext.name> <string.number> <string.number>
  ptext.move <ptext.name> <string.number> <ptext.name> <string.number>
  ptext.edit <ptext.name> <string.number> <pos1> <pos2> <text.string>
  ptext.modify <ptext.name> <string.number> <pos1> <pos2> <ptext.feature>
  ptext.remote.edit <ptext.name> <ptext.string>

Input functions:
  input.enable <technique.number> <disable.condition> <report.sequence>
  input.disable <technique.number>
  input.report <technique.number> <technique.summary>
  input.reset.system
  input.drag.set <technique.number> <seg.name>

Inquiry:
  inquire
  inquire.response <count> <response.phrase> ...
  ...sample <response.phrase>s are:
    <i.implemented.commands> <mask>
    <i.screen.coordinates> <x.left> <y.bottom> <x.right> <y.top> <count>
    <i.screen.size> <text.string> <text.string>
    <i.screen.number> <count>
    <i.terminal.name> <text.string>
    <i.terminal.type> <terminal.type.value>
    <i.intensities> <count>
    <i.line.type> <count>
    <i.characters> <mask>
    <i.character.orientations> <count> <fraction> ...
    <i.character.size> <count> <character.size.description> ...
    <i.available.input.technique> <technique.number> <text.string> ...

Miscellaneous:
  escape.protocol <text.string>
  synchronize <count>
  reset
  error.string <text.string>
```

displayed, those for accepting responses from the user via graphical input devices, and those that inform the application program of important properties of the display. The discussion of the NGP language is likewise divided into considerations of output, input, and inquiry.

Language—Output: One of the most critical requirements of an interactive graphics system, and one that might be compromised by a network, is the speed with which the display can be altered—this is the crux of many interactive dialogues. This consideration forces us to abandon the plotter protocol: to make a small change to a display of 2000 lines would require transmitting a description of the entire image (roughly 40 000 bits, even with a fairly efficient coding). Furthermore, such a technique burdens the application program by making it recompute the image from its application data structure.

An effective technique that solves these problems is the *segmented display file*. Rather than manipulate one large description of the image, the graphics system maintains a set of independent segments that together comprise the display. Each segment is assigned a numeric "name" for identification, and contains a list of graphic primitives (lines or characters) that are part of the image. Each segment also has a flag (on,off) that indicates whether the primitives described in the segment are to be displayed on the screen. The system provides facilities for specifying the contents of a specific segment, and for altering the flag. To create a segment named 8 that contains a description of the triangle in the plotter example, the application might call the following procedures in the graphics package:

OpenSegment(8)	Says primitives are to become segment 8.
MoveTo(1,1)	Primitives defining triangle.
DrawTo(2,1)	
DrawTo(2,3.5)	
DrawTo(1,1)	
CloseSegment()	Ends construction of segment 8.
PostSegment(8)	Sets segment 8 flag, so it will be displayed.

The calls simply build a display file that a hardware display processor interprets to refresh the display. Changes to the display file as a result of these calls are reflected as changes in the image on the screen.

The segment thus becomes the unit of information that is easily changed with each interaction. It is not difficult to write most application programs so that the segments correspond to logically separate parts of the display in such a way that display alterations are often limited to a small fraction of all the segments. If information within a segment must be changed, the segment is entirely rebuilt with calls such as those above. Or the segment may be deleted if its contents are no longer needed. Or the information in a segment can be retained for possible use later. This technique is useful for recurring imagery such as messages and menus.

The graphics package also provides an "update" function. The application program calls this function to identify points at which the display *must* accurately reflect all changes that have been requested by calls on the graphics system. These points usually directly precede requests for new user input: the user must view an up-to-date display to formulate his input. This function plays an important role in device independence, providing good service to storage-tube displays by reducing the number of screen erasures [31].

On a single computer, a device-independent graphics package of this sort is implemented as shown in Fig. 4(a). The package

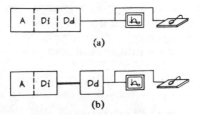

Fig. 4. The organization of a device-independent graphics package. (a) On a single computer, the software is divided into three modules: the application (A), the device-independent module (Di), and the device-dependent module (Dd). (b) The system can be adapted for a network implementation by using communications to provide the linkage between Di and Dd.

is divided into two modules, one device independent (Di), and one device dependent (Dd). Each call by the application program (A) is subjected to some Di processing, and then usually results in a call on the Dd module. The Dd module is responsible for building the segments themselves in a form that can be interpreted by the particular display processor in use. The Di module can be used with many different Dd modules with the same procedure interface—in this way, the application program can operate a variety of different display devices.

Adapting this configuration to a network environment is easy (Fig. 4(b)). The module resides with the application program and the Dd module runs in the computer that directly controls the display hardware. Network communications are used to achieve the effect of the Di module calling procedures in the Dd module. Because the procedure interface between the Di and the Dd parts is standardized to allow alternative Dd modules, the standardization is easily retained in the network protocol. Thus the segmented display file, a mechanism devised to solve problems of interactive graphics programs in single computers, turns out to be adapted easily to networks.

Language—Input: The NGP provides access to a variety of graphical input devices, for it is the interaction afforded by these devices that makes graphics an important tool in many applications. Unfortunately, achieving device independence for input is much harder than for output, in part because of the enormous range of input devices. An additional problem is that effective use of input devices requires generating on the display screen various *feedback images*, such as cursors, to allow the user to coordinate his input with images already displayed. The range of feedback techniques is even wider than the range of input devices!

An approach to device independence is to concentrate on the interactive techniques being used rather than on particular input devices. The display hardware and Dd module cooperate closely to provide rapid feedback to implement the technique. After the interaction is complete, the Dd module reports to the application program a terse summary containing essential details of the entire interaction. For example, three techniques in the repertoire are the following.

1) Positioning: The user is expected to identify a spot on the screen. He uses a coordinate input device to steer a displayed cursor to the desired spot, and then depresses a button to indicate "this is the point I mean." The summary returned to the application program contains only the coordinates of the cursor when the button was struck.

2) Stroke collection: The user is expected to draw a trace on the screen by steering the cursor at the same time the button remains depressed (the button is usually a switch on a stylus input device). The display shows the resulting trace as

feedback, which presents an effect similar to drawing. The summary reported to the application program is a list of points that lie on the trace.

3) Pointing: The user is expected to identify an item already displayed on the screen. One way to implement this technique is to steer a cursor over the item and push a button. Alternatively, a light pen can be used to identify the item. The summary reported contains a specification of which item was identified.

This entire approach focuses on input *techniques* rather than on *devices* alone. It may limit the flexibility of the application program in using some device in a clever way. However, the flexibility is available instead to the Dd module, which can implement the techniques in various ways, and can perhaps customize the implementation for a particular user.

Language—Inquiry: Not all aspects of the interface to the Dd module are completely standardized; some are parametrized. For example, some displays allow lines to be distinguished by their brightness, although devices differ in the number of brightnesses provided. A standard that assumes only one brightness prevents the use of this technique entirely. One that assumes a fixed number of brightnesses will cause confusion on a display that provides but one. A solution to problems of this sort is to let the application program or Di module *inquire* about features of the display hardware, and thereafter drive the display accordingly. Examples of parameters that can be handled this way are: number of brightnesses, number of line types (e.g., dotted, dashed), physical screen dimensions, and the kinds of input devices available.

Some inquiry results can have a profound effect on the operation of the application program. Many features of the protocol are optional and may not be implemented by the hardware or by the Dd module; inquiry establishes which features are absent. Another sort of inquiry reveals the type of display being used: is it a storage tube or a refreshed display? The application program may choose entirely different interaction styles for these two display types, because changes to storage-tube images are much slower than changes to refreshed images.

Coding: The coding for the NGP is very simple: we encode procedure calls from the Dd module to the Di module as a sequence of 8-bit bytes. The first byte identifies the procedure. Subsequent bytes provide arguments; each procedure has an associated format for arguments. The protocol was designed to avoid floating-point numbers; only integers are used.

Information returned by the Dd module to the Di module is structured symmetrically, as if the Dd module were calling procedures in the Di module to answer queries, to report interaction results, and so forth.

Transport: The coding generates a stream of bytes to be transmitted, just as the plotter protocol does. Because most of the encoded procedure calls do not return answers, the bytes can be packed into messages; messages are transmitted when full. It is occasionally necessary to transmit partial messages: for example, the "update" call forces all information encoded by Di to be transported to Dd so that the display will change. It may also be important to transmit quickly commands that alter the handling of input techniques.

Summary: We have seen that developing the ARPA NGP was primarily a matter of designing device-independent graphics package. As the package modules are designed, we find that some are device-independent and others depend on the details of particular hardware. Thus a natural division of labor between two computers is to execute device-independent mod-

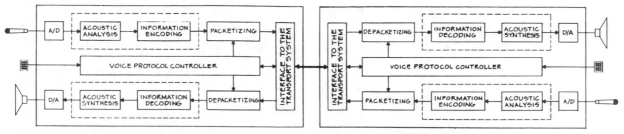

Fig. 5. The structure of processes using the network voice protocol. Processing of the protocol is divided into three parts: sending speech data, receiving speech data, and controlling the transmission. Portions enclosed by dashed lines are "vocoder dependent."

ules and the application program on one machine, and place the device-dependent modules and display hardware on another. A network provides communication between the device-independent and device-dependent modules in a straightforward way. (If we were willing to standardize the procedure interface between the application program and the device-independent module, this interface too could become a point of separation by a network.) Thus, methodology, design, and documentation of the NGP are those of a graphics package, rather than of an *ab initio* protocol design. In this setting, the network becomes a relatively unimportant artifact of the implementation: it offers interprocess communication among modules of a software system.

D. A Network Voice Protocol (NVP)

The objective of an NVP is to control the transmission of a digital representation of voice signals through a packet-switched network in real time. The transmission may be part of a man-to-man or man-to-machine communication. A protocol can provide the effect of two-party or conference calls, including user interfaces such as dialing and ringing. Or it can provide a voice message service by communicating from man to a computer capable of first recording the voice data, and and later responding to a request to repeat the data to the intended recipients. A voice protocol differs from a standard telephone connection in that applications may use the network to transmit additional digital information along with the voice data.

A voice protocol must provide natural communication between humans. On the one hand, this objective seems to require extremely good performance. Poor reproduction of the speech signal may prevent recognition of the speaker; long transmission delays may impede a dialogue; small amounts of distortion may be keenly perceived and interfere with natural communication. On the other hand, a human can tolerate many errors. Occasional noise is compensated for by the redundancy in human speech; catastrophic garbling is repaired by dialogue—the utterance is repeated.

A voice protocol should try to provide good speech quality even though data transmission rates may be severely limited by the network. Fortunately, techniques are available for encoding voice as low-bandwidth digital data; these techniques are called *vocoding techniques*. Vocoding uses real-time signal-processing algorithms to encode and decode the voice. Vocoding algorithms tend to require substantial computing to achieve both acceptable reproduction quality and low data bandwidth. High compression rates also tend to increase sensitivity to acoustic noises and communication errors. Speech quality, data rate, and processing all interact: achieving higher quality or less processing requires more transmission bandwidth. One

of the motivations for a device-independent NVP is to simplify experimentation with different compromises.

The needs of a voice HLP differ from those of a graphics HLP in several ways. The dominant concern in an NVP is the vocoding scheme used, often because special fast processing is required to vocode in real time. Language issues are relatively minor. A voice protocol requires a real-time transport system: delays, and especially delay distributions, are critical to offering real-time service; errors, however, can be tolerated. By contrast, the NGP can tolerate longer delays and greater variation in delay for "interactive" service, but cannot tolerate transmission errors.

An experiment in voice protocols has been undertaken by four sites in the ARPA network [4], [5]. Sites with differing hardware for implementing network control and vocoding algorithms were deliberately chosen in order to develop a protocol to accommodate such differences.

Language: The language for the NVP has three functions. First, it must cope with different sending and receiving hardware by achieving device independence in some way. Second, it must support user interfaces such as ringing a telephone, waiting for an answer, and hanging up. Third, it must control the transmission of a voice signal in real time. The protocol separates these functions into two distinct parts: a control protocol and a data protocol. These are separate protocols that link separate processes (see Fig. 5). The data processes are concerned only with transmitting speech data; the control processes provide the other two functions of the language.

Some of the NVP language is devoted to controlling the conversation and to exchanging information about its status. For example, the caller process tries to initiate a call with "Calling ⟨who⟩ from ⟨whom⟩," where each field addresses one of several telephone lines connecting to the NVP equipment. The answerer may reply "Ready" or "Goodbye, I am busy." If all goes well, the answerer may say "Ringing," and eventually "Ready" if the call is answered. These exchanges are simply designed to allow caller and answerer to know each other's state: ringing, ready, terminated. (See Fig. 6 for a summary of the important states of the NVP, and Table II for a summary of the protocol.)

A more interesting part of the control protocol is the negotiation of various parameters of the coding process. Although the parameters are mentioned below, we shall illustrate the negotiation process here. One of the two processes (caller or answerer) is the *negotiation master*. This process makes proposals for parameter values that the other may accept or reject. A proposal takes the form "Can you do ⟨what⟩ ⟨how⟩?" The ⟨what⟩ and ⟨how⟩ fields are coded from a small set (⟨how⟩ is actually a list of ways of doing ⟨what⟩ that are acceptable to the master). For example, the master asks "Can you do ⟨speech

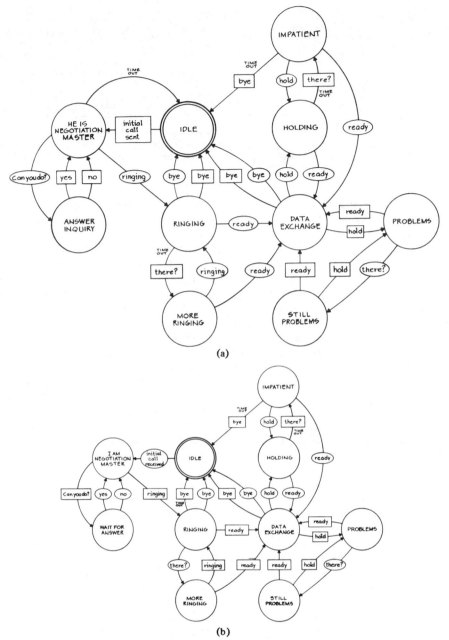

Fig. 6. The state diagram for the network voice protocol. Large circles indicate states. Transitions between states occur when a message is transmitted (arc with box) or received (arc with oval). Note that the caller and callee state diagrams are nearly symmetric.

signal sampling every⟩ ⟨62 microseconds⟩ or ⟨100 microsec-onds⟩?" The other process, the *negotiation slave*, may respond in one of two ways. A positive response is "I will do ⟨speech signal sampling every⟩ ⟨62 microseconds⟩." A negative reply says "I can't do ⟨speech signal sampling every⟩ in any way you suggested," but may optionally contain a suggested ⟨how⟩ that is acceptable. Although at any instant one of the processes is the master and one the slave, either may request renegotiation to exchange roles.

An additional *version* provision makes the negotiation more convenient. If a large number of parameters must be agreed upon, negotiating each one is tedious. We define a version to be a table of (⟨what⟩, ⟨how⟩) pairs that gives settings for a large number of parameters. Then the single negotiation "Can you do ⟨version⟩ ⟨2⟩?" will establish many parameter settings.

This negotiation scheme is designed to be extremely robust. Messages lost or delivered out of sequence will not garble the negotiation because each response repeats the question (⟨what⟩) as well as providing an answer.

Coding: Strictly speaking, the voice protocol is concerned only with controlling transmission of voice data, and not with the techniques used to generate the data. Nevertheless, good vocoding techniques, providing acceptable quality speech with modest transmission bandwidths, are the key to an NVP. A vocoder may be presented with 16 000 10-bit samples of speech waveform each second, and be required to encode this information in as few as 3500 bits. Clearly, such encodings cannot preserve all of the information in the original signal, but must strive to make errors that have only small perceptual effects.

TABLE II
SUMMARY OF ARPA NETWORK VOICE PROTOCOL MESSAGES.
DETAILS OF THE PROTOCOL ARE GIVEN IN [4]

```
Control messages:
    calling <who> <whom> <response-link>
    goodbye <code>
    negotiation.inquiry <what> <list.length> <how.list>
    positive.negotiation.response <what> <how>
    negative.negotiation.response <what> <try.this.value>
    ready
    not.ready
    inquiry
    ringing
    echo.request <id>
    echo <id>
    renegotiation.request <master.request>
    renegotiation.approval <master.request> <ok>


    ...examples of <what> is negotiated:
            <vocoding>
            <sample.period>
            <version>
            <max.msg.length>
            <LPC.degree>
            <CVSD.time.constant>
            <samples.per.parcel>
            <LPC.acoustic.coding>
            <LPC.info.coding>
            <LPC.pre.emphasis>
            <LPC.tables.set>


Data messages:
    <time.stamp> <skipped.parcels.flag> <parcel.count> <parcel> ...
```

Although a great many signal coding techniques are available [12], the ARPA NVP is currently experimenting with two: continuously variable slope delta modulation (CVSD) and linear predictive coding (LPC) [23]. These two techniques are very different; CVSD aims to produce an output waveform that *looks* close to the original, whereas LPC tries only to produce an output signal that *sounds* like the original. Experience gathered in recent years has made LPC the more popular technique for low data-rate vocoding.

Both vocoding schemes operate within a similar framework. An interval of speech is sampled and encoded by calculating the values of a number of parameters. These values are then packed into *parcels* for transmission through the network. The negotiation protocol is used to establish the type of vocoding used (LPC or CVSD), the sampling rate, the length of the period encoded in each parcel, and other details of the coding.

CVSD vocoding requires only modest processing, but does not achieve very good compression. Typically, 62 ms of speech is encoded into about 1000 1-bit parameters that are packed into a parcel for transmission, thus requiring about 16-kbits/s transmission rates. Some additional reduction in data rate comes from detecting inactivity of the speaker due to breathing, intersentence pauses, or listening to the other party. These periods of silence can be coded with very few bits; both CVSD and LPC coding take advantage of this reduction.

LPC employs two coding steps to reduce the volume of speech data. First, an *acoustic* vocoding is applied to a short period of sampled speech signal, and yields about a dozen parameters describing the signal. Second, an *information* coding step converts numeric values of these parameters to a smaller range of values and packs them into a parcel for transmission. The parcel is the unit of information flow, containing about 60 bits generated every 19.2 ms. Several parcels are packed together (up to about 14) into messages for transport through the network. Thus only 3500 bits/s are generated. This number can be reduced even further by use of "variable rate LPC" that takes advantage of acoustic redundancies (e.g., long vowels) to reduce the information content of the parameters.

The LPC acoustic vocoding algorithm fits a model of the human vocal system to a 19.2-ms interval of speech and delivers parameters describing the fit. The inverse process is applied to regenerate the speech, but it does not yield a signal identical to the original. The result is expected to *sound* like the original even though it does not *look* like the original.

The information coding step is simple compared to the LPC calculations. Although the LPC parameters vary over a wide range, the full precision need not be transmitted. The range of the parameters is broken into 32, 64, or 128 intervals with roughly equal probability of occurrence; parameter values are mapped via tables into either 5, 6, or 7 bits for transmission. The receiver inverts this nonlinear transformation.

Transport: The NVP requires real-time transport of parcels. Unfortunately, none of the standard transport facilities designed for HLP use in the ARPA network [1], [6] could provide such service; the NVP designed its own real-time protocol using only the facilities of the IMP-based communication subnet.

The real-time protocol is very simple and is applicable to real-time uses other than speech. Parcels, generated at a constant rate, are collected into messages. Each message is time-stamped with the time of creation of the first parcel in the message (the units of time measurement correspond to the time interval represented by a single parcel). During periods of silence, parcels are simply not generated, although any partially filled message will be transmitted promptly as the silence begins. (The treatment of silence is in fact somewhat tricky; see [3].) The time stamps allow the receiver to resequence messages that arrive out of order and to meter the reproduction of speech from the parcels.

Irregularities in message delays in the network cause trouble [13]. Suppose the first message experiences 340-ms delay and the receiver begins processing the first parcel of this message as it is received. If the next message experiences 360-ms delay, the receiver will finish the last parcel of the first message 20 ms before the next message arrives. What is it to do? The receiver could have delayed processing the first message somewhat in order to allow more leeway against subsequent longer network delays. This leeway can be allowed to grow as longer delays occur. However, if the *variation* in the network delay is high, the receiver's delay may become so long that an interruption by the listener is delayed awkwardly or that the speaker notices a pause when he stops speaking and begins listening. Low variation in network delay is a clear requirement for an NVP.

Very few conventional transport services are required by an NVP. No retransmission to remedy errors is required because a lost message is not catastrophic; both coding schemes are designed so that a parcel is decoded without knowledge of previous messages. Moreover, retransmission would introduce highly variable delays that cause worse perceptual damage than the loss of the message. The only effect of a lost message is an audible error for the period represented by the missing data. Because of the real-time nature of the NVP, there is also no need for user-enforced flow control: sender and receiver are processing messages at identical rates.

Results: The ARPA NVP was first used successfully in

December 1974 for real-time voice communication through the ARPA network from coast to coast. It has been implemented at five sites and has been used regularly since then. It has been used experimentally with LPC vocoding at rates between 1.8 and 5 kbit/s, and with CVSD at rates between 8 and 18 kbits/s. Although only a few sites have participated in the ARPA NVP, dissimilarities among the hardware and software environments have thoroughly exercised the device independence aims of the protocol. Some of the initial implementations used one-of-a-kind experimental devices such as the Lincoln Laboratory TX-2. A typical site uses a minicomputer attached to the network and to a fast arithmetic unit used for vocoding algorithms (e.g., PDP-11/45 and FPS AP-120A).

The NVP has been extended to handle the "higher level" functions of storing voice on files and of conferencing. In both cases, the data and negotiation protocols remained unaltered while extensions were made to the control protocol [5]. In conferencing, for example, control messages are used to establish which speaker "has the floor," and to whom speech should be sent. Additional extensions to transmit voice to a speech recognition system or from a speech synthesis system are feasible because LPC is the basis for some approaches to these goals [27]. All of these extensions are accommodated with only minor changes to the protocol because the basic NVP framework and vocoding required no alterations.

Although the voice application seems to be an unrepresentative HLP, we have seen that it offers a new perspective on several HLP functions. It shows a simple elegant negotiation mechanism. It shows the effort that must sometimes be devoted to data compression. It demonstrates a real-time end-to-end protocol. And most importantly, it places an unusual set of requirements on the transport system: low delay variation, minimal flow control, and no need for extreme reliability. Diverse needs such as these require the transport system to be flexible.

III. DESIGNING AND IMPLEMENTING HLP's

This section assembles the various techniques used to design and implement HLP's by referring liberally to the three illustrative protocols of Section III, and also to other HLP's. This compendium is a prelude to an examination of the relationship between HLP's and HLL's. Our observations are grouped into the categories of language, coding, and transport.

A. Language

The language for an HLP is clearly the most important part of the design. Meeting device independence and standardization objectives is a major challenge; it is difficult to abstract the common properties of a range of devices and applications in a design that has a simple form. It is often difficult to avoid letting quirks of inflexible operating systems or of special hardware completely destroy an otherwise simple protocol. The network is not an extrinsic contributor to the problem: it adds a few new difficulties to those encountered in designing a nonnetwork system involving multiple asynchronous communicating processes. Nevertheless, the presence of the network makes communication along such diverse computer hardware and devices possible; thus it is the reason for much of the pressure for device independence and standardization.

Device Independence: Inherent in device-independent designs is a tension between generality and standardization. As more capabilities of devices or a wider range of applications are encompassed by the design, standardization becomes more difficult. The NGP designers, for example, wanted to allow dynamically moving images to be displayed, provided that the display hardware made some provision for applying geometrical transformations to the display file rapidly enough to see motion. The attempt failed because the designers could devise no way to standardize the range of transformation facilities provided by display manufacturers. However, if aspirations of device independence were reduced, and the NGP were required to operate only displays of a certain type, dynamic images could be accommodated easily. Thus an attempt at generality was curbed by standardization problems.

Generality can also lead to complexity. Overly general designs are difficult to implement, may take a long time to devise, and often require more computing resources to process. One way to reduce this problem is to divide the facilities of an HLP into quasi-independent groups of functions with different degrees of generality. Any particular implementation may offer only a subset of the groups. The NGP, for example, recognizes four groups of commands (status and inquiry, segmented display files, positioned text, input interactions). Entire groups are optional—facilities for input interactions, for example, need not be provided. Within a group are both mandatory and optional commands. If the options are not used, a very simple implementation results. If implementers need the added features, the NGP specifies a standard way to provide them.

At the other extreme are protocols that are not very general, but are extremely simple. These unambitious HLP's can offer substantial service. A file transfer protocol that deals only with text files, or a graphics protocol that is little more ambitious than our plotter example, is remarkably useful. A design that provides a special feature in a device-independent way is worthless if it is never used!

HLP's, whether simple or general, usually provide some measure of device independence. Two approaches are used to deal with different devices.

1) The "virtual device approach." A standard is designed that specifies the operations that a process *must* implement. The plotter protocol is an example. The plotter process may be able to forward some protocol commands to the plotter hardware directly; others it may have to "simulate" in some way. For example, if the standard protocol specified colored lines, the plotter process might replace them by dashed lines if no colored pens are available. This approach derives its name from the similarity with "virtual memory:" a computer that provides a million words of virtual memory need not have that much primary memory, but a collection of mapping and paging processes simulate the effect of a million words of primary memory.

2) The "parametric approach." In this approach, the process preparing to send protocol commands will *inquire* of the plotter process information about its capabilities: How many colors can be plotted? What is the size of the plotter surface? What resolution? Given the answers to these questions, the sending process can arrange to use only features of the plotter that are available. Although this technique still requires standard ways to specify all possible plotter commands and standard ways to inquire, the burden of simulating in software those capabilities lacking in the plotter is shifted to the sender.

One benefit of the parametric approach is that the application program can be advised of the plotter's properties and can take advantage of the information. For example, if color is not available, the application program can simulate it with line textures that do not conflict with textures already used by the program. The technique also allows coding to be parametrized: for example, the plotter process could specify how many digits it requires for each coordinate value.

An important generalization of the parametric approach, called *negotiation*, makes the inquiry activity symmetric. Each process may inquire about properties of the other, often by asserting its request for a certain behavior: sender says "Can you do four colors?" and plotter replies either "Yes, I'll do four colors" or "No, I cannot do four colors." This technique allows each process to adapt to the other—they may end up being each parameterized according to some of the other's wishes. Once again, the method for negotiating, and the eventual commands that flow, must be standardized.

The basic difference between these two approaches concerns how the burden of achieving device independence is divided between the two communicating processes. The parametric approach, used by the NGP, NVP, and TELNET [7], essentially delays the specification of certain parameters until the two communicating parties are connected.

The methods used to achieve device independence can profoundly influence the structure of application programs that use the HLP. For example, the plotter protocol and the NGP are both graphics protocols, but a program must use them very differently, because they use fundamentally different techniques to make changes to the display. An application written to use a segmented display file could not be adapted easily to use the plotter protocol. Moreover, the parametric approach to standardization may induce the application to operate differently for different parameter values. For example, an interactive graphics application may drive a storage tube very differently than a refresh display (which reflects display changes more rapidly), even though the program uses the same device-independent methods to draw lines and text or to receive input.

Combining Protocols: An application may use several separate HLP's to connect its constituent parts. The different protocol uses are often independent, and use separate logical communication paths. But sometimes HLP's can unwittingly compete for resources. A good example is illustrated in Fig. 7(a), in which a user employs a TELNET protocol to control a graphics program, which in turn uses a graphics protocol connection to control a display. Most users prefer to see text and graphical output presented on the same screen (Fig. 7(b))— TELNET and the NGP thus compete for screen space. They also compete for keyboard input. But neither protocol is aware of the other's needs. The NGP design group considered allowing the NGP to control the placement of TELNET text on the screen, but abandoned the idea when it became clear such control would require synchronizing the display process (Dd) and the TELNET process (Tu) whenever screen placement changed. This problem was attacked seriously in a subsequent graphics protocol designed to allow careful control of "windows" on the screen, some of which contain TELNET text, and some graphical information [32], [35].

Robustness: An HLP provides a vital communication link in an application distributed over several computers, a link whose failure may be costly. If a person spends an hour using an interactive data-analysis program that uses the NGP to display results, and a communication error causes so much confusion that the program aborts, a great deal of work is lost. Providing the reliability to prevent these failures requires attention at all levels. The application program can save a user's state periodically in case of catastrophe; network transport facilities

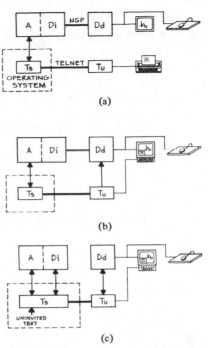

Fig. 7. Logical connections for graphics and terminal protocols. (a) Independent connections, with the display and terminal physically separate. (b) Independent connections, but "terminal text" is presented on the display. (c) A single connection for both graphics and terminal protocols, showing the insertion of "uninvited text" by an operating system.

can provide some measure of error detection and correction [1], [2], [18] and, finally, the HLP language can take steps to improve reliability, such as tolerating lost or duplicated messages. Redundant coding can be used to help detect errors. To avoid loss of synchronization in a stream of commands and arguments, a common technique is to occasionally identify the beginning of a command, for example, by marking a message to indicate that a command appears as the first item in the message.

Specification: Implementations of HLP languages usually depend on the proper interpretation of a rather detailed specification. The detail results chiefly from the requirement that all implementations of the HLP communicate with an identical language, rather than from complexity in the HLP itself. Indeed, the designer of an HLP seeks a simple elegant solution that offers the necessary services and has a straightforward implementation.

A precise HLP specification is difficult to write. Although it is similar to a specification for a "software interface" routinely used to detail the design of a module of a software system, it differs in two respects. First, it must be understood by HLP implementers accustomed to different programming languages, operating systems, conventions, and nomenclature. Second, because the implementer may not be familiar with the application addressed by the HLP, the specification must provide considerable implementation guidance. We shall argue in Section IV that notions from HLL's can be used to improve HLP specifications.

Layering: Layering helps to avoid HLP complexity: one HLP can be implemented *on top of* another. One sort of layering is exploited by all HLP's; they use some services of low-level transport protocols to provide basic communications services [1]. The plotter and NGP examples rely on this layer to provide *reliable* transmission.

HLP's can also be layered atop other HLP's. Protocols for conferencing and voice recording use the NVP as a base. An HLP that uses a coding based on character strings may be implemented on top of an HLP such as TELNET that transmits character streams between different computers.

Sometimes the opportunity to layer one HLP on top of another is impeded by poor protocol design or a shortsighted implementation. The NGP, for example, might have been layered on top of TELNET, so that the two connections of Fig. 7(a) could be reduced to one (Fig. 7(c)). This simplifies the implementation of Dd and Tu, requiring only one process. It also simplifies implementation of careful control of terminal text, as the single connection avoids the need to synchronize the display parameters in Dd to the arrival of text from Tu. However, the single connection approach was rejected by the ARPA NGP as too error-prone. Because an operating system may unexpectedly generate text to be printed on the terminal (e.g., "System going down."), it may interfere with graphical information encoded as text on the Ts–Tu connection. Clearly, the TELNET protocol and operating systems could provide a means for transmitting encoded information that would not be subject to disturbance. Such a facility, which would allow an HLP to be implemented within the TELNET protocol, was not available when the NGP was designed.

B. Coding

Coding can be a simple matter or a very complex one indeed. It is simple if we need only transmit integers or symbols from a well-specified vocabulary (e.g., an integer that identifies a command). Straightforward codings are easy to encode and decode; the NGP and NVP control messages are examples of simple codings. NVP data messages are simple encodings of parameters, although the parameters are extracted from speech samples by a complex vocoding algorithm. Although greater investment in processing can be used to compress the coding, no HLP's known to the authors use sophisticated minimum-entropy information coding techniques. This may be a result of greater attention to the less well understood problems of language and transport than to coding efficiency. Moreover, large efficiency gains can often be achieved by appropriate design of the protocol language: the segmented display file concept in the NGP offers a greater reduction in data transmission than would minimum entropy coding of entire images.

Coding problems arise when we try to encode objects that have different interpretations in different computers: "floating-point numbers" or "text characters" are examples. What happens if a "character" has no representation in the character set of the computer to which it must be transmitted? What happens when a floating-point number lies outside the range of numbers representable on the destination computer? Although it is possible to characterize precisely the acceptable ranges, it is extremely difficult to design a protocol that works properly when a sender wishes to transmit an object that cannot be interpreted by the receiver. Generally, these problems are handled by guaranteeing interpretations only on restricted subsets, such as "ASCII standard characters," or even "upper case characters."

C. Transport

An important lesson about transport systems has emerged from work on HLP's. No single abstract view of the transport facility applies to *all* HLP's; different protocols need access to transport facilities of different types. Transport facilities should be designed in a modular way to provide different *types of service* to different HLP's. The graphics and voice protocols described in this paper illustrate the range of transport services required. The NGP depends on orderly transmission of streams of bytes, and consequently requires many supporting transport mechanisms offered by IPC protocols [1], [2], [37], [38]: connections, flow control, sorting out-of-order packets, duplicate packet detection, and loss prevention. Small sacrifices in bandwidth or irregularities in transmission delay are unimportant. By contrast, the NVP requires a stable transmission delay, but can tolerate errors, lost packets, or packets discarded due to local network congestion.

Other HLP's may fall at points in between. For example, some do not need to establish network "connections," but can be designed around inquiry–response exchanges, sometimes called DATAGRAMS [26]. A protocol to look up telephone numbers might simply address a single message containing a person's name to the retrieval system; it expects a single answering message in response. If the sender receives no answer, he can repeat the request. A surprisingly large variety of protocols can be cast in this framework.

The grain of communication required of the transport system also varies among HLP's. Some will want to transmit streams of bits or bytes; others may compose indivisible messages to be delivered as atomic entities. In implementing a byte stream in a packet switching network, the transport system will attempt to buffer bytes until a message fills up. But how often should packets be sent? If a full message is assembled, presumably it should be sent immediately, subject only to flow control practices in the network. But what if a message is only partially filled, and has for several seconds seen no data added to it? Should it be sent, even though only partially full? Perhaps the receiving process is idle, and could begin working on the new data. Or perhaps the protocol is being used as part of an interactive dialog, and the user needs to see the effect of the data contained in the partial message. Or perhaps the message is partially full only because it is the last message of a long transmission (e.g., when transmitting an entire file).

The question used to resolve these questions is: on what unit of information can the receiving process take significant action? If we want the receiver to act each time a new byte is generated by the sender, we must ensure that no encoded information is buffered at the sender for very long, i.e., that partially filled messages are transmitted at short intervals. If, on the other hand, we are concerned only with finishing a long transmission as quickly as possible, using full-size packets for efficiency, we can expect the sender to indicate that transmission of the very last (partially filled) packet is required even though it's not full.

The transmission strategy used to make these decisions is determined in part by application process. Two facilities should be provided.

1) The sending process states a time interval that is the maximum time any chunk of information is buffered before sending (assuming network flow control conventions allow transmission). This time may be very long if timely transmission is unimportant, as in a file transfer, or it may be related to the amount of data accumulated for transmission [3]. (Note that such a scheme is an essential aspect of "terminal output"–characters must be periodically transmitted for the

user to see. Unfortunately, many operating systems that provide interfaces to network transport mechanisms provide this timely transmission facility *only* for terminal output; they do not implement the technique for other HLP network traffic.)

2) The sending process notifies the transport mechanism when it is important that buffered information actually be transmitted.

The needs of different HLP's are sufficiently varied to induce different behaviors in the way transport is provided: messages with time criticality of 100 ms can be treated differently than messages with 1-min delivery requirements. An HLP should make known to the transport system the *type of service* it desires. For example, NVP communications will request uniform delay. Interactive streams desire short delays, modest bandwidths, and high reliability. Transmitting a file requires high bandwidth, but can tolerate long transmission delays. In this case, packets could be routed far afield, taking advantage of idle communications lines, incurring long delays and numerous hops, but still provide large bandwidth because many packets are taking different long routes concurrently.

Most of the issues described in this section concern the implementation of transport facilities in an operating system and not the design of a communications network. As a consequence of layering, important issues in network design (naming, addressing, message sizes, internetwork operation, routing) rarely influence HLP design. An exception is our plea that the communication system respond to "type of service" requests from applications.

In summary, we believe 1) no single transport facility is universal, 2) transport systems that are assembling messages from smaller items need to transmit partial messages in response to time constraints and precise instructions from the sender, and 3) the transport needs of the application should be specified to the packet-switching network in order to provide the type of service desired.

D. Implementation

For HLP's to be useful in a resource-sharing network, implementations must be devised for many of the computers in the network. The ease with which these implementations can be constructed is often a major goal of an HLP design. Although most HLP's could be implemented easily, programming environments of many computers unfortunately complicate implementations. Many operating systems incorporate network access as an afterthought and therefore provide cumbersome facilities. Many have poor support for cooperating processes, which are used frequently in HLP implementations. And finally, tools for debugging asynchronous processes are usually poor. In a network, the problem is exacerbated by the inability to examine the state of the cooperating process or to repeat the conditions that caused an error. Even stopping the program being tested may be difficult: the other process may detect prolonged inactivity and abort!

Implementation and debugging can be aided by measures taken in the design of the HLP. Commands to reset both processes to an initial state are essential; facilities to report errors precisely can be provided. Sometimes explicit debugging aids can be built into an HLP implementation—a version of the NGP display process that types out a trace of all protocol commands received and sent greatly speeds debugging. Layering of protocols also eases implementation. If an HLP is implemented on top of a transport system deemed to transmit

streams of data reliably, many of the possibilities for timing-related errors are removed from the HLP.

IV. HIGH-LEVEL PROTOCOLS AND HIGH-LEVEL LANGUAGES

The finale of this survey of issues surrounding the design and implementation of HLP's relates the structure of HLP's to that of HLL's, and suggests techniques used in HLL's that can be applied fruitfully to problems in HLP's. In addition, HLP's point to some areas that should receive increased attention in HLL development.

A. Why an HLP Protocol Is Like An HLL

HLL's and HLP's are both abstract, but precise, definitions of a computation or communication that can be translated into the primitive operations actually provided by a computer or communication system. HLL's were born of a desire to express algorithms in a language natural to the application; a compiler fills in many details as it translates the program into the machine language of a particular computer. Similarly, an HLP is most clearly expressed in a "language" that relates closely to the application; the tedious details of coding and transport are not the primary concerns of the HLP designer and implementer.

One of the powerful ideas in HLL's is the concept of *type*: a method for defining abstract objects such as integers, characters, arrays, lists, text strings, records, sets, etc. A compiler, together with *type definitions*, chooses a way to represent these objects within the physical memory structure of the computer. With this aid, the programmer is freed from the details of encoding various objects in memory, and concentrates on harnessing these objects to ease the construction of his program.

The concept of type is just as prevalent in HLP's. Usually a message is divided into "fields," sequences of bits that are assigned particular meanings. But to the HLP designer, these fields are simply encodings of types used in the application program: integers, characters, etc.

Data structure declarations thus play a key role in both settings. They structure memory for the HLL; they structure messages for the HLP. A concrete example from the plotter protocol will further illustrate this point. The protocol is a sequence of *commands* (a type); each command specifies a *function* (a type) and possibly some *arguments* (of various types). Using PASCAL [17], we would write:

```
type PlotterFunction = (fBeginPlot,fEndPlot,fUp,fDown,
    fLineTo);
type PlotterCommand = record
  case function: PlotterFunction of
    fBeginPlot: () ;
    fEndPlot: () ;
    fUp: () ;
    fDown: () ;
    fLineTo: (x,y : int)
  end;
type PlotterProtocol = file of PlotterCommand
```

PlotterFunction is a type that can take on five values corresponding to the names fBeginPlot, fEndPlot, fUp, fDown, and fLineTo. The key type is PlotterCommand, which is a *variant record* with an entry giving the function and possible arguments—it thus specifies the structure of a single command in the plotter HLP. The type PlotterProtocol is a sequence of such commands.

The application program might generate the plotter HLP by calling five procedures corresponding to the five commands. For example, the procedure LineTo builds a PlotterCommand record consisting of the function name (fLineTo) and two argument values. The record is then "transmitted" by appending it to the PlotterProtocol sequence:

```
var c : PlotterCommand;
var pp : PlotterProtocol;

procedure LineTo (tx, ty : int );
  begin
    c.function := fLineTo; (* Build command *)
    c.x := tx; (* Insert arguments *)
    c.y := ty;
    pp↑ := c; put(pp); (*Add command to sequence *)
  end
```

Notice how type declarations and record-construction statements help specify coding and transport details.

The paradigm illustrated above is a common one in HLP's: transmitting records consisting of a command, followed by values of arguments. It is no coincidence that these records correspond to the specifications of typed objects in a procedure call; the declaration of the procedure LineTo and of the fLineTo variant of the PlotterCommand record are strikingly similar. The plotter protocol and the NGP, which use this paradigm, are essentially transmitting procedure names and arguments to the receiving process, which calls corresponding procedures. Both protocols could be expressed in terms of a "procedure call protocol," an HLP that arranges to achieve this effect [39].[2] HLP's with this flavor arise quite frequently when a single application program consisting of several modules is distributed in a network. It is precisely this methodology that we advocated for developing the NGP.

Not all HLP designs are conveniently expressed within a framework as specialized as a procedure call protocol. The NVP, for example, does not fit well into this category. However, the concept of structuring communication into records by using appropriate type declarations remains extremely valuable. These type declarations must of course, be shared by the sender and receiver to insure both parties apply the same interpretations to messages.

Although the idea of *type* is perhaps the most important, other aspects of HLL's correspond to HLP features. When two modules are *linked* together, communication methods are established between the modules (usually through procedure linkages), much the way a connection establishes a communication between two processes. The act of *binding* the two modules together might be compared to the negotiation or inquiry used to inaugurate communication, though most HLL binding is considerably less flexible than HLP parametrization. The *data abstraction* techniques in HLL's foster methods for designing software systems that are similar to the abstractions required to achieve device independence or to define standards. Finally, HLL's are increasingly concerned with methods for

specifying precisely the interface to software modules, in part so that uses of the module by other programs can be checked carefully. This problem of precise description is also key to HLP's; an accurate specification of the HLP for a service must be available to any programmer writing programs that use the HLP.

B. How HLL's Can Help HLP's

Our sketch of the relationship between HLL's and HLP's shows that many ideas developed for HLL's address corresponding needs in HLP's. However, to be fully useful in implementing HLP's, some of these ideas must be developed further.

1) Type definitions: Currently, HLL's use type definition facilities that are too loose and dependent on details of the computer on which they execute. For example, an "integer" will designate 36 bits on some machines, 32 on others, 16 on still others, etc. This definition is too vague to be useful in a heterogeneous network, i.e., one containing computers of many different sorts. Instead, we need to define integers precisely, e.g., "24-bit 2's complement integer." Also, most structural definition facilities will not allow us to split a field over a word boundary in the computer. Such a facility may be needed when interpreting a standard protocol, even though it might be folly within any given machine. Thus programming-language techniques for defining structure on word-oriented storage should be extended and applied to defining structure in bit-oriented protocol streams.

2) Interprocess communication (IPC): Many newer HLL's are beginning to offer facilities for IPC, some using the idea of transmitting typed records as we showed above [20]. However, none provides automatically the vital link between the variant record and the procedure call. The programmer can write the obvious encoder, as demonstrated in the PASCAL example, and a matching decoder that collects arguments and dispatches to call the proper procedure, but these are bulky and tedious to write. This sort of IPC is common in networks, but is neglected in programming systems. Some efforts have been devoted to this problem [11], [16], but the need has not been widely recognized.

3) Linking: HLL's must be prepared to check types used in IPC when connections are made. Ideally, a process offering an HLP service could distribute (in a standard form!) a definition of the protocol to receive service. Such a definition could be checked against the protocol definition of a potential partner when a connection is initiated—this is similar to checking caller/callee parameter declarations when linking separately compiled programs; we insist that definitions match before we allow communication.

4) Asynchrony: We need better ways to document message sequences and message exchanges. As in any multiprocessing system, we must worry about deadlock and synchronization issues. They may be especially tricky if we use a transport mechanism that sometimes delivers messages out of sequence or occasionally loses them. Assertions provided with the program, and flow analysis undertaken by a compiler, can help with certain communications problems: can a particular message be packed with others to form a larger package to transport through the network, or must it be sent immediately because a reply is required? Efforts in this area are beginning [8], [34].

5) Documentation: There is also a need for a definition at a more functional level: What are the services of the protocol?

---

[2] Strictly speaking, a "procedure call" requires that control not return to the caller until the procedure has been executed. In the plotter and NGP protocols, it is desirable to let the calling process continue execution so that several "procedure call" records can be packed together into one network message. If the procedure being called returns an answer, the calling process must of course wait for the answer.

What effect does each command have? How do the commands interact? What are possible responses to particular messages? It seems clear that a computer program, perhaps expressed as abstract operations of a process that implements the protocol, is a better documentation tool than is prose. The data abstraction languages now emerging [15], [21], [30], are working toward such definitions. Even using existing HLL's, a simple exemplary implementation of the NGP might be a much better definition of its properties than is a bulky document.

Ideally, these goals can be addressed in an integrated fashion. A new project of Feldman, Low, and Rovner [9], [10], tackles some of them with the programming language PLITS, which integrates messages and message structures into an HLL and a distributed environment DSYS, which provides the binding and debugging facilities needed to develop applications that use several communicating processes.

Developments that truly integrate protocols into programming languages and tackle interprocess communication among processes written in different programming languages would open up many new opportunities for users of HLP's. Programs using the protocols would be easier to implement and easier to change. The protocols themselves could be changed more readily, and could be described by precise definitions as well as lucid implementations.

V. Conclusion

The emergence of resource-sharing networks and the HLP's that exploit them has aroused public interest in standards. Although a standard protocol is substantially harder to design than is a set of private communication conventions, the reward is enormous: the ability to communicate effectively with a vast number of computer resources. The desire to generalize an HLP—to increase its scope to handle as many uses as possible—is countered by increased difficulty in achieving a standard. The search for simple effective standard HLP's is still in its infancy—we can expect that HLP development will continue, and can hope that further principles and methodologies will emerge to help design these protocols.

Although they have received increased attention because of the growth of computer networks, problems of standardization and generalization are not intrinsic to networks. In fact, the presence of a network often confuses the job of designing a framework to provide service to an application with the job of transmitting information in a network. Breaking the problem into issues of language, coding, and transport is a help. More importantly, the application must be understood well in simple environments, free from standardization constraints, before a standard protocol design is attempted.

The outlook for streamlining specification and implementation of HLP's is closely tied to the development of HLL's. Existing HLL's provide facilities that can be applied to simplify these tasks. The important next step is for the language designer to realize that programs written in his language will need to communicate with other programs written in other languages, on computers with different conventions. Protocol definitions must be shared among these environments in order to propagate standard protocols. Although it is a difficult goal to standardize even a simple form of interprocess communication over a wide variety of computing equipment and programming systems, ignoring this opportunity will curb the potential of resource-sharing networks. Ultimately, HLL's could be enhanced to the point that techniques used to implement

HLP's will be expressed as naturally as arithmetic expressions are now.

Acknowledgment

The authors are grateful to V. Cerf, B. Kahn, and J. Shoch for helpful comments on drafts of this paper.

References

[1] C. S. Carr, S. D. Crocker, and V. G. Cerf, "Host–host communication protocol in the ARPA network," in *AFIPS Proc.* (Spring Joint Computer Conf.), pp. 589–597, 1970.

[2] V. G. Cerf and R. E. Kahn, "A protocol for packet network interconnection," *IEEE Trans. Commun.*, vol. COM-22, p. 637, May 1974.

[3] D. Cohen, "Issues in transnet packetized voice communication," in *Proc. 5th Data Communications Symp.* (Snowbird, UT), pp. 6, 10–13, Sept. 1977, IEEE Catalog Number 77CH1260-9C.

[4] ——, "Specification for the network voice protocol," USC/Information Sciences Inst., Marina del Rey, CA, ISI/RR-75-39, DDC AD A023506, Mar. 1976.

[5] ——, "A protocol for packet switching voice communication," in *Computer Network Protocols*, A. Danthine, Ed. Liege, Belgium, Feb. 1978.

[6] W. R. Crowther, F. E. Heart, A. A. McKenzie, J. M. McQuillan, and D. C. Walden, "Issues in packet switching network design," in *AFIPS Proc.* (National Computer Conf.), p. 161, 1975.

[7] J. Davidson, W. Hathaway, J. Postel, N. Mimno, R. Thomas, and D. Walden, "The ARPANet Telnet protocol: its purpose; principles, implementation and impact on host operating system design," in *Proc. 5th Data Communications Symp.* Snowbird, UT, Sept. 1977.

[8] J. A. Feldman, "Synchronizing distant processes," Computer Science Dept., Univ. Rochester, TR 26, Oct. 1977.

[9] ——, "A programming methodology for distributed computing (among other things)," Computer Science Dep., Univ. Rochester, TR 9, Sept. 1976.

[10] J. A. Feldman, J. R. Low, and P. D. Rovner, "Programming distributed systems," *Computer Science Res. Rev.*, Univ. of Rochester, 1977–78.

[11] J. A. Feldman and R. F. Sproull, "System support for the Stanford hand-eye project," in *Proc. 2nd Int. Joint Conf. on Artificial Intelligence*, 1971.

[12] J. L. Flanagan, *Speech Analysis, Synthesis and Perception.* New York: Springer, 1972.

[13] J. W. Forgie, "Speech transmission in packet-switched store-and-forward networks," in *AFIPS Proc.* (National Computer Conf.), p. 137, 1975.

[14] D. Gojanovic, "Some experience with network graphics protocols," in *Computer Network Protocols*, A. Danthine, Ed. Liege, Belgium, Feb. 1978.

[15] A. Goldberg and A. C. Kay, *Smalltalk-72 Instruction Manual*, Xerox Palo Alto Research Center, SSL-76-6, 1976.

[16] G. Hamlin, "Configurable applications for satellite graphics," Ph.D. dissertation, Univ. of North Carolina, Chapel Hill, 1975.

[17] K. Jensen and N. Wirth, "PASCAL, user manual and report," in *Lecture Notes in Computer Science*, G. Goos and J. Hartmanis, Eds. New York: Springer, vol. 18, 1974.

[18] R. E. Kahn, "Resource-sharing computer communications networks," *Proc. IEEE*, vol. 60, pp. 1397–1407, Nov. 1972.

[19] ——, "The organization of computer resources with a packet radio network," *IEEE Trans. Commun.*, vol. COM-25, pp. 169–178, Jan. 1977.

[20] B. Lampson, J. Mitchell, and E. Satterthwaite, "On the transfer of control between contexts," in *Lecture Notes in Computer Science*, G. Goos and J. Hartmanis, Eds. New York: Springer, 1974, vol. 19. p. 181.

[21] B. Liskov, A. Snyder, R. Atkinson, and C. Schaffert, "Abstraction mechanisms in CLU," *CACM*, vol. 20, no. 8, p. 564, Aug. 1977.

[22] J. Maleson, J. Nabielsky, and R. Rashid, "Rochester image protocol," Computer Science Dep., Univ. Rochester, informal note.

[23] J. D. Markel and A. H. Gray, *Linear Prediction of Speech.* New York: Springer, 1976.

[24] W. M. Newman and R. F. Sproull, *Principles of Interactive Computer Graphics.* New York: McGraw-Hill, 1973.

[25] ——, "An approach to graphics system design," *Proc. IEEE*, vol. 62, p. 471, Apr. 1974.

[26] L. Pouzin and H. Zimmerman, "A tutorial on protocols," this issue, pp. 1346–1370.

[27] D. R. Reddy, "Speech recognition by machine: A review," *Proc. IEEE*, vol. 64, pp. 501–531, Apr. 1976.

[28] D. M. Ritchie and K. Thompson, "The UNIX time-sharing system," *CACM*, vol. 17, no. 7, pp. 365–375, July 1974.

[29] L. G. Roberts and B. D. Wessler, "Computer network development to achieve resource sharing," in *AFIPS SJCC Proc.*, vol. 36, p. 543, May 1970.

[30] M. Shaw, W. A. Wulf and R. L. London, "Abstraction and verification in Alphard: Defining and specifying iteration and generators," *CACM*, vol. 20, no. 8, p. 553, Aug. 1977.

[31] R. F. Sproull, "Omnigraph-Simple terminal-independent graphics software," Xerox Palo Alto Res. Center, CSL-73-4, 1973.

[32] ——, "InterLisp display primitives," Xerox Palo Alto Res. Center, 1977, informal note.

[33] R. F. Sproull and E. L. Thomas, "A network graphics protocol," *Comput. Graphics*, vol. 8, no. 3, Fall 1974.

[34] C. A. Sunshine, "Survey of protocol definition and verification techniques," in *Computer Network Protocols*, A. Danthine, Ed. Liege, Belgium, Feb. 1978.

[35] W. Teitelman, "A display oriented programmer's assistant," Xerox Palo Alto Res. Center, CSL-77-3, 1977.

[36] R. H. Thomas, "A resource sharing executive for the ARPAnet," in *AFIPS Proc.*, NCC, p. 155, 1973.

[37] ——, "MSG: The interprocess communication facility for the national software works," Bolt Beranek and Newman, Rep. 3483.

[38] D. C. Walden, "A system for interprocess communication in a resource-sharing computer network," *CACM*, vol. 15, no. 4, p. 221, Apr. 1972.

[39] J. E. White, "A high-level framework for network-based resource sharing," *AFIPS Proc.*, NCC, p. 561, 1976.

[40] P. A. Woodsford, "The design and implementation of the GINO 3D graphics software package," *Software Practice and Experience*, vol. 1, p. 335, Oct. 1971.

Reprinted from *The Proceedings of INFOCOM 83*, 1983, pages 196-201.
Copyright © 1983 by The Institute of Electrical and Electronics Engineers, Inc.

The Application and Presentation Layers of the Reference Model for Open Systems Interconnection

Paul D. Bartoli

American Bell Inc.

ABSTRACT

During the past year considerable progress has been made in describing the Application and Presentation layers of the Reference Model for Open Systems Interconnection (OSI). In this paper the work of ANSI, ISO and CCITT on the Application and Presentation layers is discussed. In section 2 the author discusses communication between application processes and, building on the concepts introduced, describes the role of the Application and Presentation layers in supporting communications. Section 3 contains detailed descriptions of some of the proposed capabilities of the Application and Presentation Layers.

Keywords

    Application Layer, Presentation Layer, Application, Application Process

Introduction

During the past year considerable progress has been made in describing the Application and Presentation layers of the Reference Model for Open Systems Interconnection (OSI). In this paper the work of ANSI, ISO and CCITT on the Application and Presentation layers is discussed. In section 2 the author discusses communication between application processes and builds on the concepts introduced in order to describe the role of the Application and Presentation layers in supporting communications. Section 3 contains detailed descriptions of some of the proposed capabilities of the Application and Presentation Layers.

Communication Between Application Processes

An application is the set of a user's information processing requirements. An application process is a logical element within a system which performs the information processing required for a specific application. When a application is distributed, each distributed portion of the application is an application process.

The work on the Reference Model was begun in order to provide a standard environment (guidelines, protocols) for communications among distributed portions of an application, i.e., among distributed application processes which are cooperating to perform information processing required for an application. In summary, the goal of the Reference Model and the services and protocols developed from it is to provide standard communications capabilities among application processes.

For two application processes to be able to communicate with one another (exchange meaningful information) there must be an agreement on the semantics of all aspects about which exchange of information is intended. For example, if two (or more) application processes are to cooperate to perform an airline reservation application, there must be an agreement between the application processes that airline reservations functions are to be performed, as opposed to credit checking or some other application, in order for meaningful information processing to occur. Agreement among application processes on the nature of the application at hand enables the information exchanged between application processes to be used in the proper context. We call the semantics which is shared among the application processes the <u>universe of discourse.</u>

Communication consists of the exchange of information relative to some sphere of interest of which the communicants have a shared and logically consistent view. The universe of discourse is this sphere of interest and provides the boundaries (context) within which meaningful communication can occur. In order for exchange of information to occur between application processes it is necessary to provide a means for moving <u>representations</u> of the information to be exchanged in a manner which prevents distortion of the information. The Reference Model for Open Systems Interconnection provides the framework for accomplishing undistorted transfer of information.

The OSI Reference Model involves a seven layer structure called the "Open Systems Interconnection Environment" (OSIE) [1,2]. General familiarity with the OSI Reference Model is assumed in what follows. The lower four layers of the

OSIE provide for reliable transfer of data between end systems. The Session layer (layer 5) performs the functions necessary to ensure that the representations of information are transferred between the proper communicants. These functions include provision of the proper addressing information to the Transport layer (layer 4). The lower five layers of the OSIE provide application processes the freedom to ignore the details of the underlying communications mechanism. In the discussion that follows we assume the presence of the lower five layers without further comment.

The Application Layer

The Application layer is responsible for the interpretation of the semantics of application layer protocols used to transfer information between application processes. The Presentation layer is responsible for the representation of the Application layer protocols and the information whose transfer they effect. Thus, the distinction between the Application and Presentation layers can be thought of as one of semantics versus syntax. The Application layer is concerned with the semantics and valid (allowable) sequences of Application layer protocol units which can be sent between application processes, while the Presentation layer is concerned with the concrete representation of this information.

The Application layer of the Open Systems Interconnection Environment (OSIE) provides the sole means for an application process to access the capabilities available from the OSIE. In each system the Application layer consists of a set of identifiable service elements, each of which accepts and processes requests for provision of some OSI capability or provides to the application process some response as a result of a stimulus from the OSIE. Any given subset of such service elements constitutes an application entity type and is uniquely nameable. Three examples of services (i.e., sets of service elements) which could be provided by three types of application entities are the File Transfer Service, the Virtual Terminal Service and the Job Transfer and Manipulation Service. These services are currently being defined in ISO/TC97/SC16. Logically, an application entity is the part of the application process that effectuates the application layer protocols.

Three categories of service elements are recognized: common application service elements; application specific service elements; and user specific service elements. Common application service elements provide capabilities required by application processes for purposes of information transfer between application processes independently of the nature of the application. (e.g., setting up an association between application processes and terminating an association between application processes.) Application specific service elements provide capabilities required to satisfy the needs of specific types of information transfer capabilities of broad utility (e.g., file transfer, data base access, job transfer). User specific service elements provide capabilities to satisfy the needs of particular application processes (e.g., banking, order entry, etc.) and, as such, are not generally subject to standardization. Specific application entities, however, may consist of service elements in all of the identified categories.

Section 3.1 discusses the common application service elements in detail. There are standards groups actively pursuing the definition of application specific service elements and protocols such as file transfer, data base access and job transfer service elements. These efforts are not discussed herein.

The Presentation Layer

The purpose of the Presentation layer is to represent information to communicating application entities in a way that preserves meaning while resolving syntax differences. There are three syntactic versions of the information being transferred; the source syntax, the destination syntax and the syntax of the data transferred between application entities. It should be noted that any two or all three of these syntaxes may be identical.

It is the responsibility of the Presentation layer to negtiate the syntax to be used between presentation entities (i.e., the transfer syntax) based on the source and destination syntaxes and the syntax transformation capabilities of the source and destination systems. Within the OSIE the source syntax and the destination syntax are only recognized explicitly within their own systems. From the point of view of the Presentation/Session boundary and of all lower layers, the only syntax seen is the transfer syntax. Syntax transformations are performed as internal open system functions to accomplish syntax matching between source and destination application processes and, as such, are not discussed in the Reference Model.

In general there are three ways to select the transfer syntax.

(1) by a prior agreement where, at implementation time, the transfer syntax is agreed to by all systems concerned;

(2) by referring to (selecting) a particular transfer syntax by name in the Presentation layer protocol; and

(3) by transferring a description of the transfer syntax, in some formal language,

between Presentation layer entities.*

Method (3) above is the most powerful and flexible of the methods listed. What is required here is the standardization of a syntax description language which can be used to describe transfer syntaxes. This would allow the description of a wide variety of syntaxes. The only requirement placed on a presentation layer entity is the ability to determine whether or not it can interpret and deal with a particular syntax description. This method also frees the Presentation layer from having to maintain large lists of syntaxes which could be used by communicating application processes, rather, they must be able to interpret the (single) standard syntax description language.**

Thus, the means for selecting the transfer syntax range from being very simple (a priori agreement) to being more complex but very powerful and more applicable to a wide range of applications with varying syntax requirements (syntax description method).

A key concept in the Presentation layer effort is that there is a single Presentation service and protocol which perform syntax selection and the capabilities described in Section 3.2 for all OSI applications. This is an important concept because there are many different transfer syntaxes (and presumably different required syntax transformations) required for many different applications and these are selected (and possibly negotiated) by a single presentation layer protocol. This means that it is possible for one Presentation layer protocol to exist throughout the entire OSI environment which selects and negotiates all transfer syntaxes used between Presentation entities. Each transfer syntax is referred to by name; the Transfer syntax names are conveyed by the Presentation layer protocol. Thus, within all Open Systems, one Presentation layer exists, and performs the functions mentioned above, while the number of transfer syntaxes supported by a particular open system is arbitrary and may be determined by user and system provider requirements.

----

* A Presentation layer entity is the logical element within a system that effectuates the Presentation layer protocol and provides Presentation layer capabilities to application entities.

** The ability to interpret the description language at least to the extent of determining whether a particular syntax can be dealt with, for a particular communication, is required.

Application and Presentation Layer Service Elements

This section presents the service elements that have been proposed for the Application and Presentation layers. In particular, the Common Application service elements are presented in Section 3.1 and the Presentation layer service elements are presented in section 3.2.

Common Application Service Elements

The service elements summarized below have been proposed as the Common Application Service Elements and are described in detail in the paragraphs that follow. The table below groups the Common Application Service elements into nine categories based on the capabilities they provide. Each service element is listed as being one of three types: confirmed, non-confirmed or provider initiated. A confirmed service element is a service element whose completion is indicated explicitly, by the provider of the service element, by issuing a confirmation to the invoker of the service element. A non-confirmed service element is a service element whose completion is not explicitly indicated (to the invoker) by the service element provider. A provider initiated service element is a service element which is originated by the service element provider (e.g., the Common Application Service provider) to inform the user of provider initiated actions (e.g., exception reports).

SUMMARY OF COMMON APPLICATION LAYER SERVICE ELEMENTS

Capability	Service element	Type
Origination	A_ASSOCIATE	Confirmed
Termination	A_RELEASE	Confirmed
	A_USER_ABORT	Non-confirmed
	A_PROVIDER_ABORT	Provider initiated
Context	A_CONTEXT_DEFINE	Confirmed
	A_CONTEXT_SELECT	Confirmed
Interruption	A_SUSPEND	Confirmed
	A_RESUME	Confirmed
Information Transfer	A_TRANSFER	Non-confirmed
	A_TRANSFER_CONFIRM	Confirmed
	A_TRANSFER_EXPEDITED	Confirmed
	A_PURGE	Confirmed
Status	A_STATUS	Confirmed
	A_EXCEPTION_REPORT	Provider initiated
Dialog		

control	A_PASS_TOKEN	Confirmed
	A_REQUEST_TOKEN	Non-confirmed
Synchroni-zation	A_MARK	Non-confirmed
	A_SYNCHRONIZE	Confirmed
	A_RELEASE_MARK	Confirmed
Message	A_SEND_MESSAGE	Non-confirmed

A_ASSOCIATE service element

A_ASSOCIATE is a confirmed service element used to associate two named application processes. When the request has been confirmed, an association between the two application processes has been established.

An application process may choose to accept or reject a proposed application-association.

A_RELEASE service element

A_RELEASE is a confirmed service element used to provide orderly termination of an application-association. The release is accomplished by cooperation between the associated application processes.

Where there is no agreement to release the application-association, it remains established. The application process requesting the release shall receive a response indicating whether the release has occurred or not.

A_USER_ABORT service element

A_USER_ABORT is a non-confirmed service element by means of which either application process can unilaterally terminate an application-association and have the peer application process informed of this termination. The invocation of this service element disrupts any other concurrently active service elements; in particular, information may be lost.

A_PROVIDER_ABORT service element

A_PROVIDER_ABORT is a provider initiated service element by means of which the service provider may indicate the termination of the application-association to both application processes. The invocation of this service element by the provider disrupts any other concurrently active service elements; in particular, information may be lost.

A_CONTEXT_DEFINE service element

An application context definition (A_CONTEXT) identifies application protocols which are intended to be used sometime during the application association.

A_CONTEXT_DEFINE is a confirmed service element which associates a context name with a context definition.

A_CONTEXT_SELECT service element

A_CONTEXT_SELECT is a confirmed service element that enables an application process to request that the current context be changed to the named context which must be the initial context or a context which has been previously defined in the given application-association (using the A_Context Define service element).

An application process receiving an indication of a selected context may, in its response accept or reject the proposed context. Where the proposed context is accepted, that context immediately upon confirmation becomes the current context. Where the proposed context is rejected, the current context remains unchanged.

A_SUSPEND service element

A_SUSPEND is a confirmed service element which causes an application-association to be rendered temporarily inactive until it is resumed. The total state of the association is preserved during the suspension.

A_RESUME service element

A_RESUME is a confirmed service element that requests resumption of the application-association. It may be requested by either application process, not just the one initiating the suspension. The other application process may accept or reject the request.

A_TRANSFER service element

A_TRANSFER is a non-confirmed service element that causes information to be transferred from one application process to another.

A_TRANSFER_CONFIRM service element

A_TRANSFER_CONFIRM is a confirmed service element that causes information to be transferred from one application process to another.

A_PURGE service element

A_PURGE is a confirmed service element that returns the application-association to a known state with no information remaining in that association.

A_STATUS service element

A_STATUS is a confirmed service element permitting an application process to inquire of and receive a response from the OSIE concerning the current status of a given application-association.

The parameters about which inquiries can be made are under study, including the question of whether status information unknown to the peer application-entity but generated at lower layers of the OSI can be provided.

A_EXCEPTION_REPORT service element

A_EXCEPTION_REPORT is a provider initiated service element that indicates to one or both application processes that some exceptional condition exists within the OSIE.

A_PASS_TOKEN service element

A_PASS_TOKEN is a confirmed service element permitting one application process to signal its relinquishing of the turn to send information when the two way alternate dialog discipline is being used. This service element does not cause suppression of the use of service elements other than A_TRANSFER and A_TRANSFER_CONFIRMED.

A_REQUEST_TOKEN service element

A_REQUEST_TOKEN is a non_confirmed service element permitting an application process to request the turn to send information.

A_MARK service element

A_MARK is a non-confirmed service element permitting an application process to place an identifiable mark into the information stream for synchronization purposes. It also permits indication that no more marks can be used until some are released.

A_SYNCHRONIZE service element

A_SYNCHRONIZE is a confirmed service element requesting reset of the status of an application-association to a named point.

A_RELEASE_MARK service element

A_RELEASE_MARK is a confirmed service permitting the release of synchronization point status information up to a named mark.

A_SEND_MESSAGE service element

A_SEND_MESSAGE is a non_confirmed service element permitting an application process to send information to another application process without explicit establishment of an application-association between the peers.

A_SEND_MESSAGE and the ability to provide for exception reporting in A_EXCEPTION_REPORT is an initial attempt to provide definition of the service elements required to implement connectionless message transfer.

Presentation Layer Service Elements

The service elements summarized below are proposed as the set of Presentation layer service elements and are described in detail in the paragraphs that follow. The Presentation Layer Service Elements are grouped into eight categories based on the type of capabilities provided.

SUMMARY OF PRESENTATION LAYER SERVICE ELEMENTS

Capability	Service element	Type
Establishment	P_CONNECT	Confirmed
Termination	P_RELEASE	Confirmed
	P_USER_ABORT	Non-confirmed
	P_PROVIDER_ABORT	Provider initiated
Context	P_CONTEXT_DEFINE	Confirmed
	P_CONTEXT_SELECT	Confirmed
Information transfer	P_TRANSFER	Unconfirmed
	P_PURGE	Unconfirmed
Interruption	P_SUSPEND	Confirmed
	P_RESUME	Confirmed
Status	P_EXCEPTION_REPORT	Provider initiated
Dialog Control	P_REQUEST_TOKEN	
	P_PASS_TOKEN	
	P_MARK	
Synchronization	P_SYNCHRONIZE	
	P_RELEASE_MARK	

P_CONNECT service element

P_CONNECT is a confirmed service element, used to bring into communication two application entities which are identified by name. When the request has been confirmed the two application entities have been provided with a communication channel, uniquely identifiable to themselves and an initial presentation context, within which subsequent communication takes place.

Simultaneous attempts by both application entities to establish a presentation connection between them may result in two presentation connections. An application entity may choose either to accept or reject a request for a presentation connection.

P_RELEASE service element

This service element provides confirmed orderly release of the presentation connection. The release is accomplished by cooperation between the connected application entities.

Where there is no agreement to release the presentation connection, the connection remains established. The application entity requesting this service element shall receive a response indicating whether the release has occurred or not.

P_USER_ABORT service element

This service element provides the means by which either application entity can unilaterally terminate a presentation connection and have the correspondent application entity informed of this termination. The execution of this service disrupts any other concurrently active services.

P_PROVIDER_ABORT service element

This service element is the means by which the service provider may indicate the termination of the presentation connection for reasons internal to the service provider or when the underlying Session service is not available. The execution of this service disrupts any other concurrently active services.

P_CONTEXT_DEFINE service element

A presentation context consists of a presentation transfer syntax definition.

The P_CONTEXT_DEFINE confirmed service element associates a presentation context name with a context definition. The purpose of the context definition is to specify a transfer syntax. This definition may be identified either by the proper name of the presentation transfer syntax or by a description using a syntax description language.

P_CONTEXT_SELECT service element

This confirmed service element enables an application entity to request that the current context be changed to the named context. The selected context must be one of the set of contexts previously defined (using the P_Context Define service element) or the initial presentation content.

A Presentation entity receiving an indication of the selected context may, in its response, accept or reject the selected context. Where the indicated context is accepted, the context immediately becomes the current context at the time of the response and upon receipt of the confirmation. Where the indicated context is refused, the current context remains unchanged.

P_TRANSFER service element

This unconfirmed service element transfers user data according to the current context.

P_EXCEPTION_REPORT service element

P_EXCEPTION_REPORT is a provider initiated service element that indicates to one or both application entities that some exceptional condition exists with the OSIE.

P_SUSPEND service element

P_SUSPEND is a confirmed service element which causes a P-connection to be rendered inactive until it is resumed.

P_RESUME service element

P_RESUME is a confirmed service element that requests resumption of the P_connection. It may be requested by either application entity, not just the one that initiated the P_SUSPEND. The other application entity may accept or reject the request.

SUMMARY

In the past year considerable progress has been made in the areas of Application and Presentation layer definitions. It is expected that by the end of 1983 the capabilities of the Application and Presentation layers will be further refined and agreement will be reached on the precise set of capabilities for the Application and Presentation layers.

REFERENCES

1) ISO, "Data Processing - Open Systems Interconnection - Basic Reference Model," Document ISO/TC97/SC16 N890 (DIS 7498), International Organization for Standardization, 1982.

2) CCITT, "Proposed Draft Recommendation Reference Model of Open Systems Interconnection for CCITT applications," September 1982.

Reprinted from *IEEE Journal on Selected Areas in Communications*, Volume SAC-1, Number 2, February 1983, pages 267-277. Copyright © 1983 by The Institute of Electrical and Electronics Engineers, Inc.

The Story of PLP

JOE D. WETHERINGTON, MEMBER, IEEE

Abstract—The development of information systems during the 1970's was primarily directed to the needs of commercial businesses and manufacturers. Now, with the advances in communications technology and the significant increase in microprocessor capabilities, the informational needs of the entire consumer market can be satisfied. However, to minimize the variables in developing products for the mass market that includes businesses as well as residences, the systems that are required to provide the informational vehicle must reach a high level of standardization.

Since 1978, the international arena has attempted to standardize the character sets and coding of a class of information systems referred to as Videotex. The first agreement reached was in November 1980 by the International Telegraph and Telephone Consultative Committee (CCITT), in Geneva. This CCITT recommendation was referred to as "International Information Exchange for Interactive Videotex, Recommendation S.100," and included three incompatible coding schemes.

In May 1981, a Presentation Level Protocol (PLP) was announced by AT&T which combined all of the functions of the three incompatible coding schemes of S.100, with more complete graphical and color capabilities, into a unified coding syntax. This article covers the rationale for PLP prior to May 1981 and recent progress toward a North American standard for videotex.

INTRODUCTION

IN order to develop a videotex service that will have broad usefulness at its inception, and remain functional in the future, it is necessary that it be designed with standardized capabilities. These capabilities must also meet the needs of the two primary user groups: the consumers, whose informational and transactional needs must be met in a cost effective manner, and the sponsors (i.e., information providers, advertisers, service providers), whose desires for a wide range of functions must be satisfied. It is a recognized premise that without a level of standardization to enable systems to intercommunicate, the price/performance of isolated systems will not support the creation, maintenance, and growth of a home information marketplace.

A typical videotex system can be described as having many terminals with access to a data network that connects to one or more databases (host computers). A videotex service is developed by adding informational and transactional capabilities to a videotex system.

It is possible to expand a videotex service by two methods: either by increasing the components (terminals, network, database) within the system, or by connecting the subject videotex service to another videotex service. The first method would not raise a standardization issue and would only be limited by initial design constraints on the system, such as network expandability and host computer throughput limitations. The sec-

ond method is more difficult, since the two systems would have to have been designed to the same standards. This is true at the point where the two systems connect (i.e., network interface), and also at the point where data interpretation is performed (i.e., coding interface). These two "points" in a system can generally be described within the context of the seven-layered model for open systems interconnection (OSI) under development [20] by the International Standards Organization (ISO) and the International Telegraph and Telephone Consultative Committee (CCITT). The lower four layers (i.e., physical, data link, network, transport) are sometimes referred to as the "distribution process," but in this article are lumped together in the phrase "network interface" because of its more frequent use. The upper three layers of the OSI model (i.e., session, presentation, application) include syntactical rules by which to interpret the data, and semantic execution requirements of the conforming process.

The standardization of the network interface will not be discussed further in this paper. Attention will now be given to the coding interface standards, with emphasis on the presentation layer. Following is the history and rationale of related events, a comparison of coding schemes, and a status of the videotex standardization process.

VIDEOTEX HISTORY

In May 1978, the British Post Office introduced an interactive service known as Viewdata to the CCITT in Geneva. Viewdata used a "serial coding" technique to retrieve text, block mosaic graphics, and controls, with a limit of eight possible colors, from a computer database, and displays the information on a TV screen. The connection between the computer and the TV was a telephone line.

Later that year, the French Administration proposed a similar but incompatible mosaic graphic scheme, using the parallel coding technique (serial and parallel coding techniques refer to the processing scheme of display symbols and the associated control codes). By May 1979, the Canadian Department of Communications had submitted a much different coding scheme for displaying information on a TV, which used the text and eight colors of the British and French proposals, and also the parallel coding of the French scheme. This new method, however, defined pictures, not as simple block mosaics, but in a more fundamental manner—the basic geometric primitives of point, line, arc, rectangle, and polygon. In addition, the concept of display-independent coding was introduced.

During 1978, 1979, and the first half of 1980, the technical experts of CCITT worked to develop a single coding scheme from the three proposals, for an international interactive service referred to as videotex. The primary contributors were from England, France, Germany, Canada [2], and the United States.

Manuscript received April 23, 1982; revised October 12, 1982.
The author is with AT&T, Parsippany, NJ 07054.

Numerous companies were represented by the country delegations with the exception of the U.S.A., where only AT&T actively participated.

Early in 1980 it became apparent that the need to preserve the specific coding scheme of each national system was greater than the desire to obtain the best technical solution from the three proposals. Therefore, at the final meeting of the technical committees in June 1980 at Montreal, a technical recommendation was approved which included all three proposals. This recommendation was officially adopted by CCITT in November 1980, and called "CCITT Recommendation S.100, International Information Exchange for Interactive Videotex" [11].

CONCEPTION AND DEVELOPMENT OF PLP

In 1979, AT&T wanted to continue a marketing research activity which, since 1977, had been attempting to measure the concept of a "home information" service. The mosaic graphics of the British and French proposals seemed applicable to this activity and were incorporated into the terminals used in the videotex concept trial conducted in Florida with Knight-Ridder Newspapers. To improve the display image, a capability to download custom character shapes was provided, as well as the ability to use any 16 colors from a possible palette of 512 colors. In a parallel research effort, the geometric primitives in the Canadian proposal were developed in an experimental computer database, and were being considered for other market studies.

During this same period, two unrelated activities were taking place, which add to the story. The U.S. computer/communications industry along with the International Standards Organization (ISO) were reaching substantial understanding of a seven-layer architecture for open systems interconnection (OSI). The second activity was the significant work [3] in identifying a wide range of functions possible in the computer graphics arena, motivated (since the early 1970's) by the special interest group on graphics (SIGGRAPH) in the Association for Computing Machinery (ACM).

In 1980 it was felt that in order to plan for the potential introduction of a videotex service, based on consumer needs and on the functional requirements of information providers and advertisers (sponsors), standard protocols were needed. Since it did not appear that an international standard was likely in the near term, a new protocol had to be developed. This protocol incorporated 100 percent of the features of the three incompatible coding schemes (to enable existing databases to be transcoded), and included a broader range of features (required by sponsors). The new protocol was limited to the most universal layer of the OSI model, the presentation layer, since it held the promise of permitting "all data bases to be accessed by all terminals," and because a videotex standard for all layers seemed out of reach due to the probable diversity of applications. A significant amount of the functions required by sponsors (e.g., a wide range of colors, and company logos) was contained in the work from the computer graphics area, and was therefore incorporated. However, one of the important design considerations which came into play at this point, was the need to balance the desire for rich features against the need for effective cost performance in terminal implementations. Therefore, features such as rotational viewport and full animation were not included.

Early in 1981 the decision to participate in a videotex market test in 1983 was being reached. This market test would include the Knight-Ridder Newspapers (KRN) company. A parallel activity (in early 1981) was the final stages of planning an electronic directory videotex trial to start in mid-1981 in Texas. Even though the Texas trial was to eventually be cancelled, it brought CBS Inc. into the planning picture as an information provider and trialing partner. (Note: the joint AT&T/CBS Videotex trial began in September 1982 in New Jersey.)

By the first quarter of 1981, the Presentation Level Protocol was well developed. All available protocols (French Antiope, British Prestel, Canadian Telidon, etc.) were thoroughly evaluated in order to arrive at the best technical solution possible. The technical needs of the information providers and advertisers were reviewed with the knowledgeable experts in KRN and CBS, since joint effort with AT&T in the future was possible and compatability was an obvious requirement. The CBS technical discussions brought the added benefit that PLP could be applicable to the emerging service called Teletext, which uses the vertical blanking interval (VBI) of a TV broadcast signal to transport data to a receiving television set. This conclusion was reached following technical discussions with CBS and their technical consultant, the French Television Agency, Telediffusion de France.

The provisional issue of the Bell System Videotex Standard Presentation Level Protocol (PLP) was completed in April 1981. Thereafter, the provisional PLP was announced at a scheduled meeting of the U.S. State Department's Study Group A (CCITT Preparatory Committee, made up of leading government and business interests), and copies were mailed (upon request) to its members for comments. Also, at the request of the British Post Office, technical discussions were held in early May in Geneva to inform them of the technical contents of the provisional issue of PLP.

PLP ANNOUNCEMENT AND RATIONALE

On May 20, 1981, AT&T announced the Bell System Videotex Standard Presentation Level Protocol [1] at the Videotex '81 conference in Toronto. Later that same day, official representatives of CBS, France (Telediffusion de France), and Canada (Department of Communications) acknowledged that their respective services in North America would be [4], [10], [16] compatible with PLP.

Since May 1981, over 4000 copies of PLP have been provided (on request) to individuals and organizations throughout the world. Numerous companies and countries have indicated a desire to use PLP in their own services, and the following list are some of those who have publically indicated a position in favor of PLP: KRN, CBS, Canadian Government and industries (e.g., Norpac, Microtel Pacific Research, Electrohome, Infomart), French TDF, Chemical Bank, J. C. Penney's, Apple Computer, Southeast Bank, Bank of America, Times, Inc., Times Mirror, National Semiconductor, RCA, Compuserve, General Instrument, Honeywell, Field Enterprises, Centel,

Intel, Tektronix, Digital Equipment, NBC, Westinghouse, Hazeltine, Microsoft, ICL, Xerox, Digital Research, etc.

The primary goals of the Bell System presentation protocol were to

- provide the required functionality, based upon extensive market analysis, applied research, and field trials;
- accommodate the desire for extensive features while still permitting cost-effective implementations;
- have a marketplace usefulness of many years by having a hardware-independent approach as well as by having no undefined code positions which would avoid unique terminal-dependent features (i.e., incompabilities); and
- be compatible with existing coding and code extension schemes.

The first three goals were achieved with PLP! However, the fourth goal was not realized. Functional compatibility was achieved, but coding compatibility was impossible since the three coding schemes proposed by the United Kingdom (Prestel), France (Antiope), and Canada (Telidon) were incompatible in a number of ways. The rationale for these goals was the achievement of an acceptable level of standardization essential to the existence and growth of a home information marketplace.

CODING SCHEME COMPARISONS

The CCITT Recommendation S.100 defined two mosaic graphic options (i.e., serial mode, as in Prestel; parallel mode, as in Antiope), a geometric option (as in Telidon), a general architecture for the concept of dynamically redefinable character sets (DRCS), and identified potential enhancements (based on an AT&T contribution to CCITT) such as a wide range of colors, dynamic blink, and 7 bit or 8 bit coding.

A comparison of the three schemes to PLP is made below by using the actual coding tables of S.100 and those in PLP. (It is important to recognize that since PLP was announced, Telidon was modified [22] to be identical to PLP, and the two mosaic schemes have been combined into a single document [5] which did not include the geometric capability of S.100.)

- *Text Comparison:* The text characters in S.100 apply to all three schemes, and are shown in Exhibit 1 (Fig. 3/S.100) and Exhibit 2 (Fig. 4/S.100). By comparing these to Exhibits 3 and 4 from PLP, it can be seen that they have identical codes for defined characters. The additional characters in the two PLP tables (Exhibits 3 and 4) are identical to those in the North American Broadcast Teletext Specification (NABTS) adopted [4] by CBS, the Canadian Government, and other companies. Additional text symbols may be needed which can be created by DRCS. The procedure for DRCS is completely specified in PLP, but is only briefly mentioned in S.100.

- *Block Mosaics:* A limited graphical technique is provided in S.100 using two different but very similar mosaic coding tables, Exhibits 5 and 6. By comparing these to the block mosaic table of PLP (Exhibit 7) it can be seen that PLP combined both S.100 tables into a single table by including the same image from Exhibit 5, position 7/15, and Exhibit 6, position 5/15, in their respective positions.

- *Geometric Graphics/Picture Description Instructions:* The important point here is to recognize that the concept of display-independent coding was introduced by Canada into

b7		0	0	0	0	1	1	1	1
b6		0	0	1	1	0	0	1	1
b5		0	1	0	1	0	1	0	1
b4 b3 b2 b1		0	1	2	3	4	5	6	7
0 0 0 0	0				0	@	P		p
0 0 0 1	1			!	1	A	Q	a	q
0 0 1 0	2			"	2	B	R	b	r
0 0 1 1	3				3	C	S	c	s
0 1 0 0	4				4	D	T	d	t
0 1 0 1	5			%	5	E	U	e	u
0 1 1 0	6			&	6	F	V	f	v
0 1 1 1	7			'	7	G	W	g	w
1 0 0 0	8			(	8	H	X	h	x
1 0 0 1	9			)	9	I	Y	i	y
1 0 1 0	10			*	:	J	Z	j	z
1 0 1 1	11			+	;	K		k	
1 1 0 0	12			,	<	L		l	l
1 1 0 1	13			–	=	M		m	
1 1 1 0	14			.	>	N		n	
1 1 1 1	15			/	?	O	①	o	

1 Position 5/15 can be displayed as "low line", —, or as "number sign" #, to represent the terminator function required for some existing Videotex services.

Exhibit 1. The primary set of graphic characters for international interactive videotex.

b7					0	0	0	0	1	1	1	1
b6					0	0	1	1	0	0	1	1
b5					0	1	0	1	0	1	0	1
b4	b3	b2	b1		0	1	2	3	4	5	6	7
0	0	0	0	0				°		—	Ω	ĸ
0	0	0	1	1			¡	±	`		Æ	æ
0	0	1	0	2			¢	2	´		Đ	đ
0	0	1	1	3			£	3	^		ª	ð
0	1	0	0	4			$	×	~		Ħ	ħ
0	1	0	1	5			¥	µ	¯			ı
0	1	1	0	6			#	¶	˘		Ĳ	ĳ
0	1	1	1	7			§	·	˙		Ŀ	ŀ
1	0	0	0	8			¤	÷	¨		Ł	ł
1	0	0	1	9			‘	’			Ø	ø
1	0	1	0	10			“	”	˚		Œ	œ
1	0	1	1	11			«	»	¸		º	ß
1	1	0	0	12			←	¼			Þ	þ
1	1	0	1	13			↑	½	˝		Ŧ	ŧ
1	1	1	0	14			→	¾	˛		Ŋ	ŋ
1	1	1	1	15			↓	¿	ˇ		ŉ	

Exhibit 2. The supplementary set of graphic characters for international interactive videotex.

	10	11	12	13	14	15
COLUMN / ROW	2	3	4	5	6	7
0	SPACE	0	@	P	`	p
1	!	1	A	Q	a	q
2	"	2	B	R	b	r
3	#	3	C	S	c	s
4	$	4	D	T	d	t
5	%	5	E	U	e	u
6	&	6	F	V	f	v
7	'	7	G	W	g	w
8	(	8	H	X	h	x
9	)	9	I	Y	i	y
10	*	:	J	Z	j	z
11	+	;	K	[	k	{
12	,	<	L	\	l	|
13	–	=	M	]	m	}
14	.	>	N	^	n	_
15	/	?	O	—	o	■

Exhibit 3. ASCII alphanumerics (PLP).

	10	11	12	13	14	15
COLUMN / ROW	2	3	4	5	6	7
0	SPACE	°	→	—	Ω	ĸ
1	¡	±	`	1	Æ	æ
2	¢	2	´	®	Đ	đ
3	£	3	^	©	ª	ð
4	$	×	~	TM	Ħ	ħ
5	¥	µ	¯	♪		ı
6	#	¶	˘		Ĳ	ĳ
7	§	•	˙		Ŀ	ŀ
8	¤	÷	¨		Ł	ł
9	‘	’	/		Ø	ø
10	“	”	˚		Œ	œ
11	<<	>>	¸		º	ß
12	←	1/4		1/8	Þ	þ
13	↑	1/2	˝	3/8	Ŧ	ŧ
14	→	3/4	˛	5/8	Ħ	ħ
15	↓	¿	ˇ	7/8	ŉ	■

Exhibit 4. Supplementary graphics characters (PLP).

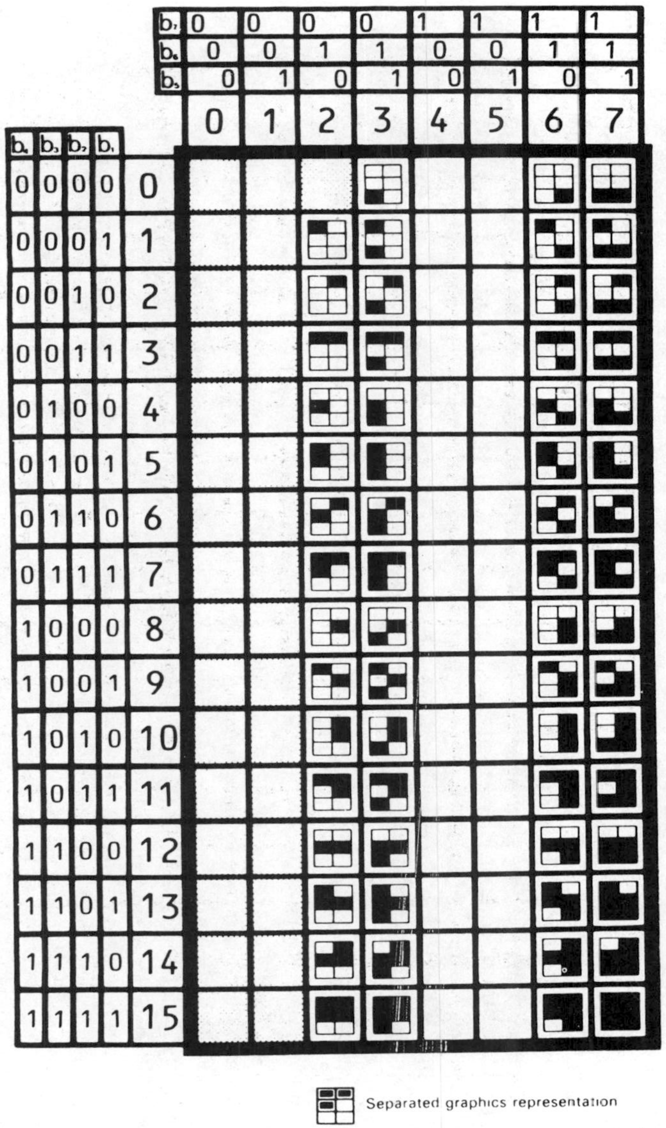

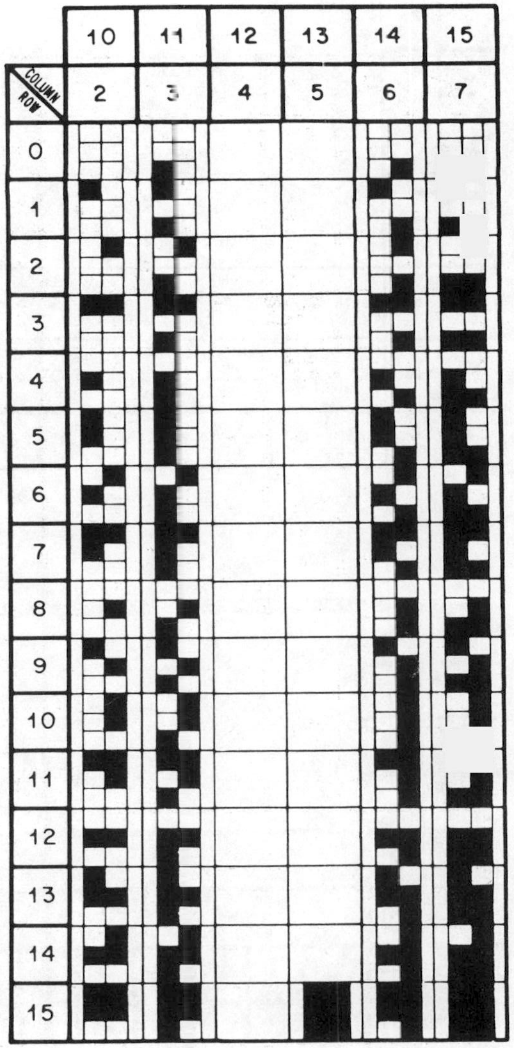

Exhibit 7. Mosaic graphics (PLP).

« Lired » mosaic character

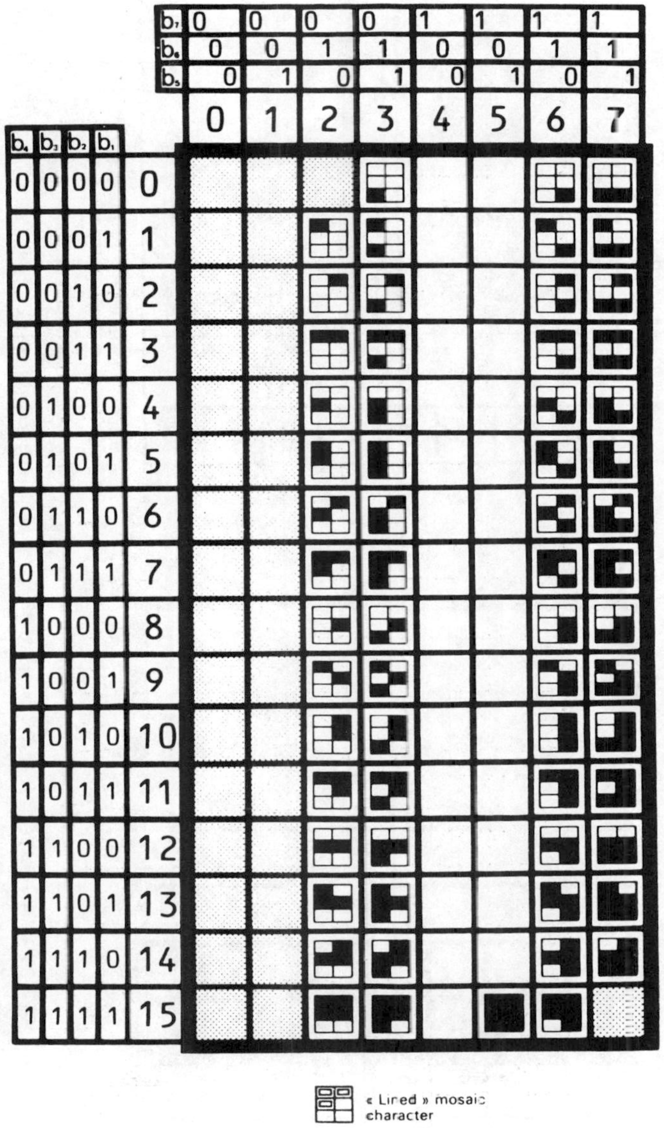

Exhibit 6. The mosaic character set—parallel mode.

Separated graphics representation

Exhibit 5. The mosaic set for the serial mode with blast-through characters in columns 4 and 5.

b7	0	0	0	0	1	1	1	1
b6	0	0	1	1	0	0	1	1
b5	0	1	0	1	0	1	0	1
b4 b3 b2 b1	0	1	2	3	4	5	6	7
0 0 0 0 0			Spare	Rect 4		Numeric data		
0 0 0 1 1						(for opcodes)		
0 0 1 0 2						or		
0 0 1 1 3						status		
0 1 0 0 4			Point 1	Poly 5		commands		
0 1 0 1 5								
0 1 1 0 6								
0 1 1 1 7								
1 0 0 0 8			Line 2	Reserved 6				
1 0 0 1 9								
1 0 1 0 10								
1 0 1 1 11								
1 1 0 0 12			Arc 3	Control 7				
1 1 0 1 13								
1 1 1 0 14								
1 1 1 1 15								

Exhibit 8. Operation code and data field assignments.

COLUMN / ROW	10	11	12	13	14	15
	2	3	4	5	6	7
0	CONTROL	RECT		NUMERIC DATA		
1						
2						
3						
4	POINT	POLY				
5						
6						
7						
8	LINE	INCR				
9						
10						
11						
12	ARC	CONTROL				
13						
14						
15						

Exhibit 9. PDI codes (PLP).

CCITT in S.100, and was retained in PLP. Exhibit 8 shows the 32 code positions in S.100. By comparing this to Exhibit 9 from PLP, it can be seen that the four versions of the five geometric primitives (point, line, arc, rectangle, polygon) have the identical coding for all 20 functions.

Exhibit 10 from PLP shows the additions to S.100 (Exhibit 8) made in the spare positions (2/0–2/3) and reserved positions (3/8–3/11). These additional codes in PLP added the enhanced textual attributes (e.g., variable character size and rotation) and graphical enhancements (e.g., incremental commands for signatures, advertising logos, and photographic-like images), which were desired by information providers and advertisers.

The code positions 3/12–3/15 on S.100 Exhibit 8 were changed as shown on PLP Exhibit 10. This provided the wide range of color capability that was required by information providers and advertisers, and the dynamic blink function for simple animation, as well as eliminating the extension (i.e., control status) to the partially-defined table in S.100 shown as Exhibit 11. This was accomplished by combining all of the functions on the Exhibit 11 (S.100) table into the op codes and operands of the PLP table, Exhibit 10.

• *Control Sets:* Each of the three coding schemes in S.100

uses the primary set of control functions found in Exhibit 12. Exhibit 13 contains the similar controls for PLP. This table has historically been referred to as the "ASCII" control set, even though it differs slightly from the control set implemented in the general trade display devices. For videotex this has been modified to provide additional controls such as SS2 and SS3 in code positions 1/9 and 1/13, respectively. These functions are identical between S.100 and PLP. However, there are some differences between Exhibits 12 and 13, such as the definitions for CAN (1/8) and US (1/15) which have been tailored to the respective service, and are therefore incompatible.

The supplementary control set in S.100 for serial mode (Exhibit 15) and the supplementary control set for parallel mode (Exhibit 14) are commonly referred to as a "C1" set. The related C1 set for PLP is in Exhibit 16. The differences between the PLP C1 set and the two S.100 C1 sets constitute the major difference between PLP and S.100. The main reasons for this are 1) S.100 was developed with two different C1 sets when only one was required, and 2) the features of PLP are so much broader than in S.100; and the code positions were required for PLP in order to implement the additional functionality. As an example, the two C1 sets (Exhibits 14 and 15) of S.100 use 16 code positions each (total of 32) to define foreground and

Exhibit 10. PDI codes (PLP)

COLUMN→ ROW↓	10 / 2	11 / 3	12–15 / 4–7
0	RESET	RECT (OUT-LINED)	
1	DOMAIN	RECT (FILLED)	
2	TEXT	SET & RECT (OUT-LINED)	
3	TEXTURE	SET & RECT (FILLED)	
4	POINT SET (ABS)	POLY (OUT-LINED)	
5	POINT SET (REL)	POLY (FILLED)	NUMERIC DATA
6	POINT (ABS)	SET & POLY (OUT-LINED)	
7	POINT (REL)	SET & POLY (FILLED)	
8	LINE (ABS)	FIELD	
9	LINE (REL)	INCR POINT	
10	SET & LINE (ABS)	INCR LINE	
11	SET & LINE (REL)	INCR POLY (FILLED)	
12	ARC (OUT-LINED)	SET COLOR	
13	ARC (FILLED)	CONTROL STATUS (WAIT)	
14	SET & ARC (OUT-LINED)	SELECT COLOR	
15	SET & ARC (FILLED)	BLINK	

Exhibit 10. PDI codes (PLP).

Exhibit 11. Control (status) and status subcommands assignment

Row	Col 0	Col 1	Col 2	Col 3	Col 4	Col 5	Col 6	Col 7
0					Clear (to black)	Line (solid)	Text (turn)	
1					Clear (to trans. parent)	Line (dotted)		
2					Clear (in black and initialize)	Line (dashed)		
3					Clear (to current colour)	Line (dot dashed)		
4					Domain (3 bytes)	Fill		
5					Domain (4 bytes)	Fill (black highlight)		
6					Domain (5 bytes)			
7					Domain (6 bytes)			
8					Drawing (blink off)			
9					Drawing (blink on)			
10								
11								
12				Control status	Tonal control (colour)	Wait (timed)		
13					Tonal control (grey)	Wait (indefinite)		
14								
15								

Exhibit 11. Control (status) and status subcommands assignment.

Exhibit 12. The primary set of control functions for international interactive videotex

Row	Column 0	Column 1
0	NUL	②
1	②	③
2	②	③
3	②	③
4	②	③
5	ENQ	③
6	②	②
7	①	②
8	APB	CAN
9	APF	SS2
10	APD	①
11	APU	ESC
12	CS	①
13	APR	SS3
14	SO	③
15	SI	③

Note 1 — Reserved for future study.

Note 2 — Reserved for transmission control characters. Their use in Videotex is for further study.

Note 3 — The definitions of these control functions are given in the relevant options.

Note 4 — As in all the code tables in this Recommendation, the shaded positions do not belong to the character set described.

Exhibit 12. The primary set of control functions for international interactive videotex.

Exhibit 15 — The supplementary set of control functions—serial mode.

Row	Col 4	Col 5
0		
1	Alpha red	Graphics red
2	Alpha green	Graphics green
3	Alpha yellow	Graphics yellow
4	Alpha blue	Graphics blue
5	Alpha magenta	Graphics magenta
6	Alpha cyan	Graphics cyan
7	Alpha white	Graphics white
8	Flashing	Conceal display
9	Steady	Contiguous graphics
10	End box	Separated graphics
11	Start box	1
12	Normal height	Black background
13	Double height	New background
14		Hold graphics
15		Release graphics

1 Reserved for further study

Note: This coding represents the final bit combination of ESC Fe sequences in a 7-bit code.

Exhibit 15. The supplementary set of control functions—serial mode.

Exhibit 14 — Supplementary set of control function—parallel mode.

Row	Col 4	Col 5
0	Black foreground	Black background
1	Red F	Red B
2	Green F	Green B
3	Yellow F	Yellow B
4	Blue F	Blue B
5	Magenta F	Magenta B
6	Cyan F	Cyan B
7	White F	White B
8	Flash	Conceal display
9	Steady	Stop lining
10	End box	Start lining
11	Start box 1	2
12	Normal size	Normal polarity
13	Double height	Inverted polarity
14	Double width	Transparent background
15	Double size	Reveal display

1 For further study
2 Reserved for CSI

CCITT 44140

Note: This coding represents the final bit combination of ESC Fe sequences in a 7-bit code.

Exhibit 14. Supplementary set of control function—parallel mode.

Exhibit 13 — C0 control set (PLP).

COLUMN / ROW	0	1
0	NUL	TC7 (DLE)
1	TC1 (SOH)	DC1
2	TC2 (STX)	DC2
3	TC3 (ETX)	DC3
4	TC4 (EOT)	DC4
5	TC5 (ENQ)	TC8 (NAK)
6	TC6 (ACK)	TC9 (SYN)
7	BEL	TC10 (ETB)
8	BS (APB)	CAN
9	HT (APF)	SS2
10	LF (APD)	SUB
11	VT (APU)	ESC
12	FF (CS)	FS
13	CR (APR)	SS3
14	SO	RS (APH)
15	SI	US

Exhibit 13. C0 control set (PLP).

Exhibit 16.   C1 control set (PLP).

	8 / 4	9 / 5
	8-BIT MODE	7-BIT MODE
0	DEF MACRO	PROTECT
1	DEFP MACRO	EDC₁
2	DEFT MACRO	EDC₂
3	DEF DRCS	EDC₃
4	DEF TEXTURE	EDC₄
5	END	WORD WRAP ON
6	REPEAT	WORD WRAP OFF
7	REPEAT TO EOL	SCROLL ON
8	REVERSE VIDEO	SCROLL OFF
9	NORMAL VIDEO	UNDER LINE START
10	SMALL TEXT	UNDER LINE STOP
11	MED TEXT	FLASH CURSOR
12	NORMAL TEXT	STEADY CURSOR
13	DOUBLE HEIGHT	CURSOR OFF
14	BLINK START	BLINK STOP
15	DOUBLE SIZE	UNPROTECT

Features	CEPT (June 1981)	PLP (May 1981)	S.100 (Nov. 1980)
o ASCII Text & Controls	X	X	X
o Supplementary Characters	X	X	X
o Dynamically Redefinable Character Set (DRCS)		X	
o Fixed Character Size	X	X	X
o Variable Text Size		X	X
o Underline	X	X	X
o Variable Character Spacing		X	
-o Variable Line Spacing		X	
o Geometric Graphics			
- Point		X	X
- Line		X	X
- Arc		X	X
- Rectangle		X	X
- Polygon		X	X
- Incremental Point		X	
- Incremental Line		X	
- Incremental Polygon (filled)		X	
o Block Mosaics - Contiguous	X	X	X
o Block Mosaics - Separate	X	X	X
o Repeat	X	X	X
o Reverse Video	X	X	X
o Cursor (On/Off)	X	X	X
o Variable Cursor		X	X
o Blink (On/Off)	X	X	X
o Dynamic Blink		X	
o Conceal/Reveal	X	X	X
o Multiple Conceal/Reveal		X	
o Different Character Path		X	X
o Rotation Text		X	X
o Eight Colors	X	X	X
o Wide Range of Colors		X	
o Controllable Stroke Width		X	
o Selectable Highlight		X	
o Programmable Texture Masks		X	
o Optional Word Wrap		X	
o Partial Screen Scrolling		X	
o Multiple Unprotected Fields		X	
o Transmit Macros		X	
o Macros		X	

Exhibit 17.   Comparison of coding schemes.

background color, where PLP uses two codes 3/12 and 3/14 (and numeric data from columns 4-7) of the PDI code table (Exhibit 10) to define color capability. Therefore, functions like defining DRCS characters (codes 4/3 and 4/5) and specifying word wrap (codes 5/5 and 5/6) could be included in the PLP C1 set (Exhibit 16).

• *Additional Sets:* There are two 96-character graphic or "G-sets" in PLP not found in S.100. These sets are reserved for macro names and for DRCS names. The DRCS capability was mentioned earlier and can be used to define 96 separate character images using any legal string of presentation code, subject to the same attributes as other "text characters." The macro table can be used to identify 96 simultaneous characters which represent an arbitrary string of presentation level code that is buffered until a "call" for the macro name is made in the received data stream. The C1 set of PLP, Exhibit 16, contains the DRCS and macro commands.

SUMMARY OF DIFFERENCES BETWEEN S.100, PLP, AND CEPT

The purpose of this article was to cover the rationale for PLP prior to May 1981. Since the CCITT Recommendation S.100 was the only specification that had any official status

relevant to a presentation level protocol at that time, PLP has been compared to it. However, since PLP was announced on May 20, 1981, many European countries have reached agreement on the coding scheme in the June 1 Recommendation No. T/CD from the CEPT Sub-Working Group CD/SE. This agreement represents an evolution over S.100 since it better defines how to code the two alphamosaic options (à la Prestel and Antiope). A comparison of features in CEPT, PLP, and S.100 is shown in Exhibit 17.

A comparison of coding schemes by merely looking at the code tables does not really do justice to the strengths of PLP. For example, the display independence of both text and graphics, provided by using the unit screen display coordinate system, and the description of attributes such as color in an implementation-independent manner should be understood to fully appreciate PLP. However, these topics will be left to the reader to investigate, and possibly to a future article.

CURRENT STATE OF STANDARDIZATION

The story of PLP would not be complete without explaining some of the procedures relating to the standardization process, and a status of the activity.

In the United States there are four U.S. Preparatory Groups chartered by the State Department to help develop technical and policy positions that should be taken by the official U.S. delegations at the various CCITT meetings. These four groups are referred to as Study Groups A, B, C, and D, and correspond to the 16 different Study Groups of CCITT. Since CCITT Study Group VIII has the charter to address the technical aspects of videotex, its counterpart in the U.S., Study Group

B, has a similar responsibility. In support of this responsibility Study Group B created a Videotex Technical Experts Panel (VTEP) following its December 1981 meeting. The purpose of this panel was to analyze the market needs of the U.S., and to recommend a standard for review and approval by U.S. Study Groups B and A. (Study Group A corresponds to CCITT Study Group I, which has the responsibility to provide the service definition of videotex.) Once a standard was approved, it would become the official U.S. position of Study Groups A and B (and also the U.S. delegation) at the subsequent meetings of CCITT Study Groups I and VIII in Geneva. Following technical discussions within CCITT, the U.S. position could be included in a world standard recommendation in 1984 by the CCITT Plenary Assembly.

A closely related standards effort was progressing in the American National Standards Institute (ANSI), in conjunction with the Canadian Standards Association (CSA). The ANSI work was being performed in a new task group (X3L2.1) and concerned the Presentation Level Protocol Syntax for Videotex and Teletext. The charter of X3L2.1 was to draft a standard by June 1982, with approval of ANSI by end of 1982. The task group used PLP as a starting document, and also considered all relevant standards (e.g., CEPT). Its task was also to coordinate with the Study Group B Videotex Technical Experts Panel to identify market needs, and to ensure complete technical agreement between the task group and the panel. The Task Group X3L2.1 would then present the draft standard to its parent ANSI committee (X3L2) for approval, who then would forward it to the full X3 committee for review and approval. Following a four-month public comment period, the draft could then become an official American National Standard.

The status as of December 1982 was as follows.

June 18, 1982–The joint ANSI/CSA Task Group unanimously adopted the standard, which was then named "Videotex/Teletext Presentation Level Protocol Syntax (North American PLPS)," dated June 18, 1982.

June 22, 1982–The VTEP agreed to send the NAPLPS (6/18/82) to Study Groups A and B as its official recommendation.

July 20, 1982–Study Groups A and B unanimously approved NAPLPS (6/18/82) with ammendments as the official U.S.A. position in CCITT. (On the same day, Canada officially adopted NAPLPS [21] as the preliminary standard in Canada.) Also approved were two other U.S.A. contributions to CCITT, which were referred to as the "win-win" proposal since they offered a solution which preserved the coding of all recognized schemes. These two documents (which are not presented in this paper) were titled "Coding Requirements For An International Videotex Recommendation" (Study Group VIII Contribution No. 79), and "Proposed Videotex Recommendation For a Unified Presentation Layer" (Study Group VIII Contribution No. 80).

August 13, 1982–U.S. State Department (Study Group B) formally submitted NAPLPS (8/1/82) and the "win-win" proposal to CCITT in Geneva [13]-[15].

September 1, 1982–The ANSI X3L2 technical committee modified and approved NAPLPS, and agreed to forward it to the full X3 committee for balloting. This draft proposed American National Standard (dpANS) was dated October 1, 1982 [9].

December 1982–Following approval by the X3 committee, the ANSI secretariat announced that the four month public comment period would begin on Janauary 21, 1983 and end May 21, 1983.

Due to the close official relationship of X3L2.1 and its counterpart subcommittee in CSA, the American National Standard and the CSA standard are expected to be technically and editorially identical. Since the U.S. Study Groups A and B have also agreed on the draft standard, a North American Videotex and Teletex Standard at the presentation layer could be achieved in 1983.

To further this optimistic tone, consider that in parallel to the ANSI process mentioned above, the goal of U.S. Study Groups A and B is to have the North American (U.S./Canada) Standard included as part of the 1984 Recommendation by the CCITT Plenary Assembly in Geneva. If this can be accomplished, a Worldwide Videotex Standard will have been achieved.

REFERENCES

[1] "Bell System Videotex Standard Presentation Level Protocol," AT&T Co., May 1981.

[2] H. G. Bown, C. D. O'Brien, W. Sawchuk, and J. R. Storey, "Picture description instructions (PDI) for the Telidon videotex systems," Dep. Commun., Canada, CRC Tech. Note 699, Nov. 1979.

[3] "Status report of the Graphics Standards Planning Committee," Comput. Graphics, Quart. Rep. SIGGRAPH-ACM, vol. 13, Aug. 1979.

[4] "North American Broadcast Teletext Specification," CBS TV Network, June 1981.

[5] "European interactive videotex service display aspects and transmission coding," CEPT Sub-Working Group CD/SE Rec. T/CD 6-1, June 1981.

[6] "SMPTE recommended practice, specifications for safe action and safe title areas, test pattern for television systems," Soc. Motion Picture and TV Eng., RP 27.3, 1972.

[7] "American National Standard code for information interchange," ANSI Standard X3.4-1977.

[8] "American National Standard code for extension techniques for use with the 7-bit coded character set of American National Standard code for information interchange," ANSI Standard X3.41-1974.

[9] "Videotex/Teletext Presentation Level Protocol Syntax (North American PLPS)," ANSI draft proposed American National Standard X3L2/82-135, Oct. 1, 1982.

[10] "Characteristics of Teletext systems," Document 11/5001-E, CCIR Rep. 957, Oct. 1981.

[11] "International information exchange for interactive videotex," CCITT Rec. S.100, Nov. 1980.

[12] "Videotex service," CCITT Rec. F.300, Nov. 1980.

[13] "Videotex/Teletext Presentation Level Protocol Syntax (North American PLPS)," U.S.A. Contrib. to CCITT Study Group VIII, No. 81, Aug. 1982.

[14] "Coding requirements for an international videotex recommendation," U.S.A. Contrib. to CCITT Study Group VIII, No. 79, Aug. 1982.

[15] "Proposed videotex recommendation for a unified presentation layer," U.S.A. Contrib. to CCITT Study Group VIII, No. 80, Aug. 1982.

[16] "Telecommunications regulatory service," Dep. Commun., Canada, Broadcast Specification BS-14, June 1981.

[17] "Data processing—7-bit coded character set for information interchange," ISO Draft Int. Standard 646, Mar. 1982.

[18] "Code extension techniques for use with the ISO 7-bit coded character set," ISO Standard 2022, 1973.

[19] "Information processing—ISO 7-bit and 8-bit coded character sets—Code extension techniques," ISO Draft International Standard 2022.2, Feb. 1982.

[20] "Data processing—open systems interconnection basic reference model," ISO Draft Proposed Standard 7498, Feb. 1982.

[21] "Videotex/Teletext Presentation Level Protocol Syntax (North American PLPS)," CSA Preliminary Standard T500, Aug. 1982.

[22] Commun. Res. Centre, Dep. Commun., Canada, Tech. Note 709E, Feb. 1982.

Joe D. Wetherington (S'66–M'68) was born in Miami, FL, on October 30, 1942. Following three years in the U.S. Navy, he received the B.S. degree in electrical engineering from the University of Florida, Gainesville, in 1968.

His first assignment was with the Government Systems Division of Western Electric, where he worked on the Sentinel and Safeguard antiballistic missile systems, doing design and development work on the computer, communications, and missile remote launch systems. In 1973, he transferred to Southern Bell and helped form the corporate communications group which developed and implemented the internal computer/communications systems. His current activities began in 1978 when he transferred to AT&T corporate headquarters to help plan the Bell System home information system. In 1979, he was the Trial Manager for the Electronic Directory test in Albany, NY, and served as the Project Manager of the joint AT&T/Knight-Ridder Newspapers videotex trial in Florida, from 1979 to 1981. His responsibilities included the development of the terminals, the network design, and trial administration. Since 1979 he has represented AT&T in the national and international standards arena, in CCITT, EIA, ISO, and ANSI, and was the key architect in the development of the Bell System's videotex standards strategy. This task also included the development responsibility for AT&T's PLP. He was instrumental in initiating the joint ANSI/CSA standards activity for videotex and teletext, culminating in the acceptance of NAPLPS as the draft American National Standard, and as part of the official U.S. State Department recommendation to CCITT for an International Videotex Standard.

A Survey of Terminal Protocols

F. Magnee

University of Liège, Department of Systems and Automatic Control, Institut d'Electricité Montéfiore B28, Sart Tilman, B-4000-Liège, Belgium

A. Endrizzi

Commission of the European Communities, Joint Research Center, Ispra Establishment, I-21020 – Ispra, Italy

J. Day

Digital Technology Incorporated, 302 East John Street, Champaign, Illinois 61820, USA

The Virtual Terminal approach has been used first by the ARPANET in the U.S. In the last few years, the problem of defining Virtual Terminal Protocols has been approached by several international organizations such as EIN, Euronet, IFIP and by national organizations such as the Belgian University Network, the German PIX Network, the French Cyclades Network and INFOREP (French' user association'). Associated manufacturers have also presented a proposal. Till now, an internationally accepted Virtual Terminal Protocol has not yet emerged.

The aim of this paper is to compare different protocols. It is divided into four main parts: 1. Presentation of the relationships between Virtual Terminal Protocol and network architecture. 2. Analysis of the different virtual terminal model. 3. Analysis of the set of primitives intended to data structure definition and management. 4. Introduction to the synchronization mechanisms of the protocol.

Keywords: Heterogeneous computer networks, protocols, terminal protocol, virtual terminal protocol.

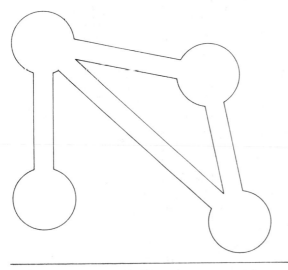

© North-Holland Publishing Company
Computer Networks 3 (1979) 299–314

1. Introduction

1.1. Terminal Protocols

One of the main goals of a computer network is to give access to the services offered by the different teleprocessing systems available through the network. Herein we shall be interested in the interaction between an operator at his terminal and an interactive application connected to the network.

Everyone knows the compatibility problems related to the heterogeneity characterizing the terminal market.

Francis N. Magnee was born in Rocourt, Belgium, in 1952. He received the Electronics Engineer's degree from the University of Liège, Liège, Belgium, in 1975. Up to now, he has been participating in a group of research on computer networks attached to the University of Liège and managed by Professor A. Danthine. His main interest is in computer network protocol design.

A. Endrizzi was born in Bolzano (Italy–1942). He received a degree in Nuclear Engineering from Politecnico di Milano in 1968. Since then he is working at the Joint Research Center Ispra Establishment. He was involved with the design of interactive languages for continuous system modelling and relational data bases for computer graphics. He is at present project leader of the European Informatics Networks and consultant for Euronet higher level protocols for which the JRC plays the role of Reference and Test Center.

John Day is a Senior Analyst with Digital Technology Incorporated in Champaign, Illinois, a network research and development firm spun off from the University of Illinois. He has been an active researcher into protocol specification, distributed data bases, and higher level protocols. He is also rapporteur for formal description techniques for ISO TC97/SC16/WG1 on Open Systems Interconnection. He has an MS in EE from the University of Illinois and is a member of ACM, IEEE, and AAAS.

This work was sponsored by the Commission of the European Communities within the framework of the research contract N° 881-78-06.

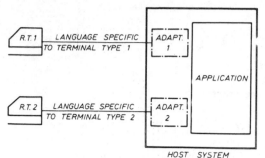

Fig. 1. R.T. = Real Terminal, ADAPT. = Adaptation Module.

In a conventional star-like time sharing system (i.e. a system made of local and remote terminals connected to one single host system), an adaptation is performed which allows the host system to explicitly support each terminal type (fig. 1).

In an heterogeneous computer network environment, the heterogeneity problem will be very likely much more difficult to live with. As a matter of fact, one can expect that a wider set of terminal types will access a variety of host systems. In such an environment, it is no longer practical to implement in each host system a set of modules performing the adequate specific adaptation. Such an approach potentially requires the implementation of (m * n) adaptation modules where m represents the number of hosts and n the number of terminal kinds connected to each host.

Terminal-oriented protocols are designed to reduce this "m * n" problem to a manageable size by establishing conventions for handling all the terminals on the network. Two basic approaches to terminal support in an heterogeneous network have emerged.

1.1.1. Virtual Terminal Approach

The first approach will consist in defining a standard language for conversation between terminal and application. Such a language will be used whenever a terminal and an application must interact via the network. In this case, each side of the connection (i.e., the terminal side and the application one) will be provided with a translation module intended to the adaptation to the standard language (fig. 2).

The primitives of the standard language together with the different mechanisms are generally called the Virtual Terminal Protocol (V.T.P.).

The support of terminals based on a standard language approach is more economic in a computer network environment as far as the number of adaptation modules to be developed is concerned. This point is illustrated in the fig. 3.

Moreover the support of one new type of terminal will require the implementation of one more adaptation module when the standard language approach is used. The other method will require the realization of m adaptation modules.

1.1.2. Parametric Approach

A second approach attempts to parameterize the

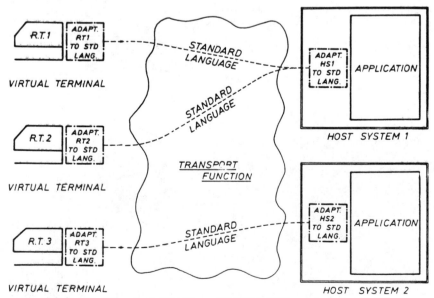

Fig. 2. R.T. = Real Terminal, ADAPT . . . TO STD LANG. = Adaptation Module.

NUMBER OF ADAPTATION MODULES	'STAR-LIKE' NETWORK .1 HOST SYSTEM .n TERM [n»]	HETEROGENEOUS NETWORK .m HOST S. [m>1] .n TERM [n»]
SPECIFIC ADAPTATION	$M1 = n$	$M'1 = n * m$
STANDARD LANGUAGE	$M2 = n+1$	$M'2 = n+m$
CONCLUSIONS	$M1 < M2$	$M'2 < M'1$

Fig. 3.

differences between terminals. The protocol is used by the host to set the various terminal parameters to the requested values. This parametric approach has been pursued primarily by the national PTT's (Postal, Telegraphy and Telephony Ministries) within the CCITT and in the U.S. by Telenet.

The CCITT [6] has approved protocols to define a Packet Assembler/Disassembler (PAD). They have been designated X.28 and X.29. Recommendation X.28 defines the protocol for use between the start/stop mode DTE (the real terminal) and the PAD. Recommendation X.29 defines the protocol for use between the PAD and the packet-mode DTE (PDTE) (the host system). There is also a recommendation X.3 which defines the PAD.

The Interactive Terminal Interface (ITI) [20] used by Telenet is very similar to X.29. There are two major differences between the two. First, Telenet supports a much more extensive set of parameters. Second, Telenet's ITI supports what is called a virtual terminal mode. This virtual terminal supports only a very primitive terminal. The only functions provided by ITI are go-ahead for half-duplex operation, an interrupt process, an abort output and a break.

This parametric approach is most successful when the primary purpose is to handle existing terminals. The PAD provides a basic, transparent mode of operation, which places most of the burden of terminal handling on the PDTE or the host. The PAD parameters allow the PDTE to shift some of this burden to the PAD. As the PAD is used to support more and more complex terminals, the number of parameters increases rapidly. X.29 has 12 parameters; an early version of Telenet's ITI had 20-some parameters and has since grown to more than 50. The PAD protocols do not allow PAD to PAD communication and it is unlikely that it will allow the PDTE's to use the PAD protocols for communication between themselves. However, symmetrical operation has been mentioned as a point for further study. Many of these problems can be avoided by using the virtual terminal approach.

This parametric approach will not be discussed in more details in the following paragraphs of the present paper. More details on this topic can be found in [9].

1.2. Virtual Terminal Protocol Proposals

The problem of defining a Virtual Terminal has been first approached in ARPANET. This protocol is known as the Telnet Protocol [1,8]. The problem of the Virtual Terminal Protocol has been considered by several international organizations, such as EIN [16, 17], Euronet [11], IFIP [12] and by national organizations such as the Belgian University Network [4], the German PIX Network [18,19], the French Cyclades Network [21] and the French' user association' INFOREP [14,15]. Associated manufacturers (CII, ICL, SIEMENS) have presented a proposal too [2].

The aim of this paper is to present a synthesis between some of those different proposals and to underline the capabilities and the functions of each of them. The analysis has been restricted to the following proposals:

— Manufacturers' proposal (CII, ICL, SIEMENS): Virtual Device Protocol [2]. This proposal defines a virtual terminal capable of supporting sophisticated classes of terminals, such as the multiforms class. This V.T. is provided with an extensive set of attributes. It is able to store multiple forms and can be provided with different auxiliary devices (e.g. a printer).
— Belgian University Network: Virtual Terminal Protocol [4].
— Euronet: Data Entry Virtual Terminal Protocol [11].
— IFIP Working Group 6.1: International Network Working Group Protocol 91 [12].
— INFOREP: Protocole Appareil Virtuel type écran [15].
— European Informatics Network: Virtual Terminal Protocol [16].

These last five proposals are rather similar. They intend to define a classical display V.T. with field and attribute capabilities. Nevertheless the definition can be easily extended to cover more sophisticated terminals (e.g. as far as the attribute capabilities are concerned).

— PIX Network: Virtual Terminal Protocol [18,19]. The capabilities offered with the PIX.VTP are quite similar to those of the five previous proposals. But the definition of this protocol is based on the concept of the "Communication variables" which is a general concept for application oriented protocol definition.

— ARPANET: Telnet Protocol [1]. This protocol defines an elementary terminal working on a line data structure with neither field nor attribute capabilities. However it does support a sophisticated echoing facility. This V.T. has been very successful within the ARPANET and is quite adequate for most ARPANET applications.

The present paper is divided into four main sections. The first one is intended to describe the services offered by the transport service which the VTP is built on. It also discusses how VTP's fit in the milieu of computer communications (and more specifically with respect to the ISO architecture). The second section describes the different VT architectures. The third section analyzes the primitives of the standard language as far as the definition and the management of the data structure are concerned. In the last section the synchronization mechanisms of the different proposals are analyzed in detail. So it is important to point out that this paper does not analyze the interface between the real terminal and the adaptation module at the terminal side.

2. Virtual Terminal Protocol and Network Architecture

Application oriented protocols, and more specifically the Virtual Terminal Protocol, are built upon a transport function which provides a set of transport services. The nature of that transport function can be very varied. As an example, it can be implemented by means of an end-to-end transport station at each side. The main point is the transport function guarantees that the virtual link [7] on which the VTP primitives are exchanged presents an adequate set of characteristics.

On the previous figure, we represent as "*Virtual Terminal Protocol* process" the whole intelligence which is necessary for translating to the standard language and for implementing the different VTP mechanisms.

In each VTP proposal, the virtual link is assumed to be a full-duplex connection on which are exchanged:

— normal messages: the transport of these messages is supposed to be performed without any loss or

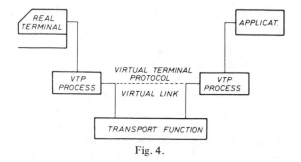

Fig. 4.

duplication of messages. Also sequencing is preserved.

With the exception of the manufacturers' VTP [2], the proposals assume that associated the virtual link is a secondary channel which allows the exchange of:

— out-of-band messages: these messages are transported with no error and it is assumed that there is neither loss nor duplication. This channel is completely independent from the previous one. It is essentially intended to allow the transport of priority [4,11,12] messages of a short length (either a few bytes long [4] or two bytes long [15] or even just one byte long [11,12,16,18]). It must be pointed out that no sequencing is assumed (except for the proposal [12]).

Since the design of these VTP's, there has been much activity by the International Organization for Standardization (ISO) in the development of a standard networking architecture for interconnecting heterogeneous ("open" in the terminology of ISO) sytems [13]. This work which is being done by ISO/TC97/SC16 (Open Systems Interconnection) has defined a seven layer architecture. The first four layers (physical, link, network and transport) of this architecture are concerned with the reliable transfer of data. The upper three layers (session, presentation and application) are the domain of higher protocols and are of concern here. Layer 4 (the transport layer) corresponds to the transport service in the ARPANET or CYCLADES. However, the VTP's described in this paper incorporate functions found in both the session and presentation layers. Most of the functions of VTP are concerned with creating and maintaining the data structure. These transformation functions are considered to be functions of the presentation layer. The functions of dialog control are considered to be session layer functions. The VTP designs described here are basically sound although they must be partitioned to correspond to the SC16 architecture. As yet no one has proposed a VTP consistent with the SC16 architecture.

3. Virtual Terminal Architecture

Several different models have been proposed for organizing a VTP. In this section we compare the overall organization of the different VTP's [9].

In some VT models [2,11,15] that have been proposed, the VT is considered from the point-of-view of the application. The virtual terminal is seen as a combination of the real terminal and whatever adaptation functions are required to make the real terminal appears as a virtual terminal from the host. At the host there is an adaptation function which converts the virtual terminal format into the local representation expected by the application. This model is asymmetrical. If the application needs to determine the current disposition of the data structure, a command must be sent to it and a reply must be generated. In order to prevent the reply from being invalidated before it is delivered by subsequent input from the user, this model relies heavily on an alternating mode to control contention for the VT. Some asynchrony is allowed by this model. The alternating (half duplex, see § 5.1) mode is seen by the designers as the primary mode of usage. All input from the terminal is displayed locally.

Another VTP model [19] is based on the "shared communication variables". The essence of this approach is to transplant the "single site" model into the network environment. In this VTP, each side takes turn accessing a single virtual data structure. This protocol is able to give the illusion of a single data structure by having a copy of the data structure at each site and restricting access to only one user at a time. This approach cannot support the asynchro-nous, full-duplex dialogues found in many systems.

In some VTP models [4,12,16], each site has a VT which represents that side's view of the state of the VT session. This model explicitly recognizes the asynchronies present in the network. Input from local user is written on the local data structure and transmitted over the network to be entered in the remote data structure. In asynchronous (or free-running, see § 5.1) dialog mode, the contents of the two data structures may be different due to concurrency of the applications and variable network delays. The same data is written on both, but the order may differ. This "free-running" dialog mode can provide greater efficiency by allowing messages to be sent at any time. This model is symmetrical and thus can easily support terminal-to-terminal and process-to-process configurations. Control of echo is not provided.

In Telnet [8], a VTP connection is seen as two virtual terminals with the keyboard of one connected to the presentation unit (or display) of the other and vice versa (fig. 5). This model takes a symmetric view of terminals and processes. A local terminal or process maps it's representation of input to its virtual terminal keyboard. The virtual representation is sent to the presentation unit of the other virtual terminal where it is mapped to the representation of the remote application. Each virtual terminal represents the state of the data structure as seen from the point-of-view of its associated partner. This model allows for considerable asynchrony between the two systems. In some applications, the information "displayed" by the two VT's may differ for a time. In other cases, the information may differ radically for long periods of time. In the Telnet protocol, echoing is controlled by means of a negotiation sequence [8]. The echoing facility in Telnet is essentially based on the observation that hosts which supply interactive

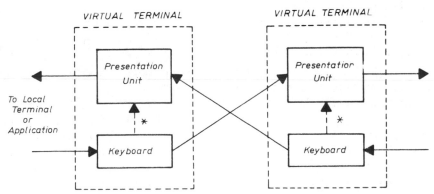

Fig. 5. * Dotted Arrows Note Optimal Echo Control (figure after J. Day [9]).

applications are optimized either for terminals which provide their own echoing or for terminals which do not, but not for both terminal types. So a set of echoing conventions which prevents an application for changing echo mode would be excessively restrictive. Servers would be burdened with users which are in the "wrong" echo mode, in which they might not have to be, and users would be burdened with remembering proper echoing modes. Those reasons lead to include in Telnet a facility for negotiating the echoing mode (see § 5.2).

4. Data Structure Management

4.1. Data Structure Organization

In the most general case, data which are exchanged on the virtual link are structured as a two-dimensional array (y lines constituted of x positions). The analogy between the data structure and the screen of a real terminal is obvious [4,11]. The data structure is generally referred to as the "virtual terminal page". Except for the Telnet protocol (see § 1.2) that page can further be divided into fields. A field is a set of contiguous positions sharing a common attribute. The set of available attributes allows one to evaluate the complexity of the data structure the V.T. is able to handle.

Table 1 gives a survey of the capabilities of each V.T. The terminology used in that table is defined in Appendix A.

It is obvious that the attributes of the V.T. do not deeply differ from the attributes available on the real terminals available in the market. Nevertheless, the search for an abstraction form prevails as a major

objective in the definition of some attributes [17]. For example, the virtual terminals are provided with the capability of contrasted display (generally, two levels of contrast are defined, i.e. normal and emphasis). In the V.T. definition, there is no indication about the implementation of the emphasis display. It is strictly a local decision (e.g. mapping in reverse video or one of two levels of brightness) which is not covered in the V.T. definition.

4.2. Data Structure Management Primitives

A position within the page of the data structure is modified by means of a pointer. As the data structure is a two dimensional array, the pointer will be a vector of two components (x, y). The current value of the pointer gives the next character position.

When the virtual terminal handles a page data structure with no field concept, the value (x_0, y_0) of the pointer modifies the x_0th position within the y_0th line of the data structure.

When the data structure consists of several fields, the values (x_0, y_0) of the pointer can take two quite different meanings:

– either it modifies the x_0th position within the y_0th line (as above). This position will be generally the x_1th position within the y_1th field of the data structure (as one field does not generally correspond to one line);

– or it modifies the x_0th position within the y_0th field [2,17]. This position will be generally the x_1th position within the y_1th line of the data structure. In this case, we consider that a "primary data structure" [17] constituted by an array of lines of X positions is obsolete. But a "secondary data structure" [17] is considered as relevant. This

Table 1
–: the feature is not available on the virtual terminal, ×: the feature is available on the virtual terminal. Note: these attributes are not applicable to Telnet Protocol.

Proposals	Field access control							
	Alpha char. access	Light-pen action	Light-pen pickable	Next form	Not addressable	Not printable	Not transmittable	Numerical access
Manufacturers'/VDP	–	–	–	×	×	×	×	×
BUN/VTP	–	×	×	–	–	–	–	×
Euronet/DEVTP	–	–	–	–	–	–	–	–
IFIP W.G. 6.1/INWG 91	–	–	–	–	–	–	–	–
Inforep/PAV	–	–	–	–	–	–	–	×
EIN/VTP	×	×	×	–	–	–	–	×
PIX/VTP	–	–	–	–	–	–	–	–

PRIMARY DATA STRUCTURE → SECONDARY DATA STRUCTURE

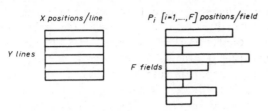

Fig. 6. (figure after Schicker and Duenki [12]).

secondary data structure is considrered as a sequence of F fields, each of them contains P_i ($i =$ 1, ..., F) positions (fig. 6).

It is clear that the former meaning of the pointer values is closely related to the existence of the screen for visualizing the field structure. So it can possibly lead to an easier mapping between the data structure and the screen coordinates. However, the latter approach is conceptually more attractive because it leads to complete independence between the data structure (which is a concept relevant as far as both the terminal and the application are concerned) and the screen (which is only a concept local to the terminal side).

The data structure management primitives can be classified into the following categories:

- *primitives for addressing the data structure:* set of primitives for moving the pointer within the data structure;
- *primitives for initializing the data structure:* allows to abandon the current data structure and to replace it by a new one which initially consists in a page full of NULL characters (displayed as blanks),
- *primitives for clearing the contents of the data structure:* the contents of the data structure are cleared but the current data structure organization is preserved. The operation of clearing can be related either to the whole data structure or just a part of it;
- *primitives for creating a data structure:* set of primitives used either for the definition of the data structure or for the fulfilling of the fields of the data structure.

Table 2 gives an overview of the different data structure management primitives available with each proposal. The precise meaning of those primitives is explained in Appendix B.

As explained in the appendix B, the NEXT LINE function is considered as an addressing primitive. However it should be mentioned that in some proposals [12], the NEXT LINE primitive is also used as an initialization primitive when the data structure consists of a single line. One can wonder if it is reasonable to perform the initialization function by means of a NEXT LINE primitive in a line data structure (since an INIT primitive already exists). As a matter of fact, the NEXT LINE primitive has a fundamentally different meaning in both cases:

- in a page environment, the pointer is set to the beginning of the next line and the previous lines within the data structure still remain addressable (e.g. accessible for the operator);
- in a line environment, the pointer is set to the beginning of the next line (i.e. the next data structure) and the previous lines (i.e. the previous data structures which have been filled in) are no longer accessible.

All the functions available on the real terminal keyboards are not exchanged on the virtual link

Protected access	Required entry	Selectable	Field adjustm. control		Field visualization control			Display control	
			Right justified (space Fill)	Right justified (Zero Fill)	Contrasted ⟨n⟩	Cursive face	Invisible	APL characters	IA5 extended
X	X	X	X	X	4	–	X	–	–
X	–	–	–	–	2	–	X	–	–
X	–	–	–	–	2	–	X	–	–
X	–	–	–	–	2	–	X	–	–
X	X	–	X	–	2	–	X	–	–
X	–	–	X	–	7	–	X	–	–
X	–	–	X	–	2	X	–	X	X

Table 2
−: the feature is not available on the virtual terminal, ×: the feature is available on the virtual terminal. Note: these functions are not applicable to Telnet Protocol.

Proposals	Primitives for addressing the data structure							
	Absolute ⟨x⟩⟨y⟩	Absolute field ⟨n⟩	Differential ⟨dx⟩⟨dy⟩	Differential ⟨dx⟩	Differential ⟨dy⟩	Home	Next field	Next horizontal tabstop
Manufacturers'/VDP	X	X	−	X	X	−	−	−
BUN/VTP	X	−	X	−	−	X	−	X
Euronet/DEVTP	X	−	−	−	−	−	−	−
IFIP W.G. 6.1/INWG 91	X	−	−	−	−	−	−	−
Inforep/PAV	X	−	−	X	−	−	−	−
EIN/VTP	X	−	X	X	−	−	X	−
PIX/VTP	X	−	−	−	−	−	−	−

between both remote VTP processes. So no VTP proposal is provided with backward sequential addressing functions (e.g. *BACKWARD HORIZONTAL TAB* – BHT, *PREVIOUS UNPROTECTED FIELD* – PUF). The reasons for excluding such backward functions are the following ones:

— as far as the human operator is concerned, BHT and PUF essentially provide the operator with a facility of moving back within the structure and correct possible typing mistakes. Such manipulations generally have only local significance and therefore do not appear in the data stream flowing on the virtual link;

— while the human operator may seem to behave in somewhat erratic way, the application can be considered as a much more structured process. So it is reasonable to assume that such backward addressing functions (as BHT and PUF) will not be used when the application builds a data structure.

The differential addressing primitives will appear as an interesting generalization of UP, DOWN, RIGHT, LEFT functions of many real terminals, because it allows multicharacter displacements in either the vertical or the horizontal direction.

As far as the data structure management primitives are concerned, it is certain that some primitives (e.g. selective unprotected field clearing) are introduced because of the personal experience of the designer. Anyway in the design of that set of primitives, a balance must be adopted between:

— the "intelligence" of the VTP process. The addition of functions causes an increase in the complexity of the process;

— the "bandwidth" of the virtual link. A restricted set of primitives must lead to use of a virtual link with a very large bandwidth.

4.3. Classes of Virtual Terminals

As mentioned in the introduction, the proposals [4,11,12,14,16,19] describe virtual terminals which are inspired by the general purpose data entry terminals (e.g. protection, contrast capabilities).

There exists such a disparity between unsophisticated real terminals (e.g. the conventional TTY) and more elaborate ones (e.g. data entry terminals) that one cannot really expect to see one single virtual terminal emerge which could satisfactorily cover the whole range of real terminals:

— if the virtual terminal is modelled after somewhat elaborate real terminals (such a described heretofore), the adaptation of simple real terminals to the virtual terminal will be impossible at a reasonable cost;

— if the virtual is modelled after simple real terminals [8], then the full range of capabilities offered on elaborate real terminals will not be taken advantage of.

In order to reconcile the need for an economical adaptation to the virtual terminal with an efficient

Next line	Next unprotected field	Start of line	Primitives for initializing the data structure Init	Primitives for clearing the data structure		Unprotected field clear from current address / from specified address to specified address		Primitives for creating a data structure		
				Clear	Current unprotected field clear	from current address	from specified address	Attribute	Character repetition	Delete attribute
X	–	–	X	X	X	–	–	X	X	–
X	X	–	X	X	–	–	–	X	–	X
X	X	–	X	X	–	–	–	X	–	X
X	X	X	X	X	–	–	–	X	X	–
X	X	–	X	X	X	X	X	X	X	–
X	–	–	X	X	–	–	–	X	–	–
–	–	–	X	X	–	–	–	X	–	–

utilization of real terminal capabilities, several virtual terminal standard classes have been defined.

The class of the virtual terminal essentially depends on the complexity of the data structure which the virtual terminal is able to handle. Five virtual terminal classes appear from the proposals:

1. The native mode V.T. [1,4,11,12,14,16] (also called real terminal mode): in this elementary mode, no adaptation of the real terminal is performed. Such a mode can be used to support exotic real terminals;

2. The scroll-mode V.T. [1,4,11,12,16,19]: this V.T. handles a homogeneous one-dimensional data structure (line). Homogeneous means that the line may not be subdivided into fields. The scroll-mode V.T. can be seen as a TTY like terminal, but is provided with a buffer capability;

3. The page-mode V.T. [2,4,12,16,19]: this V.T. handles a homogeneous two-dimensional array of Y lines with X positions. This page-mode V.T. is typically used in a dialogue with a sophisticated editor. It should be mentioned that in [4], the page-mode V.T. is provided with the protected/unprotected field capability too. So we can see here that the definition of the capabilities of the page-mode V.T. can be influenced either:

– by the current situation in the terminal market. If we accept the idea that the protection capabilities are available on most VDU real terminals, it seems natural to define the page mode V.T. as provided with such a facility or

– by the characteristics of the data structure handled by the applications. As a matter of fact, a lot of applications deal with a homogeneous two-dimensional data structure (e.g. sophisticated text editors).

4. The simple data-entry V.T. [4,11,12,14,16,19]: this V.T. is provided with a whole set of capabilities defined in various proposals, which can be characterized as a V.T. with contrast and protection facilities without storage capability.

5. The multi-form data-entry V.T. [2]: this V.T. is provided whith a whole set of facilities such as defined in [2]. It is a "super data entry V.T." with storage capability.

In [15], there is no explicit concept of V.T. classes. In that proposal, there is no strict obligation for implementing the whole set of capabilities of the data entry V.T. Moreover any subset of the V.T. may theoretically be used (via an adequate negotiation, see § 4.2).

5. VTP Fundamental Mechanisms

5.1. Data Exchange Synchronization Mechanism

Some proposals [1,4,12,16] assume that the exchange of data on the virtual link between both VTP processes can be organized according to different modes (generally called the data flow mode):

— either alternating data flow mode. In this mode, each communication partner alternately receives the right to send data from the other partner. When one of the communicating processes gives the right to send data, we generally say in short that it gives the turn to its partner. Consequently data may never be in transit between both remote VTP processes in the two opposite directions simultaneously. So the virtual link can be seen as a half duplex connection;

— or free running data flow mode. In this mode, each communication partner leaves the other perfectly free to send data at any time. Data may thus be in transit on the virtual link in the two directions at the same time. The virtual link can therefore be seen as a full duplex channel.

5.2. Negotiation Phase

Application needs, and V.T. characteristics, are quite varied. While some applications require a complex data structure (e.g. a two dimensional array with formatting capabilities), many others work with an elementary line data structure. Similar variety exists at the terminal side. This has been the basic motivation for defining several virtual terminal standard classes (see § 4.3). The consequence of such a variety is that the exchange of data is only possible if both communicating entities first agree upon a common set of capabilities.

5.2.1. Negotiable Characteristics

In the § 4.3, it appears that the most important negotiable characteristic is the virtual terminal type (except in [15]). The importance of the V.T. type mainly results from its global nature. Reaching an agreement about the V.T. type implies that the whole set of individual characteristics (e.g. attribute capabilities, set of addressing functions) which take part in its definition is accepted. In the proposal [15], each individual capability is to be negotiated and there is no global concept of standard V.T. type.

Beside the global terminal type, several individual characteristics may be negotiated.

We can mention the most important ones:

— the data flow mode. Generally [4,12,16], the negotiation is not only intended to select either free running or alternating mode. It is also responsible for indicating which side (e.g. application or terminal) will first own the turn if alternating mode is selected;

— the dimensions of the page. The virtual terminal type does not imply the dimensions of the data structure (number of positions per line, number of lines per page). Those characteristics must be negotiated apart;

— the character set (e.g. IA5. APL). The alphabet IA5 is systematically provided.

— echo. In [1], echoing is controlled by means of a negotiation sequence which allows echoing to be done by none, one or both VTP process (see chapter 3.

5.2.2. Negotiation Schemes

Two basic negotiation mechanisms have been found in the VTP's discussed here: the one used by Telnet [1] and the one found in European VTP's [11, 12,16,17].

As far as the Telnet protocol is concerned, besides negotiating whether or not a particular option is to be in effect, the mechanism allows one to specify, when appropriate, which side is to perform the function. For example, a user may negotiate the Echo option and specify whether echoing is to be done locally or remotely with respect to the initiator of the negotiation. The negotiation mechanism can be initiated by either side.

Four commands support option negotiation (DO, DONT, WILL and WONT). WILL ⟨option name⟩ is sent by either party to indicate the party's willingness to begin performing the option. DO ⟨option name⟩ and DONT ⟨option name⟩ are the positive and negative acknowledgements. Similarly, DO ⟨option name⟩ is sent to request that the other party begin performing the option. WILL ⟨option name⟩ and WONT ⟨option name⟩ are the positive and negative acknowledgements [1]. Each option specification defines the conditions for terminating the negotiation of that option.

As far as the European VTP's are concerned, the negotiation mechanism is somewhat different. A negotiated function is not seen as occuring at one side or the other. The function is either performed by the VTP process or it is not. Each VTP process supports the function for its local user wether terminal or application.

In the European proposals, we find two different negotiation schemes.

1. The Asymmetric Scheme [11,12,15]. This scheme has been conceived to be used essentially in conversation between a terminal and an application. The exchange of primitives of the mechanism is depicted in figure 7.

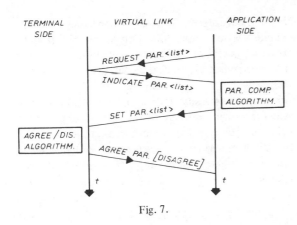

Fig. 7.

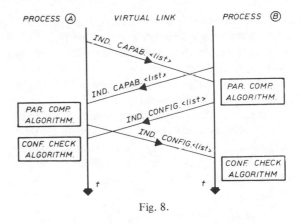

Fig. 8.

The VTP process at the application side initiates the dialogue. It asks the VTP process at the terminal side for its characteristics. In figure 7, this demand is represented by the primitive REQUEST. PAR. ⟨list⟩. The VTP process at the terminal side answers by means of the primitive INDICATE. PAR. ⟨list⟩. The list contains the values of the parameters the application side required in REQUEST. PAR. This list allows the VTP process at the application side to compute the parameters which will be used for the communication. The results of the computation process is transmitted in the list of the SET. PAR. primitive. The VTP process at the terminal side finally indicates its agreement (resp. disagreement) by sending an AGREE. PAR. (resp. DISAGREE. PAR).

If the application is not conceived to adapt, there is obviously no negotiation phase proper. In such a case, the exchanges are restricted to SET. PAR. ⟨list⟩ and AGREE. (DISAGREE). PAR.

This scheme is called "asymmetric scheme" in the sense that only one of the two communicating process is responsible for the computation of the parameters.

2. The Symmetric Scheme [17]. With this scheme there is no distinction between the terminal side and the application one. The exchange of the primitives of this negotiation scheme is depicted in fig. 8.

At the beginning, each partner sends to the other the list of its own characteristics (IND. CAPAB. ⟨list⟩).Then each partner has to analyze individually both lists of characteristics in order to find a common set of parameters. The coherence of the results of the computation process is checked by means of the IND. CONFIG. ⟨list⟩ primitives.

This scheme is called "symmetric scheme" because both communicating processes are responsible for the computation process.

As far as the asymmetric negotiation scheme is concerned, the algorithms of computation of the communication parameters can be locally defined. Each application connected to the network can be provided with its own algorithm. Thus algorithms can be different from application to application. This does not lead to any difficulty since only one side is responsible for the computation.

Such a negotiation scheme works quite well except in a homogeneous communication (i.e. a communication between either two terminals or two applications). If two terminals must negotiate, there is a deadlock situation. We have to decide which side is to compute the parameters. Some people suggest adopting a distinction between both sides based on the concept of called/calling process. But the adequacy of such a criterion is questionable because of the potential occurence of a contention situation. If two applications must negotiate via VTP processes, there classically exists two computation algorithms and those algorithms are not necessarily compatible. In

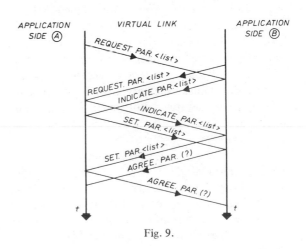

Fig. 9.

such a situation, two behaviours can be adopted:
- either we decide to allow one process to compute the parameters. In this case, the problem of choosing a criterion is still relevant;
- or we allow a double exchange of negotiation primitives (see fig. 9). In this case, both sides of the connection will compute a parameter set and check the coherency of the results with its partner algorithm.

5.3. Attention Handling Mechanism

5.3.1. Asynchronous Attention Handling

In a computer network environment, the connection between a terminal and an application is realized via a transport service (e.g. implemented by means of a packet switching network). In such an environment, the delays introduced by that transport service are no longer neglectable. So in order to allow a more efficient cooperation between the operator and the application, we must introduce some extra mechanisms.

In some special situations, a process must be able to notify its partner of an abnormal situation as quickly as possible (e.g. to spare time for data processing).

This is the reason why we introduced a secondary out-of-band channel when we defined the concept of the virtual link between both VTP processes. At the VTP level, we define the primitives "asynchronous attention". Those primitives are priority messages exchanged on the out-of-band channel.

The meaning of an attention condition can be defined:
- either at the VTP level. An example is the PLEASE attention condition defined in [11]. This primitive is used when one of the communicating processes wants to gain the turn (see § 4.1) which is hold by its partner.
- either at a higher level (convention between the operator and the application [11,12,15]). In this case, the only job of the VTP process is to transmit the information to the local user process, which has the responsibility for interpreting the information.

5.3.2. Synchronous Attention Handling

The operator at his terminal is sending a set of data to the application. At some time, he detects an error in the data previously transmitted. Thus he wants to interrupt the processing in the application. To spare data processing time he can use an out-of-band message (sent at a higher priority), but to separate obsolete data from data generated after the attention, we must introduce a special mechanism. This mechanism is generally called a "synchronous attention handling" mechanism.

In a quite general way, this mechanism reflects the need for a process to point out the occurence of an abnormal situation to its partner and to recover from that situation. Moreover such an abnormal situation can lead to an abort of previously transmitted messages on the normal data channel. So the recovery procedure requires a mechanism of synchronization of exchanges on both normal and out-of-band channels.

The structure of the most commonly used mechanism has been first introduced in [10] and further analyzed in detail in [3]. The organization of the exchanges of information during a synchronous attention handling phase is briefly described in fig. 10.

The communication between both partners consists of a succession of data phases (during which data is exchanged). These phases are interrupted by the occurence of a synchronous attention (generated either by the terminal or by the application). At that time, a synchronous attention handling phase is entered. We sequentially number the successive phases.

In figure 10, at time t_0, the process A detects an abnormal situation. So the local VTP process forwards two items on the virtual link to the VTP process which supports the process B during the synchronous attention handling phase: an out-of-band message (SYNC. ATT) and a normal message (MARK). The use of an out-of-band message for the

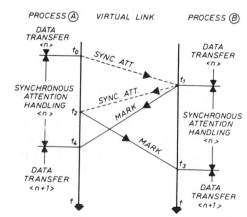

Fig. 10. SYNC. ATT = synchronous attention out-of-band messages, MARK = normal message associated with SYNC. ATT.

purpose of conveying the attention information to process B is so that the attention will be processed by the receiver as promptly as possible (recovery from an abnormal situation). However due to its priority nature, the SYNC.ATT is generally received at B before the last normal message sent by the process A during data transfer $\langle n \rangle$. As a consequence, the out-of-band message cannot indicate the point at which the arriving normal messages no longer originate from data transfer $\langle n \rangle$ but belong to data transfer $\langle n + 1 \rangle$. A clear separation between successive data transfers is nevertheless essential because data from different data transfers may have to be processed differently (whereas the data transfer $\langle n + 1 \rangle$ will normally be handed over to the destination process, those from data transfer $\langle n \rangle$ might for instance be purged on arrival at the receiver side). This separation is achieved by issuing a special purpose synchronizing normal message named MARK at some point in the synchronous attention handling. The need for a double exchange of information from the process A to process B is related to analogous considerations. The reader interested in further details can consult the references [3,4,11,12,16,18].

The meaning of the abnormal situation (and consequently of the synchronous attention) can be defined:

— either at the VTP level [4,11,12,16]. For example the primitives CLEAR [11] or PURGE [4,12,16] are typically used for reinitializing the data structure and therefore the exchanges on the virtual link.

— or at a higher level (convention between the operator and the application) [4,17,18]. In the proposals [4,17,18], on receipt of the attention condition, the interrupted process has to decide whether previously transmitted normal message is still relevant (in this case, it answers with a RESUME primitive) or obsolete and to be discarded (in this case, it answers is a purge primitive). In [9], a synchronous attention handling is rigidly associated with a reset operation at the X25 level.

Considering that synchronous attention handling establishes a transition between adjacent but otherwise independent data transfers, it may be the case that the turn inherited from the interrupted data transfer (when alternating data flow mode has been used) is not necessarily adequate for the new data transfer.

In some proposals [11,12], this resynchronization of both communicating processes associated with a

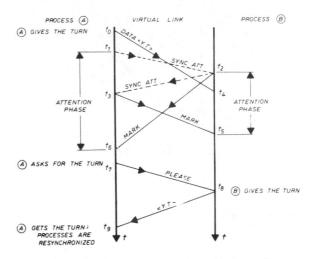

Fig. 11. DATA $\langle Y.T. \rangle$ = normal message carrying data and giving the TURN to the remote process; SYNC. ATT. = synchronous attention out-of-band message; MARK = normal message associated with SYNC. ATT; PLEASE = normal message asking for the TURN; $\langle Y.T. \rangle$ = ghost normal message as a response to the PLEASE and intended to give the TURN; TURN A (resp. B) means that at that time it is the process A (resp. B) which has the right for sending data.

synchronous attention condition is realized by means of a PLEASE primitive (see § 5.3.1 for the semantics of the PLEASE primitive). This primitive is sent on the virtual link either as a normal message [18] or as an out-of-band message [12] (see § 5.3.1 about the asynchronous attention condition).

The use of PLEASE normal message leads to a loss of performance (fig. 11) because there is no efficient transfer of information until t9. Whereas the use of a PLEASE out-of-band message can speed the resynchronization delay, but in some cases, be quite inefficient (fig. 12).

Some proposals include the resynchronization procedure within the synchronous attention handling [4,17]. Such a solution has the main advantage that the exchange of data can always start at the very beginning of the new data phase. The resynchronization process works as follows. The interrupting process sends its requirements for the turn to its partner in a special field of the attention out-of-band message. And the latter sends its own requirements in a field of the attention response out-of-band message. Then both VTP processes independently evaluate the current turn by using a common algorithm (with the requirements as inputs). Algorithms are presented in [4] and [17].

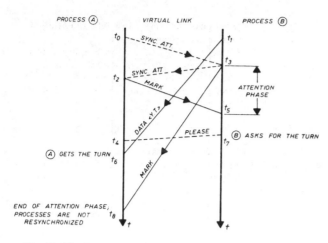

Fig. 12. The Legend of this figure is quite identical to that of Fig. 11 except for PLEASE = out-of-band message asking for the turn.

6. Conclusions

Except for the Telnet protocol [1], the VTP proposals analyzed in this paper are mainly intended to cover the class of most current VDU real terminals (i.e. they are systematically provided with facilities such as protected and contrasted fields). Nevertheless it must be pointed out that the definition is easily expandable to much more sophisticated terminals. Such an attempt has been successfully done with the manufacturer's virtual device protocol [2].

If some fundamental concepts are now widely accepted (e.g. need for a negotiation phase, general scheme of attention handling), the details are still under discussion (e.g. symmetric or asymmetric negotiation mechanism, resynchronization after synchronous attention handling). So an internationally accepted virtual terminal protocol has not yet emerged.

As far as all the proposals analyzed herein are concerned, it is to be mentioned that the dialogue is generally restricted to a unique data structure to be visualized on a presentation unit (i.e. the screen of the terminal). The existence of secondary data structures associated with auxiliary devices is not usually approached. The conept of communication variables seems to allow a systematic use of extra data structures (and auxiliary devices associated with them). But until now the problem has not been resolved. We believe that much work remains to be done on this problem in the years to follow.

Appendix A. Meaning of the Attributes Introduced in Table 1

A.1. Field Access Control Attributes

ALPHABETICAL CHARACTER ACCESS: this field is to be fulfilled via the keyboard with alphabetical characters only.

LIGHT-PEN ACTION: a light-pen entry will not only cause the field to be marked but also the current data structure contents to be forwarded to the application. The LIGHT-PEN constitutes but a restricted variety of the SELECTABLE attribute.

LIGHT-PEN PICKABLE: a light-pen entry will only result in the field receiving a mark indicating light-pen selection.

NEXT FORM: this attribute does exist in a multiforms environment only. This field contains the name of the next Form Description to be activated. The form whose name is in this field, will be active upon transmission of this forms data to the application. If the contents of this field are null, the current form remains valid.

NOT ADDRESSABLE: this field may not be repaired within the data structure. It can not be addressed during data transfers from either the application side or the terminal one. A NOT ADDRESSABLE field is by definition NOT TRANSMITTABLE, but it may be PRINTABLE (as defined hereunder).

NOT PRINTABLE: this attribute is used in order to inhibit the field from being transferred to the locally attached printer. It is obvious that this attribute is relevant only for a virtual terminal provided with a printer as auxiliary device.

NOT TRANSMITTABLE: the transfer of this field to the application is inhibited. All TRANSMITTABLE fields which are not empty (i.e. full of NULL characters) are sent from the terminal to the application within the same interaction unit. Only ADDRESSABLE fields may be TRANSMITTABLE.

NUMERICAL ACCESS: this field is to be fulfilled via the keyboard with numeric data only.

PROTECTED ACCESS: the access to this field is prevented by the terminal operator (e.g. via the keyboard). A field which is not PROTECTED may be modified by the operator.

REQUIRED ENTRY: an alphanumerical character entry must be made into this field before the field may be transmitted to the application, i.e. this field may never be sent full of NULL characters.

SELECTABLE: this field can be selected via a pointing device (e.g. a light-pen).

A.2. Field Adjustment Control Attributes

RIGHT JUSTIFIED (Space Fill): the characters entered into this field are positioned to the right-most position of the field. This field is completed with leading spaces.

RIGHT JUSTIFIED (Zero Fill): the characters entered into this field are positioned to the right-most position of the field. This field is completed with leading zeroes.

A.3. Field Visualization Control Attributes

CONTRASTED ⟨n⟩: this attribute is used for displaying a field with different levels of contrast. The level of contrast is indicated by means of the parameter ⟨n⟩. The implementation of the contrast concept can be very varying: brightness, colour, blinking, etc.

CURSIVE FACE: the contents of the field are displayed as cursive face.

INVISIBLE: this attribute is used to hide the contents of specific fields on the display (e.g. for security purposes).

A.4. Display Control Attributes

APL CHARACTERS: the contents of this field is to be displayed as APL characters.

IA5 EXTENDED: the opportunity is given for fulfilling this field with symbols which do not belong to the single IA5 alphabet. This attribute is to be used for representing the extensions of national reference versions of IA5.

Appendix B. Meaning of the Data Structure Managment Primitives Introduced in Table 2

B.1. Primitives for Addressing the Data Structure

ABSOLUTE ⟨x⟩⟨y⟩: this primitive specifies a character position directly by means of its parameters ⟨x⟩⟨y⟩. As a matter of fact, the declaration of beginning of field address by the application during the formatting of a page, is probably the most typical use of the concept of absolute addressing.

ABSOLUTE FIELD ⟨n⟩: regardless of the current position of the pointer, this primitive allows to move the pointer to the first character position of the field repaired by the parameter ⟨n⟩. It is obvious that such a primitive is used in an environment where the pointer parameter y_0 refers directly to a field number.

DIFFERENTIAL ⟨dx⟩⟨dy⟩: this primitive allows to specify a character position within the data structure by means of its relative location with respect to the current location of the pointer.

DIFFERENTIAL ⟨dx⟩: the current position of the pointer is advanced dx positions.

DIFFERENTIAL ⟨dy⟩: the current position of the pointer is advanced dy lines and set to the first column of that line.

HOME: the pointer is moved to the first effective position of the first unprotected field of the data structure. The first effective position of a field is defined as the first position of the field which is intended to be fulfilled with a data character. When the data structure is an unformatted page, the pointer is moved to the first position of the first line.

[NEXT CHARACTER (implicit): the current position of the pointer is incremented by one position].

NEXT FIELD: in a formatted page, this primitive moves the pointer to the first effective position of the next field within the data structure.

NEXT HORIZONTAL TABSTOP: in some VTP proposals, parts of a line of the data structure may be delimited by successive "horizontal tabstops". This primitive is used for moving the pointer to the next position repaired by a tabstop.

NEXT LINE: in a two-dimensional data structure, this addressing primitive moves the pointer to the first position of the next line within the data structure.

NEXT UNPROTECTED FIELD: in a formatted page, this primitive moves the pointer to the first effective position of the next unprotected field within the data structure.

START OF LINE: the pointer is moved to the first position of the current line.

B.2. Primitive for Initializing the Data Structure

INIT: this reset operation is twofold as it involves a clearing of all positions within the data structure to NULL and a moving of the pointer to the first position of the first line (reset of the contents as well as of the pointer).

B.3. Primitives for Clearing the Contents of the Data Structure

CLEAR: in a formatted data structure, this primitive is used in order to reset all the unprotected field positions to NULL and to move the pointer to the first effective position of the first unprotected field. So, the operator is intended to use the same data structure once again.

CURRENT UNPROTECTED FIELD CLEAR: the contents of the current unprotected field are reset to NULL from the current position of the pointer to the end of the current field.

UNPROTECTED FIELD CLEAR FROM CURRENT ADDRESS TO SPECIFIED ADDRESS: the contents of the unprotected fields are reset to NULL from the current position of the pointer to an address specified in the parameter list of the primitive.

UNPROTECTED FIELD CLEAR FROM SPECIFIED ADDRESS TO SPECIFIED ADDRESS: the contents of the unprotected fields, included between two addresses specified in the parameter list of the primitive, are reset to NULL.

B.4. Primitives for Creating a Data Structure

ATTRIBUTE ⟨k⟩: the current position of the pointer defines the beginning of a field whose characteristics (attribute) are given by the parameter k of the primitive ATTRIBUTE. This primitive is usually used in conjunction with the ABSOLUTE ⟨x⟩⟨y⟩ addressing primitive.

CHARACTER REPETITION ⟨k⟩⟨n⟩: the specified character k is displayed at the current position of the pointer and then repeated n times. This means that k is displayed (n + 1) times. It is obvious that the pointer is incremented once for each character of text to be displayed.

DELETE ATTRIBUTE: this primitive is used in order to delete an attribute which has been previously associated with the current character position. This primitive has no effect on the pointer.

[WRITE A CHARACTER OF FILL A FIELD (implicit): the specified character is displayed at the current position of the pointer].

References

[1] Telnet Protocol Specification, Network Working Group (NIC 18639), August 1973, 19 p.

[2] Virtual Device Protocol, Version 1, August 1977, 52 p.

[3] E. Bauwens, F. Magnee, Remarks on Negotiation Mechanism and Attention Handling, SART 77/12/13, INWG Protocol Note 72, May 1977, 22 p.

[4] E. Bauwens, F. Magnee, Definition of the Virtual Terminal Protocol for the Belgian University Network, Computer Network Protocols Symposium Proceedings, Liège, 13–15 February 1978, 14 p.

[5] CCITT (Ed.), Study Group VII, Draft Recommendation X25, Geneva, November 1976.

[6] CCITT, Proposals for Draft Provisional Recommendations for Internetworking between non-Packet Mode and Packet-Mode DTE, CCITT Study Group VII, Temporary Document, N° 62-E, Geneva 1977.

[7] A. Danthine, Host-Host Protocols and Hierarchy, IFIP-IIASA Workshop on Data Communications, IIASA, Laxenburg, September 1975, pp. 9–15.

[8] J. Davidson, W. Hathaway, J. Postel, N. Mimno, R. Thomas, D. Walden, The Arpanet Telnet Protocol: its Purpose, Principles, Implementation and Impact on Host Operating Sytem Design, Fifth Data Communications Symposium, Snowbird, Utah, 27–29 September 1977, pp. 4.10–18.

[9] J. Day, Terminal Protocols, To be published in IEEE, Transactions on Communications.

[10] A. Duenki, P. Schicker, Symmetry and Attention Handling: Comments on a Virtual Terminal, Report EIN/ZHR/77/03, February 1977, 3 p. and also in Computer Communication Review, Vol. 7, N° 3, July 1977, pp. 56–58.

[11] EURONET, Data Entry Virtual Terminal Protocol for Euronet, EEC/DG-XIII/EURONET/VTP-D/3, September 1977, 32 p.

[12] IFIP Working Group 6.1., INWG Protocol 91: Proposal for a Standard Virtual Terminal Protocol, February 1978, 52 p.

[13] International Standards Organization (ISO), Reference Model for Open System Architecture, ISO/TC97/SC16/N46, Revised Version, November 1978.

[14] N. Naffah, Protocole d'Appareil Virtuel Type Ecran, Document INFOREP, IFR 503.2, Octobre 1976. 60 p.

[15] N. Naffah, Protocol for Alphanumeric Data-Entry Terminals, Computer Networks, Vol. 2, 1978. pp. 84–94.

[16] P. Schicker, A. Duenki, The Virtual Terminal Definition, EIN/ZHR/77/018C, Computer Networks, September 1977, 48 p.

[17] P. Schicker, H. Zimmermann, Proposal for a Scroll-Mode Virtual Terminal in European Informatics Network, EIN/CCG/77/02, January 1977, 46 p.

[18] G. Schulze, A Virtual Terminal Concept, PIX/VTP/GMD/77/02, 27 p.

[19] G. Schulze, W. Börger, A Virtual Terminal Protocol based on Communication Variables, Computer Network Protocols Symposium, Liège, 13–15 February 1978, and also in Computer Networks, Vol. 2, 1978, pp. 291–296.

[20] TELENET (Ed.), Interactive Terminal Specification, Telenet Communication Corporation, September 1975, 120 p.

[21] H. Zimmermann, Proposal for a VTP, Cyclades Document, TER 533–1, July 1976, 17 p.

PROCEEDINGS OF THE IEEE, VOL. 71, NO. 12, DECEMBER 1983

The OSI File Service

DOUGLAS LEWAN AND H. GARRETT LONG, MEMBER, IEEE

Invited Paper

Abstract—The OSI File Service defines a standard for transferring, accessing, and managing information stored in or moved between open systems as files. Within the framework defined by the OSI Reference Model the OSI File Service resides within the Application Layer (OSI layer 7). The OSI File Service describes features for basic file transfer and access allowing manipulation of the data contained in a file and features for management of individual files.

To minimize the amount of detailed technical information that one needs to determine about a system before communicating with it, the OSI File Service establishes a common model for files. The model used by the OSI File Service is called the *Virtual Filestore*. Describing file transfer, access, and management in terms of the Virtual Filestore allows interconnection of a wide range of systems of different complexity. The definition of a number of optional subsets within the Virtual Filestore allows simpler systems to interwork with more sophisticated ones.

The OSI File Service defines the aims and objectives that the protocol must achieve. The application protocols for the OSI File Service support the activities required for file transfer, access, and management between open systems.

I. INTRODUCTION

THE OSI File Service defines a standard for transferring, accessing, and managing information stored in or moved between open systems as files. The file transfer, access, and management (FTAM) services allow data to be added to or removed from an information storage facility and the description of the data maintained, without needing to know how the filing system is implemented. Using the OSI File Service, otherwise incompatible filing systems may work together in any combination.

Within the framework defined by the OSI Reference Model [1], FTAM services reside within the Application Layer (OSI layer 7). The OSI File Service relies on the Presentation Layer (OSI layer 6) to resolve syntactical difference between open systems and on the Session Layer (OSI layer 5) to manage the dialogue between open systems. The FTAM protocols support the specific FTAM services defined by the OSI File Service.

The OSI File Service contains features that an application process or entity can use to exchange, create, and delete files or collections of information treated like files. The FTAM protocol implementation may be invoked directly by a human user, by a subsystem processing a queue of submitted file requests, or by a user-written application program. In each case, the same FTAM protocols will be used.

The OSI File Service describes features for basic file access allowing manipulation of any of the data contained in a file and of management of individual files, since these arise from the description of file transfer. However, a future revision of this standard will detail more complex access and management features, including the ability to manipulate groups of files.

Manuscript received August 31, 1983.
D. Lewan is with AT&T Information Systems, Lincroft, NJ 07738.
H. G. Long is with Davis Inc., Washington, DC 20001.

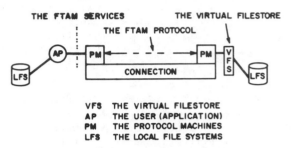

VFS THE VIRTUAL FILESTORE
AP   THE USER (APPLICATION)
PM   THE PROTOCOL MACHINES
LFS THE LOCAL FILE SYSTEMS

Fig. 1.   Architecture of the OSI File Service.

The OSI File Service does not aim to support the coordination of several distributed file repositories to provide a single unified appearance, although such support is a possible future extension. The OSI File Service defines standards for the manipulation of files by computer systems using telecommunication means; it does not apply to the interchange of files on physical media.

The ways in which file storage is implemented vary considerably between existing systems. Different systems have a wide range of styles for describing the storage of data and the means by which to access it. In keeping with the goal of OSI to minimize the amount of detailed technical information that one needs to determine about a system before communicating with it, the OSI File Service must establish a common model for files before defining protocols and procedures for file transfer, access and management. The model used by FTAM is called the *Virtual Filestore*.

Independence from file systems is realized through agreement on the Virtual Filestore and by divorcing the model from the communication-oriented aspects of the OSI File Service. Thus OSI File Service becomes concerned with three interfaces:

1) The interface between a user of the OSI File Service and the FTAM protocol, the FTAM services.

2) The interface between communicating entities, the FTAM protocol.

3) The interface between the responding FTAM entity and the remote physical filestore, the Virtual Filestore. The Virtual Filestore defines a common descriptive model for file storage.

Fig. 1 shows the structure of the file service and the relationship between its pieces and interfaces.

The Virtual Filestore is intended to motivate construction of the services and protocol in terms of files. To this end, the FTAM standard uses vocabulary generally specific to files. The formal model, however, does not bind a user or implementor to the physical reality of data storage. The model could handle tasks that are not directly related to file storage but instead conveniently describe process to process communication using a file-like structure.

As of this writing, the description of the Virtual Filestore is stable if not complete. The service description is also nearly complete. The protocol as defined by actions taken locally to one protocol machine is also nearly complete. The status of the work on the file service can be found in the current file service drafts, [2]–[5]. Versions of these documents will be put forth in October as a draft proposal by the files group in ISO/TC 97/SC 16/ WG 5.

The immediate work facing the FTAM subgroup in ISO involves a precise description of the presentation context for the OSI File Service. This presentation context would become the preferred transfer syntax for the OSI File Service. The relationship between FTAM and the common application services (CAS) must also be resolved as CAS becomes solid within OSI; in particular such a relationship will require a definition of the application context for the OSI File Service. There is also sentiment in the ISO files subgroup that a formal description of the FTAM protocol is highly desirable although it is not clear that a formal description will be a part of the standard. Formal description efforts are underway in the United Kingdom. A similar file service has been specified in [6] using an extended state approach. Beyond resolving issues arising in the OSI File Service as its structure now stands, future work on the OSI File Service also includes extension to a richer file access protocol.

II. THE MODEL OF THE FILE SERVICE

By specifying an abstraction of mechanisms for transferring, accessing, and managing files, the Virtual Filestore serves as a reference model for the OSI File Service. All aspects of the OSI File Service relating to the description of files use concepts defined by the Virtual Filestore. The conceptual framework created by the Virtual Filestore provides the context for the application protocol that supports the the OSI File Service.

Using the Virtual Filestore as a common model for describing files, a local mapping function can absorb differences in style and specifications between different systems thereby enabling them to interwork in terms that are mutually understood. Screening the details of local system environments from the external connection reduces the need to modify the existing systems and hence the initial cost of the OSI.

Describing FTAM in terms of the Virtual Filestore allows interconnection of a wide range of systems of different complexity. The definition of a number of optional subsets within the Virtual Filestore allows simpler systems to interwork with more sophisticated systems; for instance, a complex computer system could communicate with the auxiliary storage of an intelligent terminal, or with a unit-record peripheral. The Virtual Filestore not only conceals differences of style between similar kinds of data storage, but also resolves differences of type or sophistication.

The Virtual Filestore defines the following:

1) *File attributes*. The properties associated with a file. The file attributes are the object of file management.

2) *File structures*. The data contained within a file. The file contents are the object of file transfer and access.

3) *File operations*. The operations that may be performed on a file. It is through the file operations that the FTAM is realized.

A. File Attributes

The Virtual Filestore defines two classes of attributes:

file identity attributes which represent properties of the file itself and are independent of the file service session. The scope of the file identity attributes is the filestore. Examples of file identity attributes are *filename* and *date and time of creation*.

```
                    Kernel

filename
presentation context
identification structure type


                   Storage

account
date and time of creation
date and time of last modification
date and time of last read access
identity of creator
identity of last modifier
identity of last reader
file availability
possible access
future filesize


                   Security

access control
encryption name
legal qualification
```

Fig. 2. The subsets of the file identity attributes.

file activity attributes which are relevant only to the file service session in progress. The scope of the file activity attributes is the file service session. Examples of file activity attributes are *identity of initiator* and *current account*.

Appendix I discusses the individual attributes in more detail.

1) File Identity Attributes: The file identity attributes distinguish files from bulk data. They identify an individual file and are independent of the file service connection or activity within the file service. Each file identity attribute is global, in that it has one value at any particular time. All initiators which have selected the file will see the same value for a file identity attribute.

Not all of the file identity attributes defined in the Virtual Filestore are needed in all circumstances. Specifications using the Virtual Filestore definition may specify the inclusion of the groups of attributes or the restrictions on attribute values.

Three natural subsets of file identity attributes arise. The *kernel subset* consists of those file identity attributes necessary for the basic act of file transfer; it is the minimum required by the OSI File Service to characterize files. The *storage subset* of file identity attributes defines concepts associated with physical storage. The storage subset is thus concerned, for example, with restrictions imposed on file access by limitations of a storage medium or the identities of accessors. The *security subset* provides standard formats for file-related security data. Fig. 2 lists the attributes as so partitioned.

All the attributes defined by the Virtual Filestore are described in Appendix I.

2) File Activity Attributes: The file activity attributes reflect the state of the file service activity in progress. There is a different set of values for file activity attributes for each file service connection, although an entity will only have access to the state associated with activities in which it participates. The file activity attributes reflect the state of the file service activity only, but exclude the detailed state of the communication path to the filestore.

B. File Structures

1) Access Structure: The access structure describes the organization of data contained within a file as it affects access of a file's contents.

A file contains one or more identifiable data units. These data units are related in some logical fashion. In general, these relations may be sequential, hierarchical, network, or relational. The Virtual Filestore uses a tree structure to represent how the units of data within a file are related units for access purposes. This structure is called the access structure.

Each separately accessible subtree of the file data structure is a File Access Data Unit (FADU) and is a typed data object. Operations on the data contained in a file apply to FADU's.

Fig. 3 gives an example of an access structure of a file in a tree notation.

Two special cases of hierarchical access structures which are widely used are as follows:

Unstructured: The access structure of the file consists only of the root node and one data unit.

Flat: The access structure of the file consists of two levels. There are data units only on the leaf nodes. A particular special case of a flat file is a file where all the data units are instances of the same type of record.

2) Presentation Structure: FADU's are typed data objects containing atomic elements of data, called data items. The data items within a FADU are logically related by an abstract syntax called the *presentation structure*. The presentation structure of FADU's could, for example, represent records in a COBOL indexed sequential file. The Presentation Layer supports and maintains the presentation structure of each FADU.

C. File Operations

In addition to the definitions of file attributes and file structures, the Virtual Filestore also defines the valid operations on files and the data contained in them. The definition of each file operation states what it applies to and what its effects are.

The file operations are invoked by file service primitives. The OSI file service definition states what actions occur from the file operation invoked by each file service primitive.

File operations fall into two classes:

1) operations on the entire file,
2) operations on the file contents.

The filestore provider controls the use of each file operation through an access control list. The availability of a file operation is further subject to concurrency control, governing the parallel activities allowed during and after that operation. In addition, particular implementations of the Virtual Filestore may constrain the applicability and scope of some operations.

1) Operations on Entire Files: The following operations act on entire files:

Create File: The operation creates a new file and establishes the attributes of the new file.

Select File: The operation establishes a relationship between the file service initiator and a particular file. A file must be selected before using the operations described below. Note that file creation implies file selection.

Change Attribute: The operation modifies the existing value of the attribute.

Read Attribute: The operation returns the values of the requested attributes.

Open File: The operation initiates access of the currently selected file.

Close File: The operation dissolves an access relationship, previously established by the Open File operation, between the file service initiator and the selected file.

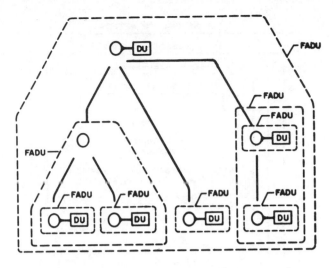

Fig. 3. Example of an access structure using a tree notation.

Delete File: The operation deletes the selected file. The filestore no longer maintains either file contents or file attributes.

Deselect File: The operation dissolves a relationship, previously established by the Select File operation, between the initiator and a particular file.

Those operations affecting the attributes of a file fall within the scope of file management.

2) Operations on File Contents: The operations on the contents of a file work within the context established by the Open File operation. The following operations act on file contents:

Locate: The operation attempts to locate the specified FADU. Parameter values are available to request location at the beginning or at the end of the file. When a file is opened, the first FADU in the file is located.

Read: The currently located FADU is read.

Insert: A new FADU is created, and is inserted into the appropriate position in the file. For sequentially organized files, the FADU's are added following the currently located FADU; for other file organizations, the positioning of the FADU's is determined by the currently located FADU, subject to constraints of implementation.

Replace: In contrast with the insert operation, use of this operation replaces the contents of an existing FADU subject to local implementation constraints. The FADU following the one written is located after the operation.

Extend: The data provided are added to the end of the currently located FADU, subject to constraints on the FADU length or relative position in the file.

Erase: The FADU is removed and the first FADU after the erased FADU is located.

For the purpose of transferring a file, all information contained in the file is handled as a single FADU.

III. OVERVIEW OF THE FILE SERVICE

The OSI File Service describes a single activity between an initiating entity, called the *file service initiator* and a responding entity associated with the filestore, called the *file service responder*. An entity may, however, be involved in more than one file service connection at any given time.

The OSI File Service is connection oriented, using the concepts of a connection between service access points as described in the OSI Basic Reference Model. The operation of the OSI File Service consists of a number of stages that create a working

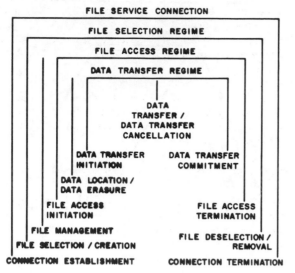

Fig. 4.   How the regimes relate to each other and the phases of the OSI File Service.

environment in which the file service initiator's desired activities can take place.

The dialogue must, in turn:

1) allow the file service initiator and the file service responder to establish each other's identity;
2) identify a selected file;
3) establish the file service initiator's authority to access the file;
4) establish the access structure for this activity;
5) establish controls on the concurrent access of the file by other file service initiators;
6) allow the file service initiator to access the attributes or contents of the currently selected file.

Each stage of the dialogue introduces a part of the operational context for the file service activity. The period for which some part of the contextual information is valid is called a *regime*. As progressively more contextual detail is established, a nest of corresponding regimes is formed. The relationship between the nesting of regimes and operations is shown in Fig. 4.

The regimes thereby delimited are as follows:

1) *File service connection regime*. The context of the file service connection regime is the existence of an application association between a user of the file service and a virtual filestore for the purpose of FTAM.

2) *File selection regime*. The context of the file selection regime identifies a particular file, its attributes and contents with a particular file service connection.

3) *File access regime*. The context of the file access regime identifies data within the currently selected file for inspection or manipulation.

4) *Data transfer regime*. The context of the data transfer regime is the inspection or manipulation of data in the file accessible within the file access regime.

Termination of a lower numbered regime implies termination of any higher numbered regimes. There is, at most, one instance of each regime at one time, but a regime may be released and a new regime of the same kind established as often as necessary. Thus for example, many files may be selected at different times over the course of a single file service connection.

A period of time in which protocol exchanges have a particular purpose, such as establishing, using, or releasing a regime is

called a *phase*. For each phase, a set of valid messages is defined. The change from one phase to another is synchronized between the peer entities, so that a common view of the set of valid messages is achieved. At any time, each entity is in precisely one phase; phases cannot be nested one within another.

The following clauses describe the sequence of phases in a typical file service activity.

A. File Service Initiation Phase

This phase is not specific to file service activity, but is a common phase that establishes the authorization and accounting information needed for communication between application entities of any sort.

B. File Selection Phase

This phase identifies a unique file to which operations in subsequent phases will apply. The current file selection continues until explicitly unset by a file deselection, a file deletion, or file service termination. The operations performed in other phases, therefore, refer to the currently selected file and do not contain explicit file identification. One form of the file selection phase is file creation.

A file selection may be in terms of a filename or as a series of constraints on other file identity attributes whose values identify the file required. A file selection request may include additional file specific access control information. The file selection phase establishes concurrency controls for the file, and a suitable access structure for identifying the data contained in the file.

C. File Management Phase

This phase allows the file service initiator to manage the currently selected file as a whole. During the file management phase, the attributes of the currently selected file may be inspected or modified.

D. File Access Initiation Phase

The file access initiation phase establishes the file access regime within which data transfer can take place.

E. Data Transfer Phase

In the data transfer phase, the file service initiator accesses individual FADU's contained in the currently selected file. Each data transfer moves a single FADU. When transferring a file, the entire contents of the file form a single FADU. Smaller data elements may be identified for presentation purposes, but they cannot be accessed individually.

Each data transfer:

1) identifies the FADU and the type of operation to be performed on that FADU;
2) transfers the data contained within the FADU;
3) concludes the transfer with a commitment exchange.

F. File Access Termination Phase

The file access termination phase closes the file access regime. The file access termination phase consolidates the actions in any earlier phases of the File Service, confirming that the requested actions have taken place and will not be revoked, and providing any final status information.

G. File Deselection Phase

The file deselection phase terminates the file selection regime. The file deselection phase may include standard accounting information, but leaves in effect any authentication or account identification established before the file selection phase.

H. File Service Termination Phase

This phase dissolves the association between the file service initiator and the file service responder, relinquishing any authentication and accounting information. After file service termination and no further context remaining, the file service activity is over.

IV. THE FILE PROTOCOL

Because the FTAM protocol operates within the OSI Application Layer, it acts on the semantics of information passed between application entities. The OSI File Protocol standard [5] specifies transmission and receipt of protocol control information at the level of complete protocol data units. The basic structure of the OSI File Protocol reflects the nesting of the file service regimes (see Section III).

Work on a preferred transfer syntax for the OSI File Service Protocol is underway. This work is detailed in [7], and closely resembles the work in CCITT on message handling [8]. The transfer syntax consists of messages, representing request and response protocol data units, and fields to carry parameters. Both messages and fields have tag-length-value constructions defined in terms of abstract data types. These abstract data types define messages and fields in terms of *integers*, *characters*, *booleans*, etc., without regard for particular representation of those data values.

V. CONCLUSION

Although file storage varies greatly from one system to the next, the OSI File Service provides a common understanding for:

1) file structures,
2) file attributes,
3) file operations.

Based on a common model of files embodied in the Virtual Filestore, the OSI File Service defines the activities required to transfer, access, and manage files between open systems. By agreeing to use the standard protocol for the OSI File Service, different systems can exchange information contained in or related to files.

APPENDIX I
ATTRIBUTES

This Appendix lists the attributes that the Virtual Filestore defines. Most names indicate quite clearly the intended meaning of the attributes. When this does not seem so clear some explanatory text has been added.

A. File Identity Attributes

1) Kernel Subset:
Filename
Presentation Context: is the presentation context under which the file was created. Thus if the user of the file service creates a file for the purpose of electronic mail its presentation context will be that of electronic mail.
Identification Structure Type: indicates whether the internal structure of the file is unstructured, flat, or hierarchical (of depth at least two).
Presentation Structure Name: names the file's presentation structure as defined in Section II-B2.

2) Security Subset:
Encryption Name: is the commonly understood name of the algorithm used to encrypt the file contents.
Legal Qualifications: is a long character string existing because of the possibly wide legal ramifications of data communications and storage.

3) Storage Subset:
Access Control: is an attribute describing the access permissions to the file.
Account
Date and Time of Creation
Date and Time of Last Modification
Date and Time of Last Read Access
Identity of Creator
Identity of Last Modifier
Identity of Last Reader
File Availability: describes simply that the file is or is not available for inspection at the time requested.
Current Filesize.

B. File Activity Attributes

Type of Access
Identity of Initiator
Password
Location of Initiator
Current Account
Current Identification Structure Type.

APPENDIX II
FILE SERVICE ELEMENTS

A. File Service Primitives

F-CONNECT—file service initiation;
F-RELEASE—file service termination (orderly);
F-ABORT—file service termination (abrupt);
F-SELECT—file selection;
F-DESELECT—file deselection;
F-CREATE—file creation;
F-DELETE—file removal;
F-READ-ATTRIB—file identity attribute inspection;
F-CHANGE-ATTRIB—file identity attribute modification;
F-OPEN—file access initiation;
F-LOCATE—FADU location;
F-ERASE—FADU removal;
F-RECOVER—file access recovery;
F-CLOSE—file access termination;
F-WRITE—data storage initiation;
F-READ—data retrieval initiation;
F-DATA—data transfer;
F-DATA-END—data transfer completion;
F-TRANSFER-END—data transfer commitment;
F-CANCEL—data transfer cancellation;
F-CHECK—data transfer checkpoint;
F-RESTART—data transfer resumption.

B. File Service Subsets

Not every implementation of the File Protocols will support all aspects of the File Service. All implementations shall support at

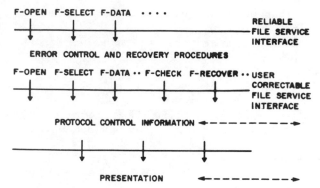

Fig. 5. Relationship between the reliable and user correctable services.

least the file transfer service subset of service elements described below.

An implementation may also support the limited file management, file access, or error control service subsets, and an implementation which supports file transfer and limited file management service subsets may support the extended file management service subset.

The service subset to be used is determined when the file service connection is established. The file service responder includes in the response a list of service subset names equal to or selected from the service subset list in the indication it receives.

File transfer service subset: The file transfer service subset provides only those facilities required to move a file's contents between open systems.

File access service subset: The file access service subset allows a user of the OSI File Service to locate, erase and move individual FADU's.

Limited and extended file management service subsets: The file management subsets give the user of the OSI File Service the ability to examine and change a file's attributes. Extended file management allows a user to create and remove files in the filestore.

Error control service subset: The error control service subset is provided for the user who prefers to control the error recovery.

Filestore management subset: Filestore management presently lies outside the scope of the OSI file service. As a possible future enhancement, filestore management may include the manipulation of groups of files.

While the spirit of open systems in part is to remove the responsibility of detailed knowledge about either the connection or the remote system, the OSI File Service has been constructed so that the operations of the File Service correspond almost one to one to protocol control information. To maintain this last property of the OSI File Service, a user may elect to perform its own error control and recovery. The facilities of the error control service subset exist for this purpose. Thus two types of service arise within the OSI File Service: a *reliable service* and a *user correctable* service. The relationship between the two classes of service is shown in Fig. 5.

C. File Service Parameters

The file service parameters form the body of the type of information needed to transfer, access, and manage files remotely. As with the file attributes, the parameters are named with a clear intent of meaning. Explanation is given where necessary.

Called Address

Calling Address

User Identity

User Account

Service Subset List: indicates at application association establishment which subset of service elements the user will use. See Appendix I.

Type of Service: shows whether or not the user would like to avoid letting the protocol machine handle error recovery.

Quality of Service: relates to the presentation quality of service.

User Charges: is the billing information associated with the file service session.

Originator: takes the values "responder" and "service provider" to indicate the apparent source of an abort.

Diagnostic

Access Structure Name: indicates the structure underlying any access operation. It takes values meaning "unstructured file," "sequential file," and "hierarchical file."

Attributes: lists the attributes to be inspected or modified.

Access Control List: specifies the conditions on which the file is being selected. The access control list parameter plays a role in authenticating and authorizing a user of the File Service for certain access priviledges.

Concurrency Control: places restrictions on simultaneous activities on the currently selected file.

Activity Identifier: names a file access activity. The activity identifier applies only within the user correctable service.

Processing Mode: shows the operations a user intends to use on the selected file.

Recovery Mode: defines possible restarting points in error recovery. The recovery mode applies only within the user correctable service.

FADU Identifier

FADU Operation: names the access operation to be performed on the located FADU.

FDI Type: names the type of the file data item (FDI) being transferred.

FDI Value: FDI type and value are the type and value information about the file content as required by the presentation layer. Note that the value of the presentation context attribute will affect the possible values of FDI type and value.

Checkpoint Identifier

Checkpoint Window: The checkpoint and checkpoint window parameters together form the basis for error recovery and application level error detection, that is failure of a peer to respond.

REFERENCES

[1] ISO/TC97/SC16/N890, "Information processing systems—Open systems interconnection—Basic reference model," ISO 7498, Feb. 4, 1982.
[2] ISO/TC97/SC16/N1453, "File transfer access and management—General description," Working Draft, Feb. 1983.
[3] ISO/TC97/SC16/N1454, "File transfer access and management—The virtual filestore," Working Draft, Feb. 1983.
[4] ISO/TC97/SC16/N1455, "File transfer access and management—The file service definition," Working Draft, Feb. 1983.
[5] ISO/TC97/SC16/N1456, "File transfer access and management—The file protocol specification," Working Draft, Feb. 1983.
[6] G. V. Bochmann, L. Henckel, and R. Popescu-Zeletin, "Formalized specification and analysis of a virtual file system," HMI-B 367, Hahn-Meitner-Institut, Berlin, Germany, Feb. 1982.
[7] ANSI X3T5/83-413, "File service data types requirements," July 1983.
[8] CCITT VII/3 and 5/TD 12, "Draft Recommendation X.MHS4: Message handling systems: Presentation transfer syntax and notation (version 1)," June 1983.

Concepts of the Document Interchange Protocol for the Telematic Services – CCITT Draft Recommendation S.a

W. Horak

SIEMENS AG, Corporate Laboratories for Information Technology, Otto-Hahn-Ring 6, D-8000 Munich 83, F.R. Germany

The CCITT Draft Recommendation S.a defines the Document Interchange Protocol for the Telematic Services. This protocol allows for the interchange of mixed text and facsimile documents by means of Teletex Mixed Mode and Group 4 Facsimile Terminals. The concept for the structuring of documents, which are based on the ISO/ECMA work on Office Document Architecture, and the concepts for the formal specification and the encoding of protocol elements, which are based on the CCITT Presentation Transfer Syntax for Message Handling Systems, are described.

Keywords: Telematic Services, Document Interchange Protocol, Teletex, Facsimile, Office Document Architecture, CCITT Draft Recommendation S.a.

Wolfgang Horak received the Diploma in Electrical Engineering from the Technical University Munich in 1968. He is presently head of the group Terminal Architecture in the Corporate Laboratories for Information Technology of SIEMENS in Munich. He joined SIEMENS in 1968 and got involved in planing of data networks and in studies concerning the impact of fiber optical transmission on broad band communication networks for picture phones and cable TV. 1974 and 1975 he was member of the "Commission for the development of the technical communication system" (KtK), which had been convoked by the German government. 1976 to 1979 he collaborated on concepts for a new public mobile radio system of the German PTT and since 1977 he works in the area of office information and communication systems. He was responsible for projects concerning text-image integration on office workstations, digital voice storage for electronic mail and interactive computer aided communication network design.

Currently W. Horak is leader of an international office system research project in the ESPRIT program of the European Commission and works since 1982 in the standardization bodies ISO/TC97/SC18/WG3, ECMA/TC29, DIN/AA18 and CCITT/SG VIII.

North-Holland
Computer Networks 8 (1984) 175–185

1. Introduction

Terminals of the Teletex service support the creation, transmission, reproduction and revision of *only* character coded documents. Facsimile terminals allow for the interchange and remote reproduction of *only* photographic coded images. However, documents often consist of a *mixture* of text and several kinds of images such as logos, signatures, drawings and photographs as shown in Fig. 1 [1]. Therefore during the present study period 1981 to 1984 CCITT is developing the Recommendation S.a for the interchange of mixed text/image documents.

The following gives an overview of the current Draft.

2. Embedding of S.a in the Telematic Protocols

The Recommendation S.a [2] defines the Document Interchange Protocol to be used above the session services within the Telematic Services when a document structure is required. This applies to Mixed Mode Teletex and Group 4 Facsimile.

Within the Teletex Service, the Mixed Mode will be a standard option. The terminals for the Group 4 Facsimile Service are divided into 4 classes. Class 1 terminals allow for pure facsimile transmission. Class 2 terminals are additionally able to receive Teletex documents as well as mixed text/facsimile documents. Class 3 terminals have provisions for sending and receiving basic Teletex documents, pure facsimile documents and mixed text/facsimile documents [3]. The Facsimile Service with Group 4 Class 3 terminals, corresponds to the Mixed Mode of the Teletex Service.

S.a is embedded in a framework of recommendations for this Telematic Services as shown in Fig. 2. S.a is bypassed for the Basic Teletex Service.

The protocol elements of S.a representing the document structure and the document's content

0376-5075/84/$3.00 © 1984, Elsevier Science Publishers B.V. (North-Holland)

SIEMENS

Mr. R.N. Smith
c/o ELECTRONIC CORP.

Cherry Hill N.J.08034
USA

Ihre Zeichen und Ihre Nachricht	Unsere Zeichen	München, Otto-Hahn-Ring 6
Sm/Br Sept. 7, 1982	Mlr	Oct. 18, 1982

Dear Sir

this letter was composed interactively at an experimental workstation (figures below) by

- *retrieval of the letter form from the disk*
- *proportional typing with different fonts and character faces*
- *scanning the photo at 200 pixels/inch, halftoning, and inserting it*
- *editing the line drawing*
- *signing on the tablet*

Regards

Müller

(Müller)

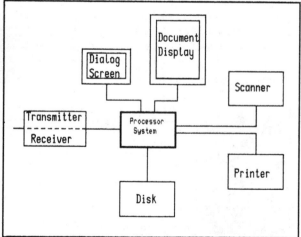

Adresse:
Siemens AG, Zentralbereich Technik
Zentrale Aufgaben Informationstechnik   Bearbeiter

Postfach 830955, D-80000 München 83

SIEMENS AKTIENGESELLSCHAFT

Zentrale Aufgaben Informationstechnik   Leitung   Dr. Heinz Schwärtzel

Fernwahl 089   Tx

Fax
Vermittlung 636-1

Vorsitzender des Aufsichtsrats: Bernhard Plettner · Vorstand: Karlheinz Kaske, Vorsitzender · Mitglieder: Theodor Baumann, Friedrich Baur, Hans Baur, Karl Heinz Beckurts, Hermann Franz, Ernst Gerhardt, Max Gunther, Heinz Gumin, Ulrich Haier, Giselher Kadegge, Claus Kessler, Gerhard Kühne, Friedrich Kurth, Heribald Närger, Hans-Gerd Neglein, Anton Peisl, Werner Poschenrieder, Dieter v. Sanden, Hans H. Schlitzberger, Wolfgang Seelig, Hans Gunther Vogelsang · Sitz der Gesellschaft: Berlin und München · Registergericht: Berlin-Charlottenburg, HRB 12300, München, HRB 6684

Fig. 1. Letter composed interactively at experimental workstation.

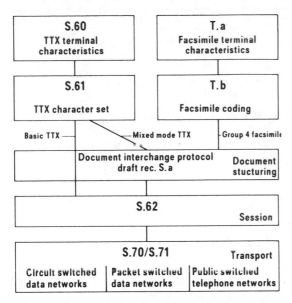

Fig. 2. Architecture of Telematic Control.

are carried inside the Session Service Data Units CSUI and CDUI of CCITT Recommendation S.62 [4].

Within S.a, two interchange formats, the Text Image Formats TIF 0 and TIF 1, are defined. TIF 0 applies to Group 4 Facsimile Class 1 terminals and TIF 1 to Mixed Mode Teletex terminals and to Group 4 Facsimile Class 2 and 3 terminals.

The terminal characteristics, the information coding and the interchange formats are negotiated during the session establishment phase. Terminal characteristics are specified in the CCITT Recom-

mendation S.60 [5] and the Draft T.a [3] and the information coding in the Recommendation S.61 [4] and the Draft T.b. [6]. Useful combinations are indicated in Fig. 3.

3. Document Architecture

3.1. Overall Architecture Model

For the purpose of S.a a *document* is an amount of text, that is interchanged between Telematic terminals.

Text is information for human comprehension that can be presented in a two-dimensional form. It consists of *graphic elements* such as *character box elements*, *geometric elements* and *photographic elements*, which constitute the *content* of a document.

S.a defines a concept for the structuring of documents. It is derived from the Office Document Architecture which is currently beeing standardized in ISO/TC97/SC18/WG3 and in ECMA/TC29 [7–9]. Fig. 4 shows the *Document Architecture* recognized in S.a. It distinguishes between layout and logical structures, which are tree structures and are composed of layout objects and logical objects. These structures provide two different but corresponding views upon the content of the document. In the current version of S.a, a logical structuring by objects such as sections, headings, footnotes and figures is not yet applied and open for further study.

Interchange-format \ Basic terminal characteristics	S.60, S.61 only	T.a, T.b only	S.60, S.61 and T.a, T.b
TIF 0	—	Group 4 Facsimile Class 1	—
TIF 1	Structured character coded document	Structured photographic coded document	Mixed text / facsimile document
Mixed Mode TTX and Group 4 Facsimile Class 2 and 3			

Fig. 3. Presentation Capabilities.

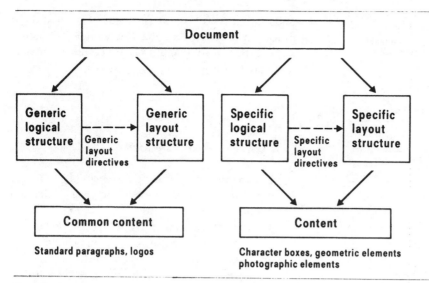

Fig. 4. Document Architecture.

3.2. Specific Layout Structure

The *specific layout structure* of a given document expresses how the document is decomposed into objects belonging to different hierarchical levels. Furthermore it relates the content of the document by means of content portions to the lowest level objects, which are the leaves of the structure tree. The *content portions* are sequences of coded character elements or photographic elements including control characters such as "line feed".

S.a knows objects of the type document, page set, page, frame and block. As Fig. 5 shows, objects of these types constitute the hierarchical levels of the specific layout structure. There can be several levels of the type page set and frame. A *page set* may represent a set of introductory pages. All objects of the type page, frame and block are rectangular areas. Frames and blocks are relatively positioned within their next higher level objects with the sides parallel to the sides of these objects.

The *page* corresponds to the interchanged image area, which may be smaller than, equal to or greater than a corresponding physical page. A *frame* (Ref. 10) may represent the area of a column or of a running header. They are optional within TIF 1. Lowest level objects are either pages as in case of TIF 0 or blocks as in case of TIF 1.

Blocks within the same frame or page can partially or fully overlay. Thereby they can be transparent or opaque. The order in which they overlay can be expressed by a ordered list of the block identifiers associated to that layout object in which the overlaying blocks are contained. This is not yet exactly specified in S.a.

As shown in Fig. 6 a frame can partially overlay other frames in a claiming manner (Ref. 11) in which case the overlaid areas can contain only blocks that belong to the claiming frame. This is not yet exactly specified in S.a.

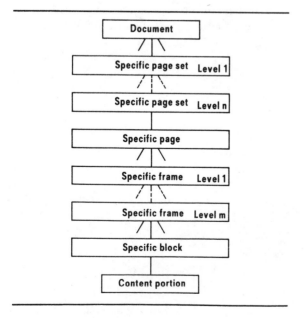

Fig. 5. Specific Layout Structure.

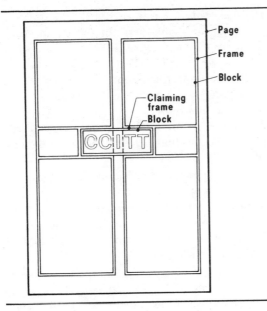

Fig. 6. Example of a Claiming Frame.

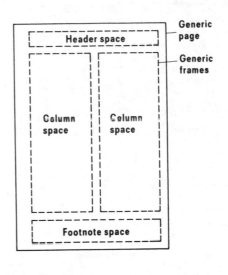

Fig. 7. Layout Template.

3.3. Generic Layout Structure

Besides the specific layout structure the Document Architecture in Fig. 4 comprises also a *generic layout structure*. The generic layout structure allows to specify predefined objects of the types page set, page, frame and block with predefined properties and predefined content portions [10]. This can be used to define a layout template for the pages of a document belonging to a certain document class. Such documents may be letters, reports, purchase orders etc. An example for a layout template is shown in Fig. 7. It consists of a generic page containing four generic frames which represent a header space, two column spaces and a footnote space with fixed positions and sizes. The generic header frame may contain a generic block with a photographic coded content portion representing a company logo. By means of a generic page set, a set of page templates for different parts of the document can be defined.

Layout templates that are interchanged, together with the document allow to facilitate and control the layout process during revision of the document by the recipient. In a document which is created according to layout templates, their generic structures may be copied repeatedly into the specific structure of the document. The specific layout objects generated thereby need not to re-peat the common properties and content portions, if they refer to the generic objects. This provides transmission efficiency especially for logo blocks and blocks of standard paragraphs that may occur repeatedly in the document. One can say, the generic objects are used like macros in programming languages.

4. Attributes

Attributes specify characteristics of objects and content portions and relations between objects and relations between objects and content portions.

4.1. Attributes of Layout Objects

The attributes of layout objects are listed in Fig. 8.

Object Type: document (0), page set (1), page (2), frame (3), block (4)

Object Identifier: 0 for generic or 1 for specific followed by the node number of the object within the tree

Reference to Corresponding Generic Object: identifier of the generic object

References to Subordinate Objects: list of identifiers of the next lower level objects

Layout objects	
Object type	M
Object identifier	O
Reference to corresponding generic object	M
References to subordinate objects	O
References to content portions	O
User-readable comments	O
Default value lists	O
Position	D (0,0 BMU)
Dimensions	D (page dimens.)
Overlay characteristics	D (transparent)
Presentation attributes	

Content portions	
Content portion identifier	O
Type of coding	D (S.61, T.b)
Number of pels per line	D
Compression	D (as in T.b)
Alternative graphic rendition	O

D defaultable   M mandatory
( ) standard default value   O optional

Fig. 8. Attributes of Layout Objects and Content Portions.

References to Content Portions: only for lowest level objects; sequence of content portion identifiers

User-readable Comments: character sequence to be interpreted by the user as comment to this object; e.g. for user names of objects

Default Value Lists: attribute value lists associated to object types; only applicable as default values to subordinate objects of that types

Content type	D (character box)
Attributes of character box content type	
Character path	D (0°)
Line progression	D (270°)
Character box orientation	D (0°)
Character box size	D (24,40 BMU as in S.61)
Character base line offset	D (14 BMU, S.61)
Character spacing	D (24 BMU, S.61)
Line spacing	D (40 BMU)
Alignment	D (left aligned)
Line layout	not yet defined
Initial offset	D (0,26 BMU)
Graphic rendition	D (as in S.61)
Attributes of photographic content type	
Pel path	D (0°)
Line progression	D (270°)
Resolution	D (1 pel/BMU)
Initial offset	D (0,0 BMU)

D   defaultable
( ) standard default value

Fig. 9. Presentation Attributes of Blocks.

Position: only for frames and blocks; positioning in the fourth quadrant of the Cartesian co-ordinate system; reference points for positioning are the top left corner; X and Y co-ordinate distances in Basic Measurement Units (BMU); each of the co-ordinates may be indicated as being either fixed or variable

Dimensions: X and Y dimensions in BMU; each of the dimensions may be indicated as being either fixed or variable

Overlay Characteristics: claiming/non claiming for frames; opaque/transparent for blocks

Presentation Attributes: category of attributes of lowest level objects; certain of these attributes may be overruled by control functions embedded in related content portions.

The *Presentation Attributes* specify how the graphic elements of the content have to be imaged. They are listed in Fig. 9.

Content Type: either character box or photographic; designates also the set of presentation attributes (character set, coding);

Attributes of Character Box Content Type:
– Character Path: 0° as default, 90°, 180°, 270°; relative to X axis, counterclockwise
– Line Progression: 270° as default, 90°, relative to X axis
– Character Box Orientation: 0° as default, 90°, 180°, 270°; relative to character path
– Character Box Size: 24,40 BMU as default; variable width for proportional spacing
– Character Box Line Offset: 14 BMU as default; relative to bottom of character box
– Character Spacing: 24 BMU as default
– Line Spacing: line spacing unit 40 BMU
– Alignment: left aligned as default, right aligned, centered, justified
– Line Layout: tabulations, identations; not yet specified
– Initial Offset: initial reference position of the first graphic element in the first line in a block; 0,26 BMU as default
– Graphic Rendition: font, style, colour, default as in Rec. S.61

Attributes of Photographic Element Content Type:
– Pel Path: 0° as default, 90°, 180°, 270°; relative to X axis
– Line Progression: 270° as default, 90°; relative to X axis

– Resolution: 200, 240, 300, 400 pels/25.4 mm; 1 pel/BMU as application dependent default
– Initial Offset: 0,0 BMU as default

4.2. Attributes of Content Portions

The Attributes of Content Portions are also listed in *Fig. 8*.

Content Portion Identifier: object identifier with additional number to identify the content portion among others belonging to the same lowest level object

Type of Coding: character box as in S.61, photographic as in T.b by default

Number of Pels per Line: implied by page or block size in case of 1 pel/BMU

Compression: compressed as in T.a by default; uncompressed

Alternative Graphic Representation: sequence of characters to be imaged instead of the content portion, when a device is not capable of decoding and/or imaging the content portion

5. Interchange Format

5.1. Structure of the Interchange Format

The document interchange format consists of a sequence of *protocol elements*. Protocol elements of three types are distinguished:

1. A *document profile descriptor*, which represents the document profile and contains a set of attributes at envelope level (reference to specific document, reference to generic document, presentation capabilities and others such as author, date, etc.).

2. *Layout descriptors*, which represent either specific or generic layout objects and contain their associated attributes.

3. *Text units*, which represent content portions and contain their associated attributes.

The transmission order of the descriptors and text units follows the natural order of the tree structure. The descriptors of generic objects follow the document profile descriptor and are followed by the descriptors of specific objects. Every text unit follows immediately the associated lowest level object.

Fig. 10 illustrates the relationships between protocol elements, their identification and their transmission order.

5.2. Formal Specification of Protocol Elements

The protocol specified in S.a is based upon the Presentation Transfer Syntax of CCITT Draft Recommendation X.MHS4 [12]. By this syntax each piece of information is considered as a *data*

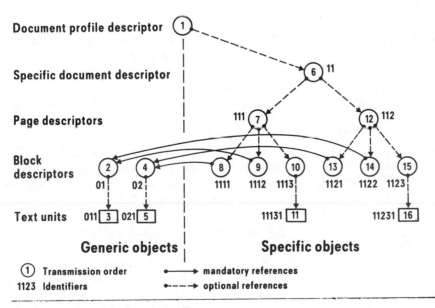

Fig. 10. Structure of the Interchange Format.

```
LayoutDescriptor            ::= SEQUENCE {
    layoutObjectType            LayoutObjectType,
    layoutDescriptorBody        LayoutDescriptorBody}

        LayoutObjectType        ::= INTEGER {document (0), pageSet (1), page (2),
                                                    frame (3), block (4)}

        LayoutDescriptorBody    ::= SET {
            objectIdentifier        ObjectReferenceName OPTIONAL,
            referencesTo            CHOICE {
                subordinateObjects  [0] IMPLICIT SEQUENCE OF ObjectReferenceName,
                contentPortions     [1] IMPLICIT SEQUENCE OF PortionReferenceName}
                                                                OPTIONAL,
            referenceToGenericObject [2] IMPLICIT ObjectReferenceName OPTIONAL,
            position                [3] IMPLICIT MeasurePair OPTIONAL,
            dimensions              [4] IMPLICIT MeasurePair OPTIONAL,
            claiming                [5] IMPLICIT Claiming OPTIONAL,
            transparent             [6] IMPLICIT Transparent OPTIONAL,
            presentationAttributes  [7] IMPLICIT PresentationAttributes OPTIONAL,
            defaultValueLists       [8] IMPLICIT SEQUENCE OF DefaultValueList
                                                                OPTIONAL,
            userReadableComments    [9] IMPLICIT CommentString OPTIONAL}

        ObjectReferenceName     ::= [APPLICATION 1] IMPLICIT PrintableString
                                        -- digits 0 to 9 with space as a delimiter

        MeasurePair             ::= SEQUENCE {Measure, Measure}

        Measure                 ::= CHOICE {
            fixedMeasure            [0] IMPLICIT INTEGER,
            variableMeasure         [1] IMPLICIT INTEGER}

        Claiming                ::= INTEGER {non-claiming (0)}
                                        -- other values for further study

        Transparent             ::= INTEGER {transparent (0)}
                                        -- other values for further study

        CommentString           ::= IA5String
                                        -- same character set as PrintableString
                                        -- plus carriage return and line feed
```

Fig. 11. Formal Definition of the Layout Descriptor.

element being an instance of a certain *data type* with a certain *data value*.

The *standard notation* defined in X.MHS4, which is an extended Backus-Naur-Form (BNF) allows for the formal specification of data elements. This notation is used to define the S.a protocol element types in terms of SEQUENCES and SETS of more elementary data types, which in turn are specified in terms of others, and finally in terms of basic data types such as INTEGER and OCTET STRING.

The protocol element type definitions provide the rules for the production of protocol elements for representation of given documents. Fig. 11 shows as an example the formal definition of the layout descriptor in X.MHS4 standard notation. The layout descriptor is of the type SEQUENCE and consists of the data elements named Layout Object Type and Layout Descriptor Body. The first component is a basic data element of the type INTEGER and indicates the type of the layout object which the descriptor represents. The second component is a composite data element of the type SET and contains any other attributes of the represented object.

In the same manner the Document Profile Descriptor, the Presentation Capabilities, the Default Value List, the Presentation Attributes and the Text Units are defined in S.a.

5.3. Description of a given Document

Applying the S.a protocol element type definitions given documents with their generic and specific objects and their content portions can be described. Fig. 12 shows a part of the description

```
page:

specificLayoutDescriptor {
    layoutObjectType page,
    layoutDescriptorBody {
        objectIdentifier "1 3",
        referencesTo
            subordinateObjects {"1 3 1", "1 3 2"},
        dimensions {fixedMeasure 1728, fixedMeasure 2400}}}


block:

specificLayoutDescriptor {
    layoutObjectType block,
    layoutDescriptorBody {
        objectIdentifier "1 3 1",
        referencesTo
            contentPortions {"1 3 1 1"},
        position {fixedMeasure 240, fixedMeasure 480},
        dimensions {fixedMeasure 1200, fixedMeasure 240}
        presentationAttributes {
            contentType characterBox,
            characterBoxAttributes {
                lineSpacing 80,
                graphicRendition {3}}}}}
```

Fig. 12. Part of a Description of a Given Document.

of a given document, which contains the description of a specific page and of a specific block in that page.

5.4. Protocol Encoding

The encoding of the S.a protocol elements bases on the *standard representation* of X.MHS4 for data values. The standard representation is the set of rules for the encoding of data values for the transmission as a sequence of octets.

The data value of a data element consists of three components, the identifier, the length and the contents, which have to appear always in that order. The *identifier* is the data element name which designates the data type and governs therefore the interpretation of the contents. The length specifies the length of the contents. The *contents* is the substance of the data element conveying its primary information. The identifier and the length each consist of one or more octets. The contents consists of zero or more octets.

Fig. 13 shows an encoding example of a layout descriptor representing the specific page described in Fig. 12. The right-hand side of Fig. 13 shows the octet-level representation of the identifiers, the lengths and contents of all data elements of this page descriptor in hexadecimal notation. It consumes an amount of 38 octets. The left-hand side of Fig. 13 contains those tables that assign identifiers to all protocol elements/data elements occurring at the right-hand side. The identifiers are represented in hexadecimal notation.

6. Conclusion

Most probably this Draft Recommendation S.a will be approved during the next CCITT/SG VIII plenary in March 1984. The current version has been developed in close liaison within CCITT between SG VIII/WP2, 3 and 4 and SG I/WP 3 and SG VII/WP 5 as well as between CCITT and ISO/TC97/SC18/WG3 and 5 and ECMA/TC29.

The Document Interchange Protocol defined in S.a supports in its current stage mainly the imag-

```
A2   Identifier: specificLayoutDescriptor
2+   Length: 36 octets
02   Identifier: layoutObjectType (INTEGER)
01   Length: 1 octet
     02 Contents: 2 (page)
31   Identifier: layoutDescriptorBody (SET)
1F   Length: 31 octets
41   Identifier: objectIdentifier (ObjectReferenceName)
03   Length: 3 octets
     312033 Contents: "1 3"
A0   Identifier: referencesTo subordinateObjects
0E   Length: 14 octets
41   Identifier (ObjectReferenceName)
05   Length: 5 octets
     312033201 Contents: "1 3 1"
41   Identifier (ObjectReferenceName)
05   Length: 5 octets
     312033202 Contents: "1 3 2"
A4   Identifier: dimensions
08   Length: 8 octets
80   Identifier: fixedMeasure
02   Length: 2 octets
     06C0  Contents: 1728
80   Identifier: fixedMeasure
02   Length: 2 octets
     0960  Contents: 2400

octet-level representation of the page (38 octets) in
hexadecimal notation,
                       two hexadecimal digits per octet
```

Context: S.a (the protocol)

Identifier	Implied data type	Data element name
A0	SET	Document Profile Descriptor
A1	SEQUENCE	Generic Layout Descriptor
A2	SEQUENCE	Specific Layout Descriptor
A3	SEQUENCE	Text Unit

Context: Layout Descriptor (SEQUENCE)

Identifier	Implied data type	Data element name
02	INTEGER	Layout Object Type
31	SET	Layout Descriptor Body

Context: Layout Descriptor Body (SET)

Identifier	Implied data type	Data element name
41	OCTET STRING	Object Identifier
A0	SEQUENCE	References to Subordinate Objects
A1	SEQUENCE	References to Content Portions
82	OCTET STRING	Reference to Generic Object
A3	SEQUENCE	Position
A4	SEQUENCE	Dimensions
85	INTEGER	Claiming
86	INTEGER	Transparent
A7	SET	Presentation Attributes
A8	SEQUENCE	Default Value Lists
89	OCTET STRING	User-readable comments

Context: Measure Pair (SEQUENCE)

Identifier	Implied data type	Data element name
80	INTEGER	Fixed Measure
81	INTEGER	Variable Measure

Fig. 13. Encoding Example of a Protocol Element.

---

ing of interchanged mixed text and facsimile documents. However, by means of its generic structure it allows to define layout templates, that can be used to control and facilitate the layout process of a document. Furtheron the substitution mechanism with generic objects provides transmission efficiency for content portions that occur repeatedly in a document.

Of course, the document can be reedited at the recipient, however, with not yet sufficient support for an automatic reformatting and relayouting. The latters would need additional architectural tools (Refs. 13, 14) in order to facilitate and control e.g. the reformatting of text in blocks of variable size, the flow of text between blocks, the repositioning of figures relative to their references, etc.. Furthermore the reediting could be supported by architectural tools allowing for an easy access to also logical objects such as sections, for an automatic renumbering of sections, an automatic update of contents lists, reference lists, etc..

Provisions have been already made within S.a to apply also the logical structure in coexistence with the layout structure in order to allow for comprehensive document processing. Its inclusion and the extension by content types for business graphics such as those of the Metafile of the Graphical Kernel System (GKS) [15] should be envisaged for the next study period. Thereby the results concerning the Office Document Architecture and the Office Document Interchange Formats, that will be achieved by ISO/TC97/S18/WG3 and ECMA/TC29 during 1984, should be taken into consideration.

S.a offers already a great enhancement of the Telematic Services and is – due to its object-orientation – open for even further improvements.

References

[1] W. Horak, "Interchanging Mixed Text Image D in the Office Environment." Comput. & Graphi No. 1, 1983, pp. 13–29

[2] CCITT/SG VIII, "Document Interchange Pr the Telematic Services". Rennes, October 1983

[3] CCITT/SG VIII/WP2/TD103, "Draft Recom T.a: Apparatus for Use in the Group 4 Facsimi Geneva, 24 May - 3 June 1983

[4] Recommendation S.62, "Control Procedures and Group 4 Facsimile Service" (Revised CCITT/SG VIII/WP4, August 1983

[5] Teletex Recommendations S.70, S.60 and S Yellow Book, Vol. VII, November 1980

[6] CCITT/SG VIII/WP2/TD28, "Draft Reco T.b". Geneva, 24 May - 3 June 1983

[7] ECMA/TC 29/83/56, "Office Document A Fourth Working Draft, July 1983

[8] ISO/TC97/SC18/WG3 N 207, "Office Doc tecture". Fourth Working Draft, September

[9] W. Horak, "Change proposals and enhancer Recommendation S.a". ISO/TC97/SC18/ April 1983

[10] W. Horak and G. Krönert, "Office docume concepts for the static and dynamic layout the generic layout structure and generic lay ECMA/TC29/83/5, January 1983

[11] W. Horak, "Overlay of Frames and Blocks SC18/WG3/N 141, March 1983

[12] Draft Recommendation X.MHS 4, "Me Systems; Presentation Transfer Syntax CCITT/SG VII/WP5, June 1983

[13] W. Horak and G. Krönert, "An Object Document Architecture Model for Docum Between Open Systems". Proc. of GLO Diego, November 1983, pp. 1245–1249

[14] W. Horak and G. Krönert, "Proposal fo ject Oriented Office Document Archi ISO/TC97/SC18/WG3 N 191, July 198

[15] ISO/DIS 7942, "Information processing System (GKS)-Functional description",

SECTION 7 GLOSSARY*

ALPHAGEOMETRIC CODING. A display technique for Videotex. In addition to characters, patterns built up from geometric primitives can be displayed.

ALPHAMOSAIC CODING. A display technique for Teletext and Videotex. In addition to ordinary characters, geometric patterns can be displayed using a 2 x 3 grid within each character space.

APPLICATION LAYER. Layer 7 of the OSI model. This layer determines the interface of the system with the user.

ASYNCHRONOUS TRANSMISSION. Transmission in which each information character is individually synchronized (usually by the use of start elements and stop elements).

AUTOMATIC REPEAT REQUEST. A feature that automatically initiates a request for retransmission when an error in transmission is detected.

BALANCED TRANSMISSION. A transmission mode in which signals are transmitted as a current that travels down one conductor and returns on the other. For digital signals, this technique is known as differential signaling, with the binary value depending on the voltage difference.

BASEBAND. Transmission of signals without modulation. In a baseband local network, digital signals (1's and 0's) are inserted directly onto the cable as voltage pulses. The entire spectrum of the cable is consumed by the signal. This scheme does not allow frequency-division multiplexing.

BIT STUFFING. The insertion of extra bits into a data stream to avoid the appearance of unintended control sequences.

BRIDGE. A device that links two homogeneous packet-switched local networks. It accepts all packets from each network addressed to devices on the other, buffers them, and retransmits them to the other network.

BROADBAND. The use of coaxial cable for providing data transfer by means of analog or radio-frequency signals. Digital signals are passed through a modem and transmitted over one of the frequency bands of the cable.

BROADCAST. The simultaneous transmission of data to a number of stations.

BUS. A local network topology in which stations are attached to a shared transmission medium. The transmission medium is a linear cable; transmissions propagate the length of the medium and are received by all stations.

CATENET. A collection of packet-switched and broadcast networks that are connected together via gateways.

CATV. Community Antenna Television. CATV cable is used for broadband local networks, and broadcast TV distribution.

CIRCUIT SWITCHING. A method of communicating in which a dedicated communications path is established between two devices through one or more intermediate switching nodes. Unlike packet switching, digital data are sent as a continuous stream of bits. Bandwidth is guaranteed, and delay is essentially limited to propagation time. The telephone system uses circuit switching.

COLLISION. A condition in which two packets are being transmitted over a medium at the same time. Their interference makes both unintelligible.

COMMUNICATIONS ARCHITECTURE. The hardware and software structure that implements the communications function.

CONNECTIONLESS DATA TRANSFER. A protocol for exchanging data in an unplanned fashion and without prior coordination (e.g., datagram).

CONNECTION-ORIENTED DATA TRANSFER. A protocol for exchanging data in which a logical connection is established between the endpoints (e.g., virtual circuit).

CONTENTION. The condition when two or more stations attempt to use the same channel at the same time.

CSMA. Carrier Sense Multiple Access. A medium access control technique for multiple-access transmission media. A station wishing to transmit first senses the medium and transmits only if the medium is idle.

CSMA/CD. Carrier Sense Multiple Access with Collision Detection. A refinement of CSMA in which a station ceases transmission if it detects a collision.

CYCLIC REDUNDANCY CHECK. An error-detecting code in which the code is the remainder resulting from dividing the bits to be checked by a predetermined binary number.

DATA CIRCUIT-TERMINATING EQUIPMENT. In a data station, the equipment that provides the signal conversion and coding between the data terminal equipment (DTE) and the line. The DCE may be separate equipment or an integral part of the DTE or of intermediate equipment. The DCE may perform other functions that are normally performed at the network end of the line.

DATAGRAM. In packet switching, a self-contained packet, independent of other packets, that does not require acknowledgment, and that carries information sufficient for

*Based on Glossary in *Data and Computer Communications*, by William Stallings, Macmillan, 1985.

routing from the originating data terminal equipment (DTE), without relying on earlier exchanges between the DTEs and the network.

DATA LINK LAYER. Layer 2 of the OSI model. Converts unreliable transmission channel to reliable one.

DATA TERMINAL EQUIPMENT. That part of a data station that serves as a data source, data sink, or both.

DIFFERENTIAL ENCODING. A means of encoding digital data on a digital signal such that the binary value is determined by a signal change rather than a signal level.

DOD REFERENCE MODEL. A communications architecture that has evolved from the ARPANET project and DOD standardization activities.

ENCAPSULATION. The addition of control information by a protocol entity to data obtained from a protocol user.

FAST SELECT. An option of the X.25 virtual call that allows the inclusion of data in the call setup and call clearing packets.

FLOW CONTROL. The function performed by a receiving entity to limit the amount or rate of data that is sent by a transmitting entity.

FULL-DUPLEX TRANSMISSION. Data transmission in both directions at the same time.

GATEWAY. A device that connects two systems, especially if the systems use different protocols. For example, a gateway is needed to connect two independent local networks, or to connect a local network to a long-haul network.

HALF-DUPLEX TRANSMISSION. Data transmission in either direction, one direction at a time.

HEADER. System-defined control information that precedes user data.

INTEGRATED SERVICES DIGITAL NETWORK. A planned worldwide telecommunication service that will use digital transmission and switching technology to support voice and digital data communication.

INTERNET PROTOCOL. An internetworking protocol that provides connectionless service across multiple packet-switched networks.

INTERNETWORKING. Communication among devices across multiple networks.

MANCHESTER ENCODING. A digital signaling technique in which there is a transition in the middle of each bit time. A 1 is encoded with a high level during the first half of the bit time; a 0 is encoded with a low level during the first half of the bit time.

MEDIUM ACCESS CONTROL (MAC). For broadcast networks, the method of determining which device has access to the transmission medium at any time. CSMA/CD and token are common access methods.

MESSAGE SWITCHING. A switching technique using a message store-and-forward system. No dedicated path is established. Rather, each message contains a destination address and is passed from source to destination through intermediate nodes. At each node, the entire message is received, stored briefly, and then passed on to the next node.

MULTIPOINT. A configuration in which more than two stations share a transmission path.

NETWORK LAYER. Layer 3 of the OSI model. Responsible for routing data through a communications network.

PACKET ASSEMBLER/DISASSEMBLER (PAD). A device used with an X.25 network to provide service to asynchronous terminals.

PACKET SWITCHING. A method of transmitting messages through a communications network in which long messages are subdivided into short packets. The packets are then transmitted as in message switching. Usually, packet switching is more efficient and rapid than message switching.

PARITY BIT. A check bit appended to an array of binary digits to make the sum of all the binary digits, including the check bit, always odd or always even.

PHYSICAL LAYER. Layer 1 of the OSI model. Concerned with the electrical, mechanical, and timing aspects of signal transmission over a medium.

PIGGYBACKING. The inclusion of an acknowledgment to a previously received packet in an outgoing data packet.

POINT-TO-POINT. A configuration in which two stations share a transmission path.

PRESENTATION LAYER. Layer 6 of the OSI model. Concerned with data format and display.

PROTOCOL. A set of rules that govern the operation of functional units to achieve communication.

PROTOCOL DATA UNIT. A block of data exchanged between two entities via a protocol.

PUBLIC DATA NETWORK. A government-controlled or national monopoly packet-switched network. This service is publicly available to data processing users.

RING. A local network topology in which stations are attached to repeaters connected in a closed loop. Data are transmitted in one direction around the ring, and can be read by all attached stations.

SERVICE ACCESS POINT. A means of identifying a user of the services of a protocol entity. A protocol entity provides one or more SAPs for use by higher-level entities.

SESSION LAYER. Layer 5 of the OSI model. Manages a logical connection (session) between two communicating processes or applications.

SIMPLEX TRANSMISSION. Data transmission in one preassigned direction only.

SLIDING-WINDOW TECHNIQUE. A method of flow control in which a transmitting station may send numbered packets within a window of numbers. The window changes dynamically to allow additional packets to be sent.

SYNCHRONOUS TRANSMISSION. Data transmission in which the time of occurrence of each signal representing a bit is related to a fixed time frame.

TELETEX. A text communications service that provides message preparation and transmission facilities.

TELETEXT. A one-way information retrieval service. A fixed number of information pages are repetitively broadcast on unused portions of a TV channel bandwidth. A decoder at the TV set is used to select and display pages.

TOKEN BUS. A medium access control technique for bus/tree. Stations form a logical ring around which a token is passed. A station receiving the token may transmit data, and then must pass the token on to the next station in the ring.

TOKEN RING. A medium access control technique for rings. A token circulates around the ring. A station may transmit by scizing the token, inserting a packet onto the ring, and then retransmitting the token.

TOPOLOGY. The structure, consisting of paths and switches, that provides the communications interconnection among nodes of a network.

TRANSPORT LAYER. Layer 4 of the OSI model. Provides reliable, transparent transfer of data between endpoints.

TREE. A local network topology in which stations are attached to a shared transmission medium. The transmission medium is a branching cable emanating from a headend, with no closed circuits. Transmissions propagate throughout all branches of the tree and are received by all stations.

UNBALANCED TRANSMISSION. A transmission mode in which signals are transmitted on a single conductor. Transmitter and receiver share a common ground.

VALUE-ADDED NETWORK. A privately owned packet-switched network whose services are sold to the public.

VIDEOTEX. A two-way information retrieval service accessible to terminals and TV sets equipped with a special decoder. Pages of information at a central resource are retrieved interactively over a switched telephone line connection.

VIRTUAL CIRCUIT. A packet-switching service in which a connection (virtual circuit) is established between two stations at the start of transmission. All packets follow the same route, need not carry a complete address, and arrive in sequence.

X.21. A network access standard for connecting stations to a circuit-switched network. Includes OSI layers 1-3 functionality.

X.25. A network access standard for connecting stations to a packet-switched network. Includes OSI layers 1-3 functionality.

X.75. An internetworking protocol that provides virtual circuit service across multiple X.25 networks.

SECTION 8 BIBLIOGRAPHY

As the reader should have gathered by now the subject of this text is both broad and rapidly evolving. No bibliography can hope to be either thorough or timely. The entries in this section were chosen using the following criteria:

- *Relevance:* This tutorial is concerned with the principles and evolving standards for communications architectures and protocols, and this is reflected in the bibliography. Few of the references describe proprietary or experimental implementations.

- *Currency:* Most of the references are of rather recent origin.

- *Representativeness:* The interested reader can pursue the topics introduced in this tutorial by consulting the references listed here. They are, however, only representative of the available literature. The articles themselves contain further references for the truly dedicated reader.

Table 8.1 provides a topical key.

TABLE 8.1 REFERENCE KEY

1. Communications Architecture					
ABRA84	CORR82	FOLT82	MART81	POUZ78	WECK80
BAER83	CYPS78	GREE80	MCFA79	RAUC78	ZIMM80
BOWE83	DAVI79	JOHN80	MCQU78	STAL85	
CERF83a	DAY83	KONA83	MEIJ82	SELV80	
CERF83b	DEAT82	LAM84	MOLD81	TANE81a	
CHAP82	ENNI83	LINI83	PADL83	TANE81b	
CHAP83	FOLT81	LOVE79	POPE84a	THUR83	

2. Physical and Data Link Protocols				
ALLA82	BROD83b	CONA83	JOSH83	STUT72
BERT80	BURR83	FLET84	LIN84	WABE82
BERT81	CARL80	FOLT80c	MCCL83	WEIS83
BLAC82	CLAN82	GRAU82	MYER82	YANO81
BROD83a	CONA80	GRAY72	PARK83	

3. The Network Interface			
ATKI80	DECI82a	FOLT80b	SAKA82
BBN81	DECI82b	GRIF82	STAL84c
BHUS83	DORR81	ROBI81	WARE83
BURG83	DORR83	RUTK82	
COLL83	FOLT80a	RYBC81	

4. Internetworking			
BURG84	GIEN79	SAPR84	STAL83
CALL83	HIND83	SCHN83	STAL84a
CERF78	NBS80a	SHEL82	UNSO82
DALA82	POST80	SHOC78	WARN80
DOD83a	POST81	SHOC79	

5. Transport and Session Protocols	
DOD83b	NBS80b
EMMO83	NEUM83
GARL77	STAL84b
KNIG83	SUNS78
MIER82	SUNS81

6. Presentation and Application Protocols			
BART83a	DAY80	KUO81	SPRO78
BART83b	HAST83	LANG83	TYDE82
BORS84	HOBE80	LEWA83	WETH82
CHIL83	HOLL83	LOWE83	
CUNN83	HOLL85	MAGN79	
CUNN84	HORA84a	NBS80c	
DAVI77	HORA84b	POPE84b	

ABRA84 Abrams, M. and Cotton, I. *Computer Networks: A Tutorial*. IEEE Computer Society Press, 1984.

A collection of reprints plus original material focusing on network applications and management issues, such as network control, security, and planning. Also covers lower level protocols and communications network technology.

ALLA82 Allan, R. "Local-Area Networks Spur Moves to Standardize Data Communications Among Computers and Peripherals." *Electronic Design*, December 23, 1982.

A fairly detailed discussion of the IEEE 802 standard.

ATKI80 Atkins, J. "Path Control: The Transport Network of SNA." *IEEE Transactions on Communications*, April, 1980.

Describes the layer of SNA that corresponds to OSI network layer plus part of OSI data link layer.

BAER83 Baer, D. and Sturch, J. "An SNA Primer for Programmers." *Computerworld*. November 14 and 21, 1983.

A lengthy and useful description of IBM's communications architecture.

BART83a Bartoli, P. "The Application and Presentation Layers of the Reference Model for Open Systems Interconnection." *Proceedings, INFOCOM 83*, 1983.

A look at standards at the two highest OSI layers. Included in this tutorial.

BART83b Bartoli, P. "The Application Layer of the Reference Model of Open Systems Interconnection." *Proceedings of the IEEE*, December, 1983.

A brief description of the ISO application protocol specification.

BBN81 Bolt, Beranek, and Newman Inc. *Specifications for the Interconnection of a Host and an IMP*. Report 1822, December 1981.

This report has had a significant influence on the evolution of network access protocols. It specifies the principle network access technique for ARPANET.

BERT80 Bertine, H. "Physical Level Protocols." *IEEE Transactions on Communications*, April, 1980.

Discusses principles and gives examples.

BERT81 Bertine, H. "Physical Level Interfaces and Protocols." in *Data Communications Network Interfacing and Protocols*, 1981.

A revised version of [BERT80]. Included in this tutorial.

BHUS83 Bhusri, G. "Optimum Implementation of Common Channel Signalling in Local Networks." *Proceedings, INFOCOM 83*, 1983.

Compares X.25 and CCITT Signaling System Number 7. The latter is a specification for signaling across a circuit switched network.

BLAC82 Black, U. "Data Link Controls: The Great Variety Calls for Wise and Careful Choices." *Data Communications*, June, 1982.

Discusses principles of data link control and examines two IBM protocols: SDLC and BSC.

BORS84 Borsook, P. "U.S. Navy Brings Out Standard for Word Processing Interchange." *Data Communications*, December, 1984.

A nontechnical description of the development of the Document Interchange Format (DIF) standard.

BOWE83 Bowers, A. and Connell, E. "A Checklist of Communications Protocol Functions Organized Using the Open System Interconnection Seven-Layer Reference Model." *Proceedings, COMPCON Fall 83*, 1983.

A useful comparison of OSI layers. Included in this tutorial.

BROD83a Brodd, W. "HDLC, ADCCP, and SDLC: What's the Difference?" *Data Communications*, August, 1983.

Defines and compares two very similar data link standards with IBM's version.

BROD83b Brodd, W. and Boudreau, P. "Operational Characteristics: BSC versus SDLC." *Data Communications*, October, 1983.

Defines and compares IBM's two data link protocols.

BURG83 Burg, F. "Design Considerations for Using the X.25 Layer in Data Terminal Equipment." *Proceedings, INFOCOM 83*, 1983.

A practical discussion of X.25 implementation. Included in this tutorial.

BURG84 Burg, F.; Chen, C.; and Folts, H. "Of Local Networks, Protocols, and the OSI Reference Model." *Data Communications*, November, 1984.

Describes approaches to internetworking of local networks via X.25. Included in this tutorial.

BURR83 Burr, W. "An Overview of the Proposed American National Standard for Local Distributed Data Interfaces." *Communications of the ACM*, August, 1983.

Describes the ANS X3T9.5 standard for high-speed (50 Mbps) local networks. Differs significantly from IEEE 802.

CALL83 Callon, R. "Internetwork Protocol." *Proceedings of the IEEE*, December, 1983.

Discusses a variety of technical issues related to internetworking in the OSI environment, including connection-oriented versus connectionless, quality of service, addressing, fragmentation, error control, flow control, and routing.

CARL80 Carlson, D. E. "Bit-Oriented Data Link Control Procedures." *IEEE Transactions on Communications*, April, 1980.

A thorough discussion of the principles of bit-oriented data link protocols, such as HDLC.

CERF78 Cerf, V. and Kristein, P. T. "Issues in Packet-Network Interconnection." *Proceedings of the IEEE*, November, 1978.

A lengthy discussion of atternative approaches to internetworking.

CERF83a Cerf, V., and Lyons, R. "Military Requirements for Packet-Switched Networks and Their Implications for Protocol Standardization." *Computer Networks*, October, 1983.

Discusses the specific requirements that led to the development of the ARPANET protocols and architecture.

CERF83b Cerf, V. and Cain, E. "The DOD Internet Architecture Model." *Computer Networks*, October, 1983.

Presents the DOD-defined architecture and protocols developed under ARPANET. Included in this tutorial.

CHAP82 Chapin, A. "Connectionless Data Transmission." *Computer Communication Review*, April, 1982.

Discusses the motivation for, and techniques of, connectionless data transfer. This service is usually associated with the network layer (datagrams), but can be provided at any layer of the architecture.

CHAP83 Chapin, A. "Connections and Connectionless Data Transmission." *Proceedings of the IEEE*, December, 1983.

Discusses and compares connection-oriented and connectionless data transfer in the context of the OSI model.

CHIL83 Childs, G. "United Kingdom Videotex Service and the European Unified Videotex Standard." *IEEE Journal on Selected Areas in Communications*, February, 1983.

Describes the European Videotex standard, which has been incorporated into the broader proposed ANSI standard.

CLAN82 Clancy, G. J., et al. "The IEEE 802 Committee States Its Case Concerning Its Local Network Standards Efforts." *Data Communications*, April, 1982.

This instructive article defends the need for standards for local networks. Its line of reasoning is applicable in a broader context.

COLL83 Collie, B.; Kayser, L.; and Rybczynski, A. "Looking at the ISDN Interfaces: Issues and Answers." *Data Communications*, June, 1983.

A readable overview of the ISDN standard at the time of writing.

CONA80 Conard, J. "Character-Oriented Data Link Control Protocols." *IEEE Transactions on Communications*, April, 1980.

Surveys the older (some would say obsolete) type of link control protocols.

CONA83 Conard, J. "Services and Protocols of the Data Link Layer." *Proceedings of the IEEE*, December, 1983.

A thorough survey of principles. Included in this tutorial.

CORR82 Corrigan, M. "Defense Data Network Protocols." *Proceedings, EASCON 82*, 1982.

A brief review of the standards being developed by DOD at all levels of their architecture.

CUNN83 Cunningham, I. "Message Handling Systems and Protocols." *Proceedings of the IEEE*, December, 1983.

A somewhat formal overview of CCITT message handling systems.

CUNN84 Cunningham, I. "Electronic Mail Standards to Get Rubber-Stamped and Go Worldwide." *Data Communications*, May, 1984.

A more informal overview of CCITT message handling standards.

CYPS78 Cypser, R. *Communications Architecture for Distributed Systems*. Addison-Wesley, 1978.

Describes one of the earliest communications architectures to be announced: SNA. Although SNA has evolved since the publication of this book, it remains the most detailed and thorough description of a working architecture.

DALA82 Dalal, Y. K. "Use of Multiple Networks in the Xerox Network System." *Computer*, October, 1982.

Looks at an internetwork approach taken for Ethernet. Exposes many of the issues a designer must face.

DAVI77 Davidson, J.; Hathaway, W.; Postel, J.; Mimno, N.; Thomas, R. and Walden, D. "The ARPANET Telnet Protocol: Its Purpose, Principles, Implementation, and Impact on Host Operating System Design." *Proceedings, Fifth Data Communications Symposium*, 1977.

Describes one of the earliest virtual terminal protocols. Although Telnet is quite limited, it is one of the few operational protocols.

DAVI79 Davies, D.; Barber, D.; Price, W.; and Solomonides, C. *Computer Networks and Their Protocols*. Wiley, 1979.

A textbook on the subject.

DAY80 Day, J. "Terminal Protocols." *IEEE Transactions on Communications*, April, 1980.

This survey covers much the same ground as [MAGN79].

DAY83 Day, J. and Zimmermann, H. "The OSI Reference Model." *Proceedings of the IEEE*, December, 1983.

A formal presentation.

DEAT82 Deaton, G. "OSI and SNA: A Perspective." *Journal of Telecommunication Networks*, Fall, 1982.

A detailed comparison of OSI to IBM's communications architecture.

DECI82a Decina, M. "Managing ISDN Through International Standards Activities." *IEEE Communications Magazine*, September, 1982.

Describes CCITT's activities and organization related to ISDN.

DECI82b Decina, M. "Progress Towards User Access Arrangements in Integrated Services Digital Networks." *IEEE Transactions on Communications*, September, 1982.

Describes the set of ISDN standards. Included in this tutorial.

DOD83a Department of Defense. *Military Standard Internet Protocol*, MIL-STD-1777, August 12, 1983.

A specification of DOD's Internet Protocol which, as of this writing, is the only standard internetwork protocol available.

DOD83b Department of Defense. *Military Standard Transmission Control Protocol*, MIL-STD-1778, August 12, 1983.

A specification of DOD's TCP, which is functionally equivalent to ISO's Class 4 Transport Protocol.

DORR81 Dorros, I. "ISDN." *IEEE Communications Magazine*, March, 1981.

A general discussion of ISDN. Does not address standards.

DORR83 Dorros, I. "Telephone Nets Go Digital." *IEEE Spectrum*, April 1983.

Describes the internal evolution of telecommunications networks that is leading toward the ISDN.

EMMO83 Emmons, W. and Chandler, A. "OSI Session Layer Services and Protocols." *Proceedings of the IEEE*, December, 1983.

A standards-oriented discussion. Included in this tutorial.

ENNI83 Ennis, G. "Development of the DoD Protocol Reference Model." *Proceedings, SIGCOMM '83 Symposium*, 1983.

A concise justification for the DOD view of communications architectures and the reasons for their lack of acceptance of the OSI model.

FLET84 Fletcher, J. "Serial Link Protocol Design." *Proceedings, SIGCOMM 84*, June, 1984.

A discussion of technical design principles for link protocols and an analysis of X.25 Level 2 based on those principles. The X.25 protocol is found wanting.

FOLT80a Folts, H. "Procedures for Circuit-Switched Service in Synchronous Public Data Networks." *IEEE Transactions on Communications*, April, 1980.

Describes the X.21 standard. Included in this tutorial.

FOLT80b Folts, H. "X.25 Transaction-Oriented Features — Datagram and Fast Select." *IEEE Transactions on Communications*, April 1980.

Describes two transaction-oriented services defined for X.25. The datagram service has not been adopted by any major implementer and will be deleted from the standard. The fast select facility, though connection-oriented, provides basically the same service as the datagram standard.

FOLT80c Folts, H. "A Powerful Standard Replaces the Old Interface Standby." *Data Communications*, May, 1980.
Describes RS-449. Included in this tutorial.

FOLT81 Folts, H. "Coming of Age: A Long-Awaited Standard for Heterogeneous Nets." *Data Communications*, January, 1981.
Describes the OSI model.

FOLT82 Folts, H. "A Tutorial on the Open Systems Interconnection Reference Model." *OSI Data Transfer*, June, 1982.
A detailed description. Included in this tutorial.

GARL77 Garlick, L. Rom, R. and Postel, J. "Reliable Host-to-Host Protocols: Problems and Techniques." *Proceedings, Fifth Data Communications Symposium*, 1977.
Discusses transport protocol principles and describes TCP.

GIEN79 Gien, M. and Zimmermann, H. "Design Principles for Network Interconnection." *Proceedings, Sixth Data Communications Symposium*, 1979.
An exhaustive analysis of interconnection issues. Included in this tutorial.

GRAU82 Graube, M. "Local Area Nets: A Pair of Standards." *IEEE Spectrum*, June, 1982.
A brief overview of the IEEE 802 standard.

GRAY72 Gray, J. "Line Control Procedures." *Proceedings of the IEEE*, November, 1972.
A discussion of the principles of data link control, published long before the OSI model was developed. The principles haven't changed.

GREE80 Green, P. "An Introduction to Network Architectures and Protocols." *IEEE Transactions on Communications*, April, 1980.
Discusses the principles of a communications architecture.

GRIF82 Griffiths, J. "ISDN Network Terminating Equipment." *IEEE Transactions on Communications*, September, 1982.
Looks at the design issues relating to the user-ISDN equipment interface.

HAST83 Hastings, T. "Conformance Requirements in the ANSI Videotex/Teletext Interchange Standard (NAPLPS). *Proceedings, COMPCON 83 Fall*, September, 1983.
Conformance requirements specify exactly what it means to conform to the standard.

HIND83 Hinden, R.; Haverty, J.; and Sheltzer, A. "The DARPA Internet: Interconnection Heterogeneous Computer Networks with Gateways." *Computer*, September, 1983.
Describes the implementation of the DOD Internet Protocol. Included in this tutorial.

HOBE80 Hoberecht, V. "SNA Function Management." *IEEE Transactions on Communications*, April, 1980.
A look at higher-layer protocols within IBM's SNA.

HOLL83 Hollis, L. "OSI Presentation Layer Activities." *Proceedings of the IEEE*, December, 1983.

A brief discussion of ISO's approach to presentation layer protocol definition.

HOLL85 Holland, G. "NAPLPS Standard Defines Graphics and Text Communications." *EDN*, January 10, 1985.
A detailed presentation of the standard.

HORA84a Horak, W. "Concepts of the Document Interchange Protocol for the Telematic Services: CCITT Draft Recommendation S.a." *Computer Networks*, June, 1984.
Describes document architecture protocols being developed by CCITT. Included in this tutorial.

HORA84b Horak, W. and Kronert, G. "An Object-Oriented Office Document Architecture Model for Processing and Interchange of Documents." *Proceedings, Second ACM-SIGOA Conference on Office Information Systems*, 1984.
A clear overview of ECMA's draft document content and document interchange architectures, which are close to those being developed under CCITT.

IEEE85 "Special Issues on Telecommunications Standards." *IEEE Communications Magazine*, January, 1985.
This special issue describes the organization and areas of interest of most relevant standards-making organizations.

JOHN80 Johnson, S. "Architectural Evolution: Digital Unveils Its DECNET Phase III." *Data Communications*, March, 1980.
An overview of DEC's communication architecture, one of the most widely-used proprietary architectures.

JOSH83 Joshi, S. and Iyer, V. "New Standards for Local Networks Push Upper Limits for Lightwave Data." *Data Communications*, July, 1984.
Describes ANSI's proposed standard for fiber ring local networks. Similar to IEEE 802.5 for twisted-pair ring.

KNIG83 Knightson, K. "The Transport Layer Standardization." *Proceedings of the IEEE*, December, 1983.
A brief description of the ISO family of transport protocols.

KONA83 Konangi, V. and Dhas, C. "An Introduction to Network Architectures." *IEEE Communications Magazine*, October, 1983.
Presents specific example architectures. Included in this tutorial.

KUO81 Kuo, F. *Protocols and Techniques for Data Communication Networks*. Prentice-Hall, 1981.
A portion of this book is devoted to higher-layer protocols.

LAM84 Lam, S. *Principles of Communication and Networking Protocols*. IEEE Computer Society Press, 1984.
A collection of reprints plus original material focusing on the techniques and protocols used to manage a communications network. Covers packet-radio, packet-switched, and local networks. Algorithms, design and analysis techniques, formal models, and verification methods are also covered.

LANG83 Langsford, A.; Naemura, K.; and Speth, R. "OSI Management and Job Transfer Services." *Proceedings of the IEEE*, December, 1983.
Briefly describes the concept of network management in the OSI environment. Then describes a protocol for job transfer and manipulation.

LEWA83 Lewan, D. and Long, H. "The OSI File Service." *Proceedings of the IEEE*, December, 1983.
Looks at the application-level protocol for file transfer. Included in this tutorial.

LIN84 Lin, S.; Costello, D.; and Miller, M. "Automatic-Repeat-Request Error-Control Schemes." *IEEE Communications Magazine*, December, 1984.
A detailed mathematical analysis of ARQ schemes used for error control in data link protocols.

LINI83 Linington, P. "Fundamentals of the Layer Service Definitions and Protocol Specifications." *Proceedings of the IEEE*, December, 1983.
Describes the terminology and modeling techniques used in the OSI model and related protocol standards. A useful reference for those who want to read the standards documents.

LOVE79 Loveland, R. "Putting DECNET into Perspective." *Datamation*, March, 1979.
A brief overview of DEC's communications architecture.

LOWE83 Lowe, H. "OSI Virtual Terminal Service." *Proceedings of the IEEE*, December, 1983.
Describes an ISO-defined set of virtual terminal services. The basic model and service commands are presented.

MAGN79 Magnee, F.; Endrizzi, A. and Day, J. "A Survey of Terminal Protocols." *Computer Networks*, November, 1979.
A review of presentation-level virtual terminal protocols. Included in this tutorial.

MART81 Martin, J. *Computer Networks and Distributed Processing*. Prentice-Hall, 1981.
A readable treatment of most of the topics in this tutorial.

MCCL83 McClelland, F. "Services and Protocols of the Physical Layer." *Proceedings of the IEEE*, December, 1983.
Provides an overview of the OSI physical layer concept, and then discusses the service specification for a variety of physical layer standards, including X.21, RS-449, and ISDN.

MCFA79 McFarland, R. "Protocols in a Computer Internetworking Environment." *Proceedings, EASCON 79,* 1979.

A discussion of communications architecture from DOD's perspective.

MCQU78 McQuillan, J., and Cerf, V. *Tutorial: A Practical View of Computer Communications Protocols.* IEEE Computer Society Press, 1978.

A collection of reprints plus extensive original material on the principles of communication protocols.

MEIJ82 Meijer, A., and Peeters, P. *Computer Network Architectures,* Computer Science Press, 1982.

This book is primarily devoted to describing specific protocols and architectures, some standard and some proprietary.

MIER82 Mier, E. "High-Level Protocols, Standards, and the OSI Reference Model." *Data Communications,* July, 1982.

Discusses the direction in higher-level protocols and the role of the various standards organizations.

MOLD81 Moldow, B. "Reality and the Proposed OSI Standard." *Data Communications,* June, 1981.

A complaint about the restrictiveness of the OSI model in forcing given functions to given layers.

MYER82 Myers, W. "Toward a Local Network Standard." *IEEE Micro,* August, 1982.

An excellent and quite thorough presentation of the IEEE 802 standard.

NBS80a National Bureau of Standards. *Features of Internetwork Protocol.* ICST/HLNP-80-8, July 1980.

NBS80b National Bureau of Standards. *Features of the Transport and Session Protocols,* ICST/HLNP-80-1, March 1980.

NBS80c National Bureau of Standards. *Features of the File Transfer Protocol (FTP) and the Data Presentation Protocol (DPP).* ICST/HLNP-80-6, 1980.

The above three reports are thoughtful analyses of the relevant issues concerning various protocols.

NEUM83 Neumann, J. "OSI Transport and Session Layers: Services and Protocol." *Proceedings, INFOCOM 83,* 1983.

A brief overview.

PADL83 Padlipsky, M. "A Perspective on the ARPANET Reference Model." *Proceedings, INFOCOM 83,* 1983.

Contrasts this model with OSI. Included in this tutorial.

PARK83 Parker, R. "Committees Push to Standardize Disk I/O." *Computer Design,* March, 1983.

Briefly describes the ANS X3T9.5 standard for high-speed local networks and places it into the context of related I/O standards.

POPE84a Popescu-Zeletin, R. "Some Critical Considerations on the ISO/OSI RM from a Network Implementation Point of View." *Proceedings, SIGCOMM 84,* June, 1984.

Discusses the experience and problems in implementing a communications capability using the OSI model. The author concludes that the OSI approach is effective.

POPE84b Pope, A. "Encoding CCITT X.409 Presentation Transfer Syntax." *Computer Communication Review,* October, 1984.

A somewhat formal description of the presentation level of CCITT's message handling standard.

POST80 Postel, J. B. "Internetwork Protocol Approaches." *IEEE Transactions on Communications,* April, 1980.

Describes and compares X.75 and DOD's internet protocol. Included in this tutorial.

POST81 Postel, J. B. Sunshine, C. A.; and Cihen, D. "The ARPA Internet Protocol." *Computer Networks,* 1981.

A thorough description of DOD's internet protocol.

POUZ78 Pouzin, L., and Zimmermann, H. "A Tutorial on Protocols." *Proceedings of the IEEE,* November, 1978.

An exhaustive treatment of protocol functions and characteristics.

RAUC83 Rauch-Hindin, W. "Upper-Level Network Protocols." *Electronic Design,* March 3, 1983.

Relates the OSI model to various working protocols and also discusses the role of various standards-making organizations.

ROBI81 Robin, G., and Treves, S. "An Introduction to Integrated Services Digital Networks." *Electrical Communication,* Vol. 56, No. 1, 1981.

A good technical discussion of ISDN mechanisms.

RUTK82 Rutkowski, A., and Marcus, M. "The Integrated Services Digital Network: Developments and Regulatory Issues." *Computer Communications Review,* July/October, 1982.

A look at the evolving standards and their implications for government regulation. Contrasts U.S. and European approaches.

RYBC80 Rybczynski, A. "X.25 Interface and End-to-End Virtual Circuit Service Characteristics." *IEEE Transactions on Communications,* April 1980.

A thorough description. Included in this tutorial.

SAKA82 Sakamoto, R. *CCITT Standards Activity: The Integrated Services Digital Network (ISDN).* Mitre Technical Report MTR-82W00169, September 1982.

This is perhaps the most complete description of the ISDN set of standards as it stood in 1982. Although ISDN work has continued to evolve, this remains a worthwhile introduction.

SAPR84 Sapronov, W. "Gateways Link Long-Haul and Local Networks." *Data Communications,* July, 1984.

This article emphasizes links between similar local networks.

SCHN83 Schneidewind, N. "Interconnecting Local Networks to Long-Distance Networks." *Computer,* September, 1983.

Discusses protocol implications and various technical approaches.

SELV82 Selvaggi, P. "The Department of Defense Data Protocol Standardization Program." *Proceedings, EASCON 82,* 1982.
Describes status and plans for DOD protocol standards.

SHEL82 Sheltzer, A.; Hinden, R. and Brescia, M. "Connecting Different Types of Networks with Gateways." *Data Communications,* August 1982.
Describes the DARPA internet.

SHOC78 Shoch, J. "Inter-Network Naming, Addressing, and Routing." *Proceedings COMPCON FALL 78,* 1978.
A useful discussion of these issues. A much-referenced paper. Also available in [LAM84].

SHOC79 Shoch, J. "Packet Fragmentation in Inter-Network Protocols." *Computer Networks,* February, 1979.
Analyzes alternative fragmentation and reassembly techniques.

SPRO78 Sproull, R. and Cohen, R. "High-Level Protocols." *Proceedings of the IEEE,* November, 1978.
Discusses principles and implementation strategies for higher-layer protocols. Included in this tutorial.

STAL83 Stallings, W. "Beyond Local Networks." *Datamation,* August, 1983.
Examines protocol, function, and performance issues in connecting local networks to long-haul networks and other local networks.

STAL84a Stallings, W. "IEEE Project 802: Setting Standards for Local-Area Networks." *Computerworld,* February 13, 1984.
A discussion of the 802 family of link, medium access, and physical layer standards. Included in this tutorial.

STAL84b Stallings, W. "A Primer: Understanding Transport Protocols." *Data Communications,* November, 1984.
A tutorial article. Included in this tutorial.

STAL84c Stallings, W. "The Integrated Services Digital Network." *Datamation,* December 1, 1984.
A survey article on ISDN.

STAL85 Stallings, W. *Data and Computer Communications.* Macmillan, 1985.
A textbook on the subject, structured along the lines of the OSI model.

STUT72 Stutzman, B. "Data Communication Control Procedures." *ACM Computing Surveys,* December, 1972.
Another (see also [Gray72]) early discussion of data link control that embodies many of the principles found in modern protocols.

SUNS78 Sunshine, C. and Dalal, Y. "Connection Management in Transport Protocols." *Computer Networks,* December, 1978.
Discusses some of the most important transport protocol mechanisms.

SUNS81 Sunshine, C. "Transport Protocols for Computer Networks." in *Protocols and Techniques for Data Communication Networks,* edited by F. Kuo, Prentice-Hall, 1981.
A functional description of transport protocols. Included in this tutorial.

TANE81a Tanenbaum, A. *Computer Networks.* Prentice-Hall, 1981.
A textbook on the subject, structured along the lines of the OSI model.

TANE81b Tanenbaum, A. "Network Protocols." *Computing Surveys,* December, 1981.
Defines protocols in the context of the OSI model. Included in this tutorial.

THUR83 Thurk, M. and Twaits, L. "Inside DEC's Newest Networking Phase." *Data Communications,* September, 1983.
An updated look at DNA, DEC's communications architecture.

TYDE82 Tydeman, J.; Lipinski, H.; Adler, R.; Nyhan, M.; Zwimpfer, L. *Teletext and Videotext in the United States.* McGraw-Hill, 1982.
A mostly nontechnical description of Teletext and Videotex.

UNSO82 Unsoy, M. "X.75 Internetworking of Datapac with Other Packet Switched Networks." *Journal of Telecommunication Networks,* Fall, 1982.
Describes practical experience with X.75. Included in this tutorial.

WABE82 Waber, K. "Considerations on Customer Access to the ISDN." *IEEE Transactions on Communications,* September, 1982.
ISDN from the subscriber's point of view.

WARE83 Ware, C. "The OSI Network Layer: Standards to Cope with the Real World." *Proceedings of the IEEE,* December, 1983.
A somewhat abstract discussion of the ISO network layer standard.

WARN80 Warner, C. "Connecting Local Networks to Long-Haul Networks: Issues in Protocol Design." *Proceedings, Fifth Conference on Local Computer Networks,* 1980.
Looks at the difficulties of using an internet protocol across dissimilar networks.

WECK80 Wecker, S. "DNA: The Digital Network Architecture." *IEEE Transactions on Communications,* April, 1980.
A thorough description of DEC's communications architecture.

WEIS83 Weissberger, A. "Bit Oriented Data Link Controls." *Computer Design,* March, 1983.

Examines functions and formats. Included in this tutorial.

WETH83 Wetherington, J. "The Story of PLP." *IEEE Journal on Selected Areas in Communications*. February, 1983.

A presentation-level standard for videotex. Included in this tutorial.

YANO81 Yanoschak, V. "Implementing the X.21 Interface." *Data Communications,* February, 1981.

A practical discussion of X.21 implementation. Included in this tutorial.

ZIMM80 Zimmermann, H. "OSI Reference Model — The ISO Model of Architecture for Open System Interconnection." *IEEE Transactions on Communications,* April, 1980.

A rather formal definition of the OSI model.

AUTHOR BIOGRAPHY

William Stallings received a PhD from M.I.T. in computer science and a B.S. from Notre Dame in electrical engineering. He is an independent consultant and president of Comp/Comm Consulting of Great Falls, VA. He has been vice president of CSM Corp., a firm specializing in data processing and data communications for the health-care industry. He has also been director of systems analysis and design for CTEC, Inc., a firm specializing in command, control, and communications systems. He has also been senior communications consultant for Honeywell, where he was involved in the planning and design of communications and network products.

Dr. Stallings is the author of numerous technical papers and the following books:

. *LOCAL NETWORKS: AN INTRODUCTION, SECOND EDITION*, Macmillan 1987

. *COMPUTER ORGANIZATION AND ARCHITECTURE*, Macmillan, 1987

. *DATA AND COMPUTER COMMUNICATIONS*, Macmillan, 1985

. *REDUCED INSTRUCTION SET COMPUTERS*, IEEE Computer Society Press, 1987

. *COMPUTER COMMUNICATIONS: ARCHITECTURES, PROTOCOLS, AND STAN-DARDS*, IEEE Computer Society Press, 1985

. *INTEGRATED SERVICES DIGITAL NETWORKS (ISDN)*, IEEE Computer Society Press, 1985

. *LOCAL NETWORK TECHNOLOGY, SECOND EDITION*, IEEE Computer Society Press, 1985

. *A MANAGER'S GUIDE TO LOCAL NETWORKS*, Prentice-Hall, 1983